GYROSCOPES: THEORY AND DESIGN

With Applications to Instrumentation, Guidance, and Control

EDITED BY

PAUL H. SAVET

Staff Scientist, Arma Division, American Bosch Arma Corporation
Adjunct Professor, Polytechnic Institute of Brooklyn

McGRAW-HILL BOOK COMPANY, INC.

New York Toronto London

1961

GYROSCOPES: THEORY AND DESIGN

 Library of Congress Catalog Card Number: 60-53355

54963

THE MAPLE PRESS COMPANY, YORK, PA.

THE AUTHORS

CHARLES T. DAVENPORT
Supervisor, Applied Research, Research Laboratory, Arma Division, American Bosch Arma Corporation (Chapters 5, 6)

PAUL S. JORGENSEN
Head, Systems Analysis Section, Arma Division, American Bosch Arma Corporation (Chapter 2)

JULIUS Y. KAPLAN
Manager, General Projects Department, Arma Division, American Bosch Arma Corporation (Chapter 4)

BERNARD LITMAN
Staff Scientist, Arma Division, American Bosch Arma Corporation (Chapter 3)

CHARLES J. MUNDO, JR.
Department Manager, Advanced Development Systems, Raytheon Manufacturing Company (Chapter 8)

GEORGE H. NEUGEBAUER
Head, Accelerometer Section, Arma Division, American Bosch Arma Corporation (Chapter 10)

THEODORE J. NEWMAN
Head, Systems Research Section, Arma Division, American Bosch Arma Corporation (Chapter 7)

SIDNEY OSBAND
Senior Engineer, Supervisor, Gyro Section, Missile Guidance Department, Arma Division, American Bosch Arma Corporation (Chapter 12)

PAUL H. SAVET
Staff Scientist, Arma Division, American Bosch Arma Corporation (Chapter 1)

MARVIN TAYLOR
Head, Gyro Section, Arma Division, American Bosch Arma Corporation (Chapter 9)

FRANCIS W. WESSBECHER
Senior Engineer, Product Evaluation Section, Arma Division, American Bosch Arma Corporation (Chapter 11)

To the Department of Defense
whose sponsorship of research
and development programs made
possible most of the devices
described herein

PREFACE

Gyroscopics, or the building of gyros and applying them to systems, is a science as well as an art. It is a science in the sense of understanding the relationship of gyros to other instruments; it is an art in the way gyros are built to attain the high level of performance required in modern applications.

The authors of this book participated for a considerable number of years in the birth and development of modern high-precision gyro instruments. They played an active role in finding new applications for these devices, which contributed substantially to extending the frontiers of the art.

The authors are fully aware of the fact that educating gyro scientists and engineers is a long, laborious task. Accordingly, they did not presuppose any such plan when, under the inspiration of Dr. Paul D. Eddy, president, and Dr. Francis K. Ballaine, dean of Adelphi College, Garden City, New York, it was suggested to the management of the Arma Division that a course in gyroscopics be initiated, starting with the spring term of 1958 at Adelphi. The plan was somewhat experimental, since no modern textbook was available and the course had never been given before in any college in the New York area. Moreover, the problem had to be faced that any designated instructor or instructors were committed—even overcommitted—in vital defense work, which practically precluded any extensive teaching assignment of such magnitude. As a result, following the suggestion made by Dr. Sherman Lowell of Adelphi, the decision was reached to split the teaching task among a group of instructors (whose names now appear at the heads of chapters in this book) and thus to convey a seminar character to the course. Actually, twelve or thirteen individual two-hour lectures were planned, each to be delivered by a different instructor, with a guest speaker to be invited at the end of the lecture series.

The decision to write a book was not reached, however, only as a result of a teaching success. It was reached essentially because the lecture notes could serve as a valuable basis for writing a more extensive presentation of the subject. Moreover, we strongly felt the need of filling an obvious gap in the technical literature. Perhaps nobody (and certainly not the authors) could hope to write a book as monumental and everlasting as F. Klein and A. Sommerfeld's "Theorie des Kreisels."

Indeed, the classical foundations of gyroscopic phenomena will hardly ever be presented better than in that masterpiece. Yet, notwithstanding that classic and some more recently published books, there was no single approach to this subject available in book form which incorporated up-to-date findings in component design as well as applications to high performance systems. It was primarily the need for a more comprehensive study that prompted the writing of the present book.

This book was written by eleven authors, of whom the undersigned was honored to be chosen editor and coordinator. The task of performing the work adequately has been a most rewarding experience, scientifically and in terms of human relationships. If we did not fall too far short of our goals, it is partly because we were all under the same roof, associated with the Arma Division. But more important were the devoted efforts of the individual authors, who did their utmost to make this book a high-quality accomplishment.

The organization of the book serves the purpose for which it was written. It is basically an introductory and, to a certain extent, a reference text in the gyro art. The subject is so broad that omissions are part of this sort of undertaking. The present book is no exception, and it is needless to say that these omissions have been voluntary and deliberate, since out of countless applications we have confined ourselves to those areas which are challenging, modern, and representative of systems in which, not just any, but high-precision gyro instruments specifically are involved. In the field of applications we have selected stable verticals, gyrocompasses, and inertial guidance systems, within limits permitted by considerations of military security. Other highly interesting applications have been left out, on purpose, mainly to limit the size of the book.

However, with these high-precision gyro applications in mind the book would have been definitely one-sided had we not strongly emphasized mechanical and electrical design considerations. Indeed, the strict observance or neglect of these (and many other processes) makes the difference between successfully designing an inertial-quality gyro and merely creating an instrument with much lower performance capability.

Such considerations underlie the organization of this book. The first three chapters are theoretical in nature and provide an introduction to the mechanics of a spinning wheel (which a gyro of any existing design essentially is). This is followed by a chapter on restraints, which is the basis of any system consideration (still theoretical, though) in which a gyro element is integrated into an instrumentation system. The integration starts, of course, at the component level and is responsible historically for generating two different types of gyro components, depending upon the number of degrees of freedom available for precession.

The chapters on stable vertical and meridian-seeking systems are the first applications offered—perhaps the most important ones, as far as engineering maturity is concerned, if the elapsed years are considered—since the pioneering work with which the names of Anschütz, Schuler, Brown, Sperry, and Arma are associated. Indeed, forty-odd years have gone by since the first attempt was made by these pioneers to utilize the rotation of the earth in space to secure a north-seeking trend or to simulate the curvature of the gravity field by what is known today as *Schuler tuning*. The two following chapters have a more modern flavor and deal with inertial guidance fundamentals.

The last four chapters are practical in nature and are intimately related to the physical gyro component, its design, performance, mechanical and electrical properties, and evaluation. We feel very strongly that these chapters, which may be less "glamorous" to a newcomer (who is liable to be overimpressed by applications to space travel), should be glamorous indeed to those called upon to build gyro components of highest performance and operational reliability.

The level of preparation of the reader need not go beyond a sound over-all engineering background and some basic knowledge of vector calculus or operational transformation—and besides, a review of these disciplines is offered in the first chapter. The book has unique features, as the reader may discover. The design chapters (9 to 12) contain a very sizable number of these. Among the salient features in the applications should be mentioned the independence of east-west velocity of the vehicle in the meridian-seeking ability of a compass, even if the vehicle were to travel at earth's rate, i.e., become stationary in inertial space; the way gravity-sensing and the curvature of the earth occur in actually establishing Schuler tuning; and the rather simplified, but inspiring, error analysis provided in the inertial guidance chapters.

To the deliberate omissions already listed, we should add two more. The first is somewhat philosophical in nature and is related to inertial space and its concept, as viewed by modern theories of physics, especially on the atomic scale. The second concerns the attempt to build "unconventional" gyros, not based on a tangible spinning wheel. We felt that while the first subject was in itself fascinating it was not yet of enough practical interest, i.e., of engineering consequence, in the present state of the art; and that the second did not reach any definite hardware stage and performance in comparison with conventional instruments.

The authors are fully aware of possible shortcomings and would be grateful to receive constructive suggestions for improving their text. A useful book, and we hope that this will be one, is a living undertaking, subject to growth. The nourishment for this growth may come from many sources, and all of them will be highly valued and considered.

The actual writing of this book was not enough of a contribution to make it be. Its birth is the result of the combined and devoted effort of many persons whose names do not appear on the title page or in chapter by-lines. Their support, encouragement, and direct help were invaluable in organizing and preparing our book. We feel deeply indebted to the management of the Arma Division, in particular to C. W. Perelle, C. T. Foss, E. D. Gittens, E. A. Goetz, A. V. Sommer, and J. C. Isbister for their direct support. Our particular thanks are due to Dr. Francis K. Ballaine, dean, and Dr. Sherman Lowell, head of graduate mathematics studies, Adelphi College, for the most valuable help and suggestions. Finally, our sincere appreciation is due to a number of people in the Arma Division, particularly to Miss Cele Bisaillon, Miss Ruth Kent, and Mrs. Doris Baer for their conscientious help in preparing this manuscript.

Paul H. Savet

CONTENTS

CHAPTER 1

FUNDAMENTALS OF VECTOR AND OPERATIONAL CALCULUS

By Paul H. Savet

Nomenclature

x, y, z = axes of a rectangular (cartesian) system of coordinates
$\bar{\imath}, \bar{\jmath}, \bar{k}$ = unit vectors along x, y, z
$\bar{u}$ = unit vector
α, β, γ = direction cosines along x, y, z
r, θ, z = system of cylindrical coordinates
$\bar{\rho}, \bar{\sigma}, \bar{k}$ = unit vectors defined in above system
r, φ, λ = system of spherical coordinates
$\bar{\rho}, \bar{\sigma}, \bar{\tau}$ = unit vectors defined in above system
∇ = nabla, differential operator
V_E = easterly velocity
V_N = northerly velocity
V_V = vertical velocity
$\bar{\omega}$ = angular-velocity vector
$\omega_x, \omega_y, \omega_z$ = projection of $\bar{\omega}$ upon x, y, z
g = acceleration of gravity
$p = d/dt$ = Heaviside operator
s = operator in Laplace transform

1-1. Introduction

Applied mathematics is a tool, and its occurrence in this book will be considered from that point of view. Broadly speaking, it may be envisaged for our present needs as a quantitative language in which relationships in the operation of a gyro (as a component or part of a system) will be expressed. Also, while it provides a means of expression, it may contribute directly to the formulation of new thoughts by derivation. It is with this point of view in mind that this chapter has been written.

In this book the mathematical level pertaining to the analysis of a gyroscope does not exceed the rudiments of vector calculus and operational transformations. Our attention will be mainly directed, therefore, to a concise presentation of these, going, however, somewhat beyond the strictly rudimentary stage. It is felt that mastering any art, including the handling of a basic mathematical apparatus, calls for an understanding on a level higher than the one directly involved in actual applications.

1-2. Definition of Vectors

Vectors represent more than a new type of notation or a condensed way of expressing known formulas.

They establish first a discrimination between so-called "undirected" magnitudes, or *scalars*, and directed ones, or *vectors*. To the first category belong such physical entities as volume, temperature, entropy, mass, density, and kinetic energy, while typical directed magnitudes or vectors encompass such notions as velocity, acceleration, force, magnetic field, and angular momentum.

Scalars are represented by algebraic (not necessarily positive) numbers, e.g., 5 ft^3, $-20°$F, 2 dyne-cm, while vectors are expressed by the association of an absolute magnitude and a direction in space. Specifying, for instance, a velocity of 30 ft/sec involves the spelling out of this magnitude, to which the definition of a direction is added, e.g., directed along the positive orientation of the OY axis in a cartesian system of coordinates.

In a formal representation there are several ways of introducing a vector. One form relies on three projections upon the axes of a cartesian reference system. These projections are directed individually, i.e., possess an origin and an end point. The addition of these projections "vectorially" (i.e., placing the origin of the second vector at the end point of the first one, and performing the same operation with the third vector, relative to the second) re-creates the original vector, which has been defined by means of its three projections. A vector is generally denoted by a boldface letter **V**, for instance, or $\vec{V}$, or again $\bar{V}$, or finally as projections upon the axes mentioned. The projections provide the algebraic operation

$$\bar{V} = \bar{V}_x + \bar{V}_y + \bar{V}_z \tag{1-1}$$

There is also another way to represent a vector directly. This method utilizes its (absolute) magnitude and direction. The latter is defined as an appropriately oriented *unit vector* in space, i.e., a vector the magnitude of which is equal to 1. If the latter is denoted by $\bar{u}$, we have

$$\bar{V} = V\bar{u} \tag{1-2}$$

where V denotes the (positive) absolute value of $\bar{V}$. If one were to define a set of three unit vectors $\bar{\imath}$, $\bar{\jmath}$, and $\bar{k}$ aligned with the three coordinate axes OX, OY, and OZ (Fig. 1-1), one would have

$$\bar{V} = V\bar{u} = V_x\bar{\imath} + V_y\bar{\jmath} + V_z\bar{k} \tag{1-3}$$

Since it is permissible to divide both sides of (1-3) by a scalar V, one has

$$\bar{u} = \frac{V_x}{V}\bar{\imath} + \frac{V_y}{V}\bar{\jmath} + \frac{V_z}{V}\bar{k} \tag{1-4}$$

We see that the absolute magnitude V does not occur in this equation; indeed, a different scale factor in space would equally affect $\bar{V}$ and its three projections upon the axes of reference. Being an invariant with

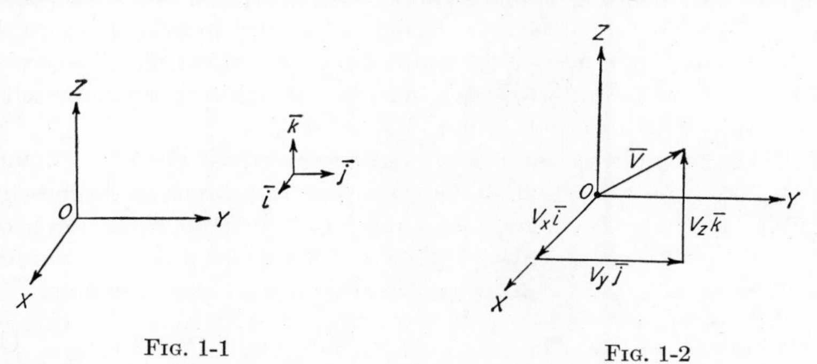

FIG. 1-1 FIG. 1-2

respect to scale, the ratios V_x/V, V_y/V, and V_z/V have an intrinsic significance attached to the unit vector $\bar{u}$. These ratios are called the *direction cosines* of $\bar{u}$ or $\bar{V}$ and are often denoted by α, β, γ in the literature. Thus,

$$\begin{aligned} \alpha &= \frac{V_x}{V} \\ \beta &= \frac{V_y}{V} \\ \gamma &= \frac{V_z}{V} \end{aligned} \tag{1-5}$$

A simple consideration of geometry provides

$$\begin{aligned} \alpha^2 + \beta^2 + \gamma^2 &= 1 \\ V_x^2 + V_y^2 + V_z^2 &= V^2 \end{aligned} \tag{1-6}$$

The introduction of a system of (cartesian) reference is a convenience, for we will often use projections upon such a system of axes in this text. It must be emphasized, however, that this is but a convenience. Vector relationships are invariant expressions, independent of any particular frame of reference chosen. As a result, the latter could be disregarded in making a reasoning involving vector relationships.

Another important, often implicitly assumed, property of vectors is their invariance with respect to *translations* parallel to themselves in (euclidean) space. In this operation the projections upon a system of axes do not change; or, expressed differently, the point of application of a vector does not enter in its definition, unless expressly stated to the contrary in some exceptional cases.

1-3. Product of Two Vectors

Basically any vector operation is equivalent to a simultaneous set of algebraic operations pertaining to projections. It may appear, therefore, that under this heading a mere condensation of a set of simultaneous operations is to be achieved. This might be true in several cases, but generally vector operations offer more than this "rewriting," especially if the last vector definition is recalled (i.e., identifying a vector with a scalar magnitude associated with a unit vector).

Considering a unit vector $\bar{u}$ and a set of three unit vectors $\bar{\imath}$, $\bar{\jmath}$, and $\bar{k}$, we have seen that the direction cosines α, β, and γ as per (1-5) are the projections of $\bar{u}$ upon $\bar{\imath}$, $\bar{\jmath}$, or $\bar{k}$. If a *scalar product* or *dot product* of two vectors $\bar{a}$ and $\bar{b}$ is defined as

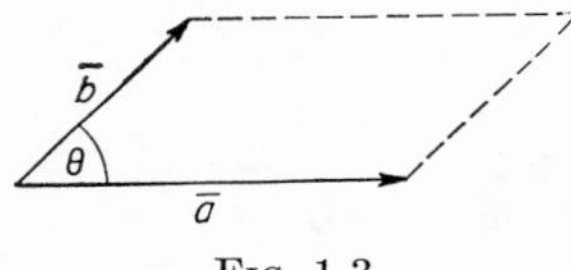

FIG. 1-3

$$\bar{a} \cdot \bar{b} = \bar{a} \cdot \bar{b} \cdot \cos\theta \tag{1-7}$$

where θ is the angle between $\bar{a}$ and $\bar{b}$ (Fig. 1-3), we see that

$$\bar{a} \cdot \bar{b} = \bar{b} \cdot \bar{a} \tag{1-8}$$

It follows that with unit vectors we should have

$$\begin{aligned} \bar{u} \cdot \bar{\imath} &= \alpha \\ \bar{u} \cdot \bar{\jmath} &= \beta \\ \bar{u} \cdot \bar{k} &= \gamma \end{aligned} \tag{1-9}$$

and generally

$$\begin{aligned} \bar{\imath}^2 = \bar{\jmath}^2 = \bar{k}^2 &= 1 \\ \bar{\imath} \cdot \bar{\jmath} = \bar{\jmath} \cdot \bar{k} = \bar{k} \cdot \bar{\imath} &= 0 \end{aligned} \tag{1-10}$$

It would appear that it is possible to derive all the rules of operation on vectors by limiting ourselves to unit vectors, remembering that the dot product of two vectors (which results in a scalar) amounts to factoring any one of the vectors with the projection of the second vector upon the first one. This point of view should be supplemented by another type of product, called *cross product* or *vector product*, denoted by $\bar{a} \times \bar{b}$, the result of which is a vector equal in magnitude to $a \cdot b \cdot \sin\theta$ and oriented in a way to represent the direction of penetration of a right-hand screw when the rotation of this fictitious screw carries $\bar{a}$ into the direction of $\bar{b}$, with $0 < \theta < \pi$.

On the earth, if $\bar{a}$ is a radial vector in the equatorial plane carried toward $\bar{b}$ by the rotation of the earth, $\bar{a} \times \bar{b}$ (for a rotation less than 180°) is oriented from the South to the North Pole along the axis of the earth.

Geometrically, $\bar{a} \times \bar{b}$ in absolute value represents the area of a parallelogram defined by vectors $\bar{a}$, $\bar{b}$, as shown in Fig. 1-3, including the dotted lines. As a particular instance, if vectors $\bar{a}$ and $\bar{b}$ are aligned with each other ($\theta = 0$), $\bar{a} \cdot \bar{b} = a \cdot b$ and $\bar{a} \times \bar{b} = 0$, whereas if they are perpendicular to each other ($\theta = \pi/2$), one has $\bar{a} \cdot \bar{b} = 0$ and $|\bar{a} \times \bar{b}| = a \cdot b$ in absolute value, oriented according to the definition mentioned above.

Since $\sin(-\theta) = -\sin\theta$, let us also remember that

$$\bar{a} \times \bar{b} = -\bar{b} \times \bar{a} \tag{1-11}$$

Summarizing these results as applied to unit vectors, we have in addition to Eqs. (1-10) the following:

$$\begin{aligned} \bar{\imath} \times \bar{\imath} &= \bar{\jmath} \times \bar{\jmath} = \bar{k} \times \bar{k} = 0 \\ \bar{\imath} \times \bar{\jmath} &= -\bar{\jmath} \times \bar{\imath} = \bar{k} \\ \bar{\jmath} \times \bar{k} &= -\bar{k} \times \bar{\jmath} = \bar{\imath} \\ \bar{k} \times \bar{\imath} &= -\bar{\imath} \times \bar{k} = \bar{\jmath} \end{aligned} \tag{1-12}$$

A rather interesting fact should be noted at this point. Basically the association (by means of a cross product) of two unit vectors along two different cartesian axes yields a unit vector along the third axis. This is so by definition, notwithstanding the fact that $\bar{\imath} \times \bar{\jmath}$ or $\bar{k} \times \bar{\imath}$, etc., are not vectors in the strict sense of the word but tensors of a special kind. Essentially a vector has as many components as the number of degrees of freedom in space. In a four-dimensional continuum, for instance, the cartesian unit vectors, say $\bar{e}_1$, $\bar{e}_2$, $\bar{e}_3$, and $\bar{e}_4$, can be associated not in four but in six different combinations with each other. One has six components created by these associations, viz., $\bar{e}_1 \times \bar{e}_2$, $\bar{e}_1 \times \bar{e}_3$, $\bar{e}_1 \times \bar{e}_4$, $\bar{e}_2 \times \bar{e}_3$, $\bar{e}_2 \times \bar{e}_4$, and $\bar{e}_3 \times \bar{e}_4$. Generally in an n-dimensional space the cross products mentioned number $n(n-1)/2$; since it happens that for $n = 3$ dimensions the expression $n(n-1)/2$ is also equal to 3, a vector definition as per Eqs. (1-12) becomes possible and legitimate in consistency.

With the rules just established, the elementary operations of linear algebra can be extended and applied directly to vectors or to scalars derived from vectors. In particular, the laws of commutation, association, and distribution are generally applicable, remembering, of course, that in the case of vector products the order of sequencing becomes important. Thus,

$$\begin{aligned} \bar{a} \cdot (\bar{b} + \bar{c}) &= \bar{a} \cdot \bar{b} + \bar{a} \cdot \bar{c} \\ &= (\bar{b} + \bar{c}) \cdot \bar{a} = \bar{b} \cdot \bar{a} + \bar{c} \cdot \bar{a} \\ \bar{a} \times (\bar{b} + \bar{c}) &= \bar{a} \times \bar{b} + \bar{a} \times \bar{c} \\ (\bar{b} + \bar{c}) \times \bar{a} &= -\bar{a} \times \bar{b} - \bar{a} \times \bar{c} \end{aligned} \tag{1-13}$$

As a last remark, it is permissible to divide a vector equation with a scalar or to multiply a vector equation (either as a dot or as a cross operation) with a vector. It would be impossible, however, to divide a vector or scalar equation with a vector.

1-4. Composite Products

If two vectors are associated with each other as a dot product, the result is a scalar. The multiplication of this scalar with another vector yields a trivial result, namely, that the length (but not the orientation) of the latter is changed by a factor numerically equal to the scalar.

On the other hand, if two vectors are multiplied with each other as a cross operation, this yields a vector, which in turn could be multiplied with another vector as a dot or cross product, ultimately providing a scalar or a vector, respectively. Thus the combination

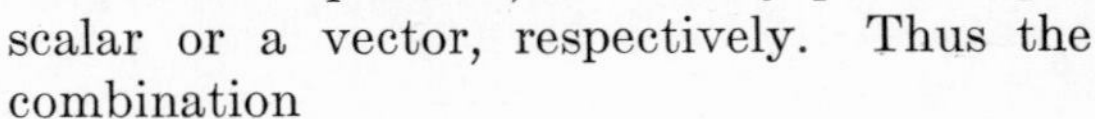

$$V = (\bar{a} \times \bar{b})\bar{c} \tag{1-14}$$

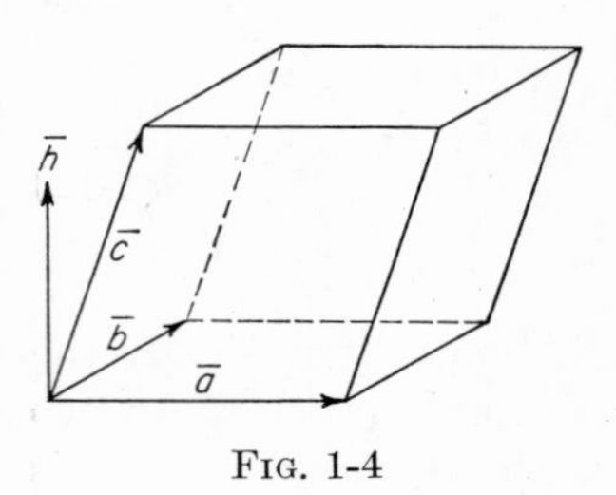

FIG. 1-4

also called a *mixed product*, is a scalar, the interpretation of which is as follows. The cross product $\bar{a} \times \bar{b} = \bar{h}$, as shown in Fig. 1-4, is oriented as defined previously (Sec. 1-3) and is equal in magnitude to the area of the base of the parallelepiped shown. The scalar product $\bar{h} \cdot \bar{c}$ will then represent the positive *volume* of this parallelepiped, provided the angle between $\bar{h}$ and $\bar{c}$ is less than 90°. From the above relationships it also follows that

$$\begin{aligned} V &= (\bar{a} \times \bar{b})\bar{c} = (\bar{b} \times \bar{c})\bar{a} = (\bar{c} \times \bar{a})\bar{b} \\ &= -(\bar{b} \times \bar{a})\bar{c} = -(\bar{c} \times \bar{b})\bar{a} = -(\bar{a} \times \bar{c})\bar{b} \end{aligned} \tag{1-15}$$

which again points out the fact that a vector, as defined by (1-14) and (1-15), is independent of the system of coordinates chosen. It also follows that, if $\bar{a} = \bar{b}$ or $\bar{b} = \bar{c}$ or $\bar{c} = \bar{a}$, the mixed product V is equal to zero.

If a vector $\bar{a} \times \bar{b}$ is multiplied with $\bar{c}$ as a cross operation, say $\bar{U} = \bar{c} \times (\bar{a} \times \bar{b})$, another vector $\bar{U}$ is obtained, which of course should not be confused with $(\bar{c} \times \bar{a}) \times \bar{b}$. Also, let it be noted that writing the above as $\bar{a} \times \bar{b} \times \bar{c}$ does not make sense, as the composite products are not equal to each other.

Let us consider $\bar{U} = \bar{c} \times (\bar{a} \times \bar{b})$. The parenthesis represents a vector perpendicular to the plane defined by $\bar{a}$ and $\bar{b}$. Then $\bar{U}$, which results from the cross product of a vector $\bar{c}$ with $\bar{m} = \bar{a} \times \bar{b}$, should be perpendicular to both $\bar{c}$ and $\bar{m}$. But being perpendicular to $\bar{m}$ is equivalent to saying that $\bar{U}$ should be contained in the plane defined by $\bar{a}$ and $\bar{b}$.

Therefore,

$$\bar{U} = \lambda\bar{a} + \mu\bar{b}$$

where λ and μ are two constants to be determined.

On the other hand, as seen above, $\bar{U} \cdot \bar{c} = 0$, since it is a mixed product with two identical (or identically oriented) factors. As a result,

$$\lambda(\bar{a} \cdot \bar{c}) + \mu(\bar{b} \cdot \bar{c}) = 0$$

Or again, introducing a new constant p, we have

$$\lambda = p(\bar{b} \cdot \bar{c})$$
$$\mu = -p(\bar{a} \cdot \bar{c})$$

which yields

$$\bar{U} = p[(\bar{b} \cdot \bar{c})\bar{a} - (\bar{a} \cdot \bar{c})\bar{b}]$$

Taking as a particular instance $\bar{a} = \bar{\imath}$, $\bar{b} = \bar{c} = \bar{\jmath}$, we have

$$\bar{U} = \bar{c} \times (\bar{a} \times \bar{b}) = \bar{\jmath} \times (\bar{\imath} \times \bar{\jmath}) = \bar{\jmath} \times \bar{k} = \bar{\imath},\ (\bar{b} \cdot \bar{c})\bar{a} = \bar{\imath}$$

and therefore $p = 1$.
Consequently,

$$\bar{U} = \bar{c} \times (\bar{a} \times \bar{b}) = \bar{a}(\bar{b} \cdot \bar{c}) - \bar{b}(\bar{a} \cdot \bar{c}) \tag{1-16}$$

In a similar way, we have

$$(\bar{a} \times \bar{b})(\bar{c} \times \bar{d}) = (\bar{a} \cdot \bar{c})(\bar{b} \cdot \bar{d}) - (\bar{a} \cdot \bar{d})(\bar{b} \cdot \bar{c}) \tag{1-17}$$

$$\begin{aligned}(\bar{a} \times \bar{b}) \times (\bar{c} \times \bar{d}) &= (\bar{a},\bar{b},\bar{d})\bar{c} - (\bar{a},\bar{b},\bar{c})\bar{d} \\ &= (\bar{a},\bar{c},\bar{d})\bar{b} - (\bar{b},\bar{c},\bar{d})\bar{a}\end{aligned} \tag{1-18}$$

where $(\bar{a},\bar{b},\bar{c})$ denotes the mixed product $(\bar{a} \times \bar{b})\bar{c}$, as can be shown by simple derivation. Briefly, if $\bar{a} \times \bar{b}$ is denoted by $\bar{A}$, we have the mixed product

$$\bar{A}(\bar{c} \times \bar{d}) = \bar{c}(\bar{d} \times \bar{A}) = \bar{c}[\bar{d} \times (\bar{a} \times \bar{b})]$$

The bracket is developed according to Eq. (1-16), which provides

$$\bar{a}(\bar{b} \cdot \bar{d}) - \bar{b}(\bar{a} \cdot \bar{d})$$

and multiplying as a dot product with $\bar{c}$, Eq. (1-17) follows.

In a similar way, and using again the above-mentioned notation, i.e., $\bar{A} = \bar{a} \times \bar{b}$, we have

$$\bar{A} \times (\bar{c} \times \bar{d}) = \bar{c}(\bar{A} \cdot \bar{d}) - \bar{d}(\bar{A} \cdot \bar{c}) = \bar{c}(\bar{a},\bar{b},\bar{d}) - \bar{d}(\bar{a},\bar{b},\bar{c})$$

Or again, if $\bar{D} = \bar{c} \times \bar{d}$ is introduced, $(\bar{a} \times \bar{b}) \times \bar{D}$ becomes $\bar{b}(\bar{a},\bar{c},\bar{d}) - \bar{a}(\bar{b},\bar{c},\bar{d})$, as shown in Eq. (1-18).

More general expressions might be derived by the procedures outlined, although we will not insist on them because of their limited interest in present applications.

1-5. Projection upon a Cartesian System

All the formulas derived previously show the independence of vector relationships from any system of reference considered. As a result, the derivation or restatement of these relationships in terms of projections (upon a cartesian reference) may not appear to be necessary. There are instances in applications, however, when these projections are required, and accordingly a brief restatement of some of the established results in a projected form becomes desirable.

Let us assume two vectors $\bar{a}$ and $\bar{b}$ and consider their projections a_x, a_y, a_z and b_x, b_y, b_z, defined as

$$\bar{a} = a_x\bar{\imath} + a_y\bar{\jmath} + a_z\bar{k}$$
$$\bar{b} = b_x\bar{\imath} + b_y\bar{\jmath} + b_z\bar{k}$$

The scalar product or dot product then appears as

$$\bar{a} \cdot \bar{b} = a_xb_x + a_yb_y + a_zb_z \tag{1-19}$$

which is derived by recalling the operations upon unit vectors as defined by Eqs. (1-10) and (1-12). In a similar way, the cross product becomes

$$\bar{a} \times \bar{b} = (a_yb_z - a_zb_y)\bar{\imath} + (a_zb_x - a_xb_z)\bar{\jmath} + (a_xb_y - a_yb_x)\bar{k} \tag{1-20}$$

The mixed product $(\bar{a} \times \bar{b})\bar{c}$ may be written

$$\begin{aligned}(\bar{a} \times \bar{b})\bar{c} &= (a_yb_z - a_zb_y)c_x + (a_zb_x - a_xb_z)c_y + (a_xb_y - a_yb_x)c_z \\ &= \begin{vmatrix} a_x & a_y & a_z \\ b_x & b_y & b_z \\ c_x & c_y & c_z \end{vmatrix}\end{aligned} \tag{1-21}$$

as can be immediately established after simple inspection. A similar procedure would offer projected expressions of more complex relationships, such as shown in Eqs. (1-16), (1-17), etc.

Another interesting derivation is based on the expression of dot and cross products squared. Since

$$\bar{a} \cdot \bar{b} = a \cdot b \cdot \cos\theta$$
$$\bar{a} \times \bar{b} = a \cdot b \cdot \sin\theta \times \text{a unit vector}$$

we have, by squaring,

$$(\bar{a} \cdot \bar{b})^2 + (\bar{a} \times \bar{b})^2 = a^2b^2 \tag{1-22}$$

Or, explicitly, remembering that $\cos^2\theta + \sin^2\theta = 1$,

$$\begin{aligned}(a_xb_x + a_yb_y + a_zb_z)^2 + (a_yb_z - a_zb_y)^2 + (a_zb_x - a_xb_z)^2 \\ + (a_xb_y - a_yb_x)^2 = (a_x^2 + a_y^2 + a_z^2)(b_x^2 + b_y^2 + b_z^2)\end{aligned} \tag{1-23}$$

which is a famous identity, originally derived by Lagrange, using purely algebraic considerations.

1-6. Differentiation of Vectors

Individual projections of a vector may depend on a number of independent variables, and a linear combination of these will also depend on these variables, assuming, of course, that the unit vectors $\bar{\imath}$, $\bar{\jmath}$, and $\bar{k}$ are fixed in space. The latter hypothesis might (and eventually will) be removed when the motion of a body with respect to a moving reference (such as the earth) is considered. In what follows we assume, provisionally at least, that $\bar{\imath}$, $\bar{\jmath}$, $\bar{k}$ are fixed references. Under these conditions the rules of differentiation applied to scalars are directly extended to vectors. Suppose, for instance, that $\bar{a}$ and $\bar{b}$ depend on a scalar variable λ. The derivative $d\bar{a}/d\lambda$ implies the derivation of a_x, a_y, a_z separately, and thus $d\bar{a}/d\lambda$ becomes $\bar{\imath}\, da_x/d\lambda + \bar{\jmath}\, da_y/d\lambda + \bar{k}\, da_z/d\lambda$. It should be noted, however, that the independent variable λ is a *scalar*. No study has ever been made (on a systematic basis) of vector functions depending on other vector magnitudes in other than a linear way. For this reason (and for lack of applications to gyroscopics) they will not be considered here.

Consider, however, the products $\bar{a} \cdot \bar{b}$ and $\bar{a} \times \bar{b}$, and take their derivative with respect to λ. One has

$$\begin{aligned} \frac{d}{d\lambda}(\bar{a} \cdot \bar{b}) &= \frac{d\bar{a}}{d\lambda} \cdot \bar{b} + \bar{a} \cdot \frac{d\bar{b}}{d\lambda} \\ \frac{d}{d\lambda}(\bar{a} \times \bar{b}) &= \frac{d\bar{a}}{d\lambda} \times \bar{b} + \bar{a} \times \frac{d\bar{b}}{d\lambda} \end{aligned} \tag{1-24}$$

The proof is offered by establishing the validity of these formulas along their projections, although a direct proof might as well (and easily) be established. In a similar way, the derivation of a mixed product $(\bar{a},\bar{b},\bar{c})$ yields

$$\frac{d}{d\lambda}(\bar{a},\bar{b},\bar{c}) = \left(\frac{d\bar{a}}{d\lambda}, \bar{b},\bar{c}\right) + \left(\bar{a}, \frac{d\bar{b}}{d\lambda}, \bar{c}\right) + \left(\bar{a},\bar{b}, \frac{d\bar{c}}{d\lambda}\right) \tag{1-25}$$

the proof of which is identical to the one mentioned previously.

1-7. Differentiation of Unit Vectors; Angular and Linear Velocity; Acceleration

For the sake of simplicity, let us consider first a two-dimensional case, say the plane of this paper. Suppose that a unit vector $\bar{\rho}$ is defined by its orientation with respect to a fixed reference direction OX by means of an angle θ, counted counterclockwise (Fig. 1-5). We shall also introduce a unit vector $\bar{\sigma}$ perpendicular to $\bar{\rho}$ directed at an angle $\theta + \pi/2$ with respect to reference OX. If θ is a variable itself, i.e., undergoing a small increment $\Delta\theta$, the end point A of $\bar{\rho}$ will move to B, corresponding to a vector (Fig. 1-6).

$$\overline{AB} = \overline{OB} - \overline{OA} = \bar{\rho}(\theta + \Delta\theta) - \bar{\rho}(\theta)$$

Since $\Delta\theta$ is a scalar, it can be used as a divisor of the above equation. We have

$$\frac{\bar{\rho}(\theta + \Delta\theta) - \bar{\rho}(\theta)}{\Delta\theta} = \frac{\overline{AB}}{\Delta\theta}$$

For small values of $\Delta\theta$ the left-hand side becomes the derivative of $\bar{\rho}$ with respect to θ, while the right-hand side is oriented along a direction

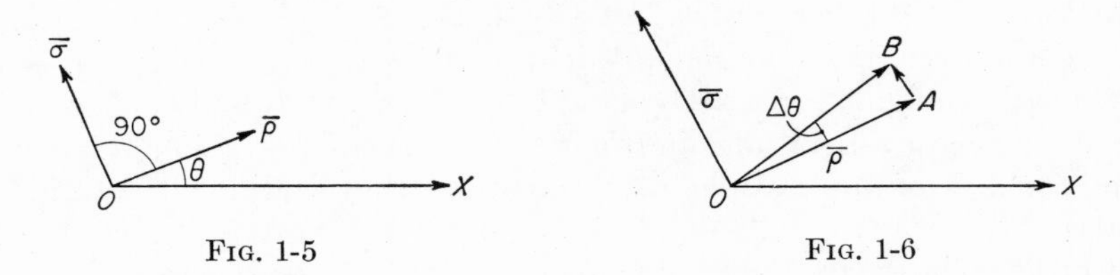

FIG. 1-5

FIG. 1-6

of $\theta + \pi/2$ with an absolute value equal to unity. It thus becomes a unit vector, previously defined as $\bar{\sigma}$. In conclusion we have

$$\frac{d\bar{\rho}}{d\theta} = \bar{\sigma}$$
$$\frac{d\bar{\sigma}}{d\theta} = -\bar{\rho} \tag{1-26}$$

Equation (1-26) also provides

$$\bar{\rho}\,\frac{d\bar{\rho}}{d\theta} + \bar{\sigma}\,\frac{d\bar{\sigma}}{d\theta} = 0$$

Moreover, we have separately

$$\bar{\rho}\,\frac{d\bar{\rho}}{d\theta} = 0 \qquad \text{and} \qquad \bar{\sigma}\,\frac{d\bar{\sigma}}{d\theta} = 0$$

since the square of a unit vector is a constant, viz., $\bar{\rho}^2 = 1$ and $\bar{\sigma}^2 = 1$, which directly provides $\bar{\rho}\,d\bar{\rho}/d\theta = 0$, etc., pointing out that $d\bar{\rho}/d\theta$ is perpendicular to $\bar{\rho}$, as anticipated.

Let us assume now that the angular orientation θ is a function of time t. The scalar magnitude $d\theta/dt$ defines the angular velocity of unit vector $\bar{\rho}$ or $\bar{\sigma}$ in the plane considered. Later on we shall give a more correct (vectorial) definition of the angular velocity, but for the time being we assume it to be a scalar $d\theta/dt$. Introduce the *position vector* in the xy plane, defined by $\bar{r} = \bar{\imath}x + \bar{\jmath}y$, relative to a fixed origin O. (A more general definition of the position vector in space should include the additional term $\bar{k}z$.) Like any vector, the position vector $\overline{OP} = \bar{r}$, in Fig. 1-7, might be defined as the absolute value r multiplied by the appropriately oriented unit vector $\bar{\rho}$. Thus, $\overline{OP} = \bar{r} = r\bar{\rho}$.

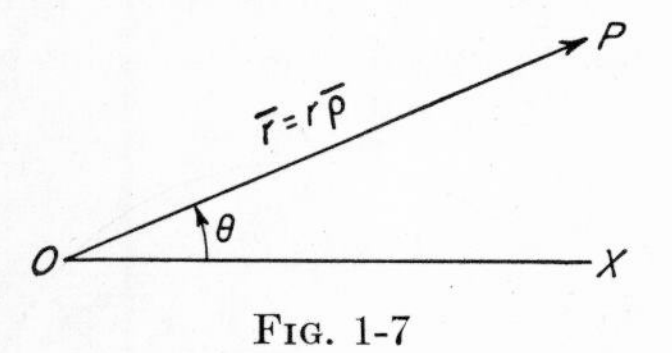

FIG. 1-7

The derivative of $\bar{r}$ with respect to time is obtained as follows. The absolute value r is differentiated directly, remembering that $\bar{\rho}$ contains the intermediate variable θ. Thus, for $\bar{\rho}$ and $\bar{\sigma}$ we have

$$\begin{aligned} \frac{d\bar{\rho}}{dt} &= \frac{d\bar{\rho}}{d\theta}\frac{d\theta}{dt} = \bar{\sigma}\frac{d\theta}{dt} \\ \frac{d\bar{\sigma}}{dt} &= \frac{d\bar{\sigma}}{d\theta}\frac{d\theta}{dt} = -\bar{\rho}\frac{d\theta}{dt} \end{aligned} \tag{1-27}$$

The time derivative of $\overline{OP}$, i.e., the velocity vector $\bar{V}$ in the xy plane (or $r\theta$ plane), thus becomes

$$\bar{V} = \frac{d\bar{r}}{dt} = \frac{dr}{dt}\bar{\rho} + r\frac{d\bar{\rho}}{dt} = \frac{dr}{dt}\bar{\rho} + r\frac{d\theta}{dt}\bar{\sigma} \tag{1-28}$$

The first term dr/dt represents the radial velocity directed along $\bar{\rho}$, while the second term is the product of the distance r from the origin O with the angular velocity $d\theta/dt$; it represents the tangential or circumferential velocity of $\bar{r} = \overline{OP}$ (or point P) and is oriented in the positive direction of $\bar{\sigma}$, if $d\theta/dt > 0$.

An additional time derivation applied to (1-28) yields the acceleration

$$\begin{aligned} \frac{d\bar{V}}{dt} &= \left(\frac{d^2r}{dt^2}\bar{\rho} + \frac{dr}{dt}\frac{d\bar{\rho}}{dt}\right) + \left(\frac{dr}{dt}\frac{d\theta}{dt}\bar{\sigma} + r\frac{d^2\theta}{dt^2}\bar{\sigma} + r\frac{d\theta}{dt}\frac{d\bar{\sigma}}{dt}\right) \\ &= \left[\frac{d^2r}{dt^2} - r\left(\frac{d\theta}{dt}\right)^2\right]\bar{\rho} + \left[2\frac{dr}{dt}\frac{d\theta}{dt} + r\frac{d^2\theta}{dt^2}\right]\bar{\sigma} \end{aligned} \tag{1-29}$$

In the first parenthesis (directed radially) we have the radial acceleration d^2r/dt^2, which hardly requires an explanation; this is combined with the centrifugal component $-r(d\theta/dt)^2$ originated by the $(r\, d\theta/dt)(d\bar{\sigma}/dt)$ term, i.e., due to the change in direction of the supposedly constant tangential velocity component $r\, d\theta/dt$. The second parenthesis contains two terms. The first is the combination of the time derivative of r in the expression $\bar{\sigma}r\, d\theta/dt$, which is $\bar{\sigma}(dr/dt)(d\theta/dt)$, and the time derivative of $\bar{\rho}$ in $\bar{\rho}\, dr/dt$, which is again $\bar{\sigma}(dr/dt)(d\theta/dt)$; altogether, $2\bar{\sigma}(dr/dt)(d\theta/dt)$ is obtained, which represents what is known as the *Coriolis acceleration;* the second term is the tangential acceleration due to a time-variable angular velocity $d\theta/dt$.

In many applications it is useful to know the acceleration of a point in space, assuming that the position vector $\bar{r}$ is represented, as before, by an absolute magnitude r and the corresponding unit vector $\bar{\rho}$, i.e., $\bar{r} = r\bar{\rho}$.

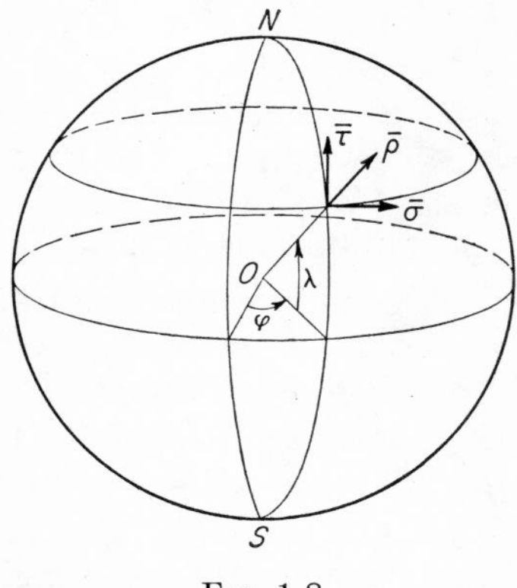

Fig. 1-8

Figure 1-8 represents a set of geographical coordinates upon a sphere of radius r. The latitude is denoted by λ (positive, upon the Northern Hemisphere) and the longitude by φ, counted eastward from a reference meridian. Three unit vectors are defined, viz., $\bar{\rho}$ directed vertically upward, $\bar{\sigma}$ oriented to the east, $\bar{\tau}$ directed toward the north. The following relationships, generalizing those offered in Eq. (1-26), prevail, as can be shown directly by taking into consideration the components of unit vectors involved in a change in direction when λ or φ varies. We have, successively,

$$\begin{aligned} \frac{\partial\bar{\rho}}{\partial\lambda} &= \bar{\tau} & \frac{\partial\bar{\rho}}{\partial\varphi} &= \cos\lambda\bar{\sigma} \\ \frac{\partial\bar{\sigma}}{\partial\lambda} &= 0 & \frac{\partial\bar{\sigma}}{\partial\varphi} &= -\cos\lambda\bar{\rho} + \sin\lambda\bar{\tau} \\ \frac{\partial\bar{\tau}}{\partial\lambda} &= -\bar{\rho} & \frac{\partial\bar{\tau}}{\partial\varphi} &= -\sin\lambda\bar{\sigma} \end{aligned} \tag{1-30}$$

Since these partial derivatives are known, the position vector $\bar{r} = r\bar{\rho}$ can be differentiated to get velocity and acceleration. Remembering that

$$\frac{d}{dt} = \frac{dr}{dt}\frac{\partial}{\partial r} + \frac{d\lambda}{dt}\frac{\partial}{\partial\lambda} + \frac{d\theta}{dt}\frac{\partial}{\partial\theta}$$

and without going through intermediate calculations [identical to those of (1-28) and (1-29)], we have a velocity expressed by

$$\frac{d\bar{r}}{dt} = \bar{\rho}\frac{dr}{dt} + \bar{\sigma}r\cos\lambda\frac{d\varphi}{dt} + \bar{\tau}r\frac{d\lambda}{dt} \tag{1-31}$$

which is a combination of a radial or vertical velocity dr/dt, an easterly velocity $r \cos \lambda\, d\varphi/dt$, and a northerly velocity $r\, d\lambda/dt$. A second differentiation yields

$$\frac{d^2\bar{r}}{dt^2} = \left[\frac{d^2r}{dt^2} - r\left(\frac{d\lambda}{dt}\right)^2 - r\cos^2\lambda\left(\frac{d\varphi}{dt}\right)^2\right]\bar{\rho} + \left[2\cos\lambda\frac{dr}{dt}\frac{d\varphi}{dt} - 2r\sin\lambda\frac{d\lambda}{dt}\frac{d\varphi}{dt} + r\cos\lambda\frac{d^2\varphi}{dt^2}\right]\bar{\sigma} + \left[2\frac{dr}{dt}\frac{d\lambda}{dt} + r\sin\lambda\cos\lambda\left(\frac{d\varphi}{dt}\right)^2 + r\frac{d^2\lambda}{dt^2}\right]\bar{\tau} \quad (1\text{-}32)$$

One recognizes the radial acceleration d^2r/dt^2 and two centrifugal terms in the $\bar{\rho}$ direction. The first of these, namely, $-r(d\lambda/dt)^2$, is due to a northerly velocity. The easterly velocity provides a centrifugal component $-r\cos\lambda(d\varphi/dt)^2$ which is parallel to the equatorial plane, thus giving both $\bar{\rho}$ and $\bar{\tau}$ components, i.e., $-r\cos^2\lambda(d\varphi/dt)^2\bar{\rho}$ and $r\sin\lambda\cos\lambda(d\varphi/dt)^2\bar{\tau}$. There are two tangential accelerations present, viz., $r\cos\lambda\, d^2\varphi/dt^2\bar{\sigma}$ and $r\,d^2\lambda/dt^2\bar{\tau}$, the first directed to the east and the second to the north. Finally, all the acceleration terms with a coefficient 2 represent Coriolis accelerations resulting from the combination in different pairs of three first derivatives dr/dt, $d\lambda/dt$, and $d\varphi/dt$, as anticipated. Another way of writing these expressions becomes possible by making the eastern velocity V_E, the northern velocity V_N, and the vertical velocity V_V appear explicity. We have by definition

$$V_V = \frac{dr}{dt} \qquad V_E = r\cos\lambda\frac{d\varphi}{dt} \qquad V_N = r\frac{d\lambda}{dt} \quad (1\text{-}33)$$

Therefore, the complete velocity vector becomes

$$\frac{d\bar{r}}{dt} = V_V\bar{\rho} + V_E\bar{\sigma} + V_N\bar{\tau} \quad (1\text{-}34)$$

while the acceleration vector may be expressed as

$$\frac{d^2r}{dt^2} = \left(\frac{dV_V}{dt} - \frac{V_N{}^2 + V_E{}^2}{r}\right)\bar{\rho} + \left(2\frac{V_VV_E}{r} - 2\tan\lambda\frac{V_NV_E}{r} + \frac{dV_E}{dt}\right)\bar{\sigma} + \left(2\frac{V_VV_N}{r} + \tan\lambda\frac{V_E{}^2}{r} + \frac{dV_N}{dt}\right)\bar{\tau} \quad (1\text{-}35)$$

Depending on the particular application, Eq. (1-32) or the expressions offered by (1-35) might be preferred. It should also be noted that in the polar regions $\tan\lambda$ becomes infinite and V_E zero. The east and north components of the acceleration appear indeterminate in (1-35), while this difficulty is absent in Eq. (1-32).

1-8. The Operator ∇

This differential operator, written as an inverted Greek Δ and called *nabla* or *del*, is expressed in a cartesian system as

$$\bar{\nabla} = \bar{\imath}\frac{\partial}{\partial x} + \bar{\jmath}\frac{\partial}{\partial y} + \bar{k}\frac{\partial}{\partial z} \tag{1-36}$$

It also has an intrinsic significance, since it is independent of the orientation of the cartesian reference system. This can be shown by means of a linear transformation, causing one cartesian system to be rotated into another. If $\bar{r}$ is the position vector (as defined in Sec. 1-7) and $\bar{\rho}$ the unit vector $\bar{r}/r$, directed as $\bar{r}$, we have

$$\begin{aligned}\bar{\rho}\frac{\partial}{\partial r} &= \bar{\rho}\left(\frac{\partial}{\partial x}\frac{dx}{dr} + \frac{\partial}{\partial y}\frac{dy}{dr} + \frac{\partial}{\partial z}\frac{dz}{dr}\right) \\ &= \bar{\imath}\frac{\partial}{\partial x} + \bar{\jmath}\frac{\partial}{\partial y} + \bar{k}\frac{\partial}{\partial z}\end{aligned} \tag{1-37}$$

Or again

$$\begin{aligned}\bar{\imath}\frac{\partial}{\partial x} + \bar{\jmath}\frac{\partial}{\partial y} + \bar{k}\frac{\partial}{\partial z} &= \bar{\imath}\frac{\partial}{\partial r}\frac{\partial r}{\partial x} + \bar{\jmath}\frac{\partial}{\partial r}\frac{\partial r}{\partial y} + \bar{k}\frac{\partial}{r}\frac{\partial r}{\partial z} \\ &= \frac{\partial}{\partial r}\left(\bar{\imath}\frac{x}{r} + \bar{\jmath}\frac{y}{r} + \bar{k}\frac{z}{r}\right) = \bar{\rho}\frac{\partial}{\partial r}\end{aligned} \tag{1-38}$$

which shows that the differential vector operator $\bar{\nabla}$ is equal to $\bar{\rho}\dfrac{\partial}{\partial r}$.

From a formal viewpoint $\bar{\nabla}$ is a vector and can be associated as a multiplier to a scalar A, which provides the gradient $\bar{\nabla}A$ of the scalar. In application to a vector $\bar{V}$ it yields either a divergence $\bar{\nabla} \cdot \bar{V}$ or div $\bar{V}$, if the product is a scalar or dot operation; or a curl $\bar{\nabla} \times \bar{V}$ or curl $\bar{V}$, or again rot $\bar{V}$, if $\bar{\nabla}$ is applied as a cross product to $\bar{V}$.

Since, in addition to being a vector, $\bar{\nabla}$ is a differential operator, both the association with other (vector or scalar) magnitudes and the order of sequencing become of primary importance. Thus $(\bar{a} \cdot \bar{\nabla})\bar{b}$ should not be confused with $\bar{a}(\bar{\nabla} \cdot \bar{b})$ or $\bar{\nabla}(\bar{a} \cdot \bar{b})$, etc.

Applied to a scalar A, the gradient $\bar{\nabla}A$ appears when the total differential of A with respect to x, y, and z is taken, which provides

$$dA = \frac{\partial A}{\partial x}dx + \frac{\partial A}{\partial y}dy + \frac{\partial A}{\partial z}dz = (\bar{\nabla}A) \cdot d\bar{r} \tag{1-39}$$

with
$$\bar{\nabla}A = \bar{\imath}\frac{\partial A}{\partial x} + \bar{\jmath}\frac{\partial A}{\partial y} + \bar{k}\frac{\partial A}{\partial z}$$

and
$$d\bar{r} = \bar{\imath}\,dx + \bar{\jmath}\,dy + \bar{k}\,dz$$

In absolute value dA is $|\bar{\nabla} A|\, dr \cos\theta$, where θ represents the angle between vectors $\bar{\nabla} A$ and $d\bar{r}$. If $d\bar{r}$ is *any* vector in a plane tangent to the surface $A(x,y,z) = \text{const}$ at (x,y,z), the variation dA vanishes, i.e., $\cos\theta = \pi/2$.

Therefore, $\bar{\nabla} A$ is perpendicular to surface $A = \text{const}$, and for a given absolute value of dr the variation dA is maximum for $\theta = 0$, i.e., along the normal to $A = \text{const}$. Vector $\bar{\nabla} A$ is oriented in this direction and is called the *gradient* of scalar A.

Associated with a vector $\bar{V}$ as a dot product, the divergence $\bar{\nabla} \cdot \bar{V}$ is obtained. This is expressed in cartesian coordinates as

$$\bar{\nabla} \cdot \bar{V} = \frac{\partial V_x}{\partial x} + \frac{\partial V_y}{\partial y} + \frac{\partial V_z}{\partial z} \tag{1-40}$$

If a cube $dx\,dy\,dz$ is considered (Fig. 1-9), the flux of velocity across the $dy\,dz$ face at x is $V_x\,dy\,dz$, entering the cube (if $V_x > 0$); at $x + dx$ the flux of velocity which leaves the cube across $dy\,dz$ is $[V_x + (\partial V_x/\partial x)\,dx]\,dy\,dz$.

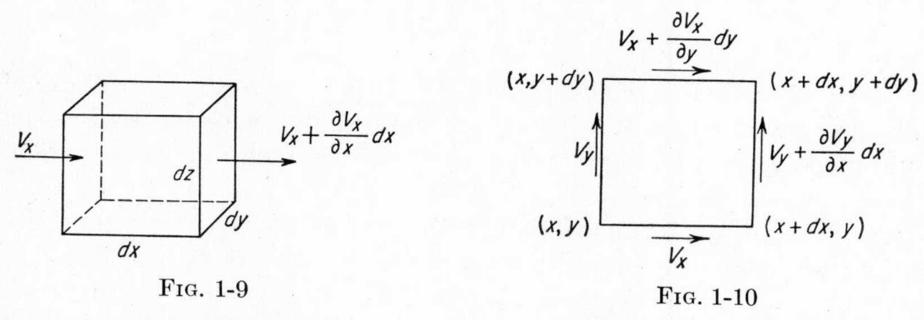

FIG. 1-9

FIG. 1-10

The excess of flux leaving the cube in the x direction is $(\partial V_x/\partial x)\,dx\,dy\,dz$; the sum of these effects along the three axes is $\bar{\nabla} \cdot \bar{V}\,dx\,dy\,dz$. As a result, the divergence of $\bar{V}$ represents the rate of depletion of the mass content of a unit volume per unit time, if $\bar{V}$ is the velocity, and the density is equal to 1.

Consider now the cross product of $\bar{\nabla}$ and vector $\bar{V}$. In a cartesian system its expression is

$$\bar{\nabla} \times \bar{V} = \text{curl}\,\bar{V} = \bar{\imath}\left(\frac{\partial V_z}{\partial y} - \frac{\partial V_y}{\partial z}\right) + \bar{\jmath}\left(\frac{\partial V_x}{\partial z} - \frac{\partial V_z}{\partial x}\right) + \bar{k}\left(\frac{\partial V_y}{\partial x} - \frac{\partial V_x}{\partial y}\right)$$

$$= \begin{vmatrix} \bar{\imath} & \bar{\jmath} & \bar{k} \\ \dfrac{\partial}{\partial x} & \dfrac{\partial}{\partial y} & \dfrac{\partial}{\partial z} \\ V_x & V_y & V_z \end{vmatrix} \tag{1-41}$$

In order to provide an interpretation, consider, for instance, the $\bar{k}$ component, i.e., $\partial V_y/\partial x - \partial V_x/\partial y$.

In moving from x to $x + dx$ the vertical velocity V_y undergoes a variation of $(\partial V_y/\partial x)\,dx$, which appears as tending to rotate the $x + dx$ face counterclockwise with respect to z at an angular rate equal to $\partial V_y/\partial x$. The horizontal component V_x, in turn, undergoes an increment of $\partial V_x/\partial y$ when y becomes $y + dy$. A clockwise rotation ensues at an angular rate of $+\partial V_x/\partial y$ or at a counterclockwise angular rate of $-\partial V_x/\partial y$. The average value of these contributions is an angular rate

$$\omega_z = \frac{1}{2}\left(\frac{\partial V_y}{\partial x} - \frac{\partial V_x}{\partial y}\right) \tag{1-42}$$

A similar reasoning applied to the $\bar{\imath}$ or $\bar{\jmath}$ components yields corresponding results, so that three components of angular velocity

$$\begin{aligned} \omega_x &= \frac{1}{2}\left(\frac{\partial V_z}{\partial y} - \frac{\partial V_y}{\partial z}\right) \\ \omega_y &= \frac{1}{2}\left(\frac{\partial V_x}{\partial z} - \frac{\partial V_z}{\partial x}\right) \\ \omega_z &= \frac{1}{2}\left(\frac{\partial V_y}{\partial x} - \frac{\partial V_x}{\partial y}\right) \end{aligned} \tag{1-42a}$$

are derived, which verifies Stokes's interpretation in hydrodynamics that the curl is twice the instantaneous angular velocity that a small liquid particle would have if the surrounding medium were suddenly annihilated.

It is appropriate to mention that the curl of a vector is essentially a particular association of individual vector components in pairs. If n represents the number of components, the number of associations is $n(n-1)/2$. It happens that in a three-dimensional space we have $n(n-1)/2 = n$ or $n = 3$, and as a result the three components of curl appear as a vector. In a four-dimensional space, however, $n(n-1)/2 = 6$, and therefore no vectorial representation is possible. The curl of a vector, considered as another vector, is thus artificial; it is possible in three dimensions only.

Let us note that the curl is actually a skew symmetrical tensor of the second order.

In more complex associations of $\bar{\nabla}$, we should underline the one which results from the derivation of a scalar (or vector) magnitude as a function of time, with a position function entering as an intermediate variable. Thus we have

$$\begin{aligned} \frac{d}{dt} f(x,y,z,t) &= \frac{\partial f}{\partial t} + \frac{\partial f}{\partial x}\frac{dx}{dt} + \frac{\partial f}{\partial y}\frac{dy}{dt} + \frac{\partial f}{\partial z}\frac{dz}{dt} \\ &= \frac{\partial f}{\partial t} + \left(\frac{d\bar{r}}{dt}\cdot\bar{\nabla}\right) f \end{aligned} \tag{1-43}$$

As stated above, f could be a scalar or a vector. Note the association of $\bar{\nabla}$ with $d\bar{r}/dt$ as a dot product, i.e., a scalar entity, bearing in mind, however, that, as an operator, $\bar{\nabla}$ affects f but not $d\bar{r}/dt$. If f is a velocity vector, $\bar{v}$, its time derivative, i.e., the acceleration, appears as

$$\frac{d\bar{v}}{dt} = \frac{\partial \bar{v}}{\partial t} + (\bar{v} \cdot \bar{\nabla})\bar{v} \tag{1-44}$$

in which the first term defines a local acceleration, followed by what may be called the *acceleration of displacement.* Indeed, this is the acceleration that a particle undergoes as it enters, within a time interval dt, a new environment in which a different velocity prevails with respect to the one that the particle would maintain owing to its own inertia. This change of velocity per unit time is described as the acceleration of displacement and appears in the second term of Eq. (1-44). Another way of interpreting the acceleration of displacement appears by the development of the formula

$$\bar{a} \times (\bar{\nabla} \times \bar{b}) = \bar{\nabla}_b(\bar{a} \cdot \bar{b}) - (\bar{a} \cdot \bar{\nabla})\bar{b}$$

where subscript b is a reminder that $\bar{\nabla}$ applies only to $\bar{b}$ as a differential operator. Exchanging $\bar{a}$ and $\bar{b}$ yields

$$\bar{b} \times (\bar{\nabla} \times \bar{a}) = \bar{\nabla}_a(\bar{a} \cdot \bar{b}) - (\bar{b} \cdot \bar{\nabla})\bar{a}$$

or, altogether,

$$\bar{\nabla}(\bar{a} \cdot \bar{b}) = \bar{a} \times (\bar{\nabla} \times \bar{b}) + \bar{b} \times (\bar{\nabla} \times \bar{a}) + (\bar{a} \cdot \bar{\nabla})\bar{b} + (\bar{b} \cdot \bar{\nabla})\bar{a}$$

If $\bar{a} = \bar{b} = \bar{v}$ is introduced, we get

$$(\bar{v} \cdot \bar{\nabla})\bar{v} = \bar{\nabla}\left(\frac{\bar{v}^2}{2}\right) - (\bar{\nabla} \times \bar{v}) \times \bar{v} \tag{1-45}$$

This formula provides still another interpretation of the acceleration of displacement, namely, as a gradient of kinetic energy combined with the Coriolis acceleration.

1-9. Angular Velocity

Several instances were encountered in this chapter where the notion of angular velocity entered. One of these occurred in the time differentiation of a unit vector and still another in connection with the curl of a velocity vector.

A rather descriptive way of defining the angular velocity about an axis in space is offered by specifying it as a vector oriented along the axis of penetration of a "right-hand screw," if the latter follows the rotation involved. The absolute magnitude of the angular-velocity vector depends on the units chosen.

Consider a unit vector in space $\bar{u}$ which under the influence of an angular velocity (vector $\bar{\omega}$) undergoes a rate of change in direction. The end point of $\bar{u}$ moves within the plane of rotation which is defined by the motion $d\bar{u}/dt$ as a function of time. We have, by definition,

$$\frac{d\bar{u}}{dt} = \bar{\omega} \times \bar{u} \qquad \text{or} \qquad \bar{\omega} = \bar{u} \times \frac{d\bar{u}}{dt} + m\bar{u} \tag{1-46}$$

where m = arbitrary scalar
This equation defines the time derivative of a unit vector within a rotating frame of reference. On the other hand, if the position vector $\bar{r} = r\bar{u}$ is considered, issued from any point of the axis of rotation, and assuming that r in absolute value is a constant, Eq. (1-46) yields

$$\frac{d\bar{r}}{dt} = \bar{\omega} \times \bar{r} \tag{1-47}$$

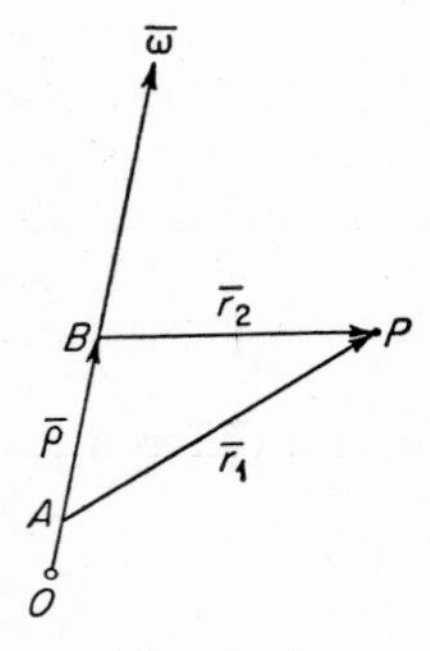

FIG. 1-11

Thus the linear velocity is the cross product of $\bar{\omega}$ and the distance from the axis of rotation of the point considered. The origin of $\bar{r}$ upon the axis of rotation is immaterial, since if one denotes by A or B two points of application (Fig. 1-11) with $\overline{AB} = \bar{\rho}$ and $\bar{r}_1 = \bar{\rho} + \bar{r}_2$, we have

$$\bar{\omega} \times \bar{r}_1 = \bar{\omega} \times (\bar{\rho} + \bar{r}_2) = \bar{\omega} \times \bar{r}_2 \tag{1-48}$$

as already stated, because of $\bar{\rho}$ being parallel to $\bar{\omega}$.

If a vector field of velocity is generated by a rotation $\bar{\omega}$ as defined by Eq. (1-47), i.e., $\bar{V} = \bar{\omega} \times \bar{r}$, the curl of the field becomes

$$\nabla \times \bar{V} = \bar{\nabla} \times (\bar{\omega} \times \bar{r}) = \bar{\omega}(\bar{\nabla} \cdot \bar{r}) - (\bar{\omega} \cdot \bar{\nabla})\bar{r} = 2\bar{\omega} \tag{1-49}$$

at least for a constant $\bar{\omega}$, since $\bar{\nabla}\bar{r} = 3$ and $(\bar{\omega} \cdot \bar{\nabla})\bar{r} = \bar{\omega}$. This is in agreement with Stokes's findings, as explained previously.

A point of great importance should be mentioned, however, relative to the "vector" nature of rotations. Two angular velocities $\bar{\omega}_1$ and $\bar{\omega}_2$ can be added to each other vectorially, and the end result is a vector, behaving as an actual vector sum. *Finite* rotations cannot be added, however, as they do not represent vectors in the sense defined by Eq. (1-46). Let us take $\bar{\omega} = d\bar{\theta}/dt$, for instance, which applied to $\bar{u}$ during time dt transforms $\bar{u}$ into $\bar{u} + \bar{\omega}\, dt \times \bar{u}$ or $\bar{u} + d\bar{\theta} \times \bar{u}$. This is an expression which cannot be integrated for finite angular displacements in θ. Forcibly it is not possible to consider two *finite* rotations and add them. An arbitrary definition of finite rotation "vectors" might be adopted, however, and a special procedure followed in their addition. A somewhat cumbersome, but interesting, method has been outlined by Webster.* The procedure might be useful in certain applications.

* A. G. Webster, "Dynamics of Particles and of Rigid, Elastic, and Fluid Bodies," 2d ed., p. 202, Dover Publications, New York, 1959.

Normally, however, when finite rotations do occur, the use of a system of eulerian coordinates is more appropriate, as will be seen in other chapters of this book.

1-10. Relative Motion

In the investigation of problems related to kinematics it is often required to express phenomena referred to a system of axes which is itself in motion (of translation and rotation) with respect to another (supposedly fixed) frame of reference. This is particularly true in gyroscopic phenomena as they occur upon the earth, since the latter turns around its own axis at a sidereal rate and communicates its rotation to the frame of reference attached (at a certain location) to the earth.

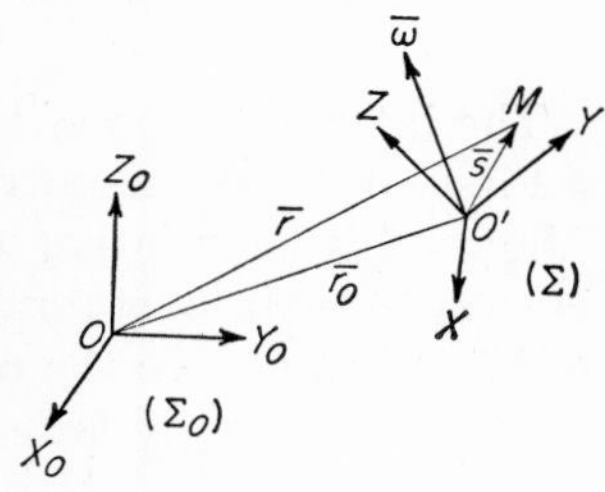

FIG. 1-12

We assume a fixed reference system Σ_0 in space, with respect to which a second frame of reference Σ moves in a clearly distinct way (Fig. 1-12). The latter is defined by the combination of a vector $\bar{r}_0 = \overline{OO'}$ and the angular-velocity vector $\bar{\omega}$, as seen at any instant in system Σ. The position vector of a point M referred to Σ is denoted by $\bar{s}$, so that the absolute position vector (with respect to Σ_0) becomes $\bar{r} = \bar{r}_0 + \bar{s}$, wherein each term may be a function of time.

If a vector $\bar{p}$ were stationary, as seen in Σ, its absolute velocity would still be $\bar{\omega} \times \bar{p}$, according to the definition of $\bar{\omega}$. Thus the time derivative of $\bar{p}$ ought to be

$$\frac{d\bar{p}}{dt} = \frac{\partial \bar{p}}{\partial t} + \bar{\omega} \times \bar{p}$$

where $\partial \bar{p}/\partial t$ is the local time derivative referred to Σ. One exception to this rule is offered by the angular velocity itself, since $\bar{\omega} \times \bar{\omega} = 0$, and thus

$$\frac{d\bar{\omega}}{dt} = \frac{\partial \bar{\omega}}{\partial t}$$

Let us consider now a point defined in system Σ by a relative position vector $\bar{s}$. We have

$$\bar{r} = \bar{r}_0 + \bar{s} \tag{1-50}$$

Taking the first derivative with respect to time, we get the absolute velocity

$$\bar{V} = \frac{d\bar{r}}{dt} = \frac{d\bar{r}_0}{dt} + \frac{\partial \bar{s}}{\partial t} + \bar{\omega} \times \bar{s} \tag{1-51}$$

This absolute or inertial velocity contains three terms. The first $(d\bar{r}_0/dt)$ is the entrainment or drag velocity, the second $(\partial\bar{s}/\partial t)$ is the relative velocity, while the third $(\bar{\omega} \times \bar{s})$ might be called the induced velocity due to the rotation of Σ in inertial space.

Another time derivative yields the inertial acceleration, i.e.,

$$\begin{aligned}\bar{A} &= \frac{d^2\bar{r}_0}{dt^2} + \frac{d}{dt}\left(\frac{\partial\bar{s}}{\partial t} + \bar{\omega} \times \bar{s}\right) \\ &= \frac{d^2\bar{r}_0}{dt^2} + \frac{\partial}{\partial t}\left(\frac{\partial\bar{s}}{\partial t} + \bar{\omega} \times \bar{s}\right) + \bar{\omega} \times \left(\frac{\partial\bar{s}}{\partial t} + \bar{\omega} \times \bar{s}\right) \\ &= \frac{d^2\bar{r}_0}{dt^2} + \frac{\partial^2\bar{s}}{\partial t^2} + \frac{\partial\bar{\omega}}{\partial t} \times \bar{s} + 2\bar{\omega} \times \frac{\partial\bar{s}}{\partial t} + \bar{\omega} \times (\bar{\omega} \times \bar{s}) \qquad (1\text{-}52)\end{aligned}$$

The interpretation of these terms is as follows:

First we have the entrainment or drag acceleration $d^2\bar{r}_0/dt^2$. This is followed by the relative acceleration $\partial^2\bar{s}/\partial t^2$ and the angular acceleration $(\partial\bar{\omega}/\partial t) \times \bar{s}$; the next term represents the Coriolis acceleration $2\bar{\omega} \times \partial\bar{s}/\partial t$, and finally we have the centrifugal acceleration $\bar{\omega} \times (\bar{\omega} \times \bar{s})$.

In gyroscopics it is necessary to emphasize the importance of these terms—of unequal relative significance, to be sure, when orders of magnitudes are compared. Analysis within a moving frame of reference becomes necessary when dealing with a spinning wheel within a rotating frame of coordinates, where, owing to high values of ω, the Coriolis and centrifugal effects outweigh the rest of the terms; such analysis is also necessary when considering the behavior of a gyroscopic instrument on the surface of the earth, where the problem of earth rotation enters, the Coriolis term thus outweighing the centrifugal contribution. The following chapters will provide a series of examples of analysis carried out relative to a moving frame of reference.

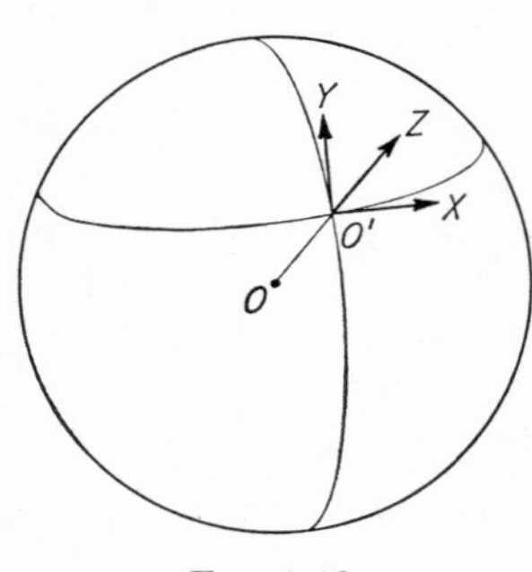

Fig. 1-13

It might be of interest to give a simple example of the application of Eq. (1-52), e.g., that of a raindrop falling to the earth when the air resistance is neglected. Consider the Northern Hemisphere of latitude λ and a cartesian frame of reference $O'XYZ$, with $O'Z$ pointing vertically upwards, $O'X$ oriented to the east, and $O'Y$ directed to the north. The sidereal angular-velocity vector is directed from the South to the North Pole of the earth and is denoted by $\bar{\omega}$. The prevailing acceleration of gravity is equal to $-\bar{k}g$, where $\bar{k}$ is part of the $\bar{\imath}, \bar{\jmath}, \bar{k}$ system of unit vectors attached to $O'XYZ$ and g is the absolute value of gravity, supposed to be constant. Because of the low value of $\omega \approx 2\pi/24$ radians/hr, the centrifugal term is disregarded; so is $d^2\bar{r}_0/dt^2$ and, of course, $\partial\bar{\omega}/\partial t$. Since $\bar{\omega}$ is a constant, we have

$$\bar{\omega} = \omega(\cos\lambda\bar{\jmath} + \sin\lambda\bar{k})$$

$$\bar{\omega} \times \frac{\partial\bar{s}}{\partial t} = \omega(\cos\lambda\bar{\jmath} + \sin\lambda\bar{k}) \times \left(\bar{\imath}\frac{\partial x}{\partial t} + \bar{\jmath}\frac{\partial y}{\partial t} + \bar{k}\frac{\partial z}{\partial t}\right)$$

$$= \omega\left[\left(\cos\lambda\frac{\partial z}{\partial t} - \sin\lambda\frac{\partial y}{\partial t}\right)\bar{\imath} + \sin\lambda\frac{\partial x}{\partial t}\bar{\jmath} - \cos\lambda\frac{\partial x}{\partial t}\bar{k}\right]$$

The equations of motion become

$$\frac{\partial^2 x}{\partial t^2} + 2\omega\left(\cos\lambda\frac{\partial z}{\partial t} - \sin\lambda\frac{\partial y}{\partial t}\right) = 0$$

$$\frac{\partial^2 y}{\partial t^2} + 2\omega\sin\lambda\frac{\partial x}{\partial t} = 0 \tag{1-53}$$

$$\frac{\partial^2 z}{\partial t^2} - 2\omega\cos\lambda\frac{\partial x}{\partial t} = -g$$

In further approximations $\partial y/\partial t$ in the bracket of the first equation will be neglected as compared with $\partial z/\partial t$, while the second equation might be disregarded altogether, since $\omega\partial x/\partial t$ is of the second order of magnitude; finally the $\omega\partial x/\partial t$ term in the third equation is omitted in the presence of $\partial^2 z/\partial t^2$.

After all these simplifications, we have

$$\frac{\partial^2 x}{\partial t^2} + 2\omega\cos\lambda\frac{\partial z}{\partial t} = 0$$

$$\frac{\partial^2 z}{\partial t^2} = -g \tag{1-54}$$

The initial conditions are for $t = 0$, $z = h > 0$, $x = 0$, $\partial x/\partial t = 0$, and $\partial z/\partial t = 0$. Integration yields

$$\frac{\partial x}{\partial t} = 2\omega\cos\lambda(h - z)$$

$$z = h - \frac{gt^2}{2}$$

or

$$h - z = \frac{gt^2}{2}$$

Thus

$$\frac{\partial x}{\partial t} = \omega\cos\lambda g t^2$$

and

$$x = \frac{1}{3}\omega\cos\lambda g t^3 = \frac{2^{3/2}}{3}\frac{\omega\cos\lambda h^{3/2}}{g^{1/2}} \tag{1-55}$$

This equation shows that there is a deviation to the east and, according to the second equation in (1-53), a very slight deviation to the south, at least on the Northern Hemisphere.

1-11. Operational Methods of Calculation

As in previous paragraphs, the attitude taken here is practical. We rely more on needs in applications than on exhaustive and rigorous establishment of a mathematical discipline for its own sake.

In the following chapters we will have to solve differential equations representing steady-state or transient phenomena in gyros or discuss the behavior of components pertaining to complex gyro systems. In most instances we will encounter one or several simultaneous linear differential equations with constant coefficients and a time-dependent forcing function. The latter may again be a linear combination (with constant coefficients) of a function and its successive derivatives with respect to time. In all cases occurring here time will be the independent variable.

The solution of the type of equations mentioned involves the linear combination of a transient homogeneous solution (depending on initial conditions) and the response to the forcing function. The latter does not depend on any initial condition. Since by following well-known rules of calculus, the solutions mentioned might be derived directly, it would appear somewhat artificial (or superfluous) to apply any other method of derivation and discussion. As will be shown later, however, so-called "operational calculus" offers a number of advantages over the classical approach of solving differential equations. The most important advantages are as follows:

1. The interpretation of the transient, steady-state, and initial behavior, together with the response to a forcing function, appears almost directly, without necessarily having to solve the complete equation in the most general way. Indeed, particular initial conditions are inserted before deriving the solution of the equation.

2. In many instances the behavior of a system is more apparent in operational form than in a time-dependent expression, especially since operational symbolism is quite general and applicable to any particular forcing function considered.

3. Because of the foregoing, should there be any discontinuity in the forcing function, it will not restrict the applicability and effectiveness of the operational rules followed.

1-12. Operational Calculus; Heaviside's Notation

In a general way a linear differential equation such as

$$\frac{d^n y}{dt^n} + a_1 \frac{d^{n-1} y}{dt^{n-1}} + \cdots + a_{n-1} \frac{dy}{dt} + a_n y = \varphi(t) \tag{1-56}$$

may be written symbolically as

$$F(y) = \varphi(t) \tag{1-57}$$

where F denotes the algebraic and differential operations applied to $y(t)$ which result in the transformation of this variable into the time function $\varphi(t)$. The usual solution of (1-56) or (1-57) ultimately amounts to expressing y as a function of t. The calculations required on $\varphi(t)$ to derive $y(t)$ may contain time differentiations and integrations. Also, there are n arbitrary constants which occur in $y(t)$. Their determination calls for the introduction of the same number of initial conditions known at the outset of operations.

In a symbolic way, if $p = d/dt$ denotes a differential operator, as used in Heaviside's approach, Eq. (1-56) may be written

$$(p^m + a_1p^{n-1} + \cdots + a_{n-1}p + a_n)y = \varphi(t) \tag{1-58}$$

in which the sequencing of p^m and y should be strictly observed. If the parenthesis is assimilated to a polynominal in p of degree n, say $H(p)$, equation

$$H(p)y = \varphi(t) \tag{1-59}$$

might be solved (formally at least) by writing

$$y = \frac{\varphi(t)}{H(p)} \tag{1-60}$$

Disregarding, for the time being, the rigor of reasoning, and proceeding according to intuition, the polynomial $H(p)$ of the denominator [which also yields the characteristic equation $H(p) = 0$] can be decomposed into factors $(p + \beta_1)(p + \beta_2) \cdots (p + \beta_n)$, where β_i are real or complex numbers (and in the latter case associated in conjugate pairs if H is real). The ratio $1/H(p)$ might therefore be written as the sum of n partial fractions. Thus we are led to a formal solution

$$y = \sum_{i=1}^{n} \frac{A_i}{p + \beta_i} \varphi(t) \tag{1-61}$$

where A_i are appropriate constants. With any one of the partial fractions in mind, we have

$$py + \beta_i y = A_i\varphi \tag{1-62}$$

the time solution of which is explicitly

$$y_i = (y_i)_0e^{-\beta_it} + A_ie^{-\beta_it} \int_0^t \varphi(t)e^{\beta_it}\, dt \tag{1-63}$$

For $t = 0$, we have $y_i = (y_i)_0$, as appears immediately by inspecting (1-63). In particular, if we assume that φ is a constant, equal to unity, for instance, we have

$$y_i = (y_i)_0e^{-\beta_it} + \frac{A_i}{\beta_i}(1 - e^{-\beta_it}) \tag{1-64}$$

For $t = 0$, we find again that $y_i = (y_i)_0$, while for large values of t, y_i becomes A_i/β_i, provided that the real part of β_i is positive.

If $\beta_i = 0$, Eqs. (1-62) and (1-63) degenerate into

$$y_i = \frac{A_i\varphi(t)}{p} = (y_i)_0 + A_i \int_0^t \varphi(t)\, dt \tag{1-65}$$

which shows that the symbolic character of the time differential operator $p = d/dt$ can be extended to reciprocal values, viz., $q = 1/p$. This symbol denotes a time integration, as per operation (1-65).

Finally, if $\varphi(t)$ is a periodic function, e.g., $\varphi(t) = \exp\,(j\omega_i t)$ where $j = \sqrt{-1}$ (as used by electrical engineers; usually the notation $i = \sqrt{-1}$ is considered), the second term of (1-63) may be computed explicitly. This yields

$$y_i = (y_i)_0 e^{-\beta_i t} + A_i \frac{e^{j\omega_i t} - 1}{\beta_i + j\omega_i} \tag{1-66}$$

or $$y_i = \text{transient solution (with initial condition)} + \frac{A_i}{j\omega_i + \beta_i} \tag{1-67}$$

In other words, y_i pertaining to any value of β_i is derived from (1-61) by substituting $j\omega$ for p and solving (1-59) as if it were a purely algebraic equation. As far as the response to the forcing function is concerned, the procedure is certainly legitimate, so that one may also write in a general way

$$y = \frac{\varphi(t)}{H(j\omega)} \tag{1-68}$$

If φ is developed into Fourier series, every frequency component will correspond to a steady-state time response equal to

$$y_k = \frac{\varphi(t)}{H(j\omega k)} \tag{1-69}$$

It is apparent from the foregoing that the Heaviside method of solving differential equations is a very powerful, practical tool, which in many instances provides quick solutions and a relatively easy discussion of the response of a linear system to certain inputs.

Unfortunately, the Heaviside method is not rigorous in its formulation and contains hidden pitfalls, particularly when the forcing function is not of the simplest kind. Moreover, it has a basic shortcoming in that the transient response, together with the insertion of the corresponding initial conditions, is artificial and extraneous to the Heaviside calculus.

In order to alleviate these drawbacks and to put operational calculus on a more rigorous foundation, the historically older yet more powerful method of the Laplace transform has been revived and perfected by modern scientists.

1-13. The Laplace Transform

Historically, the transformation introduced by Laplace was intended for deriving the solution of a class of linear differential equations in which the coefficients were also linear functions of the independent variable. For this purpose Laplace made use of an integral of the form

$$y(t) = \int_{(L)} Z(u)e^{ut}\,du \tag{1-70}$$

where the function $Z(u)$ and the path of integration (L) had to be determined by imposing a set of conditions, depending on the nature of the equation involved. Laplace's method yielded, among others, solutions in terms of Bessel functions, represented as definite integrals known as Poisson integrals and Sommerfeld integrals.*

Let us restrict ourselves to differential equations with constant coefficients, as represented by (1-56) and (1-57), and introduce a definite integral as a function of time, defined by the formula

$$\mathfrak{L}[\varphi(t)] = F(s) = \int_0^\infty \varphi(\tau)e^{-s\tau}\,d\tau \tag{1-71}$$

This integral is called the *Laplace transform* of $\varphi(t)$, and it yields a function $F(s)$ of the variable s occurring in the exponential. This parameter s, upon which the definite integral depends, is a complex number, generally restricted to those (necessarily positive) values of its real part greater than a minimum c necessary to assure the convergence of integration and thus the existence of the function $F(s)$. Expression (1-71) is recognized as a particular case of the more general operation (1-70) originally introduced by Laplace. In accepted terminology, it transforms the time function $\varphi(t)$ into the s function $F(s)$ or transforms the function $\varphi(t)$ from the time domain to the complex frequency domain defined by s. The Laplace transform appears then as an extension into the complex domain of the Fourier transform which is a particular case of (1-71) when the real part of s becomes equal to zero. The inverse Laplace transform carrying the complex frequency domain into the time domain is a definite integral of s; in this operation time t enters as a constant parameter

$$\mathfrak{L}^{-1}[F(s)] = \varphi(t) = \frac{1}{2\pi j}\int_{c-j\infty}^{c+j\infty} F(s)e^{st}\,ds \tag{1-72}$$

and is analogous to the inversion of the Fourier transform corresponding to a purely imaginary value of s. Moreover, in this integral the constant c enters as the minimum value required for the convergence, thus

* Jahnke-Emde, "Tables of Higher Functions," 6th ed., revised by Dr. Friedrich Lösch, pp. 145–152, McGraw-Hill Book Company, Inc., New York, 1960.

assuring the existence of $\varphi(t)$ as derived from $F(s)$. In all the operations mentioned it is generally assumed that $t \geq 0$.

If the Laplace transform of both sides of Eq. (1-56) or (1-57) is taken, the relationship in the time domain is replaced by an equation in the s domain. However, since $F(y)$ in (1-57) contains differential operations, this transformation would become particularly useful if the time derivative of y or $\varphi(t)$ became a purely algebraic operation carried out on $F(s)$.

Yet this is precisely what happens when one or several successive differentiations with respect to time are applied to $\varphi(t)$. Thus Eq. (1-71) appears as

$$\mathfrak{L}\left(\frac{d\varphi}{dt}\right) = \int_0^\infty \frac{d\varphi}{d\tau} e^{-s\tau}\, d\tau = -\varphi(+0) + s\mathfrak{L}(\varphi)$$
$$= -\varphi(+0) + sF(s) \tag{1-73}$$

and in a similar way

$$\mathfrak{L}\left(\frac{d^2\varphi}{dt^2}\right) = -\varphi'(+0) - s\varphi(+0) + s^2F(s) \tag{1-74}$$

and so on. As far as integration is concerned, application of well-known elementary rules provides the relationship

$$\mathfrak{L}\left[\int_0^t \varphi(t)\, dt\right] = -\frac{\varphi^{(-1)}(+0)}{s} + \frac{F(s)}{s} \tag{1-75}$$

The most fundamental difference between this and the Heaviside method (which leaves the time domain unchanged) appears immediately. While a time derivative in the Heaviside operation involves a mere multiplication with $p = d/dt$, the Laplace transform offers the same formalism (with s instead of p), supplemented, however, with the introduction of the initial conditions upon which the transient solution depends. Thus the latter is offered directly by the Laplace transform, while it is inserted in a rather artificial way in the Heaviside operations. Also s is not a differential operator alone, as is obvious not only in Eqs. (1-73) to (1-75) but also when the time derivative of $\varphi(t)$ in (1-72) is taken, i.e.,

$$\frac{d\varphi}{dt} = \frac{1}{2\pi j} \int_{c-j\infty}^{c+j\infty} sF(s)e^{st}\, ds \tag{1-76}$$

Indeed, s is within the integral sign and not outside of it as would be required if s were merely an operator d/dt, as in Heaviside's notations.

As a particular example, consider the simple differential equation

$$\tau \frac{dy}{dt} + y = 1$$

with the initial condition of $y = 0$ for $t = 0$. The $\mathfrak{L}$ transform of 1 (as will be seen in Sec. 1-14) is $1/s$. If $F(s)$ denotes the Laplace transform of $y(t)$, we have by virtue of (1-73)

$$\tau[-y(+0) + sF(s)] + F(s) = \frac{1}{s}$$

or

$$F(s) = \frac{1}{s(1 + s\tau)} = \frac{1}{s} - \frac{\tau}{1 + s\tau}$$

Taking the inverse transform as shown in Table 1-1, we get

$$y(t) = \mathfrak{L}^{-1}[F(s)] = 1 - e^{-t/\tau} \tag{1-77}$$

a solution which contains both the steady-state response ($y = 1$) to the forcing function and the transient term of the decay exponent ($-t/\tau$), as expected.

1-14. Transform Pairs

It appears from the foregoing that in order to apply practically the Laplace transform method to the solution of differential equations, it is necessary to list the most current Laplace transforms as they occur in this book. Table 1-1 provides a sample of these transform pairs which are typical enough, though far from being complete. For a more extensive list, special treatises should be consulted or the excellent brochure by Foster and Campbell[7] utilized.

Yet incomplete as the list given in Table 1-1 may appear, it offers a representative selection of transform pairs which occur in the most usual linear differential equations with constant coefficients. The only exception is the transform of the forcing function, if the latter is of a very special kind involving, for instance, discontinuities, etc. It is mostly for cases such as these that special treatises should be consulted.

1-15. Particular Solutions

Essentially, the practical success of the Laplace transform method in interpreting the solution of a differential equation directly is intimately dependent upon the possibility of splitting an inverse polynomial into a sum of partial fractions. For example, consider a function $y(t)$ as occurs in Eq. (1-56) and its Laplace transform $Y(s)$. Making use of formulas of differentiation as indicated by (1-73), (1-74), etc., we have

$$Y(s) = \frac{G(s)}{H(s)} \tag{1-78}$$

where $H(s)$ is a polynomial of degree n, identical with $H(p)$ as it contains the same terms, while the initial values of y affect only the numerator $G(s)$, composed of the Laplace transform $F(s)$ of $\varphi(t)$, supplemented by the additional terms imposed by the initial data. Thus the interpretation of $Y(s)$ gets reduced to a linear combination of simple operations, every one of which provides in the time domain the steady response to the forcing function and the transient solution, i.e., the over-all solution of the problem involved.

TABLE 1-1

$$F(s) = \int_0^\infty e^{-st}\varphi(t)\,dt \qquad \varphi(t) = \frac{1}{2\pi j}\int_{c-j\infty}^{c+j\infty} e^{st}F(s)\,ds$$

$\varphi(t)$	$F(s)$
1	$\frac{1}{s}$
t	$\frac{1}{s^2}$
t^n	$\frac{n!}{s^{n+1}}$
e^{-at}	$\frac{1}{s+\alpha}$
$\sin \omega t$	$\frac{\omega}{s^2+\omega^2}$
$\cos \omega t$	$\frac{s}{s^2+\omega^2}$
$e^{-\alpha t}\cos t$	$\frac{s+\alpha}{(s+\alpha)^2+\omega^2}$
$\frac{t^n}{n!}e^{-\alpha t}$	$\frac{1}{(s+\alpha)^{n+1}}$
$\varphi(t-a)$	$e^{-as}F(s)$

As a particular case, consider the steady-state response to a harmonic forcing function. This solution might be obtained in a way similar to Heaviside's method by writing $s = j\omega$ directly in the expression of $H(s)$, i.e., $H(j\omega)$, which will carry the interpretation of the solution into the time domain. Indeed, one would have [since in this case $G(s) = F(s)$]

$$H(j\omega)Y(s) = F(s) \tag{1-79}$$

and therefore, by performing an inverse Laplace transform,

$$H(j\omega)y(t) = \varphi(t) \tag{1-80}$$

or

$$y(t) = \frac{\varphi(t)}{H(j\omega)} \tag{1-81}$$

Initial conditions do not figure in this operation, as we restrict ourselves to the steady-state response of $y(t)$ to $\varphi(t)$. Take, for instance, the differential equation of a periodic forcing function $\varphi(t) = \exp(j\omega t)$ of circular frequency ω applied to a linear mechanical oscillatory system, having a spring constant, an inertia, and a viscous damping. This is essentially the schematic representation of an accelerometer excited by a harmonic forcing function and is governed by the differential equation

$$I\frac{d^2y}{dt^2} + f\frac{dy}{dt} + ky = e^{j\omega t} \tag{1-82}$$

where I is the mass, f the damping coefficient, and k the spring constant of the instrument. Performing the operations as suggested by Eq. (1-81), one is led to a steady-state response given by

$$y = \frac{e^{j\omega t}}{(k - I\omega^2) + jf\omega} \tag{1-83}$$

which is a well-known expression and yields easily the in-phase and quadrature components of the response by a straightforward calculation performed on complex variables.

As for the transient solution (in which the initial conditions to the problem do occur), we have

$$H(s)Y(s) = \mathfrak{L}(\varphi) + I[y'(0) + sy(0)] + fy(0) \tag{1-84}$$

where $H(s) = Is^2 + fs + k$ and $y(0)$, $y'(0)$ are initial values for $t = 0$. Equation (1-84) can be solved formally for $Y(s)$, and the result can be converted back to the time domain after applying usual procedures in partial fractions and consulting tables of transform pairs for the conversion from the s to the time domain. In this operation $\varphi(t)$ could be any (not necessarily a continuous) function of time, provided that $\mathfrak{L}(\varphi)$ exists. In the particular case of $\varphi(t)$ being a periodic time function as in (1-82), we find again a steady-state response, as given by (1-83), plus a transient solution decaying exponentially to zero owing to viscous damping, represented by the term $f\,dy/dt$ in (1-82).

In addition to the steady-state and transient solutions, it is often of great interest to explore two particular conditions in the transient response, namely, its limit behavior at $t = 0$ and at $t = \infty$. In order to evaluate these so-called "initial value" and "final value" conditions, let us consider again Eq. (1-73). If the variable s becomes nil, the exponential under the integral sign tends toward unity. As a result, the integral becomes $\varphi(+\infty) - \varphi(+0)$, which assimilated with the right side of Eq. (1-73), viz., $-\varphi(+0) + sF(s)$, provides

$$\lim_{s\to 0} sF(s) = \lim_{t\to\infty} \varphi(t) \tag{1-85}$$

On the other hand, should s increase to infinity (with its real part staying positive), the definite integral in (1-73) vanishes. As a result,

$$\lim_{s\to\infty} sF(s) = \lim_{t\to 0} \varphi(t) \tag{1-86}$$

As an application, consider a single-degree-of-freedom integrating gyro, the output angle of which is denoted by y and the input angle by x. The latter is supposed to be a unit step function at time $t = 0$. The equation $y(x)$, which is given here without derivation (as it will be handled in other chapters in more detail), is

$$I\frac{d^2y}{dt^2} + c\frac{dy}{dt} = H\frac{dx}{dt}$$

or

$$I\frac{dy}{dt} + cy(t) = Hx(t) \tag{1-87}$$

with the initial conditions of $t < 0$, $x = 0$, $t \geq 0$, $x = 1$, and $y = 0$. In this equation I denotes the moment of inertia, c the viscous damping coefficient, and H the angular momentum of the gyro. If, for the sake of simplicity, the Laplace transforms are denoted by $x(s)$ and $y(s)$, respectively, we have

$$I[sy(s) - y(0)] + cy(s) = \frac{H}{s}$$

or

$$y(s) = \frac{H}{s(c + Is)} \tag{1-88}$$

An expression similar to (1-86) is derived from (1-74), namely,

$$\lim_{t\to 0}\frac{dy}{dt} = \lim_{s\to\infty} s^2y(s) \tag{1-89}$$

which is valid only if $y(0) = 0$, as in the present case. Thus

$$\left(\frac{dy}{dt}\right)_{t\to 0} = \lim_{s\to\infty}\frac{Hs}{c + Is} = \frac{H}{I} \tag{1-90}$$

which is independent of the time constant $\tau = I/c$ of the gyro, as anticipated. On the other hand, for $t = \infty$, Eq. (1-85) yields

$$y(\infty) = \lim_{s\to 0} sy(s) = \frac{H}{c} \tag{1-91}$$

which shows that the maximum amplitude of response is proportional to the time constant; or the ratio

$$\frac{y(\infty)}{\tau} = \left(\frac{dy}{dt}\right)_{t=0} = \frac{H}{I} \tag{1-92}$$

is independent of damping, i.e., is a function only of the geometry and speed of rotation of the gyrowheel.

PROBLEMS

1-1. If

$$\frac{d\bar{a}}{dt} = \bar{\omega} \times \bar{a} \qquad \text{and} \qquad \frac{d\bar{b}}{dt} = \bar{\omega} \times \bar{b}$$

show that

$$\frac{d(\bar{a} \times \bar{b})}{dt} = \bar{\omega} \times (\bar{a} \times \bar{b})$$

1-2. A ship travels with a northerly component of velocity V_N and an easterly component V_E. Because of earth rotation, show that the resulting Coriolis accelerations are

(*a*) $2\omega_E V_N \sin \lambda$, directed toward west
(*b*) $2\omega_E V_E \sin \lambda$, directed toward north
(*c*) $2\omega_E V_E \cos \lambda$, directed downward

where ω_E is earth's angular velocity and λ is the latitude angle.

1-3. All accelerations, that is, rates of change of velocity, may be divided into two classes: changes in magnitude (speeding up or slowing down) and changes in direction (centrifugal acceleration or turning). Considering each of the Coriolis accelerations of Prob. 1-2 separately, which of the following does each represent?

(*a*) Change in magnitude
(*b*) Change in direction
(*c*) One-half change in magnitude and one-half change in direction.

BIBLIOGRAPHY

1. Phillips, H. B.: "Vector Analysis," John Wiley & Sons, Inc., New York, 1933.
2. Lass, H.: "Vector and Tensor Analysis," McGraw-Hill Book Company, Inc., New York, 1950.
3. Weatherburn, C. E.: "Advanced Vector Analysis," G. Bell & Sons, Ltd., London, 1944.
4. McLachlan, N. W.: "Complex Variable Theory and Transform Calculus, with Technical Applications," 2d ed., The Macmillan Company, New York, 1953.
5. Gardner, M. F., and J. L. Barnes: "Transients in Linear Systems," John Wiley & Sons, Inc., New York, 1942, 2 vols.
6. Churchill, R. V.: "Operational Mathematics," 2d ed., McGraw-Hill Book Company, Inc., New York, 1958.
7. Campbell, G. A., and R. M. Foster: Fourier Integrals for Practical Applications, *Bell Telephone System, Tech. Monograph* B-584, 1942.

CHAPTER 2

THEORY OF THE GYROSCOPE—PART 1

By Paul S. Jorgensen

Nomenclature

x, y, z = axes of rectangular (cartesian) system of coordinates; body-fixed coordinates
x', y', z' = inertial set of coordinates
v_x, v_y, v_z = velocity components along x, y, z
a_x, a_y, a_z = acceleration components along x, y, z
$\bar{v}$ = velocity vector
$\bar{a}$ = acceleration vector
$\bar{M}$ = momentum
$\bar{F}$ = force
P = potential energy
K = kinetic energy
$\bar{H}$ = angular momentum
$\bar{T}$ = torque
T_x, T_y, T_z = projections of $\bar{T}$ upon x, y, z
$\bar{\omega}$ = angular velocity
$\omega_x, \omega_y, \omega_z$ = projections of $\bar{\omega}$ upon x, y, z
$\bar{\imath}, \bar{\jmath}, \bar{k}$ = unit vectors aligned with x, y, z
ρ = mass density
dV = differential volume
A, B, C, D, E, F = moments and products of inertia
I = moment of inertia
θ, φ, ψ = eulerian angles

2-1. Dynamics of a Point Mass

Basic Concepts. Before discussing the dynamics of a rotating body, we should review some of the main ideas concerning simple linear motion. A first step in introducing the subject is to consider the idea of a point mass, the concept of all the material of a body having a finite weight being concentrated in an infinitesimal volume. Thus the location of the mass may be described simply as a point in space or as a set of three numbers in a selected coordinate system.

For this purpose, consider a rectangular cartesian coordinate system as shown in Fig. 2-1. These right-hand coordinates will be taken as being fixed in inertial space, so that the position of the point mass m in inertial space is defined by the coordinates x, y, and z. Furthermore, by differentiating these quantities with respect to time, the velocity of the point mass is defined, and, likewise, a second differentiation yields its acceleration. Thus we have for the three components of velocity and acceleration

$$v_x = \frac{dx}{dt} \qquad v_y = \frac{dy}{dt} \qquad v_z = \frac{dz}{dt} \tag{2-1}$$

and

$$a_x = \frac{dv_x}{dt} = \frac{d^2x}{dt^2} \qquad a_y = \frac{dv_y}{dt} = \frac{d^2y}{dt^2} \qquad a_z = \frac{dv_z}{dt} = \frac{d^2z}{dt^2} \tag{2-2}$$

At this point, the use of vector notation to describe the above quantities will be introduced. First, a set of unit vectors $\bar{\imath}$, $\bar{\jmath}$, and $\bar{k}$ will be introduced on the coordinate system, as shown on Fig. 2-1, $\bar{\imath}$ along the x coordinate, $\bar{\jmath}$ along y, and $\bar{k}$ along z. This permits the location of the point mass m to be expressed as a position vector $\bar{r}$, where

$$\bar{r} = x\bar{\imath} + y\bar{\jmath} + z\bar{k} \tag{2-3}$$

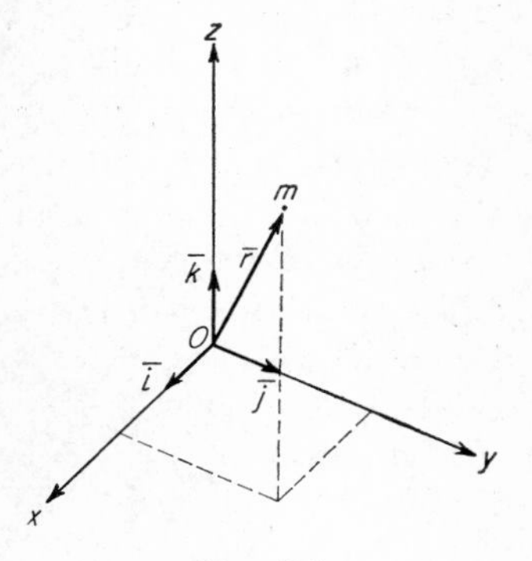

FIG. 2-1

The above expression follows directly from the rules of vector addition. $\bar{r}$ is a vector which originates at the origin of the coordinate system and terminates at the point mass. Furthermore, the velocity and acceleration of the point mass are obtained by successive differentiations of $\bar{r}$. Thus we have the velocity and acceleration vectors given by

$$\bar{v} = \frac{d\bar{r}}{dt} = \frac{dx}{dt}\,\bar{\imath} + \frac{dy}{dt}\,\bar{\jmath} + \frac{dz}{dt}\,\bar{k} \tag{2-4}$$

or

$$\bar{v} = v_x\bar{\imath} + v_y\bar{\jmath} + v_z\bar{k}$$

and

$$\bar{a} = \frac{d\bar{v}}{dt} = \frac{dv_x}{dt}\,\bar{\imath} + \frac{dv_y}{dt}\,\bar{\jmath} + \frac{dv_z}{dt}\,\bar{k} \tag{2-5}$$

or

$$\bar{a} = a_x\bar{\imath} + a_y\bar{\jmath} + a_z\bar{k}$$

It should be noted that in formally differentiating the above, the derivatives $d\bar{\imath}/dt$, $d\bar{\jmath}/dt$, and $d\bar{k}/dt$ do not appear. They are zero by virtue of taking the coordinates to be an inertial or space-fixed coordinate system.

Force. The point mass may have a force acting on it. Physically this may be mechanical, gravitational, electrostatic, or magnetic. However, whatever the origin of this force may be, having an intrinsic directional character it may always be expressed as a vector quantity as follows:

$$\bar{F} = F_x\bar{\imath} + F_y\bar{\jmath} + F_z\bar{k} \tag{2-6}$$

where F_x, F_y, and F_z are the components of the force along the x, y, and z directions, respectively.

Newton's law of motion as applied to the point mass is the well-known vector equation

$$\bar{F} = m\bar{a} \tag{2-7}$$

which simply states that the rate of change of velocity of a body multiplied by its mass must equal the force on the body.

At this point it would be well to consider two special types of acceleration. The first case is that in which the force on a moving body is directed along the same direction as its velocity; the body will simply speed up or slow down, its direction of travel remaining unchanged. The second is when the force is always at right angles to the velocity vector. Here the direction of the velocity will be continuously changing, but its magnitude will remain constant. The reason particular attention is directed to these elementary cases is primarily the analogy they possess with rotational dynamics, which will be discussed later. To anticipate the treatment of rotational motion, the first case is analogous to the speeding up and slowing down of a wheel when the applied torque is along the same direction as the spin. The second case is analogous to the motion experienced by a spinning wheel when the applied torque is at right angles to the spin.

Momentum. The momentum of a point mass is simply defined as the product of its mass and velocity and thus is a vector quantity given by

$$\bar{M} = m\bar{v} \tag{2-8}$$

Upon differentiating and substituting in Eq. (2-7), we have the following alternative formulation for Newton's law of motion:

$$\bar{F} = \frac{d\bar{M}}{dt} \tag{2-9}$$

which states that the rate of change of momentum $\bar{M}$ of a body is equal to the force acting on the body.

Energy of a Point Mass. When a force is applied to the point mass, potential energy is imparted to the mass. The mass accepts this in the form of kinetic energy. Thus a conversion from potential to kinetic energy (or vice versa) is obtained.

The incremental change in potential energy is given by the dot product

$$\Delta P = -\bar{F} \cdot \Delta \bar{r} \tag{2-10}$$

where $\Delta \bar{r}$ is an incremental change in the position of the mass. Thus the time rate of change of potential energy is given by

$$\frac{dP}{dt} = -\bar{F} \cdot \frac{d\bar{r}}{dt} = -\bar{F} \cdot \bar{v} \tag{2-11}$$

The negative sign indicates a loss of potential energy. Physically, this is because of the conversion from potential to kinetic energy.

The kinetic energy of the mass is given by

$$K = \tfrac{1}{2}mv^2 = \tfrac{1}{2}m\bar{v} \cdot \bar{v} = \tfrac{1}{2}\bar{M} \cdot \bar{v} \tag{2-12}$$

Upon differentiating, we have the time rate of change of kinetic energy given by

$$\frac{dK}{dt} = \tfrac{1}{2}m\bar{a} \cdot \bar{v} + \tfrac{1}{2}m\bar{v} \cdot \bar{a} = m\bar{a} \cdot \bar{v} \tag{2-13}$$

Upon substituting Eq. (2-7), we obtain from (2-11) and (2-13) the relation

$$\frac{dP}{dt} + \frac{dK}{dt} = 0$$

or, upon integrating,

$$P + K = \text{const} \tag{2-14}$$

The above relation is, of course, simply a restatement of the conservation of energy.

In the above discussion, we spoke of a loss of potential energy resulting in a gain of kinetic energy. Of course, the reverse is equally likely. It all depends on the direction of the velocity vector $\bar{v}$ relative to the vectors $\bar{F}$ and $\bar{a}$.

Torque and Angular Momentum. In this section two angular or rotational concepts will be defined. These will be used in the next section where rigid-body dynamics is introduced.

Consider first the concept of torque. Crudely stated, we speak of torque as acting about some reference point, which, for our purposes, is considered to be the origin of the coordinate system. It may be thought of as a twisting action resulting from some force being applied at a point other than the reference point. Mathematically defined, the torque due to a force on the point mass is given by the vector cross product

$$\bar{T} = \bar{r} \times \bar{F} \tag{2-15}$$

Thus torque has a directional property. A simple illustration is the use of a screwdriver by a right-handed person (inserting the screw). The four fingers indicate the direction of the forces, the radius of the screwdriver handle represents the distance, and the blade points in the direction of the torque.

Next, the idea of angular momentum about the origin of the coordinate system is considered. This vector quantity is related to linear momentum in a manner analogous to the way torque is related to force. Thus the angular momentum of the point mass is given by

$$\bar{H} = \bar{r} \times \bar{M} \tag{2-16}$$

Differentiation of Eq. (2-16) yields

$$\frac{d\bar{H}}{dt} = \bar{v} \times \bar{M} + \bar{r} \times \frac{d\bar{M}}{dt}$$

but $\bar{v} \times \bar{M} = \bar{v} \times m\bar{v} = 0$
and substituting Eqs. (2-9) and (2-15)

$$\bar{T} = \frac{d\bar{H}}{dt} \tag{2-17}$$

This states that the rate of change of angular momentum equals the applied torque.

2-2. Dynamics of a Rigid Body

Rigid Body in Space. So far the dynamics of only a single point mass in space has been considered. Now the idea of a rigid body of finite dimensions will be introduced.

In order to limit the treatment of the subject only to matters of interest in the study of gyroscopics, certain assumptions regarding the rigid body will be made. First, the center of gravity of the body is considered to be fixed in space (or simply moving at a constant velocity). This enables us to consider only the rotational motion of the body about its space-fixed center of gravity.

We will now define our set of coordinates x, y, and z as being fixed relative to the body with the origin of the coordinates at the center of gravity of the body. And as previously in the discussion of a point mass, a set of unit vectors $\bar{\imath}$, $\bar{\jmath}$, and $\bar{k}$ along x, y, and z, respectively, is defined. It must be clearly understood that having body-fixed coordinates is quite different from employing inertial coordinates as was previously done. As the body rotates, the coordinates x, y, and z rotate in space accordingly. Similarly, the unit vectors rotate so that the derivatives $d\bar{\imath}/dt$, $d\bar{\jmath}/dt$, and $d\bar{k}/dt$ will, in general, have finite values.

Angular Velocity. At a given instant of time there will exist a certain straight line in the body about which the body rotates. Each point in the body on this line will have zero velocity while every other point will have a finite velocity in space. It should be noted that, in general, the attitude of the line may be continuously changing both relative to the body and relative to space.

The angular velocity of the body is defined as a vector along this line of zero linear velocity. It is proportional to the rate of change of angular position in space, with the direction of the vector defined by the right-hand-screw rule; the four fingers illustrate the body motion and the blade of the screw points in the direction of the angular-velocity vector. It is generally given in units of radians per unit time.

The actual velocity of any point in the body is the product of the angular velocity and the perpendicular distance from the point to the angular-velocity line. If $\bar{\omega}$ is the angular-velocity vector and $\bar{r}$ is the position vector of a point in the body, the velocity of this point is conveniently expressed by the following vector relation:

$$\bar{v} = \frac{d\bar{r}}{dt} = \bar{\omega} \times \bar{r} \tag{2-18}$$

As an example, consider the effect of the body rotation on the unit vectors $\bar{\imath}$, $\bar{\jmath}$, and $\bar{k}$. Equation (2-18) may be used to determine the time rate of change of these vectors. Thus, if

$$\bar{\omega} = \omega_x\bar{\imath} + \omega_y\bar{\jmath} + \omega_z\bar{k}$$

the derivatives of the unit vectors are given by

$$\begin{aligned} \frac{d\bar{\imath}}{dt} &= \bar{\omega} \times \bar{\imath} = \omega_z\bar{\jmath} - \omega_y\bar{k} \\ \frac{d\bar{\jmath}}{dt} &= \bar{\omega} \times \bar{\jmath} = \omega_x\bar{k} - \omega_z\bar{\imath} \\ \frac{d\bar{k}}{dt} &= \bar{\omega} \times \bar{k} = \omega_y\bar{\imath} - \omega_x\bar{\jmath} \end{aligned} \tag{2-19}$$

Moments and Products of Inertia. In this section certain quantities related to the mass distribution of the body will be defined. These are the moments of inertia and the products of inertia. These quantities are related to rotational dynamics in a manner analogous to mass in the dynamics of a simple point mass. They are defined relative to the coordinates chosen and thus are a function of the attitude of these coordinates relative to the body.

The moments of inertia of the rigid body about the x, y, and z axes are defined by the volume integrals

$$\begin{aligned} A &= \iiint \rho(y^2 + z^2)\, dV \\ B &= \iiint \rho(z^2 + x^2)\, dV \\ C &= \iiint \rho(x^2 + y^2)\, dV \end{aligned} \tag{2-20}$$

where ρ is the mass density of the body, $dV = dx\,dy\,dz$ is the differential volume, and the above integrations are taken over the entire volume of the body in question. Similarly, the products of inertia in the yz, zx, and xy planes are defined by the volume integrals

$$\begin{aligned} D &= \textstyle\iiint \rho yz\,dV \\ E &= \textstyle\iiint \rho zx\,dV \\ F &= \textstyle\iiint \rho xy\,dV \end{aligned} \tag{2-21}$$

Now let us consider some arbitrary line L in the body which passes through its center of gravity. Let α, β, and γ be the direction cosines of this line relative to the coordinates x, y, and z, respectively. Furthermore, let $\bar{\mu}$ be a unit vector along this line, so that $\bar{\mu}$ is therefore given by

$$\bar{\mu} = \alpha\bar{\imath} + \beta\bar{\jmath} + \gamma\bar{k} \tag{2-22}$$

Let $\bar{r}$ be the position vector of any point in the body and let p be the perpendicular distance from this point to the line L. The magnitude of this perpendicular distance is given by the vector cross product

$$p = |\bar{\mu} \times \bar{r}| \tag{2-23}$$

In a manner similar to the definition of moment of inertia about the x, y, and z axes, the moment of inertia about the line L is defined by

$$I = \textstyle\iiint \rho p^2\,dV \tag{2-24}$$

Upon substitution of Eq. (2-23) and cross-product multiplication, the moment of inertia is given by

$$I = \textstyle\iiint \rho[(\beta z - \gamma y)^2 + (\gamma x - \alpha z)^2 + (\alpha y - \beta x)^2]\,dV$$

Expanding the above and substituting Eqs. (2-20) and (2-21), we finally have for the moment of inertia about the line L

$$I = A\alpha^2 + B\beta^2 + C\gamma^2 - 2D\beta\gamma - 2E\gamma\alpha - 2F\alpha\beta \tag{2-25}$$

Thus it has been shown that the moment of inertia about any arbitrary line may be expressed in terms of the moments and products of inertia relative to the x, y, and z axes and the direction cosines of the line relative to these axes.

Ellipsoid of Inertia. Attention is now directed to the rather wide generality of Eq. (2-25). The quantities A to F were defined with coordinates having an arbitrary attitude relative to the body; in addition, the attitude of the line L was arbitrary. As will be shown, some simplicity is obtained by placing a constraint on the attitude of the body-fixed coordinates.

Suppose we measure off from the origin a distance $\bar{d}$ along the line L which is equal to the reciprocal of the square root of the moment of inertia I. This displacement vector $\bar{d}$ is collinear with $\bar{\mu}$ and is given by

$$\bar{d} = x\bar{\imath} + y\bar{\jmath} + z\bar{k} \tag{2-26}$$

where the position coordinates now have the units of the reciprocal square root of moment of inertia and are given by

$$x = \frac{\alpha}{\sqrt{I}} \qquad y = \frac{\beta}{\sqrt{I}} \qquad z = \frac{\gamma}{\sqrt{I}} \tag{2-27}$$

Substitution for α, β, and γ in Eq. (2-25) yields the following implicit relationship between x, y, and z and the moments and products of inertia:

$$Ax^2 + By^2 + Cz^2 - 2Dyz - 2Ezx - 2Fxy = 1 \tag{2-28}$$

This three-dimension quadratic equation describes a surface in space which is an ellipsoid. The only constants in the equation are the moments and products of inertia of the rigid body. Thus the ellipsoid fully describes the inertia properties of the body and is therefore referred to as the "ellipsoid of inertia." Another designation is "momental ellipsoid."

Now let us consider this ellipsoid from a geometrical point of view. From solid geometry we know that for any ellipsoid there exist three principal axes and that, if the x, y, and z axes are selected to coincide with these, the equation for the surface collapses to the form

$$Ax^2 + By^2 + Cz^2 = 1 \tag{2-29}$$

This purely geometrical consideration demonstrates that it is possible to select a set of coordinates for any rigid body for which the product-of-inertia terms vanish. This particular set of coordinates in the body are its principal axes of inertia. One of these axes is the axis about which the body has a maximum moment of inertia and another is the axis about which the moment of inertia is a minimum.

Angular Momentum of a Rigid Body. In an earlier discussion the angular momentum of a point mass was defined [Eq. (2-16)]. The definition for a rigid body is simply an extension of this; namely, the angular momentum of a rigid body is the volume integral of the angular momentum of all the differential point masses that make up the body. Thus the angular momentum of a rigid body is given by

$$\bar{H} = \iiint \rho(\bar{r} \times \bar{v})\, dV \tag{2-30}$$

But from Eq. (2-18) it follows that $\bar{r} \times \bar{v} = \bar{r} \times (\bar{\omega} \times \bar{r})$, and from the triple cross-product formula the expression for the angular momentum becomes

$$\bar{H} = \iiint \rho[r^2\bar{\omega} - (\bar{r} \cdot \bar{\omega})\bar{r}]\, dV$$

Substituting $\bar{r} = x\bar{\imath} + y\bar{\jmath} + z\bar{k}$ and $\bar{\omega} = \omega_x\bar{\imath} + \omega_y\bar{\jmath} + \omega_z\bar{k}$ and letting $\bar{H} = H_x\bar{\imath} + H_y\bar{\jmath} + H_z\bar{k}$, we obtain for the three components of angular momentum

$$\begin{aligned} H_x &= \iiint \rho[(y^2 + z^2)\omega_x - xy\omega_y - xz\omega_z]\, dV \\ H_y &= \iiint \rho[(z^2 + x^2)\omega_y - yz\omega_z - yx\omega_x]\, dV \\ H_z &= \iiint \rho[(x^2 + y^2)\omega_z - zx\omega_x - zy\omega_y]\, dV \end{aligned}$$

Substituting for the definitions of moments and products of inertia of a rigid body, we have the components of angular momentum as follows:

$$\begin{aligned} H_x &= A\omega_x - F\omega_y - E\omega_z \\ H_y &= B\omega_y - D\omega_z - F\omega_x \\ H_z &= C\omega_z - E\omega_x - D\omega_y \end{aligned} \tag{2-31}$$

The above equations are general in that they apply to any arbitrary set of body-fixed coordinates. Let us assume, for simplicity, that the coordinates x, y, and z were selected to be the principal axes of inertia of the body. The product-of-inertia terms vanish, and A, B, and C are the principal moments of inertia of the body. The expression for the angular-momentum vector is now given by

$$\bar{H} = A\omega_x\bar{\imath} + B\omega_y\bar{\jmath} + C\omega_z\bar{k} \tag{2-32}$$

It should be clearly noted that, unless a body rotates about a principal axis, the angular-momentum and angular-velocity vectors are not collinear.

Euler's Equations of Rotation. In an earlier discussion of the dynamics of a point mass, Eq. (2-17) was developed which states that the rate of change of angular momentum equals the applied torque. Since a rigid body may be thought of as consisting of an infinity of point masses, this relationship must also be true for a rigid body. To repeat,

$$\bar{T} = \frac{d\bar{H}}{dt} \tag{2-17}$$

Again, assuming that the x, y, and z coordinates coincide with the principal axes of inertia, we see that differentiating Eq. (2-32) yields an expression which must equal the torque applied to the body so that

$$\bar{T} = A\left(\frac{d\omega_x}{dt}\,\bar{\imath} + \omega_x\frac{d\bar{\imath}}{dt}\right) + B\left(\frac{d\omega_y}{dt}\,\bar{\jmath} + \omega_y\frac{d\bar{\jmath}}{dt}\right) + C\left(\frac{d\omega_z}{dt}\,k + \omega_z\frac{d\bar{k}}{dt}\right)$$

Substituting the expressions for the derivatives of the unit vectors [Eq. (2-19)], we obtain the following relations for the three components of the applied torque:

$$
\begin{aligned}
T_x &= A\,\frac{d\omega_x}{dt} - (B - C)\omega_y\omega_z \\
T_y &= B\,\frac{d\omega_y}{dt} - (C - A)\omega_z\omega_x \\
T_z &= C\,\frac{d\omega_z}{dt} - (A - B)\omega_x\omega_y
\end{aligned}
\tag{2-33}
$$

where $\bar{T} = T_x\bar{\imath} + T_y\bar{\jmath} + T_z\bar{k}$

The above relations are Euler's equations of rotation of a rigid body. They provide an essential tool for developing gyroscopic theory. It should be emphasized that in the above formulation both torque and angular velocity are expressed in body-fixed coordinates which are whirling around with the rotating body. Consequently, they are difficult to interpret physically from the point of view of an observer in a nonrotating coordinate system. In a later section these equations will therefore be modified to express the dynamics of a rotating body in nonrotating coordinates. This modified formulation is more adaptable to a further study of gyroscopic phenomena.

For the moment, however, let us consider a special case of Eq. (2-33). Suppose $T_z = 0$ and $A = B$. This results in $d\omega_z/dt = 0$, which means that the component of angular velocity ω_z is constant. Thus Eq. (2-33) collapses to two differential equations with two dependent variables, ω_x and ω_y, as follows:

$$\frac{d\omega_x}{dt} - \frac{(A - C)\omega_z}{A}\,\omega_y = \frac{T_x}{A} \tag{2-34}$$

$$\frac{(A - C)\omega_z}{A}\,\omega_x + \frac{d\omega_y}{dt} = \frac{T_y}{A} \tag{2-35}$$

For example, let the applied-torque components T_x and T_y be constant. The solutions to Eqs. (2-34) and (2-35) are therefore given by

$$\omega_x = \frac{T_y}{(A - C)\omega_z} + C_1 \sin\frac{(A - C)\omega_z t}{A} + C_2 \cos\frac{(A - C)\omega_z t}{A} \tag{2-36}$$

$$\omega_y = \frac{-T_x}{(A - C)\omega_z} + C_1 \cos\frac{(A - C)\omega_z t}{A} - C_2 \sin\frac{(A - C)\omega_z t}{A} \tag{2-37}$$

where C_1 and C_2 are constants of integration. Certain interesting observations may be made concerning the above solutions. First, consider the constant part of the solutions, namely, the contribution due to the applied torque. Note that the torque about the y axis results in angular velocity about the x axis and, similarly, torque about the x axis results in angular velocity about the y axis. This paradoxical conclusion is typical of gyroscopic action, often making the subject difficult to grasp. The important idea to keep in mind is that a torque acting on a rotating body may change the direction as well as the magnitude of the angular velocity just as a force acting on a moving point mass may similarly affect the velocity of the mass. These ideas will be further clarified when gyroscopic action in nonrotating coordinates is described.

The second aspect of the solutions of Eqs. (2-36) and (2-37) to observe is the inherent oscillatory character of a rotating rigid body. The natural frequency of oscillation is given by

$$\omega_n = \frac{A - C}{A}\,\omega_z \tag{2-38}$$

For $A = C$, this frequency equals zero. Furthermore, if A and C are approximately equal, the slowly changing oscillatory angular velocity about the x and y axes appears to an observer on the body as a conical wander of the axis about which the body is rotating. A practical example of this phenomenon is the rotation of the earth. Because of its oblate shape, the moment of inertia of the earth is a maximum about the polar axis and a minimum about an axis in the equatorial plane. The earth does, in fact, experience a slow conical shift of its axis of rotation, with the period for a complete cycle of this phenomenon being about once every 440 days. This type of oscillatory motion will be discussed later from the point of view of an observer on a nonrotating coordinate system.

Eulerian Angles. In the previous section we discussed an example in which a solution for the angular velocity of a rigid body was obtained. To be specific, what was obtained was the instantaneous angular velocity as a function of time, expressed as three components along the principal axes of inertia of the body. But what does this tell us about the attitude of a body in space as viewed by an observer not rotating with the body? The general approach taken to obtain this knowledge is to describe the attitude of the body coordinates relative to the space-fixed coordinates by means of a set of angles called *eulerian angles.* These are three angles of rotation, ψ, θ, and ϕ, which can specify any arbitrary attitude of the rigid body. Since the body is rotating, these angles are continuously changing. The generation of these angles is illustrated in Fig. 2-2. Again, let x, y, and z be the body-fixed coordinates and, likewise, let x', y', and z' be a set of coordinates fixed in inertial space.

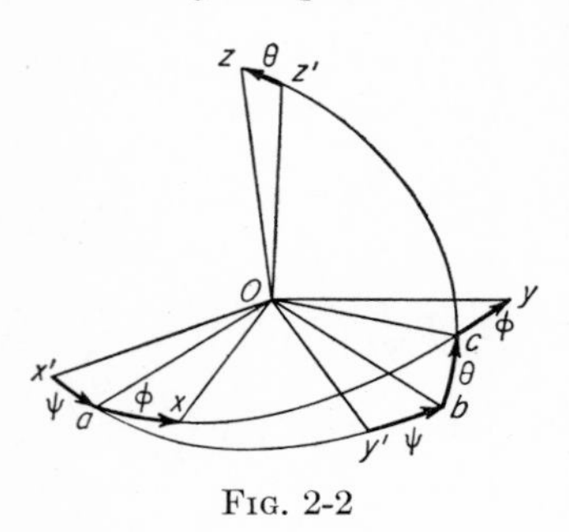

FIG. 2-2

The approach is to perform a set of successive coordinate transformations by a rotation about one of the coordinates. In this manner, we begin with the space-fixed coordinates and end up in the body coordinates, as described below.

First, a rotation is made about the z' axis by the angle ψ. This generates an intermediary set of coordinates a, b, and z'. Next, a rotation is made by the angle θ about the line Oa, thereby generating the second set of intermediary coordinates a, c, and z. Finally, the body coordinates x, y, and z are generated by a rotation about the z axis by the angle ϕ.

The angular velocity of the rigid body, which has been expressed as components along body-fixed coordinates, is related to the eulerian angles by the following equations:

$$\omega_x = \cos\phi \frac{d\theta}{dt} + \sin\phi \sin\theta \frac{d\psi}{dt} \tag{2-39}$$

$$\omega_y = -\sin\phi \frac{d\theta}{dt} + \cos\phi \sin\theta \frac{d\psi}{dt} \tag{2-40}$$

$$\omega_z = \cos\theta \frac{d\psi}{dt} + \frac{d\phi}{dt} \tag{2-41}$$

Having thus obtained a solution for ω_x, ω_y, and ω_z, we could solve Eqs. (2-39) to (2-41) to determine the attitude of the body in space. These equations are, except for the simplest cases, generally too complex to obtain an analytic solution, and consequently it is most often necessary to resort to numerical methods for solving them.

Energy of Rotation. The energy relations for a rotating body are completely analogous to those previously developed for a point mass. Therefore, the explanation which follows is largely a parallel of the previous discussion on the energy of a point mass.

When a torque is applied to a body, potential energy is imparted to the body, which accepts it in the form of kinetic energy. This results in a conversion between potential and kinetic energy.

The incremental change in potential energy is given by the dot product

$$\Delta P = -\bar{T} \cdot \overline{\Delta\theta} \tag{2-42}$$

where $\overline{\Delta\theta}$ is an infinitesimal angular displacement of the body. (NOTE: Infinitesimal angles may be regarded as vector quantities. This is not possible with finite angles.) Thus the time rate of change of potential energy is given by

$$\frac{dP}{dt} = -\bar{T} \cdot \frac{d\bar{\theta}}{dt} = -\bar{T} \cdot \bar{\omega} \tag{2-43}$$

The above expression may be derived from Eq. (2-11), the corresponding relation for the rate of change of potential energy of a point mass. Consider now an infinitesimal volume of the rigid body; let $\bar{F}$ be the force acting on this incremental part of the body and $\bar{v}$ its velocity. The rate of change of potential energy is given by

$$\frac{dP}{dt} = -\bar{F} \cdot \bar{v} \tag{2-11}$$

But

$$\bar{v} = \bar{\omega} \times \bar{r} \tag{2-18}$$

and therefore

$$\frac{dP}{dt} = -\bar{F} \cdot (\bar{\omega} \times \bar{r})$$

The above scalar triple product may be rewritten as follows:

$$\frac{dP}{dt} = -(\bar{r} \times \bar{F}) \cdot \bar{\omega}$$

But $\bar{r} \times \bar{F} = \bar{T}$ [Eq. (2-15)], the torque being applied to the infinitesimal volume. Thus again we have

$$\frac{dP}{dt} = -\bar{T} \cdot \bar{\omega} \tag{2-43}$$

which may be extended to the entire rigid body. This is valid, since $\bar{\omega}$ must be the same for all points in the body and the torque acting on the body is the vector sum of the torque on all the incremental parts that constitute the body.

The kinetic energy of the mass is given by the following dot product:

$$K = \tfrac{1}{2}\bar{H} \cdot \bar{\omega} \tag{2-44}$$

Upon differentiating, we have the time rate of change of kinetic energy given by

$$\frac{dK}{dt} = \frac{1}{2}\frac{d\bar{H}}{dt} \cdot \bar{\omega} + \frac{1}{2}\,\bar{H} \cdot \frac{d\bar{\omega}}{dt}$$

But considering A, B, and C as the principal moments of inertia, we have

$$\bar{H} = A\omega_x\bar{\imath} + B\omega_y\bar{\jmath} + C\omega_z\bar{k}$$

also

$$\bar{\omega} = \omega_x\bar{\imath} + \omega_y\bar{\jmath} + \omega_z\bar{k}$$

Now if the above formulations are substituted into each of the two terms on the right-hand side of dK/dt, it can be shown that the terms are equal. Therefore, it may be written as

$$\frac{dK}{dt} = \frac{d\bar{H}}{dt} \cdot \bar{\omega} \tag{2-45}$$

Upon substituting Eq. (2-17) into Eq. (2-45) and comparing with Eq. (2-43), we again obtain the following relation between potential and kinetic energy:

$$\frac{dP}{dt} + \frac{dK}{dt} = 0$$

Or, upon integrating, we have

$$P + K = \text{const} \tag{2-14}$$

Attention is directed toward the similarity of the energy relations for a point mass and those for a rotating body. In particular, Eqs. (2-17), (2-42), (2-43), (2-44), and (2-45) are analogous to Eqs. (2-9), (2-10), (2-11), (2-12), and (2-13), respectively.

The expression for the kinetic energy of a rotating body [Eq. (2-44)] may be derived by a summation of the kinetic energy of all the particles that make up the body. (This is the same approach which was previously used to develop the relation for the angular momentum of a rigid body.) Thus the kinetic energy of the body is given by the volume integral

$$K = \tfrac{1}{2}\iiint \rho v^2 \, dV \tag{2-46}$$

where ρ is the mass density of the body, $dV = dx\,dy\,dz$ is the differential volume, $\bar{v}$ is the velocity of this differential volume, and the above integration is taken over the entire volume of the body.

But $$v^2 = \bar{v} \cdot \bar{v} = (\bar{\omega} \times \bar{r}) \cdot (\bar{\omega} \times \bar{r})$$
where $$\bar{\omega} = \omega_x \bar{\imath} + \omega_y \bar{\jmath} + \omega_z \bar{k}$$
and $$\bar{r} = x\bar{\imath} + y\bar{\imath} + z\bar{k}$$

Upon substitution of the above expressions for $\bar{\omega}$ and $\bar{r}$ in Eq. (2-46), the following is obtained:

$$K = \tfrac{1}{2}\iiint \rho[(\omega_y z - \omega_z y)^2 + (\omega_z x - \omega_x z)^2 + (\omega_x y - \omega_y x)^2] \, dV$$

Expanding the above and substituting Eqs. (2-20) and (2-21), the definitions for the moments and products of inertia of a rigid body, we have the kinetic energy given by

$$K = \tfrac{1}{2}(A\omega_x^2 + B\omega_y^2 + C\omega_z^2 - 2D\omega_y\omega_z - 2E\omega_z\omega_x - 2F\omega_x\omega_y) \tag{2-47}$$

The above expression is equivalent to Eq. (2-44). This can be shown by substituting Eq. (2-31) into (2-44). It should be noted that if A, B, and C are the principal moments of inertia of the body, Eq. (2-47) collapses to the simple form

$$K = \tfrac{1}{2}(A\omega_x^2 + B\omega_y^2 + C\omega_z^2) \tag{2-48}$$

PROBLEMS

2-1. Express the angular velocity $\bar{\omega} = \omega_x'\bar{\imath} + \omega_y'\bar{\jmath} + \omega_z'\bar{k}$ in terms of the eulerian angles, where ω_x', ω_y', and ω_z' are space-fixed components. A set of relations for ω_x', ω_y', and ω_z' similar to Eqs. (2-39) to (2-41) for the body-fixed coordinates will be obtained.

2-2. From the differential Eqs. 2-33 for $A = B$ and $T_z = 0$, obtain the general solution for ω_x, ω_y, and ω_z. Assume T_x and T_y are constant torques applied to the body. Also, let $A > C$.

2-3. Derive Eqs. 2-31 from Eq. (2-16), and derive Eqs. 2-33 from Eq. (2-31).

BIBLIOGRAPHY

1. Klein, F. and A. Sommerfeld: "Über die Theorie des Kreisels," B. G. Teubner Publisher, Leipzig, 1897–1910, 4 vols.

2. Webster, A. G.: "Dynamics of Particles and of Rigid, Elastic and Fluid Bodies," 2d ed., Dover Publications, New York, 1959.

3. Grammel, R.: "Der Kreisel," Friedrig Vieweg und Söhne, Brunswick, Germany, 1920.

4. Whittaker, E. T.: "Analytical Dynamics of Particles and Rigid Bodies," 4th ed., Cambridge University Press, New York, 1937.

5. Joos, Georg: "Theoretical Physics," translated by Ira Freeman, 2d ed., Hafner Publishing Company, New York, 1950.

6. Deimel, R. F.: "Mechanics of the Gyroscope," Dover Publications, New York, 1950.

7. Ferry, E. S.: "Applied Gyrodynamics," John Wiley & Sons, Inc., New York, 1932.

CHAPTER 3

THEORY OF THE GYROSCOPE—PART 2

By Bernard Litman

Nomenclature

x, y, z = system of rectangular body-fixed axes
x', y', z' = system of rectangular axes fixed to gyro housing
$\bar{T}$ = torque vector
$\bar{\omega}$ = angular-velocity vector
T'_x, T'_y, T'_z = projection of $\bar{T}$ upon x', y', z'
$\omega'_x, \omega'_y, \omega'_z$ = projection of $\bar{\omega}$ upon x', y', z'
H = angular momentum
A, B, C = moments of inertia
g = acceleration of gravity
K = kinetic energy

3-1. Performance Equations with Respect to "Stationary" Reference Axes

The previous chapter derived a set of equations for moment of inertia and angular momentum of a body with respect to coordinate axes x, y, and z which were fixed to the body. The equations resulted in torque expressions (Euler's equations) with respect to these same body-fixed axes. These formulations are useful in developing body motions as seen by one who is stationary with respect to the axes. An example would be the motion of the earth as seen by an observer on the earth. Thus, the angular velocities obtained would represent the apparent angular motion of the stars.

In all the work we will pursue involving a high-speed gyrowheel, these relations turn out to be quite inconvenient, since they are expressed in coordinates which rotate around rapidly with respect to an external observer. Accordingly, we will pick another set of coordinate axes, fixed with respect to the gyro housing rather than to the rotating flywheel. The rotor bearings will compel one axis to coincide with one of the axes of the body-fixed system, and we will call this the *spin axis* z. The other axes fixed to the gyro housing are x' and y'. Note that this is not a truly stationary set of axes, since the gyro housing will move through space and hence the axes will too. However, this set of "housing-fixed" axes will turn out to be the most convenient one for most gyroscopic instrument problems. The relative orientation of the two sets of axes is shown in Fig. 3-1. From inspection of the figure, we may write the following relations for torque and angular velocity in the new coordinate system:

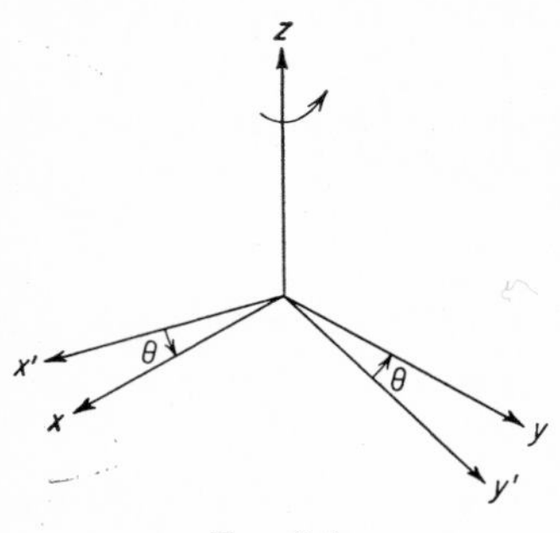

Fig. 3-1

$$
\begin{aligned}
T'_x \cos\theta + T'_y \sin\theta &= T_x \\
-T'_x \sin\theta + T'_y \cos\theta &= T_y \\
\omega'_x \cos\theta + \omega'_y \sin\theta &= \omega_x \\
-\omega'_x \sin\theta + \omega'_y \cos\theta &= \omega_y
\end{aligned}
\tag{3-1}
$$

We will now substitute these expressions into Euler's equations (2-33). We will also let $B = A$, which makes our gyrowheel a figure of revolution, as would be the case for any practical gyro. Substitution yields (note that $d\theta/dt = \omega_z$)

$$
\begin{aligned}
T'_x \cos\theta + T'_y \sin\theta &= A(\dot{\omega}'_x \cos\theta - \omega'_x\omega_z \sin\theta + \dot{\omega}'_y \sin\theta + \omega'_y\omega_z \cos\theta) \\
&\quad + (A - C)(\omega'_x\omega_z \sin\theta - \omega'_y\omega_z \cos\theta) \\
-T'_x \sin\theta + T'_y \cos\theta &= A(-\dot{\omega}'_x \sin\theta - \omega'_x\omega_z \cos\theta + \dot{\omega}'_y \cos\theta - \omega'_y\omega_z \sin\theta) \\
&\quad + (A - C)(\omega'_x\omega_z \cos\theta + \omega'_y\omega_z \sin\theta) \\
&\quad T_z = C\dot{\omega}_z
\end{aligned}
\tag{3-2}
$$

If we multiply the first of Eqs. (3-2) by $\cos\theta$ and the second by $-\sin\theta$ and add, we obtain T'_x. Similarly, if we multiply the first by $\sin\theta$ and the second by $\cos\theta$ and add, we obtain T'_y. The reader can verify that the results of this algebraic manipulation yield the following:

$$
\begin{aligned}
T'_x &= A\dot{\omega}'_x + C\omega_z\omega'_y \\
T'_y &= A\dot{\omega}'_y - C\omega_z\omega'_x \\
T_z &= C\dot{\omega}_z
\end{aligned}
\tag{3-3}
$$

Again we note that these torques are expressed with respect to axes fixed to the gyro case. The z axis coincides with the spin axis.

When no net torques are applied to the spin axis, $T_z = C\dot{\omega}_z = 0$ and $\omega_z = \text{const}$. This is the case in a gyro when the motor-driving torque just balances the friction torques so that the wheel is running at constant speed. If $C\omega_z = H_z$, then

$$
\begin{aligned}
T'_x &= A\dot{\omega}'_x + H_z\omega'_y \\
T'_y &= A\dot{\omega}'_y - H_z\omega'_x
\end{aligned}
\tag{3-4}
$$

The first term in each of the above expressions represents the familiar inertia force. A should also include the moment of inertia of the housing so that the torques represent total torques applied to housing and gyro-wheel. The second term represents the gyroscopic force. We note that this force (unlike the inertia force) is proportional to the velocity at right angles to the torque being considered.

We are now in a position to examine the motion of a gyroscopic body when subjected to torques, and we shall take several typical cases.

3-2. Fixed Torque Applied to a Gyro

If the applied torques T'_x and T'_y are assumed constant with time, the differential Eqs. (3-4) have solutions of the form

$$\omega'_x = \frac{-T'_y}{H_z} \qquad \omega'_y = \frac{T'_x}{H_z} \tag{3-5}$$

as well as

$$\begin{aligned} \omega'_x &= K_1 \sin \frac{H_z t}{A} + K_2 \cos \frac{H_z t}{A} \\ \omega'_y &= -K_1 \cos \frac{H_z t}{A} + K_2 \sin \frac{H_z t}{A} \end{aligned} \tag{3-6}$$

where K_1 and K_2 are arbitrary constants. (These solutions may be verified by direct substitution.) A complete solution is obtained by combining (3-5) and (3-6) and selecting K_1 and K_2 to meet the initial conditions.

We note that (3-5) represents a steady motion, proportional to and at right angles to the applied torque. This steady motion is called the *precession* of the gyro. Equations (3-6) represent an oscillatory motion superimposed on the steady motion. This is the *nutation* of the gyro. It has a frequency given by $H_z/2\pi A$. Magnitude A, which is the inertia at right angles to the spin axis, includes not only the inertia of the wheel but that of any stationary parts affixed to it, such as gyro housing, motor stator, etc.

Let us assume that we start at $t = 0$ from a stationary condition of $\omega'_x = \omega'_y = 0$ and suddenly apply a fixed torque T'_x. (For simplicity, we will not apply a torque T'_y.) Then, substitution of the initial conditions into (3-5) and (3-6) enables us to obtain K_1 and K_2. The final solution is

$$\begin{aligned} \omega'_x &= \frac{T'_x}{H_z} \sin \frac{H_z t}{A} \\ \omega'_y &= \frac{T'_x}{H_z}\left(1 - \cos \frac{H_z t}{A}\right) \end{aligned} \tag{3-7}$$

Substitution of typical numbers shows that the oscillatory part is usually very small in amplitude and moderately high in frequency (a sizable fraction of the rotational frequency of the wheel).

3-3. Damping Present on the Gyro

Normally there will be reasonable damping forces on the gyro (friction, viscous drag, etc.), and these will cause the nutation to damp out quickly after application of a torque. To demonstrate this we will assume a damping torque about each axis x' and y' proportional to the angular velocities ω_x' and ω_y'. Equations (3-4) then become

$$\begin{aligned} T_x' &= A\dot{\omega}_x' + f\omega_x' + H_z\omega_y' \\ T_y' &= A\dot{\omega}_y' + f\omega_y' - H_z\omega_x' \end{aligned} \tag{3-8}$$

Solutions equivalent to (3-5) and (3-6) now become

$$\omega_x' = \frac{fT_x' - H_zT_y'}{H_z^2 + f^2} \qquad \omega_y' = \frac{H_zT_x' + fT_y'}{H_z^2 + f^2} \tag{3-9}$$

and

$$\begin{aligned} \omega_x' &= e^{-ft/A}\left[K_1 \sin\left(\frac{H_zt}{A}\right) + K_2 \cos\frac{H_zt}{A}\right] \\ \omega_y' &= e^{-ft/A}\left[-K_1 \cos\left(\frac{H_zt}{A}\right) + K_2 \sin\frac{H_zt}{A}\right] \end{aligned} \tag{3-10}$$

It is evident that the nutation terms are now associated with an exponential damping term. We note that the steady-state (precession) term is also altered somewhat by the damping term. In most modern applications, however, the damping term will not affect the steady precession, because the gyro is used with a power-driven follow-up servo. This means that the gyro and its housing are maintained in a fixed angular relation with respect to their external enclosure, so that no net viscous drag appears. Thus the steady-state motion will really be represented by Eqs. (3-5). On the other hand, the servo will not normally be capable of keeping up with the rapid nutation oscillations. Therefore, the viscous drag will remain at the nutation frequencies, and we can continue to use Eqs. (3-10) with accuracy.

3-4. The Spinning Top

We shall now treat a case where the torques on a gyro are not fixed but depend on the position of the gyro. This is represented by a top spinning close to the vertical. The torques acting on the top are caused by gravity acting on the mass of the top. The magnitude of the torque is closely proportional to the angular deviation of the top's spin axis from the vertical. We will find a critical speed below which the top will not sustain itself but will topple. Figure 3-2 shows such a top making an angle ϕ with the vertical. A complete analysis should include large values of ϕ. However, we will illustrate the same point with simpler algebra by assuming ϕ to be small. Similarly (for algebraic simplicity), we have selected one of our axes, x', to be horizontal at the instant we look at the top. From an inspection of Fig. 3-2, we observe

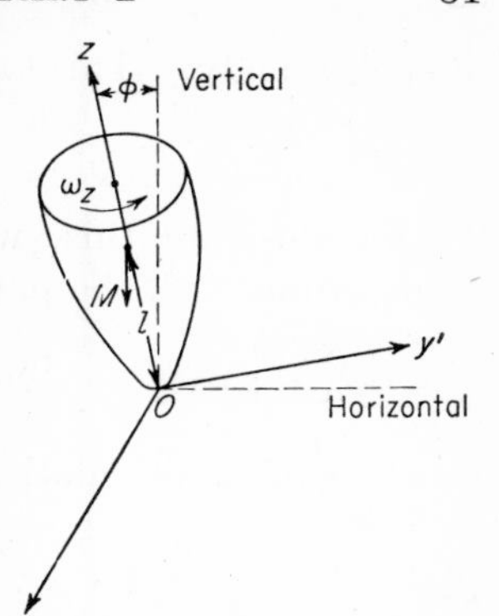

FIG. 3-2

$$\begin{aligned} T'_x &= Mgl \sin \phi \cong Mgl\phi \\ T'_y &= 0 \\ \omega'_x &= \dot{\phi} \end{aligned} \tag{3-11}$$

Substituting these terms into Eqs. (3-4), we have

$$\begin{aligned} Mgl\phi &= A\dot{\omega}'_x + H_z\omega'_y \\ 0 &= A\dot{\omega}'_y - H_z\omega'_x \end{aligned} \tag{3-12}$$

We can differentiate the first of Eqs. (3-12) and then replace $\dot{\phi}$ and $\dot{\omega}'_y$ from the expressions in (3-11) and (3-12), yielding

$$Mgl\omega'_x = A\ddot{\omega}'_x + \frac{H_z{}^2\omega'_x}{A} \tag{3-13}$$

or

$$\ddot{\omega}'_x + \left(\frac{H_z{}^2}{A^2} - \frac{Mgl}{A}\right)\omega'_x = 0 \tag{3-14}$$

If the expression in the parenthesis is positive, the roots of the differential equation in ω'_x are imaginary, and ω'_x will go through a steady oscillation (nutation) so that the motion is stable. If the expression is negative, one of the roots for ω'_x is positive, which indicates a steady exponential increase for ω'_x (toppling). Hence, our criteria are

$$\text{Stable: } H_z{}^2 > Mgl\,A \qquad \text{Unstable: } H_z{}^2 < Mgl\,A \tag{3-15}$$

3-5. Energy

A powerful tool in determining the behavior of many physical systems is the principle of conservation of energy. Thus, in a simple nondissipative system, we can state that the sum of the kinetic and potential energy is a constant. Expressed differently, we can say that the work put into a system by external forces is equal to the gain in kinetic energy. The work input is obtained by multiplying each force (or torque) by the linear (or angular) displacement along the direction of the force (or torque). The reader has probably used this tool previously in linear mechanics, for instance, to determine the motion of a particle in the earth's gravity field. The result is, of course, the same as if one directly utilized Newton's law ($\bar{F} = m\bar{a}$), but a complete statement is often more easily obtained by using the energy expression.

The same principle can be applied with ease to a rotating rigid body, such as a gyroscope, if we write a simple expression for the kinetic energy of such a body. This expression is given by

$$K = \tfrac{1}{2}\bar{\omega} \cdot \bar{H} \tag{3-16}$$

To demonstrate this, we expand $\bar{H}$ as a summation of the angular momentum of all the particles.

$$\tfrac{1}{2}\bar{\omega} \cdot \bar{H} = \tfrac{1}{2}\bar{\omega} \cdot \sum_i (\bar{r}_i \times m_i\bar{v}_i)$$

By a simple manipulation of vector algebra, we can rewrite this as

$$\tfrac{1}{2} \sum_i [m_i(\bar{\omega} \times \bar{r}_i) \cdot \bar{v}_i]$$

However, $\bar{\omega} \times \bar{r}_i$ is the velocity of the particle due to its rotation. Our expression now becomes

$$\tfrac{1}{2} \sum_i (m_i\bar{v}_i \cdot \bar{v}_i) = \tfrac{1}{2} \sum_i (m_i v_i^2)$$

This is the sum of the kinetic energy of all the particles in the body. Thus our original expression is indeed the total kinetic energy of the rotating body.

Example. We may take the solutions of Eqs. (3-7) and apply our energy expression (3-16). Expressing this vector equation in terms of its components, we have $\tfrac{1}{2}(\omega'_x H_x + \omega'_y H_y + \omega_z H_z)$. Since ω_z is constant, the change in kinetic energy will be given by the first two terms, viz.,

$$\Delta K = \tfrac{1}{2}(\omega'_x H_x + \omega'_y H_y)$$

Since we are using principal axes, the expressions for H_x and H_y are directly given by $H_x = A\omega'_x$ and $H_y = A\omega'_y$. Hence

$$\Delta K = \frac{A}{2} (\omega'^2_x + \omega'^2_y)$$

Substituting the values of ω'_x and ω'_y from Eqs. (3-7), we get

$$\Delta K = A \frac{T'^2_x}{H_z^2} \left(1 - \cos \frac{H_z}{A} t\right) \tag{3-17}$$

The work done by the external torque T'_x is

$$\int_0^t T'_x \, d\theta'_x = \int_0^t T'_x \omega'_x \, dt$$

and substituting the values of ω'_x from (3-7) we get

$$A \frac{T'^2_x}{H_z^2} \left(1 - \cos \frac{H_z}{A} t\right) \tag{3-18}$$

As expected, this is equal to the change in kinetic energy.

PROBLEMS

3-1. A gyro has 10^6 cgs units of angular momentum and rotates at 12,000 rpm. The moment of inertia at right angles to the spin axis (including housing, etc.) is $1\frac{1}{2}$ times that about the spin axis. A fixed torque of 1 oz-in. is suddenly applied and maintained about the x' axis. What is the precession rate? What is the nutation frequency? What is the maximum angular offset in the direction of the applied torque?

3-2. What is the value of the damping constant needed to give a decay rate of 50 per cent per complete nutation cycle in the above gyro?

What is the maximum value of damping force that would exist for the torque applied in Prob. 3-1?

3-3. Find the permanent offset θ_x' taken by the gyro after the nutation is damped out. What is the total work done by the applied torque? NOTE: In Probs. 3-2 and 3-3 assume that the damping acts only at the nutation frequency and not for the steady-state motion.

3-4. Rederive Eqs. (3-3) without making the assumption that $B = A$. This will cover the case of an object which is not a figure of revolution (such as an airplane propeller). Show that a steady precession no longer causes only a constant reaction torque but, in addition, an oscillating torque with a frequency of oscillation equal to twice the frequency of rotation.

BIBLIOGRAPHY

1. Klein, F. and A. Sommerfeld: "Über die Theorie des Kreisels," B. G. Teubner Publisher, Leipzig, 1897–1910, 4 vols.

2. Webster, A. G.: "Dynamics of Particles and of Rigid, Elastic and Fluid Bodies," 2d ed., Dover Publications, New York, 1959.

3. Grammel, R.: "Der Kreisel," Friedrig Vieweg und Söhne, Brunswick, Germany, 1920.

4. Whittaker, E. T.: "Analytical Dynamics of Particles and Rigid Bodies," 4th ed., Cambridge University Press, New York, 1937.

5. Joos, Georg: "Theoretical Physics," translated by Ira Freeman, 2d ed., Hafner Publishing Company, New York, 1950.

6. Deimel, R. F.: "Mechanics of the Gyroscope," Dover Publications, New York, 1950.

7. Ferry, E. S.: "Applied Gyrodynamics," John Wiley & Sons, Inc., New York, 1932.

CHAPTER 4

FUNCTIONAL CHARACTERISTICS AND RESTRAINTS

By Julius Y. Kaplan

Nomenclature

ω_p = angular rate of precession
I, I_z = moment of inertia of gyrowheel
ω_z = angular rate of spin of gyrowheel
ω_n = natural circular frequency
H = angular momentum
T = torque
θ_x, θ_y = spin-vector angular displacement with respect to inertial space
θ'_x, θ'_y = gyro housing angular displacement with respect to inertial space
C, C_x, C_y = viscous drag coefficients
K, K_{ex}, K_{ey} = elastic restraint constants (torsional gradients)
IA = input axis
OA = output axis
SRA = spin reference axis
τ = time constant
δ = coefficient of critical damping
e_x, e_y = relative angular displacements of gyrowheel and gyro housing

4-1. Introduction

The idea to produce desired gyro characteristics through restraints received impetus in the 1940s when the designers of fire control and vehicle stabilization systems drew away from the conventional reliance on a "master gyro reference." From a system viewpoint it was sometimes convenient to handle each axis of stabilization separately. Early experimentation showed that a gyro constrained to precess only about one axis (the so-called "single-degree-of-freedom" gyro) would have the desired characteristic of responding to space inputs essentially only about the desired input axis. Further, by restraining its precession with linear springs, the resulting precessional displacement would be a direct measure of rate with respect to inertial space. Other convenient forms of restraint appeared evident, e.g., pure viscous. This gave the property of proportionality (with a slight time constant) of precession angle to input axis motion with respect to inertial space. A long period of developing these single-degree-of-freedom gyros has resulted in a versatile line of single-axis "space tachometer" and "space synchro" transducers particularly suitable to fire-control-system and vehicle-motion stabilization. Painstaking experimentation has brought the accuracy of these devices into the precision inertial class.

The single-axis restrained gyro has thus provided an important asset to the system designers, who have found ready use for this transducer in multiloop stabilization requirements.

Beyond the single-axis gyro there is a large overlapping field where the two-axis or two-degree-of-freedom gyro is used. The application of restraints here may not be as obvious, since the spin axis is not normally constrained. However, it is important to understand the effect of secondary (undesired) restraints on gyro performance, as well as the purposeful use of primary restraints in some cases to achieve desired functional characteristics. In general, the effect of undesired restraints and the resulting deleterious effect on gyro performance are extremely important to the design and application of gyros in both the single- and the two-degree-of-freedom class.

The previous chapters dealt with the basic mechanics of the gyroscope. Succeeding chapters will be concerned with the problems of detailed gyro design, system applications, and methods of test. In this chapter we will develop as foundation material some of the basic functional gyro configurations. We will see how these configurations, each with its characteristic behavior, are achieved through the intelligent combination of gimbaling arrangements and systems of restraints.

In today's complex systems involving a variety of carefully interwoven electrical, mechanical, hydraulic, and chemical devices, it has become necessary to look for a convenient "common denominator" way, mathematically, of representing the characteristics of the system and the elements which comprise it. Classical mathematics is much too unwieldy. So in order to meet this end, operational mathematics utilizing the Laplace transform has been developed. By this means both transient and steady-state characteristics may be represented. With a little familiarity the physics of a particular system element may be written directly in transform notation, and its transient and steady-state performance may be easily understood therefrom. There are a number of good references on this operational mathematics, some of which are given in the Bibliography at the end of the chapter.

With the aid of this operational notation, the variety of basic gyro configurations are developed from fundamental gyro equations. The features of each configuration are explored and their advantages and limitations described.

4-2. Role of the Gyro

Before deciding on a particular gyro configuration, the system designer first must establish clearly the specific stabilization role to be performed by the gyro. If the gyro is to perform directly the physical task of stabilization, by furnishing a gyroscopic corrective effort, then the accuracy of the gyroscopic reference embodied in the spin vector is necessarily compromised. This is so because the rate at which the spin vector precesses is directly proportional to gyro reaction torque. Today such use of the gyro is found only in relatively crude applications. This is in contrast to the past, where most gyroscopic stabilization was of the brute-force type, using massive flywheels spinning at relatively high speeds to develop the stabilizing torques directly.

In today's technology, with its extreme emphasis on accuracy and miniaturization, the drive motor of a servomechanism, rather than the gyro itself, is normally called upon to provide the muscle power of corrective effort.* Precision low-power lightweight sensor devices (e.g., potentiometers, tachometers, gyros, etc.) are used to measure accurately and often remotely the error between command and output. This error is fed back as an order to the servomotor which will drive the output untiringly until the output-input error is virtually eliminated. Since a power amplifier is normally provided between the sensor and the servomotor, negligible power is drawn from the sensor. Thus the gyro, in the role of the sensor, need not sacrifice accuracy of its attitude reference by doing work. As an added feature, the null circuit of the servomechanism provides a convenient "adding loop" for a variety of inputs which may be used to shape the response of the output. We shall see in Chap. 5 how this feature is used to advantage, for example, in building a modern gyrocompass.

It is on this role of the gyro as a sensor that we shall concentrate our attention. The system designer must ensure that the gyro is used in such a way as to prevent the inadvertent tapping of work from it; the gyro designer must work closely with him to evaluate carefully the environment to which the gyro will be exposed to be sure that the level of disturbing torques excited by the environment (e.g., shock, vibration,

* It should be noted that in some applications the gyro stabilizing effort may be relied upon as an aid to providing *transient* rigidity, at no serious sacrifice to steady-state performance. This is done when it is not efficient to provide the capacity of servo corrective effort required at high frequencies.

temperature, etc.) as well as power-supply fluctuations do not exceed the required limits for the time period under consideration.

The gyro designer has many paths open to him. Some applications call for a truly space-fixed attitude reference; others may require a controlled angular rate in space (i.e., space tachometer). Alternatives include the use of one or more gimbals and a variety of restraining mechanisms operating in an open- or closed-loop fashion. Whatever the choice (and he must make it in coordination with the system engineer), the designer's most challenging task is to devise unique and reliable means to prevent spurious torques, usually of microscopic level, from disturbing the spin or angular-momentum vector. This must be accomplished while the "wanted" torques, intentionally designed in restraints, are acting to give the characteristic gyro response desired. The procedural steps in composing a gyro configuration are treated in the following section.

4-3. Functional Design of the Gyro

Starting with the concept of a spin vector in inertial space, we may consider the basic functional design of a gyro to be accomplished in five steps as follows:

Step 1. Embody the spin vector into a flywheel caused to rotate at high speed on an axle.

Step 2. Mount the axle in a gimbal set having at least one or possibly two degrees of freedom with respect to an external housing.

Step 3. Provide suitable means for restraining the angular motion or precession of the axle, thereby shaping the transient and steady-state response of the gyro to inputs of angular rate or torque.

Step 4. Provide a means (pick-off device) for measuring the motion of the external housing relative to the axle.

Step 5. Furnish a means (caging device) for initially setting the axle to a desired attitude, subsequently causing it to move in a prescribed manner (ordered precession).

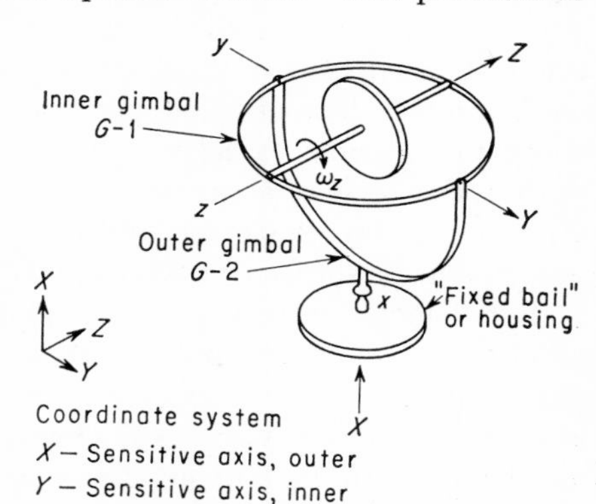

FIG. 4-1. Functional stick diagram of two-axis gyro. It is also variously referred to as a two-degree-of-freedom gyro, three-frame gyro, displacement or positional gyro, and free gyro. For ideal conditions of perfect balance and no gimbal friction, the gyro axle is not affected by any motions of the housing; once the wheel has reached its speed, the axle will maintain its orientation fixed in inertial space. Observe, too, that either axis X or Y performs in the dual role of input or output axis.

These steps are illustrated in Fig. 4-1, the stick diagram of a two-axis gyro. This type of gyro is referred to by several names, including two-degree-of-freedom gyro, three-frame gyro, displacement or positional gyro, and free gyro. The axle of the flywheel is bearing-mounted in an inner gimbal G-1, which is in turn pivoted in an outer gimbal G-2. The outer gimbal G-2 is pivoted in an external housing or "fixed bail." Assuming, for the moment, the ideal conditions of no friction (or other restraining torques) at the gimbal pivots and perfect gimbal balance, we see that the rotor axle, once set spinning, will remain pointing in the same direction in inertial space without regard to the movement of the housing. Since the axle, or spin vector, is gyroscopically held fixed in inertial space, the displacement of the housing with respect to it may be measured or described by the angular motion about the two sets of gimbal pivots. It is this property which gives rise to the term *displacement gyro*. The term *free gyro** is derived from the fact that the spin vector is, ideally, not disturbed by any angular motion of the housing. The other names identify the degrees of freedom of the gimbaling and the number of frames of support, i.e., two degree of freedom and three frame. In some circles the terms *space gyro*, *space synchro*, and *space potentiometer* are applied for this type of gyro; these are all "use" connotations, expressing the system designer's viewpoint of the role the gyro is to play.

For some applications it is found useful to suppress one degree of freedom by eliminating the outer gimbal G-2. This is illustrated by Fig. 4-2*a*, the stick diagram of a single-axis gyro. Synonym names are single-degree-of-freedom and two-frame gyro. Since the outer gimbal does not exist, it can be seen that rotation of the housing about the vertical axis X will apply a coercive torque on the spinning wheel. As long as the housing is caused to rotate, the axle will precess (about Y) until it is aligned with the X axis, i.e., until the axis of rotation or applied torque and the axis of spin are coincident. The axle rate of precession, as we have learned, is directly proportional under steady-state conditions to the applied torque and inversely proportional to the angular momentum, or explicitly

$$\omega_P = \frac{T}{H} = \frac{T}{I_z \cdot \omega_z}$$

Conversely, the gyroscopic torque of precession is proportional to the angular rate of housing rotation. It is this property which permits us to construct a so-called "single-axis" rate gyro, depicted in Fig. 4-2*b*. Rather than let the axle precess until the effect of the coercive torque disappears, i.e., until the axis of spin has moved into coincidence with the

* It should be emphasized that a truly "free" gyro is ideally achieved only when *all* restraints to precession are removed. For this to be possible, there need to be at least two degrees of freedom.

axis of housing rotation, a pair of restraining springs is attached between gimbal G-1 and the fixed bail. Now, as the axle precesses, a restraining torque is developed by the springs proportional to the angle precessed. Under these conditions it will be found that the axle will precess until the restraining-spring torque matches the gyroscopic precession torque developed as a reaction to the rotation of the housing. Since the torque of precession is proportional to the rate at which the housing is rotated, the angle through which the axle precesses is directly a measure of the angular

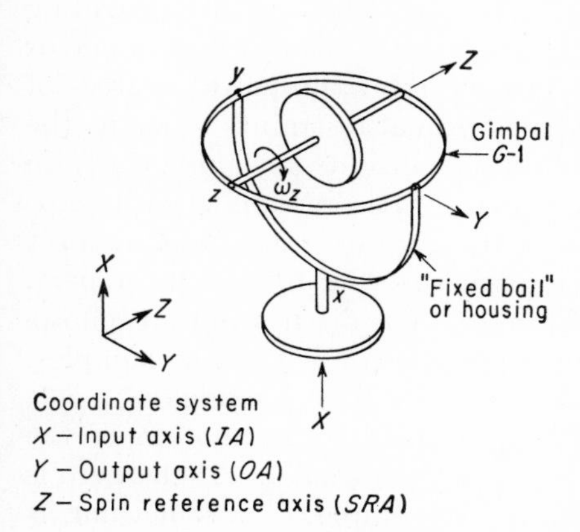

FIG. 4-2*a*. Functional-stick diagram of single-axis gyro. This gyro is also variously referred to as single-degree-of-freedom or two-frame gyro. If the housing is rotated about the vertical axis X, the axle Z will precess until it is vertical, i.e., aligned with X.

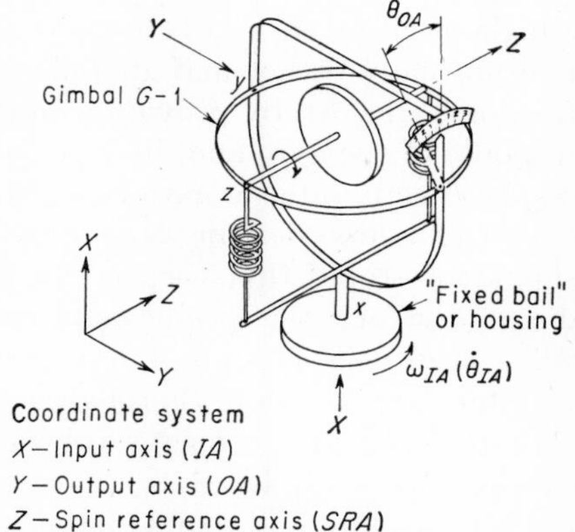

FIG. 4-2*b*. Functional-stick diagram of single-axis rate gyro. Springs attached between gimbal G-1 and housing provide linear elastic restraint. In the presence of angular rotation ω_{IA} of the housing, the axle will precess through angle θ_{OA} until the restraining torque of the springs balances the gyroscopic precession torque due to the housing rotation. The gyro thus indicates directly by the angular displacement θ_{OA} a measure of the input rate ω_{IA}.

rate of housing rotation. We thus have constructed, by applying a linear spring restraint, a rate (measuring) gyro, sometimes called a *space tachometer*.

Similarly, it can be seen that the application of other types of restraining torques, singly or in combination, to equate the precessional torque can be used to alter the functional gyro characteristic. For example, in the case illustrated above, should a linear first-order viscous restraint be used in place of the linear elastic restraint, the precession torque produced as a result of housing rotation rate is balanced off by a viscous torque, formed as the product of viscous restraint coefficient by the rate of axle precession. In effect, the rates of axle precession and housing rotation are equated, which is equivalent to saying that the displacement of the axle is proportional to the housing motion. This is really an integrating action where the precession of the axle about Y is an integral of the angular rate of the housing about X. Such a gyro is known as a *rate-integrating gyro.* These relationships and the methods for producing a variety of gyro functions through the application of suitable restraints will be treated more extensively later.

In what has been discussed above, we have seen how the first three basic steps in configuring a gyro may be accomplished: (1) by providing a high-speed flywheel; (2) by mounting the axle of this flywheel in one or two mutually orthogonal gimbals to provide the appropriate degrees of freedom; and (3), by providing suitable torsional restraints to shape the response of the gyro and, in effect, to functionalize its basic use, e.g., as a displacement, rate, or rate-integrating gyro. The remaining two steps concern the practical implementation of the gyro design. Here again it should be stated that the system requirements will, for the most part, dictate the form the specific design will take. The discussion that follows will serve to clarify steps 4 and 5 by reference to a few typical examples. In later chapters more thorough design details will be provided.

Step 4 provides a means (pickoff) for measuring the motion of the external housing relative to the axle (spin reference axis). If the gyro is not a sealed unit and remote indication is not required, then something as simple as a pointer on the inner gimbal moving over an accurate (say, vernier) scale on the outer gimbal or housing might suffice. Even in such a simple case, however, the effect of any unbalance of the pointer and stability of balance must be evaluated for consistency with the accuracy demanded of the gyro. In most cases remote indication is a definite requirement. Perhaps the most straightforward means would be a resistance potentiometer of the low-torque type. However, for any reasonably accurate gyro, the lower friction available in induction potentiometers would probably be in order. Where higher-gain outputs are required, low-reluctance magnetic inductor devices are used. The danger here is in the potentially troublesome magnetic reaction torques. To obviate this inductive air-coil pickoffs are sometimes used, sacrificing appropriate angular gradient, of course. Occasionally capacitor-type pickoffs may be used. Again the effect of electrostatic forces must be assessed. For most all-electric pickoffs the problem of electric lead-in wires exists. These are inevitable sources of torsional restraint which the designer must minimize and finally account for (see Chap. 11 for more details).

Step 5 furnishes a means for ordering angular motion of the axle. It might seem paradoxical, after so much emphasis on the integrity of the axle as an attitude reference, to introduce the concept of applying a "disturbing" torque to cause the spin vector to be precessed. Notwithstanding, for practical reasons this is mandatory, if the gyro is to be useful in a system. First, the axle must be set to a precise reference attitude. Secondly, the system might require that the axle not be fixed in space but rather to the earth. This means that the axle must be an accurately prescribed *moving* reference.

Let us look at an example. Consider the case of an inertial navigator used to guide a submarine for extended periods of time through the oceans. At the outset, the gyroscopic reference, the axle, must be accurately aligned to a known reference. For this purpose, a star tracker might be used to establish a reference with the fixed stars. The gyro axle must then be precessed into coincidence with the stellar reference. This can be done by an automatic servo loop, excited from a null signal, measuring the deviation of the axle from the stellar reference. This error signal, suitably amplified, will actuate the gyro torquer. The torquer will then automatically precess the axle until coincidence with the stellar reference is achieved. The gyro is now ready for inertial navigation to commence. If "free gyro" mode is to be used, ideally no further torquing of the gyro is required. Practically speaking, however, advantage is sometimes taken of "known" gyro behavior in the expected environment, i.e., attempt is made to cancel the predictable drift characteristic through the application of experimentally derived torque patterns using electromagnetic torquers. This is a case of torquing for second-order correction. A first-order use of torquing is demonstrated by the case where the gyro spin axis is slaved to the local vertical automatically (by Schuler tuning, which will be discussed later). This slaving is accomplished by means of accurate torquing of the spin vector.

Initial setting of the spin vector to a known orientation is sometimes referred to as "caging." In some of the less accurate applications, mechanical means are used to lock the axle in the desired position before start-up. In most high-performance gyros used in servo loops, however, caging is accomplished conveniently by the use of small-angle mechanical stops to locate the axle approximately. The torquer is used for precise positioning via the automatic servo loop. The stop angles are made large enough to prevent "tumbling"* for the largest expected servo lag error. On the other hand, they are made small enough to prevent any overstressing of the delicate restraining members of the suspension (e.g., electric lead-in flexes). The small stop angles also ensure a reasonably small settling or erection time for the gyro and its platform. If very wide angle stops were used, excessive torque levels would be required to

* Tumbling is a condition of sudden upset of a gyro or gyro platform evidenced by a sudden and rapid precession of the spin axis due to large torque disturbance such as the spin axle striking the mechanical stops.

bring the gyro and its slaved platform to the reference attitude in a minimum time interval.

In order to tie together the five steps discussed above, let us examine a few typical gyros to see how they are in fact accomplished. Figure 4-3 is a diagram of a type of two-axis displacement gyro, built by the Arma Division of the American Bosch Arma Corp., which is useful as a two-axis reference in space inertial and terrestial guidance.

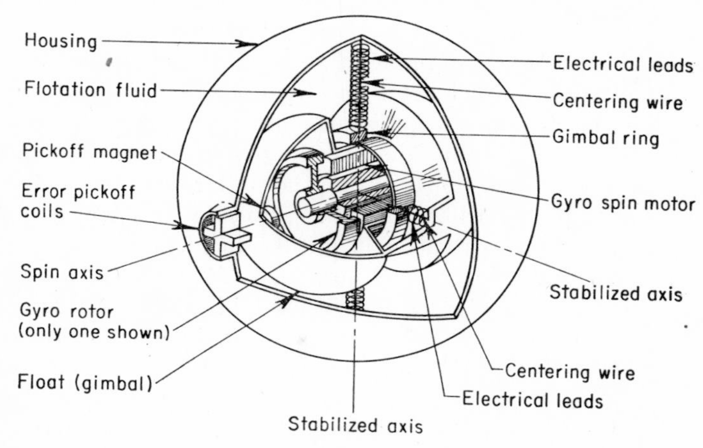

FIG. 4-3. Cutaway drawing of a two-axis gyro developed by the Arma Division, American Bosch Arma Corporation, Garden City, N.Y. The gyrowheel rotates inside a hermetically sealed float. The gap between float and housing (several thousandths of an inch) is filled with a fluid of equal density to the float. Pairs of fine filament wires stretched from float to gimbal ring and gimbal ring to housing center the float in the housing. A zero friction suspension is accomplished because there are no bearings. The float is "weightless" in the neutral-density fluid and, therefore, does not experience any disturbing forces when the housing is accelerated.

Figure 4-4 is a diagram of a type of single-axis rate-integrating gyro developed by the Massachusetts Institute of Technology Instrumentation Laboratory for use as a single-axis reference in fire control and inertial guidance applications. The methods peculiar to each gyro in accomplishing the previously discussed design steps are tabulated for comparison in Table 4-1. No attempt is made to establish the advantage of one scheme over another. Subtle differences can be properly understood only with respect to the specific system application for which the gyro is intended.

As one might expect, there is a tremendous variety in approaches taken in accomplishing each phase of a gyro design. As material and technique breakthroughs occur, new design concepts are developed to take advantage of them. Whereas Figs. 4-3 and 4-4 depict gyro designs based on some of the latest know-how in fluid-supported gimbals, Fig. 4-5 illus-

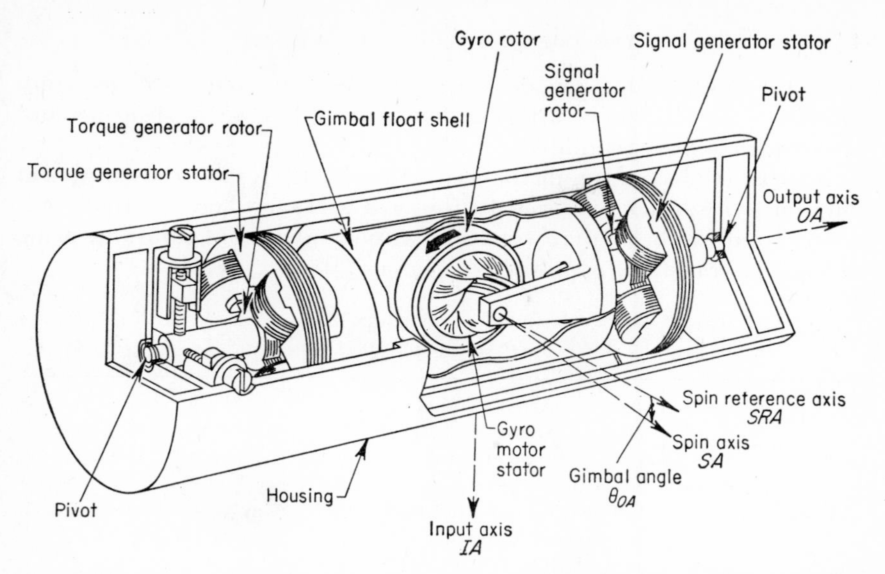

FIG. 4-4. Cutaway drawing of a single-axis gyro developed by the M.I.T. Instrumentation Laboratory. The gyrowheel rotates inside the cylindrical, hermetically sealed gimbal float shell. A small (few thousandths of an inch) gap filled with a high-density fluid separates the float from the housing. The float is neutrally buoyant in the fluid (weightless) and is centered in the gap by jewel pivot bearings at the housing extremities along the output axis. Since the float is essentially weightless, the normal force on the pivot bearings is very low, reducing friction and consequently drift. (*Aeronautical Engineering Review.*)

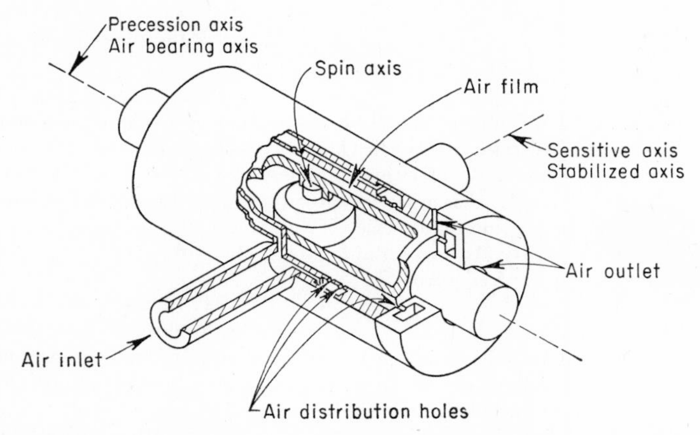

FIG. 4-5. Cutaway drawing of a single-axis gyro developed by U.S. Army Ballistic Missile Agency, Redstone Arsenal, Ala. Suspension of the output axis is by a unique air bearing. A thin film of compressed air separates the "floated" output axis from the housing. The air gap between float and housing is about 1.5 thousandths of an inch. The distribution holes feeding air into the gap are a few thousandths of an inch in diameter. (*Journal of the Institute of Navigation.*)

trates still another approach, developed by Redstone Arsenal of the Army Ballistic Missile Agency, utilizing the principle of an air-bearing-supported single-axis gyro gimbal.

Now that we have been introduced to the basic steps in the functional design of gyros, let us proceed to the next section where we shall synthesize, from the basic gyro equation, various gyro configurations using the Laplace transform operator notation as a tool.

TABLE 4-1. COMPARISON OF DESIGN APPROACHES FOR TWO TYPICAL PRECISION GYROS

Design step	Arma two-axis displacement gyro (see Fig. 4-3)	M.I.T. single-axis rate-integrating gyro (see Fig. 4-4)
1. Flywheel	Ball-bearing-mounted flywheel, driven by three-phase synchronous motor	Same as for Arma two-axis displacement gyro
2. Gimbaling	Flywheel-motor system encased in hermetically sealed spherical float, neutrally buoyant at operating temperature in high-density fluid. Float G-1 centered and pivoted to outer gimbal G-2 by fine wire filaments; neutrally buoyant gimbal G-2 centered and pivoted to housing by fine wire filaments. Electric lead-in provided by wire filaments plus helical flexes	Flywheel-motor system encased in hermetically sealed cylindrical float, neutrally buoyant at operating temperature in high-density fluid. Float G-1 suspended to outer case by jewel and pivot. Electric lead-in provided by "watch-spring" flexes
3. Restraints	Torsional: extremely low torsional restraint due to wire filaments and flexes. No friction (filament support). Viscous: very low viscous drag due to low-viscosity fluid and relatively large fluid gaps. Result: free gyro	Torsional: extremely low torsional restraint due to flexes. Very low pivot friction. Viscous: high viscous drag coefficient due to high-viscosity fluid and narrow fluid gap. Result: rate-integrating gyro
4. Pickoff	Two-axis, air-coil displacement pickoffs excited by electromagnets mounted to float G-1 at extremities of spin axis	Electromagnetic microsyn (multipole) pickoff; rotational type mounted on shaft of output axis G-1
5. Caging and ordered precession	Caging: via small-angle stops plus torquer. Ordered precession: two-axis, air-coil torquers (winding superimposed on pickoff block) react with electromagnets on float	Caging: same. Ordered precession: single-axis microsyn torquers on shaft of output axis G-1

4-4. Gyro Transfer Function—Operational Notation

The synthesis and analysis of complex systems require that all elements be described in common mathematical terms. For this purpose, operational mathematics, using the Laplace transform notation, has been generally applied. This permits the writing of the so-called "transfer-function" characteristic, which expresses in operational form the ratio of output to input. Both steady-state and transient characteristics are expressed in this combined notation. With a little training, the reader will find it comparatively easy to correlate factors in the ratio with their equivalence in steady-state and transient response. By means of this ratio, or transfer function, the gyro can truly be considered a "black box" and can be treated as such in the over-all system analysis.

For reference purposes, the nomenclature outline below summarizes the various symbols used. Starting with the basic gyro equations, we will develop a variety of gyro types, showing their functional (transfer) diagrams and transfer-function characteristics.

Let us consider first a momentum vector in inertial space, physically embodied in a flywheel of momentum H.* The equations of motion are then

$$T_x = H\dot{\theta}_y + I_x\ddot{\theta}_x + C_x(\dot{\theta}_x - \dot{\theta}'_x) + K_{ex}(\theta_x - \theta'_x) \quad (4\text{-}1)$$
$$T_y = -H\dot{\theta}_x + I_y\ddot{\theta}_y + C_y(\dot{\theta}_y - \dot{\theta}'_y) + K_{ey}(\theta_y - \theta'_y) \quad (4\text{-}2)$$

Nomenclature for Gyro Transfer-function Analysis

1. Coordinate system

   a. An orthogonal coordinate system (X,Y,Z) on the gyro is defined.

   b. The spin axis is defined as Z. Using the right-hand-spin convention, positive z is defined such that the spin vector is positive.

   c. The X and Y axes are defined as being collinear with the pickoff axes (axes of input and/or output). Positive directions are defined so that a right-handed coordinate system is established.

2. Functional characteristics of the gyro

   H = angular momentum $I_z\omega_z$ or $I_z\dot{\theta}_z$

   θ_x, θ_y = spin-vector angular displacements (about X, about Y) with respect to inertial space

   θ'_x, θ'_y = housing angular displacement with respect to inertial space

   T_x, T_y = total torques applied to gyro

   T_{xe}, T_{ye} = electrical torques (command) applied via torquer

   T_{xu}, T_{yu} = internal torques acting on gyro in its environment, e.g., unbalance torques

* For the purpose of this analysis, the flywheel is considered to have a fixed inertia and to be rotating at a constant angular speed $\omega_z = \dot{\theta}_z$, i.e., H is constant.

K_{ex}, K_{ey} = elastic restraint constants (torsional gradients)
C_x, C_y = viscous drag coefficients
I_x, I_y = flywheel assembly inertias (about X, about Y)
s = differential operator d/dt

For the purpose of generating transfer functions with appropriate diagrams, the above equations of motion have been limited to elastic, viscous, and inertial restraints. By substituting $s\theta$ for $\dot{\theta}$ and $s^2\theta$ for $\ddot{\theta}$, we may write Eqs. (4-1) and (4-2) in operational notations.

$$T_x = Hs\theta_y + I_x s^2\theta_x + C_x s(\theta_x - \theta_x') + K_{ex}(\theta_x - \theta_x') \qquad (4\text{-}3)$$
$$T_y = -Hs\theta_x + I_y s^2\theta_y + C_y s(\theta_y - \theta_y') + K_{ey}(\theta_y - \theta_y') \qquad (4\text{-}4)$$

Equations (4-3) and (4-4) provide the possibility of deriving transfer functions for a variety of gyro types.

Let us take the case of a single-axis gyro (see Fig. 4-2*a*). Assume, for the moment, that the output axis Y_{OA} is constrained in frictionless pivots. The flywheel system Z_{SRA} is free to move only about Y_{OA} but is constrained from rotating about X_{IA}. Consequently, θ_x and θ_x' become identical (zero net motion), resulting in the following simplifications of Eqs. (4-3) and (4-4):

$$T_x = Hs\theta_y + I_x s^2\theta_x \qquad (4\text{-}3a)$$
$$T_y = -Hs\theta_x + I_y s^2\theta_y + C_y s(\theta_y - \theta_y') + K_{ey}(\theta_y - \theta_y') \qquad (4\text{-}4a)$$
or
$$T_y = -Hs\theta_x + (I_y s^2 + C_y s + K_{ey})\theta_y - (C_y s + K_{ey})\theta_y'$$

Since IA and OA are more familiar to those in the single-axis-gyro field, a conversion from subscripts x to IA and y to OA will be made at this point. We have

$$T_{IA} = Hs\theta_{OA} + I_{IA}s^2\theta_{IA} \qquad (4\text{-}3b)$$
$$T_{OA} = -Hs\theta_{IA} + (I_{OA}s^2 + C_{OA}s + K_{OA})\theta_{OA} - (C_{OA}s + K_{OA})\theta_{OA}' \qquad (4\text{-}4b)$$

Equation (4-3*b*) defines the torque T_{IA}, which is the torque or couple acting on the gimbal pivots. This is of interest in designing the gyro so that the resulting normal forces acting on the pivots do not cause excessive friction.

Equation (4-4*b*) may be depicted in a transfer-function diagram by suitably grouping terms. For simplicity's sake, the subscripts are dropped for the coefficients

$$T_{OA} + \theta_{IA}(Hs) + \theta_{OA}'(Cs + K) = \theta_{OA}(Is^2 + Cs + K) \qquad (4\text{-}4c)$$

This may be represented schematically as shown in Fig. 4-6. Note that T_{OA} is the sum of all torques applied to the gyro, including command torques via the torquer, as well as internal torques resulting from such imperfections as unbalance and nonisoelasticity.

The transfer-function diagram as presented in Fig. 4-6 may be used directly or may be even further simplified for any particular system to which a single-axis gyro is applied. For torque command inputs, the gyro transfer function is

$$\frac{\theta_{OA}}{T_{OA}} = \frac{1}{Is^2 + Cs + K} \tag{4-5}$$

For input angular rates the transfer function is

$$\frac{\theta_{OA}}{s\theta_{IA}} = \frac{H}{Is^2 + Cs + K} \tag{4-6}$$

To achieve a particular characteristic in any given gyro design the ratios of the linear restraints may be adjusted. As an example, consider

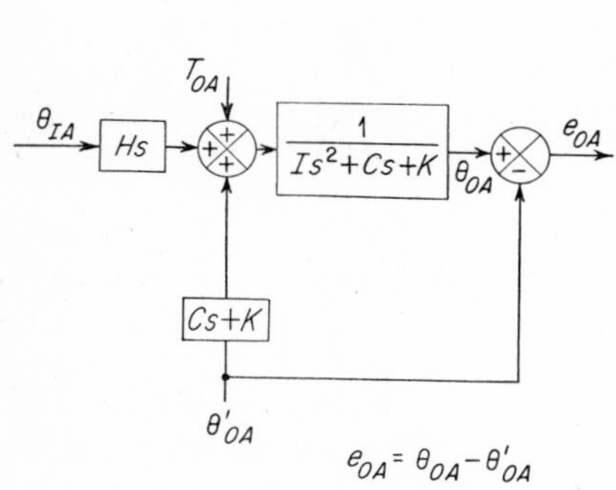

FIG. 4-6. General transfer-function diagram of a single-axis gyro.

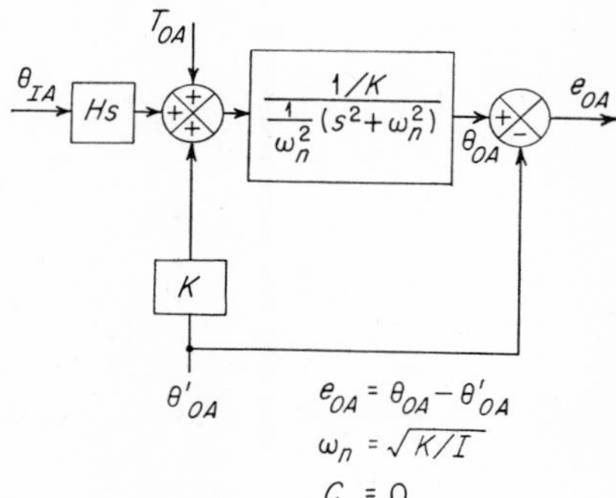

FIG. 4-7a. Single-axis rate gyro transfer-function produced by using high spring restraint K. Diagram shows a limiting condition of no damping, $C = 0$.

the single-axis rate gyro of Fig. 4-2b. Here, the ratio K/C is made purposely large. For the moment, assume a limiting condition of no damping ($C = 0$). Equation (4-4c) may then be simplified to

$$T_{OA} + \theta_{IA}(Hs) + \theta'_{OA}K = \theta_{OA}K\,\frac{s^2 + K/I}{K/I} \tag{4-7}$$

Substituting $\omega_n{}^2$ for K/I (ω_n = natural circular frequency), we have

$$T_{OA} + \theta_{IA}(Hs) + \theta'_{OA}K = \theta_{OA}K\,\frac{s^2 + \omega_n{}^2}{\omega_n{}^2} \tag{4-8}$$

Figure 4-7a shows a functional representation of this equation in a diagram of a single-axis spring-restrained rate gyro. For input angular rates, the gyro transfer function is

$$\frac{\theta_{OA}}{s\theta_{IA}} = \frac{H/K}{(1/\omega_n{}^2)(s^2 + \omega_n{}^2)} \tag{4-9}$$

or

$$\theta_{OA} = (s\theta_{IA}) \frac{H/K}{(1/\omega_n{}^2)(s^2 + \omega_n{}^2)} \tag{4-10}$$

For steady-state conditions $\theta_{OA} = \omega_{IA}(H/K)$, where $\omega_{IA} = s\theta_{IA}$, equal to the steady input axis angular rate; or, expressed in words, the output angle θ_{OA} is a product of the input rate ω_{IA} by the proportionality constant H/K. Thus the spring restraint on the output axis produces a rate-measuring gyro.

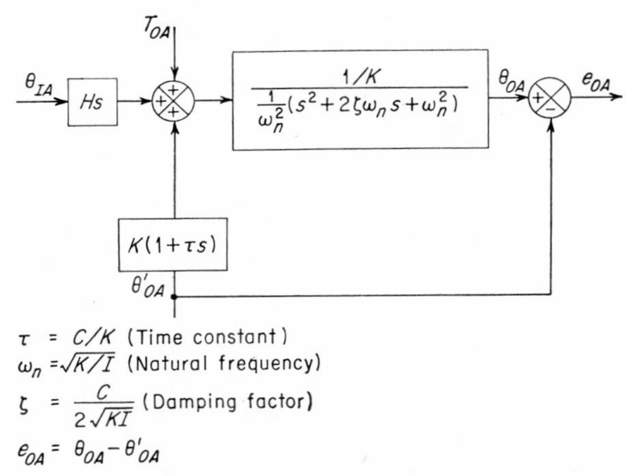

FIG. 4-7*b*. Single-axis rate gyro transfer function produced by using high spring restraint K. Diagram shows a damped rate gyro, i.e., $C > 0$.

As a practical matter, it is necessary to prevent the oscillatory condition indicated by the absence of damping in the quadratic $(s^2 + \omega_n{}^2)$. By introduction of damping about the output axis, the diagram of Fig. 4-6 is expanded to that of Fig. 4-7*b*.

A very popular form of single-axis gyro is the so-called "single-axis rate-integrating gyro," shown in Fig. 4-4. To obtain the rate-integrating characteristic, it is necessary virtually to suppress or make quite negligible the spring restraint K with respect to the viscous drag coefficient C. For simplicity's sake, assume K to be zero. Figure 4-6 may then be redrawn as shown in Fig. 4-8*a* to achieve a rate-integrating gyro. Normally the transfer-function diagram does not show the effect of θ'_{OA}, i.e., the motion of the housing about the output axis. This simplifies even further the diagram shown in Fig. 4-8*b*.

The two basic transfer characteristics corresponding to this case are

$$\frac{\theta_{OA}}{\theta_{IA}} = \frac{Hs}{Cs(\tau s + 1)} = \frac{H}{C}\frac{1}{\tau s + 1} \tag{4-11}$$

where τ represents the time constant I/C.

$$\frac{\theta_{OA}}{T_{OA}} = \frac{1}{Cs}\frac{1}{\tau s + 1} \tag{4-12}$$

Equation (4-11) shows that the output-input angle ratio may be scaled by adjusting the H/C ratio. The single-order time delay τ is made negligible by virtue of the high damping C and relatively low inertia I about the output axis. This low time constant is consistent with the

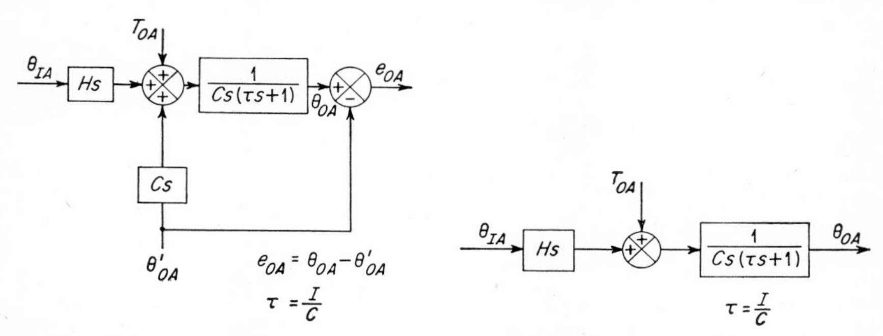

FIG. 4-8*a*. Single-axis rate-integrating gyro produced by keeping low elastic restraint K and using high viscous coefficient C.

FIG. 4-8*b*. By eliminating consideration of the housing motion θ'_{OA}, Fig. 4-8*a* is simplified to the case shown here.

stability requirements of closed-loop control systems. It should be observed, however, that the low value of τ also results in a sacrifice in gain (H/C). For those applications where high gain through the gyro is desired (perhaps to minimize the need for high electronic gain, which may cause noise problems), less damping is used. This, through the increase in time delay, puts a burden on the use of external stabilizing networks in the servo system.

Let us also note that owing to Eq. (4-11) we have

$$\frac{s\theta_{OA}}{\theta_{IA}} = \frac{H}{C}\frac{s}{1 + s\tau} = \frac{H}{I}\frac{s\tau}{1 + s\tau} \tag{4-11a}$$

which shows that the initial slope at $\tau = 0$ (or $s = \infty$) of the $\dot{\theta}_{OA}$ versus θ_{IA} curve is H/I, independent of the particular value selected for the damping C. This slope is therefore independent of the gyro time constant τ.

It is possible to convert the rate-integrating gyro of Fig. 4-8*b* to a rate gyro by the use of feedback. The output θ_{OA} (pickoff) signal is amplified by a factor K and fed back as the input to the torquer. This is shown diagrammatically in Fig. 4-9.

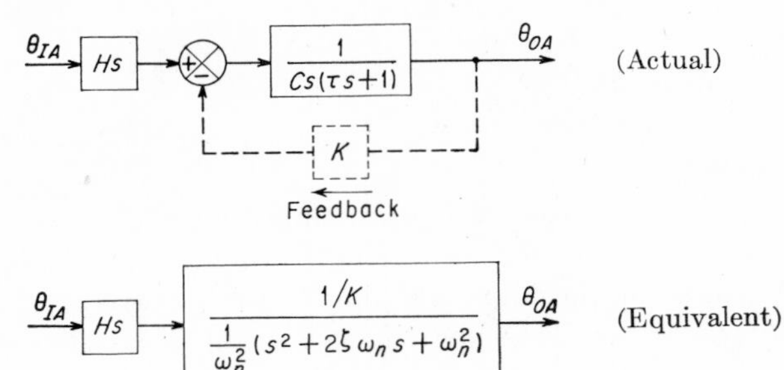

Fig. 4-9. The output θ_{OA} (pickoff) signal of a rate-integrating gyro is amplified by a factor K and applied as the input to the torquer.

The mathematics of this closed-loop approach to a rate gyro is as follows:

Let the forward gain of closed loop be according to Eq. (4-12)

$$A = \frac{1}{Cs(\tau s + 1)}$$

while the assumed feedback factor is a constant

$$B = K$$

The closed-loop expression may then be written

$$\frac{\theta_{\text{out}}}{\theta_{\text{in}}} = \frac{\theta_{OA}}{\theta_{IA}(Hs)} = \frac{A}{1 + BA} = \frac{1}{B}\frac{BA}{1 + BA} \tag{4-13}$$

Since

$$BA = \frac{K}{Cs(\tau s + 1)}$$

we have

$$\frac{BA}{1 + BA} = \frac{K/Cs(\tau s + 1)}{1 + [K/Cs(\tau s + 1)]} = \frac{K}{Cs(\tau s + 1) + K} = \frac{K}{s^2\tau C + sC + K} \tag{4-14}$$

Also, since $\tau = I/C$,

$$\frac{BA}{1 + BA} = \frac{K}{s^2 I + sC + K} = \frac{K}{I[s^2 + (C/I)s + K/I]}$$

$$= \frac{\omega_n{}^2}{s^2 + (C/I)s + \omega_n{}^2} \tag{4-14a}$$

The damping factor C/I is usually expressed in terms of the coefficient of critical damping ζ and ω_n. This conversion is made as follows:

$$\frac{C}{C_0} = \frac{C}{2\sqrt{KI}} \qquad (4\text{-}15)$$

where C_0 = critical damping value of C equal to $2\sqrt{KI}$
Therefore, $C = 2\zeta\sqrt{KI}$, and

$$\frac{C}{I} = 2\zeta\sqrt{\frac{K}{I}} = 2\zeta\omega_n \qquad (4\text{-}16)$$

Substituting (4-16) into (4-14*a*), we get

$$\frac{BA}{1 + BA} = \frac{\omega_n{}^2}{s^2 + 2\zeta\omega_n s + \omega_n{}^2} \qquad (4\text{-}14b)$$

The transfer function then becomes

$$\frac{\theta_{OA}}{\theta_{IA}Hs} = \frac{1/K}{(1/\omega_n{}^2)(s^2 + 2\zeta\omega_n s + \omega_n{}^2)} \qquad (4\text{-}13a)$$

It is apparent by inspection that the feedback factor K has converted the single-axis rate-integrating gyro to a rate gyro of the same functional characteristic as that produced by using an elastic spring restraint K. The equivalence of Fig. 4-7*b* and Fig. 4-9 (equivalent diagram) is obvious.

In the above discussion we have shown how the suppression of one degree of angular freedom, together with the adjustment of the various torsional restraints about the output axis (axis of precession), has produced a variety of gyro characteristics. This class of gyro has found considerable use as rate, rate-integrating (displacement), and occasionally as a rate double-integrating gyro. Together with electronic amplifiers in feedback systems, the single-axis gyro is indeed a versatile device.

Although it is not frequently depicted in a transfer-function diagram, the two-axis gyro may be conveniently so represented. Such a diagram shows in directly understandable terms the various restraints acting on the gyro. The effects of these upon shaping the gyro response may be seen by inspection. The two-axis gyro is frequently thought of in terms of a free or displacement gyro. For this reason, the transfer-function diagrams which point up the characteristic response resulting from restraints are not usually drawn. Realistically, restraints are employed, e.g., the two-axis gyro used in a gyrocompass where elastic torsional restraints provide compass damping as well as precise means for introducing corrections via servo loops.

Let us develop the transfer-function diagram for the two-axis gyro, as shown by Fig. 4-1. For this purpose, the basic gyro equations (4-3) and (4-4) are applicable.

Let

$$e_x = \theta_x - \theta'_x$$
$$e_y = \theta_y - \theta'_y$$

We have

$$T_x = Hs\theta_y + I_x s^2\theta_x + e_x(C_x s + K_{ex}) \quad (4\text{-}3c)$$
$$T_y = -Hs\theta_x + I_y s^2\theta_y + e_y(C_y s + K_{ey}) \quad (4\text{-}4d)$$

With the equations in this form, we are now in a position to draw the transfer-function diagram (Fig. 4-10*a*) with a simplified representation, as shown in Fig. 4-10*b*, which neglects the inertias about each sensitive axis I_x and I_y.

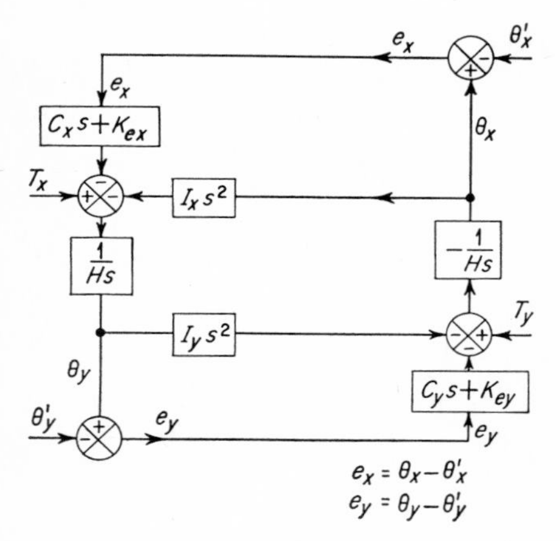

Fig. 4-10*a*. Two-axis gyro transfer-function diagram.

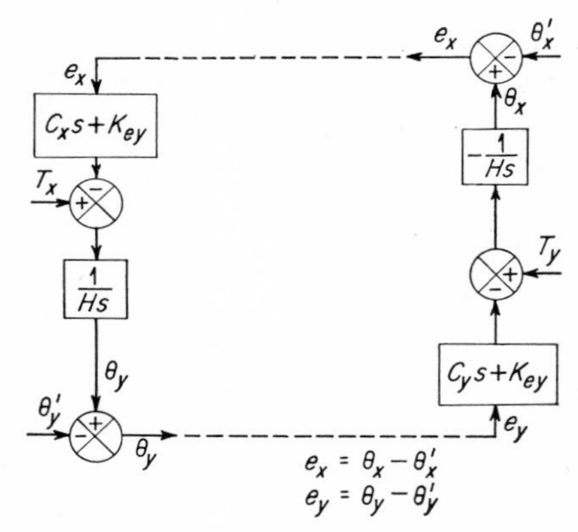

Fig. 4-10*b*. This diagram is a simplification of Fig. 4-9 made by neglecting I_x and I_y. Further simplification could be made if C_x, C_y and K_{ex}, K_{ey} were neglected. By so doing, an *ideal* "free gyro" would be depicted.

The significant properties of this type of gyro are apparent from inspection of the diagram and may be tabulated as follows:

1. Two inertially stabilized reference axes are provided. Each axis x and y serves as both input and output axes, e.g., T_y causes precession about x and T_x creates a precession about y.

2. Error signals with respect to inertial space are obtained directly without significant time delay and without making the gyro precess. This is in contrast to the single-axis gyro, as explained previously. Calibration of H and C is not required, since the gain is independent of these magnitudes and there is no significant time constant.

3. The spin vector is not coerced by the gimbaling system, i.e., is theoretically unrestrained angularly, except by the viscous and spring coupling between the housing and the spin vector. This latter coupling is normally made quite negligible. Thus, there is no significant disturbing torque to affect the rigidity of the gyro reference.

4. Ordered precession may be applied to the gyro by application of the appropriate torque (T_x or T_y) via torquers. In addition to these intentional torques, the other disturbing torques are those resulting from design imperfections (T_{xu}, T_{yu}). For diagrammatic purposes, all these disturbing torques may be considered applied as T_x, T_y. A simplified presentation of the two-degree-of-freedom gyro may be obtained by neglecting the inertias I_x, I_y, since the Coriolis torques such as $H\dot{\theta}_x$ are enormously higher than the purely inertial terms such as $I_x\ddot{\theta}_x$.

4-5. Some Application Notes

In the treatment above we have considered the gyro as a black box. One might question the extent to which this is valid. Let us examine this matter and see what nonideal factors must be considered. The representation below categorizes the picture quite simply.*

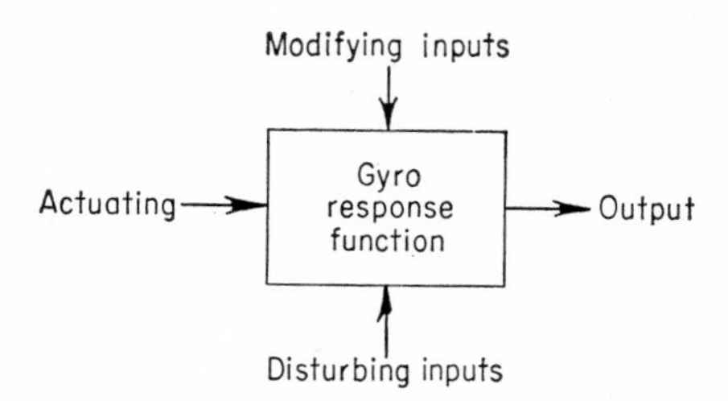

Actuating input is defined as angular motion (of gyro housing) with respect to inertial space and/or command signals.

Modifying input is considered to be any input which modifies the response function.

Disturbing inputs are considered to be those uncontrolled inputs which give rise to spurious outputs by exciting changes in the internal gyro parameters.

Response function expresses the ratio of output to actuating input. This may be in two forms. First, it may be a mathematical ratio (usually in Laplace transform notation); specifically the transfer function expresses the theoretical ratio of output to actuating input. Secondly,

* This material is based in part on notes of meetings, held in 1956, in which the author participated as a member of the Gyro Terms and Test Procedures Task Committee, a subcommittee of the Ordnance Advisory Committee of the National Security Industry Association.

it may be expressed as a transfer characteristic, the plot (theoretical or experimental) of the gyro output as a function of frequency of the actuating input. The plot is usually represented as both amplitude ratio and phase angle difference. Modifying inputs are of interest in that they may alter the response-function parameters in both predictable and sometimes unknown fashions.

There are, in general, two aspects of gyro performance of interest. First are the functional characteristics determined by the detailed design, including the nature and type of geometric and torsional restraints. As discussed earlier in the chapter, these determine the functional identity and response of the gyro as a system element. The second aspect concerns the accuracy with which the gyro performs its basic function of providing a spatial reference. It is in this latter area that disturbing inputs are of concern, since they give rise to a so-called "drift" of the attitude reference in both predictable and undetermined fashions. It should be apparent that an input may potentially be both "modifying" as well as "disturbing." For example, an increase in power-supply frequency would raise H by a finite amount, thus modifying the transfer function, and would also give rise to greater core losses causing a thermal-mechanical shift of the motor mass, thus disturbing the over-all mechanical balance. The balance change under the influence of gravity might cause a spurious torque resulting in drift of the gyro attitude reference.

A list of modifying and disturbing inputs which could affect a gyro should be made up by the reader. In this way it may be seen how many factors there are that should be taken into account before the gyro design is finalized and any performance quoted.

As an introduction the various undesired torques which can act on the gyro are summarized below. These will form a convenient check list in evaluating the effect that a particular gyro design feature will have in the presence of a disturbing input.

1. Constant torques: independent of acceleration
2. Unbalance torques: proportional to acceleration
3. Anisoelasticity torques: proportional to the product of two acceleration components, viz., A_x, A_y
4. Elastic restraint torques: due to some flexible mechanical coupling to the gyro
5. Friction torques: due to normal forces on bearings and viscous coupling of surfaces (static, running, and viscous friction)
6. Electromagnetic or electrostatic torques: due to interacting and stray fields, e.g., pickoffs, torquers, motors, etc.
7. Thermal torques: due to convection, irregular heating, etc.
8. Random torques: undetermined sources and/or pattern

The last item should be clarified further, since these torques ultimately limit the performance of high-precision gyros.

If all the environmental conditions of the gyro were to be fixed, it would be possible to categorize the gyro drift rate into constant or varying components. The constant drift results from a variety of generally known effects, such as unbalance, anisoelasticity, elastic restraint, etc. The superimposed varying drift is the random drift. This can only be experimentally observed and is not assignable to a known, systematic, physical effect.

4-6. Conclusions

The material presented in this chapter has been provided to bridge the gap between the basic mechanics of the gyroscope presented in the preceding chapters and the theoretical and practical aspects of design, test, and application to follow in subsequent chapters. In today's complex systems it is not sufficient to understand the gyro in itself, for it is not really an independent element in the true sense. Fortunately, as has been demonstrated, the gyro may be considered as a black box. As such, its response may be conveniently written in the language of the system designer. Through the use of one or more gimbaling arrangements and various restraining mechanisms the characteristic response may be intentionally shaped. Beyond this, the use of feedback in combination with other system elements makes it possible to shape further the gyro characteristics. Of course, the environment to which the gyro is exposed, fluctuations in power supplies, internal gyro disturbances alone and in response to the inputs must all be considered in judging whether or not the gyro will in fact be suitable for its intended application.

It should be pointed out that of necessity the treatment of restraints as offered in this chapter has been on a fairly simple plane. However, it should be apparent that the evaluation of the effect of nonlinear restraints in varying combinations may be made rather efficiently with the aid of simulation on analog computers.

PROBLEMS

4-1. Given a rate-integrating single-axis gyro, draw a family of curves showing the amplitude of transfer characteristic θ_{OA}/θ_{IA} versus time as a function of the viscous restraint coefficient C. Indicate graphically the steady-state value of θ_{OA}/θ_{IA} (gain) and the time constant τ. Refer to Fig. 4-8*b*.

4-2. It is desired to utilize a single-axis rate-integrating gyro as an element in a closed-loop system for measuring linear acceleration. Determine the restraints to be imposed on the gyro and their relative values to permit such measurement. Draw the functional diagram and indicate the transfer functions.

4-3. Show how, through the use of feedback, a single-axis rate-integrating gyro may be used to space-stabilize a platform in one axis. Draw the transfer-function diagram of the closed-loop system (use Fig. 4-8*b* as reference). Similarly, show how a two-axis gyro (Fig. 4-10*b*) may be used to space-stabilize a platform in two axes.

4-4. Considering the gyro as a black box, list the various inputs to the gyro which could alter its transfer characteristic or cause the gyro reference to drift. List as many as you can. Categorize as "modifying inputs" or "disturbing inputs."

4-5. Using Fig. 4-10*b*, determine qualitatively what would happen if a sudden displacement of the housing about X (i.e., $\Delta\theta_x'$) were to occur. What will determine whether the disturbance will settle out? What effect do the various restraints have? Is there any time delay in the pickoff signal indication of $\Delta\theta_x'$? Describe the situation for an input axis (IA) displacement in a single-axis gyro.

BIBLIOGRAPHY

1. Rawlings, A. L.: "The Theory of the Gyroscopic Compass and Its Deviations," The Macmillan Company, New York, 1944.

2. Scarborough, J. B.: "The Gyroscope: Theory and Applications," Interscience Publishers, Inc., New York, 1958.

3. Richardson, K. I. T.: "The Gyroscope Applied," Philosophical Library, Inc., New York, 1954.

4. Draper, C. S., W. Wrigley, and L. R. Grohe: The Floating Integrating Gyro and Its Application to Geometric Stabilization Problems on Moving Bases, *Aeronaut. Eng. Rev.*, vol. 15, no. 6, p. 46, 1956. NOTE: This article is a condensation of complete paper of same title presented at the Institute of the Aeronautical Sciences, Jan. 27, 1955, and as subsequently revised for publication as S.M.F. Fund Paper FF-13.

5. Klass, P. J.: Inertial Navigation, *Aviation Week*, vol. 64, Jan. 2, 9, 16, 23, 1956.

6. Weems, W. R.: An Introduction to the Study of Gyroscopic Instruments, M.I.T. Rept. Department of Aeronautical Engineering, January, 1948.

7. O'Donnel, C. F.: Inertial Navigation, *J. Franklin Inst.*, vol. 266; part I, p. 257, October, 1958; part II, p. 373, November, 1958.

8. Mueller, F. K.: Considerations on Inertial Guidance for Missiles, *Navigation*, vol. 6, no. 4, p. 240, 1959.

9. Brown, G. S., and D. P. Campbell: "Principles of Servomechanisms," John Wiley & Sons, Inc., New York, 1948.

10. Lauer, H., P. Lesnick, and L. E. Matson: "Servomechanism Fundamentals," McGraw-Hill Book Company, Inc., New York, 1947.

11. Chestnut, H., and R. W. Mayer: "Servomechanisms and Regulating System Design," John Wiley & Sons, Inc., New York, 1951, vol. I.

12. Klein, F., and A. Sommerfeld: "Über die Theorie des Kreisels," B. G. Teubner Publisher, Leipzig, 1897–1910, 4 vols.

13. Ferry, E. S.: "Applied Gyrodynamics," rev. ed., John Wiley & Sons, Inc., New York, 1933.

CHAPTER 5

THE GYROCOMPASS

By Charles T. Davenport

Nomenclature

a = acceleration
a_{NS} = north-south component of acceleration
C = vehicle course
C' = compass-card reading
c = viscous-damping coefficient
E = surface speed of earth at equator (902.464 knots)
e = base of natural logarithms (2.718282. . .)
F = force
F_C = centrifugal force
g = acceleration of gravity
H = angular momentum
h = distance to center of roll
j = operator $\sqrt{-1}$
K = $(4\ M_P\ H\omega_E \cos \lambda - M_D{}^2)^{1/2}$ (used in vertical damping equations)
k = ratio by which viscous damping attenuates pendulum motion
l = pendulum length
M = mass of pendulum bob
M_D = damping factor
M_P = gyro pendulous factor
R = earth's radius (20.9×10^6 ft); roll angle
r = turning radius
s = differential operator d/dt
T = period
T_H = horizontal-axis torque
T_I = input torque to horizontal-damping device
T_O = output torque from horizontal-damping device
T_V = vertical-axis torque
t = time
v = velocity
v_E = east component of velocity

α = pendulum angle from vertical
β = input-axis tilt
γ = phase angle between pendulum and acceleration
ϵ = north velocity error
ϵ' = settling point error caused by speed corrector
θ = spin-axis tilt
λ = latitude
τ = time constant
ϕ = angle between spin axis and north
ω = angular velocity of roll
ω_E = earth's angular velocity (72.9211×10^{-6} radian/sec)
ω_H = horizontal component of earth's angular velocity
ω_N = pendulum undamped natural frequency
ω_V = vertical component of earth's angular velocity

5-1. Definition and History

The term *gyrocompass* is often incorrectly employed to designate ordinary directional gyroscopes or to refer to gyros which are slaved to a magnetic heading transmitter. The true gyrocompass is so instrumented that the gyro senses the earth's rotation and utilizes this information to precess the gyro until its spin axis lies in the plane containing the earth's axis. The unique feature of the gyrocompass is that it seeks out and indicates true geographic north and that this action in no way depends upon the earth's magnetic field.

The gyrocompass was invented about 1906 by Dr. Hermann Anschütz-Kaempfe of Kiel, Germany, and it probably represents the most ingenious application of the gyroscope to date. The device is extremely sensitive; it detects rotational rates with respect to inertial space of the order of a few hundredths of a degree per hour. Yet, it is rugged enough to withstand the extremely severe environmental conditions encountered on naval combat vessels, land vehicles, and aircraft. Its success is a tribute to the resourcefulness, ingenuity, and engineering ability of the pioneer designers. The fluid suspension principle employed by Anschütz-Kaempfe in his first compass is still used in the most modern inertial navigation systems.

5-2. Advantages over Magnetic Compass

Compared with the conventional marine-type magnetic compass, the gyrocompass has a number of important advantages. It is far more accurate, being capable of indicating true north to within a small fraction of one degree. It has no *variation* error. Variation (sometimes called *declination*) is the difference between true north and magnetic north at any particular spot on the earth. For example, a magnetic compass in

Boston points about 15° west of true north; in San Francisco it points about 18° east of true north. Therefore, in order to compute the direction of true north from a magnetic compass reading it is necessary to know the geographic location quite closely, and this is obviously unfeasible in many instances. In addition, the value of variation changes slowly over long periods of time, and it is subject to large short-term errors caused by magnetic "storms" such as result from sunspots or the aurora borealis.

Although a gyrocompass completely loses its north-seeking action at the poles, it performs well even above 80° latitude, where a magnetic compass would be completely unusable because of the erratic nature of the variation error in that part of the world. A moderately high-speed aircraft, for example, proceeding along the 60° north latitude line may experience a rate of change of variation of over 1°/min.

The gyrocompass has no magnetic *deviation* error. It is necessary to compensate a magnetic compass for the effect of magnetic materials located in the general vicinity. Any change in the distribution of these magnetic materials requires a new deviation calibration which involves "swinging the ship." Thus, a change in cargo, or even training a large turret on a battleship, might alter the deviation error. A gyrocompass is practically a necessity in a submarine where the shielding effect of the steel hull makes a magnetic compass nearly inoperable. Magnetic compasses aboard ship are also subject to *heeling* error, an effect due to the rolling of the vessel changing the inclination of its magnetic parts with respect to the earth's field.

When a ship or aircraft experiences violent motion, the card of its magnetic compass swings erratically, making it very difficult to read. The dial of a gyrocompass, on the other hand, remains perfectly steady by virtue of the inherent rigidity of plane of the gyroscope. Another advantage of the gyrocompass over the conventional marine magnetic compass is that its heading information can be transmitted electrically to remote locations. The so-called "master compass" may be located below decks, near the center of roll of the vessel, where it has maximum protection and is least affected by ship's motion. On naval vessels the gyrocompass electrical output is employed for azimuth stabilization of guns, searchlights, optical sights, radar antennas, and the like. Repeater compasses are located at such points as the steering stations, the chart room, the captain's cabin and are also gimbal-mounted in pelorus stands for sighting the true bearing of distant objects during piloting operations.

5-3. Advantages over Magnetically Slaved Gyro

Some of the disadvantages of the simple magnetic compass are avoided by the technique of using a directional gyro "slaved" to a magnetic heading transmitter (sometimes called a *flux valve*). This has the effect of averaging out the magnetic heading information during periods of violent ship or aircraft motion, resulting in a steadier course indication. As on the gyrocompass, this indication may be transmitted electrically to repeaters. Since the magnetic heading transmitter is very small, it may be mounted on the extreme wing tip of an aircraft, for example, away from highly magnetic parts such as the motors and cargo, thereby reducing the deviation and heeling errors to some extent. However, the centrifugal force experienced during a turn of the aircraft will cause the pendulous gimbal-mounted transmitter to tilt, so that it no longer shows the direction of the earth's field in the horizontal plane. This results in a false indication of heading. This effect is alleviated in some designs by automatically disconnecting the slave gyro during turns. Provision is sometimes made for inserting the variation correction by hand or automatically from a cam driven by other navigational equipment. However, it should be noted that an accurate knowledge of location is still required and that operation above 60° latitude is not too practicable. It is customary to disconnect the slaving control at very high latitudes and to operate on a directional gyro basis.

5-4. Advantages over Directional Gyro.

A directional gyro must be set on north, and its performance thereafter is dependent upon its drift rate. Although the pure directional gyro is independent of the earth's magnetic field, it is subject to large drift errors on long flights and must be reset periodically. The error increases with time. A gyrocompass, on the other hand, because of its north-seeking action, has an error that *decreases* with time. Although disturbances may cause the gyrocompass to oscillate with a small amplitude across the meridian, its long-time average is true north, which makes it much more satisfactory as a navigational device. The directional gyro must also be corrected for earth's rotation, which requires an accurate knowledge of the local latitude. For example, an error of only 1° in the corrector setting at 40° latitude will result in an apparent drift rate of about 0.2°/hr. Although a gyrocompass requires a correction for latitude, it is by no means as critical. Furthermore, as will be shown presently, the directional gyro is far more susceptible than the gyrocompass to errors caused by minute center-of-mass shifts in the gyro.

5-5. Recent Applications

The outstanding advantages of the gyrocompass have long been recognized in naval and maritime activities, and its use on ships is practically universal. However, it was not until several years after World War II that a gyrocompass sufficiently small and rugged was developed for use on Army combat vehicles. Further miniaturization has now made it feasible for aircraft use. The gyrocompass requires a correction for the ground speed of the vehicle in which it is mounted. The recent successful development of air-borne Doppler radar has resulted, for the first time, in a method of measuring ground speed accurately enough for gyrocompass correction purposes. Another factor which delayed the application of the gyrocompass to aircraft was the belief that an airplane traveling westward at the speed of the earth would, in effect, "stop the earth" and completely nullify the north-seeking action of the compass. It will be shown, however, that the north-seeking effect of a speed-corrected gyrocompass is completely independent of the ground speed of the vehicle in which it is installed.

5-6. Effects of Earth's Rotation on Gyro

In order to indicate true north the spin axis of the gyroscope in a gyrocompass should lie in the north-south plane and should, for convenience, be horizontal. The instrumentation of the gyrocompass is so arranged that the gyro is automatically precessed toward this position by utilizing the rotation of the earth. In order to understand how this is achieved, it is necessary to know how the earth's rotation affects a gyroscope when the spin axis is tilted and not in the plane of the meridian.

Consider the gyroscope shown in Fig. 5-1. The case of the gyro is trunnioned about a horizontal axis in a fork-shaped gimbal, the stem of which, in turn, is pivoted about the vertical axis. This form of gimbaling is actually employed in many types of azimuth gyros. The gyro illustrated has been turned about the vertical axis so that the vertical plane containing the spin axis lies clockwise, a small angle ϕ from the north-south plane. At the same time, the gyro has been rotated in its horizontal-axis trunnions so that the end of the spin axis nearest north is tilted upward by an angle θ. Assuming that the gimbal bearings are frictionless and that the gyro is perfectly balanced, we see that the spin axis maintains a fixed direction in inertial space. However, the rotation

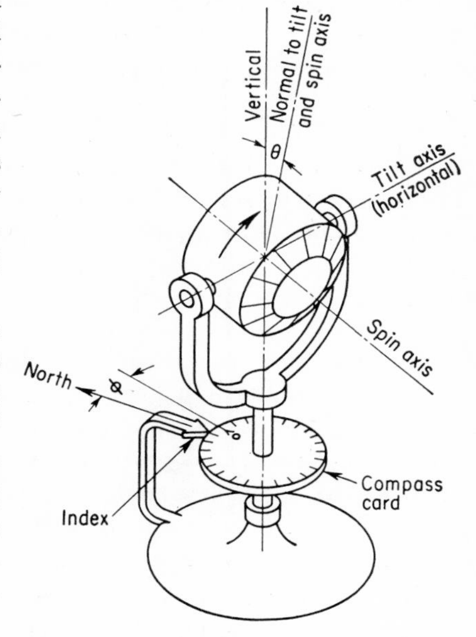

Fig. 5-1. Gyroscope with spin axis tilted and out of north-south plane.

of the earth causes a relative motion between the gyro and the earth. Components of earth rotation will now be determined about the spin axis and two other axes mutually perpendicular to the spin axis and to one another. For convenience, these latter two axes have been selected with one passing through the horizontal trunnions (the tilt axis) and the other normal to the tilt and spin axes. This last axis, then, lies in the vertical plane containing the spin axis but is tilted from the vertical by the angle θ (see Fig. 5-1).

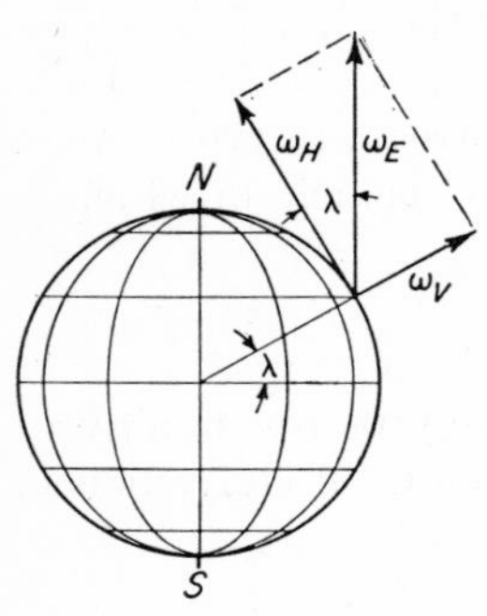

FIG. 5-2. Vertical and horizontal components of earth's rotation.

Since the gyroscope is an inertial reference device, it is necessary to consider the rate of rotation of the earth with respect to inertial space and *not* with respect to the sun. This is known as the *sidereal* rate. Although a given spot on the earth faces the sun 365 times in a year, the earth also makes a complete revolution about the sun in that time, so that it faces the so-called "fixed" stars 366 times. The sidereal rate of the earth is, therefore, slightly more than one turn per day and is indicated by ω_E, which can be expressed in a number of ways; for example, 1.00274 turns in 24 hr; 15.0411°/hr; 72.9211×10^{-6} radian/sec. At any latitude the rotation of the earth can be split into vertical and horizontal components (see Fig. 5-2). Thus, at any latitude λ the vertical and horizontal components ω_V and ω_H are

$$\omega_V = \omega_E \sin \lambda \tag{5-1}$$

$$\omega_H = \omega_E \cos \lambda \tag{5-2}$$

Figure 5-3 is a vector diagram showing how the components of earth's rotation are determined along the spin axis, the tilt axis, and the axis normal to the tilt and spin axes of the gyro shown in Fig. 5-1. The first and third of these axes contain components of both ω_V and ω_H. However, the tilt axis, being horizontal, is affected only by ω_H.

The horizontal component of earth's rotation is broken up into two right-angle components, the first, $\omega_E \cos \lambda \sin \phi$, along the gyro tilt axis, and the other, $\omega_E \cos \lambda \cos \phi$, along the intersection of the horizontal plane and the vertical plane which contains the spin axis. This latter component can, in turn, be split into two other components, one, $\omega_E \cos \lambda \cos \phi \cos \theta$, along the spin axis, and the other, $\omega_E \cos \lambda \cos \phi \sin \theta$, directed downward, normal to the tilt and spin axes. The vertical component of earth's rotation $\omega_E \sin \lambda$ is divided into two components, the first, $\omega_E \sin \lambda \sin \theta$, along the spin axis, and the second, $\omega_E \sin \lambda \cos \theta$, normal to the spin and tilt axes. Note that this last component is in the opposite direction to $\omega_E \cos \lambda \cos \phi \sin \theta$.

The components of earth rate felt about the three axes are then

Spin axis:	$\omega_E \cos\lambda \cos\phi \cos\theta + \omega_E \sin\lambda \sin\theta$	(5-3)
Tilt axis:	$\omega_E \cos\lambda \sin\phi$	(5-4)
Normal to tilt and spin axes:	$\omega_E \sin\lambda \cos\theta - \omega_E \cos\lambda \cos\phi \sin\theta$	(5-5)

The spin-axis component is usually completely negligible. In the worst case, where the spin axis lies parallel with the earth's axis, a gyro spinning at 12,000 rpm, for example, would have its angular momentum

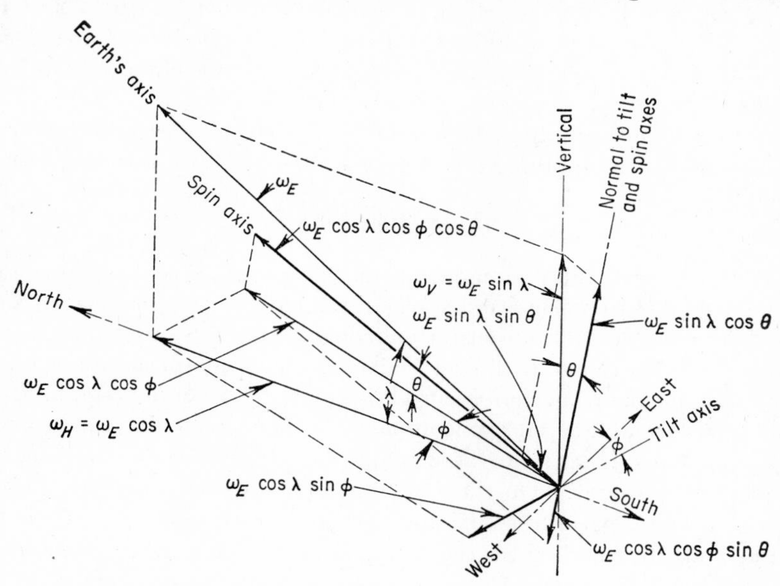

FIG. 5-3. Components of earth's rotation acting on gyro.

changed, because of earth rotation, by a factor of only six parts in a billion.

Since on a gyrocompass θ is usually very small, the second terms in Eqs. (5-3) and (5-5) may also be neglected, and the cosine of θ, which appears in the first terms, may be considered as unity. The axis of Eq. (5-5) may therefore be assumed vertical without serious error.

The angle ϕ represents the compass error. Although it may not be neglected, it will usually be small enough so that the sine can be considered as equal to the angle and the cosine as equal to unity.

Eqs. (5-4) and (5-5) may then be simplified.

Tilt axis:	$\phi\omega_E \cos\lambda$	(5-6)
Vertical axis:	$\omega_E \sin\lambda$	(5-7)

However, for special situations where θ and ϕ are not small, Eqs. (5-4) and (5-5) should be employed. It is also necessary to consider the second term of Eq. (5-5) in the case of highly accurate, nonpendulous directional gyros which are not perfectly leveled.

Equations (5-6) and (5-7) show that an untorqued horizontal-shaft gyroscope will behave as follows:

1. With respect to the earth, it will tilt at the rate $\phi\omega_E \cos \lambda$. The end of the spin axis *east* of the meridian will appear to *rise;* the end *west* of the meridian will appear to *dip*.

2. With respect to the earth, it will rotate in azimuth at the rate $\omega_E \sin \lambda$. In *northern* latitudes it will appear to drift *eastward;* in *southern* latitudes it will appear to drift *westward*. At the equator this term vanishes.

The first effect is employed to make the gyro seek north. The second is compensated by applying a torque T_H about the tilt axis equal to

$$T_H = H\omega_E \sin \lambda \tag{5-8}$$

where H is the angular momentum of the gyro. The direction of the torque is such as to precess the gyro counterclockwise in northern latitudes and clockwise in the Southern Hemisphere, thus keeping it fixed with respect to the earth about the vertical axis. This compensation is known as the *latitude* or *earth rotation* correction and must be made on all directional gyros as well as on gyrocompasses. The correction was formerly made by means of an adjustable weight which could be moved parallel to the gyro spin axis. On the most modern gyros electrical torquing is employed which permits continuous automatic computation of the correction and does not upset the gyro, as is the case when a manually adjusted weight is reset.

It is interesting to compute the rates shown by Eqs. (5-6) and (5-7) for a practical case. Consider a horizontal-shaft gyro which is 1° off the meridian at 40° latitude

$$\begin{aligned}\text{Tilt rate} &= 0.01745 \times 15.04 \times 0.766 \\ &= 0.201^\circ/\text{hr} \\ \text{Azimuth rate} &= 15.04 \times 0.643 \\ &= 9.67^\circ/\text{hr}\end{aligned}$$

5-7. Action of Pendulous Gyro

The tilting effect which occurs when the gyro spin axis is not exactly in the north-south plane (Fig. 5-1) can be made to precess the gyro toward the meridian by adding a pendulous weight to the gyroscope (Fig. 5-4). Suppose the north end of the gyro is east of the meridian, as in Fig. 5-1. The north end rises, elevating the weight and producing a couple about the tilt axis equal to

$$T_H = M_P \sin \theta$$

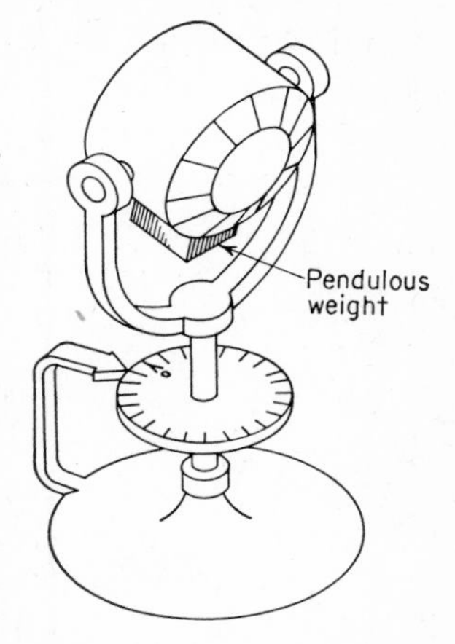

FIG. 5-4. Gyroscope with pendulous weight.

where θ is the tilt angle and M_P the pendulous factor of the gyro—the product of the weight and its distance from the tilt axis. Since θ is small, the equation may be written as

$$T_H = M_P\theta \tag{5-9}$$

If the direction of spin of the gyro is as shown, the torque will precess the spin axis *toward* the meridian, regardless of whether the initial position of the gyro is east or west of north. This is due to the fact that the direction of tilt is reversed on opposite sides of the meridian.

5-8. Equations of Motion—Pendulous Gyro

Assuming that the latitude correction [Eq. (5-8)] is applied, we may now write the differential equations describing the motion of a pendulous gyro with respect to the earth as follows:

$$\begin{aligned} \frac{d\theta}{dt} &= \phi\omega_E \cos \lambda \\ \frac{d\phi}{dt} &= -\frac{M_P\theta}{H} \end{aligned} \tag{5-10}$$

In accordance with Fig. 5-1, θ is assumed to *increase* when the end of the spin axis nearest north *rises*, and ϕ is measured clockwise from *north.* Since a positive value of θ causes the gyro to precess *counterclockwise,* the term $M_P\theta/H$ must bear a minus sign.

Assume that when $t = 0$, $\phi = \phi_0$ and $\theta = 0$. Then, the solution of these equations gives

$$\theta = \phi_0 \left(\frac{H\omega_E \cos \lambda}{M_P}\right)^{1/2} \sin \left(\frac{M_P\omega_E \cos \lambda}{H}\right)^{1/2} t \tag{5-11}$$

$$\phi = \phi_0 \cos \left(\frac{M_P\omega_E \cos \lambda}{H}\right)^{1/2} t \tag{5-12}$$

Equations (5-11) and (5-12) show undamped harmonic oscillations of the gyro about both the tilt and the azimuth axes, the two oscillations being displaced by a quarter period.

When the quantity $(M_P\omega_E \cos \lambda/H)^{1/2}t$ is equal to 2π, the time t becomes the undamped period T. Then

$$T = 2\pi \left(\frac{H}{M_P \omega_E \cos \lambda} \right)^{1/2} \tag{5-13}$$

Figure 5-5 shows the tilt and azimuth oscillations plotted for an undamped gyrocompass at 40° latitude, where the angular momentum is 4,000,000 g-cm²/sec and the pendulous factor of the gyro is 80,000 dyne-cm. The value of t is assumed to be zero when the gyro is 10° east of the meridian with the spin axis horizontal.

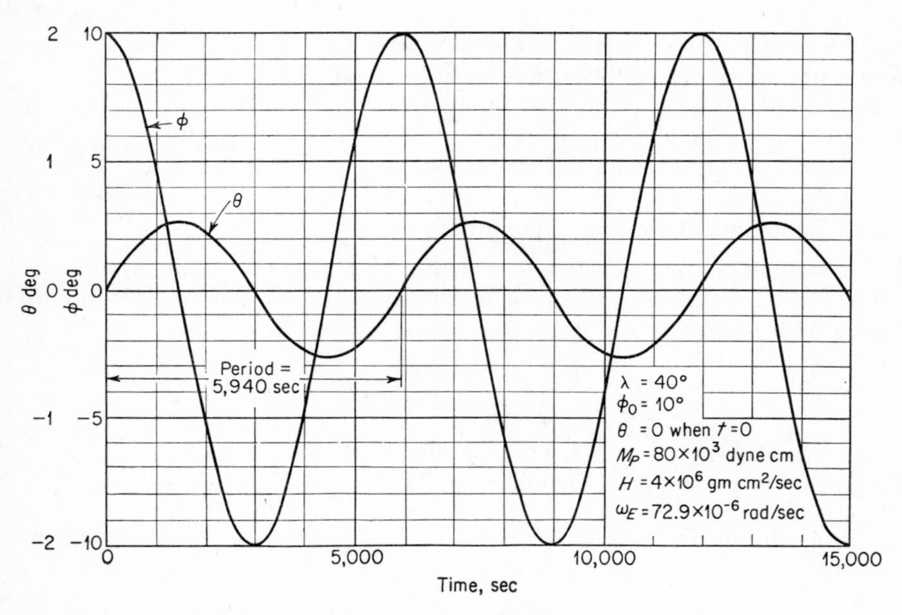

Fig. 5-5. Undamped oscillations of a gyrocompass.

From Eq. (5-11)

$$\theta = 10 \left(\frac{4 \times 10^6 \times 72.9 \times 10^{-6} \times 0.766}{80 \times 10^3} \right)^{1/2} \sin \left(\frac{80 \times 10^3 \times 72.9 \times 10^{-6} \times 0.766}{4 \times 10^6} \right)^{1/2} t$$

$$= 0.528 \sin 0.001058t$$

From Eq. (5-12)

$$\phi = 10 \cos \left(\frac{80 \times 10^3 \times 72.9 \times 10^{-5} \times 0.766}{4 \times 10^6} \right)^{1/2} t$$

$$= 10 \cos 0.001058t$$

From Eq. (5-13)

$$T = 2\pi \left(\frac{4 \times 10^6}{80 \times 10^3 \times 72.9 \times 10^{-6} \times 0.766} \right)^{1/2}$$
$$= 5{,}940 \text{ sec or } 99.0 \text{ min}$$

The path of the end of the spin axis is an ellipse (see Fig. 5-6). This is the line which would be traced on a screen by a searchlight mounted on the gyro case and aimed along the spin axis.

It is interesting to examine the effect on this "searchlight" diagram of varying the different parameters.

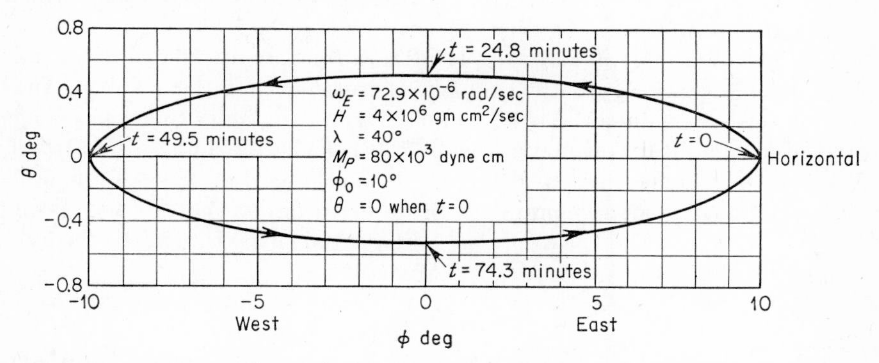

FIG. 5-6. Path traced by spin axis of an undamped gyrocompass (θ scale increased 5 to 1).

1. For a given set of compass constants at any one latitude, the ratio of the major to the minor axis of the ellipse is a constant. For the example shown, the major axis is 20° and the minor axis 1.056°. If ϕ_0 is changed from 10 to 5°, the major axis is 10° and the minor axis 0.528°.

2. An increase in gyro angular momentum increases the undamped period. Changing the angular momentum from 4,000,000 to 8,000,000 g-cm²/sec would increase the period from 99 to 140 min.

3. Increasing the pendulousness of the gyro decreases the period. A change from 80,000 to 100,000 dyne-cm would decrease the period from 99 to 88.5 min.

4. The period becomes longer with increasing latitude. A compass with a period of 99 min at 40° latitude would have a period of 208 min at a latitude of 80°.

5. For a given value of major axis at any one latitude, the minor axis of the ellipse is directly proportional to the period.

5-9. Vertical Damping

The undamped compass just discussed would be useless as a navigational device aboard ship. Some method is required to damp the oscillations so that the gyro spin axis comes to rest in a horizontal position in the north-south plane. Since on a given undamped compass at a fixed location the ratio of the major to the minor axis of the ellipse traced by the end of the spin axis is independent of the amplitude of the oscillation, any method which will shrink one axis will decrease the other in the same proportion. If the "squeeze" is applied to the minor axis, the process is called *vertical damping*. This is the technique employed on the most advanced gyrocompasses now being built. However, many types of compass have used horizontal damping where the major axis is compressed. Each method has certain advantages and disadvantages, which will be discussed later.

Vertical damping involves applying a torque about the vertical axis proportional to the gyro tilt in such a direction that the resulting precession tends to reduce the tilt. On older gyrocompasses this was accomplished mechanically or pneumatically. Electrical torquing is employed, however, on the most recent designs. It is also used in place of a pendulous weight on modern compasses in order to apply the gravity couple about the tilt axis to make the gyro north-seeking.

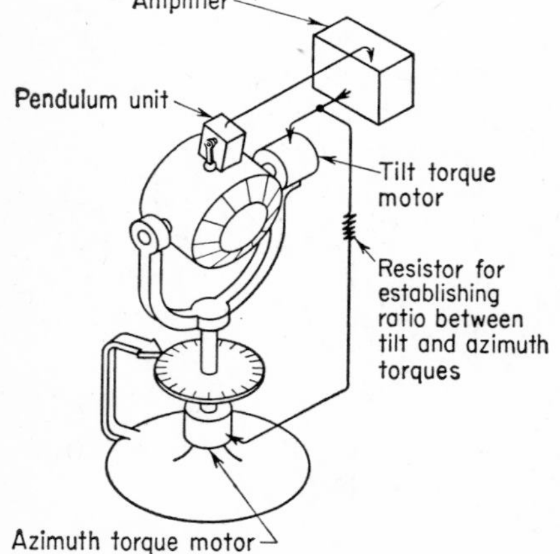

FIG. 5-7. Electrically torqued gyrocompass with vertical damping.

Figure 5-7 shows a simplified version of an electrically torqued gyrocompass with vertical damping. Mounted on the gyro case is a pendulum unit which gives a small voltage proportional to gyro tilt. Electrical torque motors are located on both the tilt and the azimuth axes. This type of torquer may be likened to a stalled two-phase induction motor whose torque is directly proportional to the voltage applied to one field, the other field being held at constant voltage. The pendulum output is amplified and applied in the correct proportions to the control fields of the tilt and azimuth torque motors in order to provide, respectively, both north-seeking action and vertical damping. The combination of pendulum and horizontal torque motor gives precisely the same effect as a pendulous weight on the gyro. Whenever the gyro tilts, a horizontal torque proportional to the tilt angle is applied to the gyro. All equations previously derived still apply. However, the quantity M_P should now be thought of as the torque per radian of tilt rather than as the pendulousness of the gyro.

Electrical control of the gyro has the following advantages:

1. Being nonpendulous, the gyro itself is unaffected by vehicle accelerations. Accelerations having components in the north-south plane cause a pendulous compass to precess in azimuth and thus develop an error. Although the pendulum unit itself is susceptible to such accelerations, it may be compensated electrically so as to correct the errors. Compensation for accelerations due to changes in vehicle speed, for example, could be computed by differentiating the output of the vehicle's speed indicator.

2. The period and/or damping of the compass may be readily changed, by simple switching, to the optimum value for any particular operating condition. For example, a very short period is desirable for rapid initial settling.

3. Damping may be accomplished more simply.

5-10. Equations of Motion—Vertical Damping

The differential equations for a vertically damped compass are similar to those for the undamped case, except that the damping term is added to the expression for $d\theta/dt$.

$$\frac{d\theta}{dt} = \phi\omega_E \cos\lambda - \frac{M_D\theta}{H}$$
$$\frac{d\phi}{dt} = -\frac{M_P\theta}{H} \tag{5-14}$$

M_D is the damping factor and is the vertical torque applied per radian of gyro tilt. The minus sign shows that the damping tilt rate opposes the tilt rate due to the rotation of the earth. As when solving Eqs. (5-10), the assumption is made that, when $t = 0$, $\theta = 0$ and $\phi = \phi_0$. The solutions are

$$\theta = \frac{2\phi_0 H\omega_E \cos\lambda}{K} e^{-M_D t/2H} \sin\frac{Kt}{2H} \tag{5-15}$$

$$\phi = \phi_0 \left(\frac{M_D}{K} \sin\frac{Kt}{2H} + \cos\frac{Kt}{2H}\right) e^{-M_D t/2H} \tag{5-16}$$

where $K = (4M_P H\omega_E \cos\lambda - M_D^2)^{1/2}$

The time t becomes the undamped period T when the quantity $Kt/2H$ is equal to 2π. Then

$$T = \frac{4\pi H}{K} \tag{5-17}$$

Equations (5-15) to (5-17) become the same as the undamped equations (5-11) to (5-13), respectively, when M_D is equal to zero. Figures 5-5 and 5-6 show the tilt and azimuth motions for the undamped case where $\lambda = 40°$, $H = 4{,}000{,}000$ g-cm²/sec, $M_P = 80{,}000$ dyne-cm, and $\phi_0 = 10°$, when $t = 0$ and $\theta = 0$. Assume that vertical damping is added to this compass, so that $M_D = 3{,}000$ dyne-cm.

From Eq. (5-15)

$$K = [4 \times 80 \times 10^3 \times 4 \times 10^6 \times 72.9 \times 10^{-6} \times 0.766 - (3 \times 10^3)^2]^{1/2}$$
$$= 7{,}910$$
$$\theta = \frac{2 \times 10 \times 4 \times 10^6 \times 72.9 \times 10^{-6} \times 0.766}{7{,}910} e^{-(3\times 10^3 t)/(2\times 4\times 10^6)} \sin \frac{7{,}910t}{2 \times 4 \times 10^6}$$
$$= 0.565e^{-0.000375t} \sin 0.000988t$$

From Eq. (5-16)

$$\phi = 10\left(\frac{3 \times 10^3}{7{,}910} \sin \frac{7{,}910t}{2 \times 4 \times 10^6} + \cos \frac{7{,}910t}{2 \times 4 \times 10^6}\right) e^{-(3\times 10^3 t)/(2\times 4\times 10^6)}$$
$$= 10(0.379 \sin 0.000988t + \cos 0.000988t)e^{-0.000375t}$$

From Eq. (5-17)

$$T = \frac{4\pi \times 4 \times 10^6}{7{,}910}$$
$$= 6{,}360 \text{ sec or } 106 \text{ min}$$

Figure 5-8 shows θ and ϕ plotted against time. Damping has increased the period from 99 to 106 min. The azimuth oscillation no longer leads

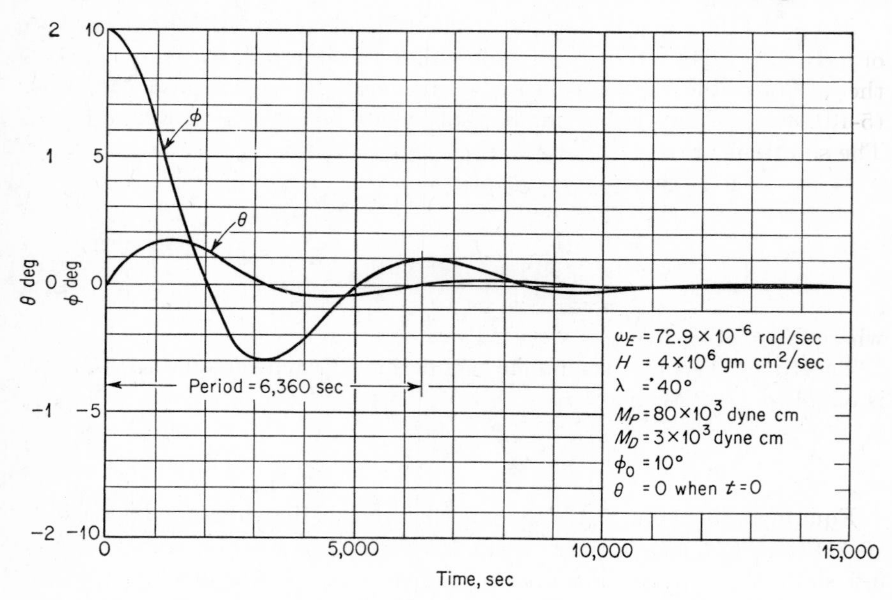

FIG. 5-8. Oscillations of a gyrocompass with vertical damping.

the tilt oscillation by 90°, as in the undamped case. This phase lead has been decreased to about 69°. Every half-cycle the amplitude of the oscillations is decreased approximately two-thirds. By the end of the 4 hours the amplitude of the azimuth oscillation has decreased from 10° to about 2′ of arc.

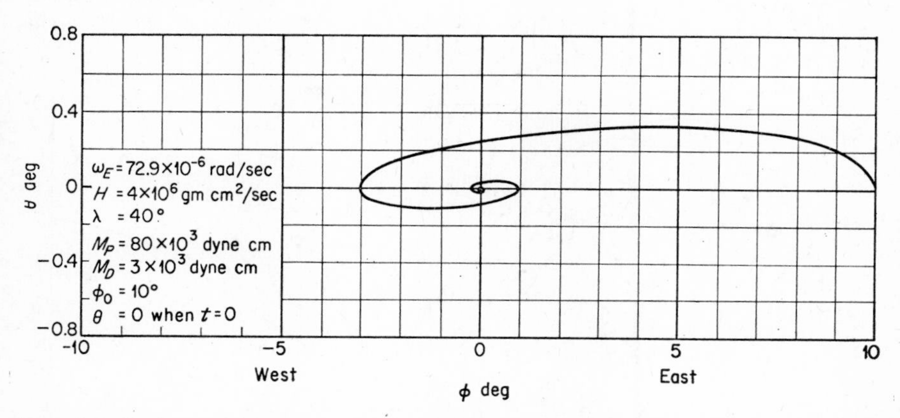

FIG. 5-9. Path traced by spin axis of gyrocompass with vertical damping (θ scale increased 5 to 1).

The spiral path traced by the spin axis is shown in Fig. 5-9, where ϕ is plotted against θ.

5-11. Horizontal Damping

In a horizontally damped gyrocompass the damping action is applied to the major axis of the ellipse traced by the end of the spin axis rather than to the minor axis, as in the case of vertical damping. This requires a horizontal-axis torque superimposed on the torque resulting from the normal gravity couple. For maximum effect this damping torque should be in quadrature with the pendulous torque, leading it by 90° (see Fig. 5-10). This diagram assumes that the azimuth oscillation is started with the gyro spin axis horizontal. During the first and third quarter periods, when the spin axis is going *toward* the meridian, the damping torque is *aiding* the righting torque. This will have the effect of hurrying the spin axis *toward* the zero position. In the second and fourth quarter periods the spin axis is going *away* from the meridian, and the damping torque is *opposing* the righting torque, thus slowing down the motion *away* from the zero position.

Since with harmonic motion the velocity is a quarter period out of phase with the displacement, a torque proportional to $d\theta/dt$, the rate of gyro tilt, would give the desired result. However, in practice it is difficult to produce such a torque. In the first place, an extremely accurately stabilized horizontal reference would be required from which to measure the rate of gyro tilt, and this would present a serious problem aboard a rolling and pitching vehicle. Secondly, the rates involved are so small that they cannot conveniently be measured by conventional techniques, such as by the use of tachometer generators. For example, when a gyrocompass is oscillating in azimuth $\pm 0.25°$ at 40° latitude, $d\theta/dt$ varies between zero and a maximum of only 0.05°/hr.

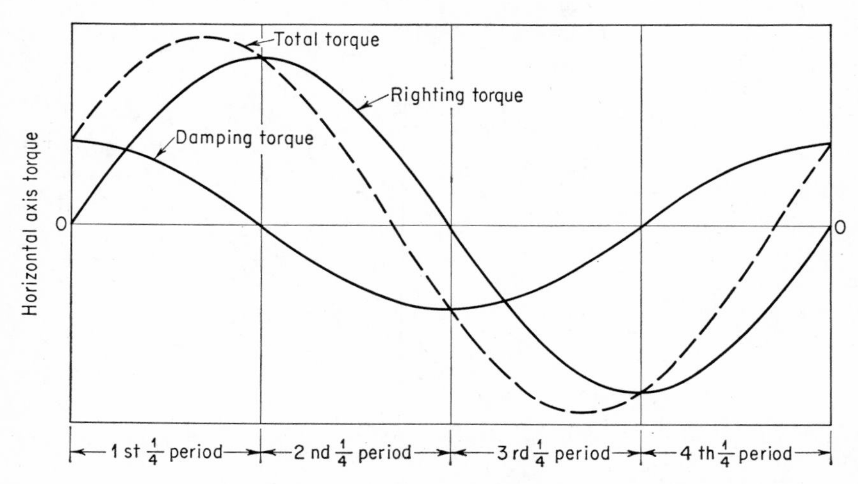

FIG. 5-10. Effect of horizontal-axis damping torque in quadrature with righting torque.

A technique which has been successfully employed is to obtain an out-of-phase effect by applying a horizontal torque, proportional to gyro tilt, via some type of time-delay device. These devices are such that the output approaches the input exponentially with respect to time. Let the input torque be T_I and the output torque T_O. Then

$$T_O = T_I - T_I e^{-t/\tau} \tag{5-18}$$

where t is time and τ the time constant of the device.

Some compasses employing electrical torquing use a thermal delay element where the input voltage is applied to a heater winding which, in turn, changes the temperature (and hence the resistance) of an adjacent winding on the same core. The change in resistance, however, is delayed because of the thermal inertia of the assembly. The change in resistance is used to control the output voltage, and this results in a mathematical relationship between input and output voltages such as given by Eq. (5-18) above.

A more common method of horizontal damping involves the use of viscous fluid carried in a pair of vessels mounted on the gyro and connected by a restricted pipe. Figure 5-11 shows the general arrangement. The fluid vessels are in the plane of the spin axis, and when the gyro is tilted, the transfer of fluid develops a torque which opposes the normal pendulous righting couple. However, because of the opposition to free flow of fluid between the vessels, this toppling torque is delayed and is therefore out of phase with the pendulous moment. Since the rate of fluid flow is proportional to the difference in head of the fluid in the two tanks, the output torque has the exponential characteristic given by Eq. (5-18).

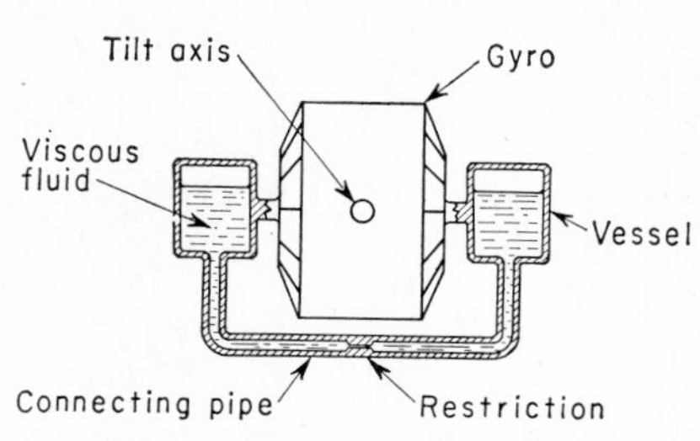

FIG. 5-11. Horizontal damping by means of a viscous fluid.

With devices of this type the desired phase relationship between righting and damping torques is not immediately established if the compass is suddenly disturbed in azimuth from the settled condition. With the fluid damping, for example, the fluid at time $t = 0$ would be at the same head in both vessels. Hence, horizontal damping, obtained by means of a delay device, is not as efficient in the initial stages as vertical damping. The advantages and disadvantages of horizontal versus vertical damping will be discussed after the equations for horizontal damping are derived.

5-12. Equations of Motion—Horizontal Damping

The case of an electrically torqued compass will be considered. The pendulum output is divided, part going directly to the tilt-axis torquer and another portion feeding the torquer via a thermal integrator. The torque resulting from the first part is the normal gravity couple $M_P\theta$, where M_P is the torque per radian of gyro tilt and θ the tilt angle. The input to the thermal integrator [T_I in Eq. (5-18)] is $M_D\theta$, where M_D is the torque per radian of gyro tilt. In practice, M_D is always made smaller than M_P; otherwise the compass would be unstable in the steady state. Equation (5-18) may now be written

$$T_O = M_D(1 - e^{-t/\tau})$$

A more convenient form is obtained by differentiating T_O.

$$\tau \frac{dT_O}{dt} + T_O = M_D\theta \tag{5-19}$$

The azimuth precession rate is proportional to the total tilt-axis torque.

$$\frac{d\phi}{dt} = -\frac{M_P\theta}{H} + \frac{T_O}{H} \tag{5-20}$$

(It is assumed that the earth rotation correction torque $\omega_E \sin \lambda$ is also applied.)

The tilt rate due to earth's rotation is given by Eq. (5-10):

$$\frac{d\theta}{dt} = \phi\omega_E \cos \lambda \tag{5-10}$$

By combining Eqs. (5-10), (5-19), and (5-20), we obtain two linear third-order differential equations for the solution of θ and ϕ.

$$\begin{aligned} \frac{\tau H}{\omega_E \cos \lambda} \frac{d^3\theta}{dt^3} + \frac{H}{\omega_E \cos \lambda} \frac{d^2\theta}{dt^2} + \tau M_P \frac{d\theta}{dt} + (M_P - M_D)\theta = 0 \\ \tau H \frac{d^3\phi}{dt^3} + H \frac{d^2\phi}{dt^2} + \tau M_P\omega_E \cos \lambda \frac{d\phi}{dt} + (M_P - M_D)\phi\omega_E \cos \lambda = 0 \end{aligned} \tag{5-21}$$

Because of the complexity of these equations, a general solution is impractical, and numerical values should be substituted for the constants before one is attempted. The procedure involves setting up an auxiliary equation of the form $ax^3 + 3bx^2 + 3cx + d = 0$ and solving for the three roots. Calling these roots x_1, x_2, and x_3, we have a solution in the form

$$C_1e^{x_1t} + C_2e^{x_2t} + C_3e^{x_3t}$$

The constants C_1, C_2, and C_3 are obtained by assuming that at time $t = 0$, $\phi = \phi_0$, $\theta = 0$, and $T_O = 0$.

Because the two components $-M_P\theta/H$ and T_O/H of Eq. (5-20) are in phase at the time $t = 0$, the full damping action does not start immediately. Horizontal damping is not as efficient as vertical damping in the initial stages. However, after a complete period of azimuth oscillation has been accomplished, the steady-state phase relationships are practically established.

In order to evaluate horizontally damped gyrocompasses, the U.S. Navy[1,*] specifies a value for an average percentage of damping over the first three peaks by the following formula:

$$\text{Damping percentage} = \frac{a - c}{a - b} \times 100 \tag{5-22}$$

where a = amplitude of first peak
b = amplitude of second peak
c = amplitude of third peak

Assume that a horizontally damped compass is started with the gyro spin axis level and 10° off the meridian. On the next swing the peak of

* Superscript numbers indicate references listed in the Bibliography at end of the chapter.

the oscillation is observed to be $-5°$, while on the successive swing it reaches $1°$.

Then, by Eq. (5-22),

$$\text{Damping percentage} = \frac{10 - 1}{10 + 5} \times 100 = 60.0\%$$

5-13. Effect of Spurious Vertical and Horizontal Torques

Before discussing the relative merits of horizontal and vertical damping, it is necessary to understand the effect of spurious vertical and horizontal torques on a gyrocompass. A steady spurious torque about the vertical axis will cause the compass to settle with the spin axis off the meridian. The settling-point error will be such that the tilt precession rate resulting from the spurious torque will be matched by an equal and opposite tilt rate due to the earth's rotation. Then, calling the spurious vertical torque T_V, we have

$$\frac{T_V}{H} = \omega_E \cos \lambda \sin \phi \approx \phi \omega_E \cos \lambda$$

$$\phi = \frac{T_V}{H \omega_E \cos \lambda} \tag{5-23}$$

A gyrocompass is often said to have a "directive effort" of so many dyne-centimeters per degree. This is the value of vertical torque which will cause it to settle $1°$ off the meridian. For example, if $H = 4{,}000{,}000$ g-cm²/(sec) and $\lambda = 40°$, the directive effort is

$$\begin{aligned} T_V &= H \phi \omega_E \cos \lambda \\ &= 4 \times 10^6 \times 0.01745 \times 72.9 \times 10^{-6} \times 0.766 \\ &= 3.90 \text{ dyne-cm/°} \end{aligned}$$

In order for a gyrocompass to be accurate it is obviously necessary to hold spurious vertical torques to an extremely low level.

A steady spurious horizontal-axis torque results in the compass settling with the spin axis tilted. The tilt will be of such magnitude that the pendulous righting moment will exactly balance the spurious torque, or

$$T_H = M_P \sin \theta \approx M_P \theta$$

$$\theta = \frac{T_H}{M_P} \tag{5-24}$$

Such spurious horizontal torques can result from center-of-mass shifts along the gyro spin axis, such as those caused by creep of materials, or from thermal expansion due to temperature changes. Another cause might be an improperly set latitude correction [see Eq. (5-8)].

5-14. Comparison of Horizontal and Vertical Damping

With vertical damping a vertical torque equal to $M_D\theta$ is developed whenever the gyro is tilted. Therefore, on a vertically damped compass a spurious horizontal torque will cause the instrument to develop an azimuth error, since such torques cause the gyro to settle with a tilt in accordance with Eq. (5-24). The error is found as follows:

$$T_V = M_D\theta = \frac{M_D T_H}{M_P}$$

$$\phi = \frac{T_V}{H\omega_E \cos\lambda} = \frac{M_D T_H}{M_P H \omega_E \cos\lambda} \qquad (5\text{-}25)$$

A horizontally damped compass, on the other hand, does not develop a vertical torque when the spin axis is tilted. Therefore, its accuracy is not affected by spurious horizontal torques. However, because of the inverted pendulum effect of the damping, the tilt angle will not be in accordance with Eq. (5-24) but will be

$$\theta = \frac{T_H}{M_P - M_D}$$

On older gyrocompasses horizontal damping was extensively employed, because the gyros of that era were quite subject to mass shifts. Furthermore, the latitude correction was inconvenient to reset, since it was adjusted by moving a weight on the gyro, which upset the compass whenever the setting was changed. However, with the advent of electrically torqued gyros and gyros with highly stable center of mass, vertical damping has become more popular because it is much simpler to instrument and gives a more efficient damping action immediately following a disturbance.

5-15. Gyrocompasses Employing Single-degree-of-freedom Gyros

A single-degree-of-freedom rate gyro can be made to indicate north, provided that it is sensitive enough. The input axis is rotated in the horizontal plane until zero rate is indicated. The input axis must then lie east-west, since that is the only direction where no horizontal component of earth rotation exists. North is therefore 90° from the input axis under this condition. When the input axis is at an angle ϕ from the east-west plane, it is exposed to a rate of $\omega_E \cos\lambda \sin\phi$ with respect to inertial space. This is, of course, exactly the same as the rate of tilt of a conventional gyrocompass when it is off north by an angle ϕ [see Eq. (5-4)]. Hence, for both types of compass, for the same north-seeking accuracy, the ratio of spurious torques to angular momentum must be kept below the same level. However, the single-degree-of-freedom compass can be made to settle more quickly, and the construction of the gyro is simpler than that of a two-degree-of-freedom type.

Care must be taken to maintain the input axis horizontal. Otherwise (except at the equator), the input axis will be exposed to a component of that portion of the earth's rotation which lies along the vertical axis. Assume that the input axis is tilted from the horizontal by a small angle β. Since the vertical component of the earth's rotation is $\omega_E \sin \lambda$ [see Eq. (5-1)], the component about the input axis is $\omega_E \sin \lambda \sin \beta$. The input axis will measure zero rate at some angle ϕ from east-west such that

$$\omega_E \sin \lambda \sin \beta = \omega_E \cos \lambda \sin \phi$$
$$\sin \phi = \sin \beta \tan \lambda$$

Since both β and ϕ are small,

$$\phi = \beta \tan \lambda \tag{5-26}$$

Thus, at 45° latitude a given tilt error produces an equal settling-point error. Proper leveling becomes extremely important at high latitudes. At 80°, for example, the azimuth error is about 5⅔ times the tilt of the input axis.

A rate gyro type of compass can give excellent results when it is mounted on a rigid tripod and carefully leveled. However, on a moving vehicle it would have to be isolated from rolling and pitching motion, since the angular rates of the vehicle would be enormous compared to the minute component of earth rate which the gyro must measure to indicate north. The best available gyro-stabilized platforms do not even approach the required degree of stability. However, a second single-degree-of-freedom gyro can be employed for azimuth stabilization of the platform, with its output axis torquer actuated by the rate signal of the primary north-indicating gyro. The secondary gyro is therefore "slaved" to the first gyro and integrates out the short-term rate signals due to imperfect stabilization, thus providing an averaging effect. Since a relatively weak coupling must exist between the two gyros, the advantage of rapid settling time is lost to some extent. Furthermore, two gyros (plus roll and pitch stabilization) are required to do a job which could be performed by one two-degree-of freedom gyro employed in the conventional gyrocompass instrumentation.

As a tripod-mounted surveying device, the rate gyro type of compass has proved to be practicable and capable of indicating north rapidly and accurately. Although the rate signal might be employed to orient the gyro automatically in azimuth, manual adjustment, with the aid of a null meter, has proved to be perfectly satisfactory and is much simpler and less costly. Spirit levels, similar to those used on surveyer's transits, permit hand leveling to within a small fraction of a minute of arc.

Single-degree-of-freedom rate-integrating gyros have been employed in the Dynatrol[2] air-borne gyrocompass. Figure 5-12 shows the principle of an early model which used two such gyros in a two-axis gimbal system.

When the instrument is settled on the meridian, the input axis of the reference gyro is horizontal and in the east-west plane. The input axis

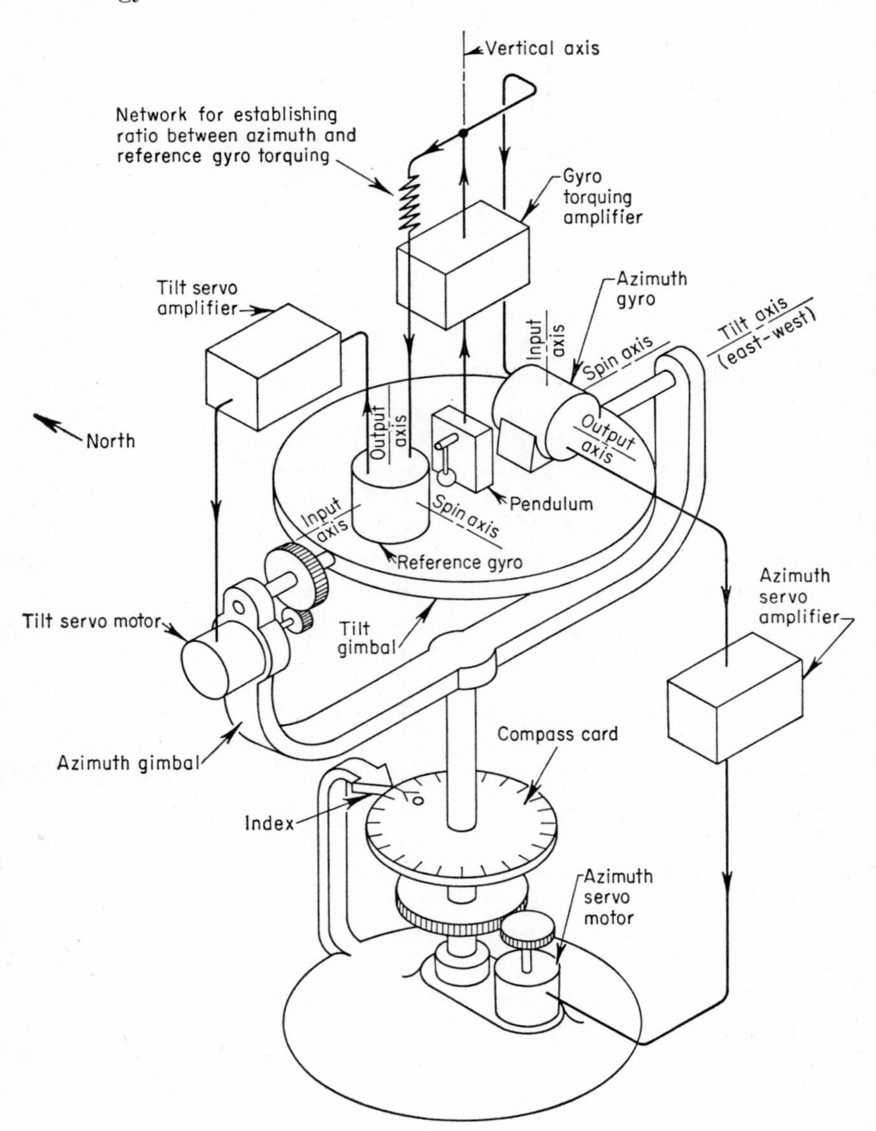

FIG. 5-12. Gyrocompass employing rate-integrating gyros.

of the azimuth gyro under this condition is vertical, and the pendulum unit is nulled. The pendulum unit is connected via a torquing amplifier and appropriate scaling networks to the output axis torquers on both gyros.

Now, if the tilt axis becomes displaced an angle ϕ from the east-west plane, a component of earth rotation (again $\omega_E \cos \lambda \sin \phi$) causes the gimbal carrying the gyros and the pendulum to tilt with respect to inertial space.

This motion takes place about the input axis of the reference gyro. Since this is a rate-integrating type of unit, an output axis rotation builds up, causing a pickoff signal to be developed. This signal is amplified and applied to the tilt-axis servomotor in such a direction that the resulting motor rotation precesses the gyro to a null. This causes the gimbal to tilt with respect to the earth, and the pendulum develops an output signal. That proportion of the pendulum signal going to the azimuth gyro torquer causes the gyro to develop a pickoff signal. The signal is amplified and fed to the azimuth servomotor in the proper phase to drive the azimuth gimbal in the direction to restore the tilt axis to the east-west plane.

The part of the pendulum signal going to the reference gyro torquer provides vertical damping to the system in that it is in the direction to make the tilt servomotor reduce the pendulum tilt. Thus the system settles in exactly the same manner as a two-degree-of-freedom vertically damped gyrocompass.

A later model of Dynatrol compass employs a three-axis gimbal system, three rate-integrating gyros, and two pendulums. Unless the two-axis system is perfectly level in the east-west plane, a settling-point error will occur, as in the rate gyro type of north-seeking compass. In aircraft applications, where prolonged angle-of-attack changes often occur, such errors might be serious, especially at high latitudes. The three-gyro design eliminates this error and also certain gimbal geometry errors (see Sec. 5-22). In addition, the system provides a source of roll and pitch information for the stabilization of other equipment.

Although each of the rate-integrating gyro approaches requires one more gyroscope than the more common two-degree-of-freedom gyro designs, there is the advantage that the types of gyros and pendulums employed are readily available from a number of manufacturers.

5-16. Vehicle-motion Errors

In general, a gyrocompass is required to indicate the heading of a land, sea, or air vehicle. Thus far, the effects of vehicle motion have been ignored. The only errors considered have been those due to earth rotation and spurious torques.

Because of the earth's curvature, vehicle velocities over its surface cause rotation of the compass with respect to inertial space, which, if uncompensated, results in serious errors. Linear accelerations acting on the gravity reference are another potential source of error. Such accelerations result from changes in speed and course, from rolling and pitching of the vehicle, and from Coriolis and centrifugal effects. So-called "gimbaling errors" can result from improper gimbal geometry or from imperfect roll and pitch stabilization of the gimbal system. Considerable ingenuity has been displayed by gyrocompass designers in combating all the above types of errors, and they have been successful in reducing them to negligible levels.

5-17. North Velocity Error

Consider the case of a gyrocompass mounted on a vehicle proceeding at a velocity v on a course C at a latitude λ. (Course angle is measured clockwise from north.) In order to determine the motion of the compass with respect to inertial space, it is necessary to combine the vehicle velocity with the surface speed of the earth. With a perfectly spherical earth (which is sufficiently accurate in this instance), the eastward velocity of the earth's surface is $R\omega_E \cos \lambda$, where R is the earth's radius (20.9×10^6 ft) and ω_E the earth's sidereal rate. The resultant motion of the vehicle relative to inertial space may be calculated from Fig. 5-13 and, for the case shown, is north of east by an angle ϵ. It is apparent that

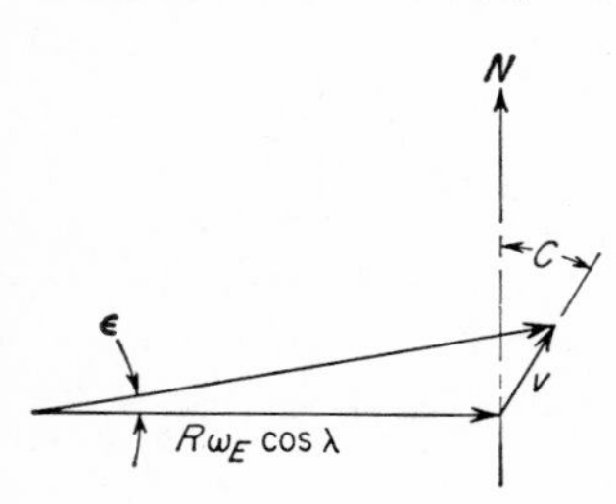

FIG. 5-13. North velocity error.

$$\epsilon = \tan^{-1} \frac{v \cos C}{R\omega_E \cos \lambda + v \sin C} \tag{5-27}$$

From the standpoint of the gyrocompass the earth appears to be rotating about an axis making an angle ϵ with the true polar axis. The compass will therefore settle with a westward error of ϵ.

This type of error is common to all gyrocompasses and, if uncompensated, could reach serious proportions. For example, on an aircraft proceeding north at 300 knots at 60° latitude

$$v = \frac{300 \times 6{,}080}{3{,}600} = 507 \text{ ft/sec}, \qquad C = 0^\circ$$

$$\epsilon = \tan^{-1} \frac{507}{20.9 \times 10^6 \times 72.9 \times 10^{-6} \times 0.500}$$

$$= \tan^{-1} 0.665 = 33.6^\circ$$

Note that this error vanishes on an east (90°) or west (270°) course. The maximum value for a given latitude does not occur on exactly a north or a south course but on a heading that is west of the meridian by the angle ϵ. Then, the vector v is perpendicular to the resultant. The maximum error for this situation is

$$\epsilon_{\max} = \sin^{-1} \frac{v}{R\omega_E \cos \lambda}$$

and will occur at headings of $360° - \epsilon$ and $180° + \epsilon$. Thus, for the case of the 300-knot aircraft considered above,

$$\epsilon_{\max} = \sin^{-1} 0.665 = 41.7°$$

It would occur on headings of 318.3 or 221.7°. In the first instance the compass would point west of north; in the second the error would be eastward.

An analog computer, having inputs of speed, latitude, and course, can be employed to obtain ϵ automatically. The compass card (or the card index) may then be offset by the angle ϵ so that the instrument reads correctly at all times. Many compasses have employed this method of correction.

The technique used on modern electrically torqued compasses is to apply a vertical-axis torque to the gyro proportional to the north component of vehicle speed. This method is independent of latitude, which simplifies the computation of the correction. The theory of operation is shown in Fig. 5-14.

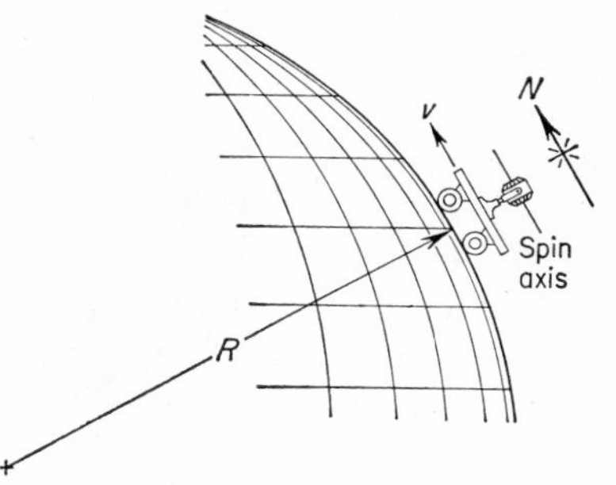

FIG. 5-14. Gyro on vehicle proceeding north.

A gyro, with the spin axis horizontal and in the meridian plane, is shown mounted on a vehicle proceeding north at a velocity v. Because of the curvature of the earth, the vehicle is rotating in the north-south plane at an angular velocity of v/R, where R is the radius of the earth. Unless otherwise corrected, the north end of the gyro will tilt, relative to the earth, at the same rate. If the gyro is pendulous (as on a gyrocompass), it will precess counterclockwise. This is the reason why a gyrocompass develops a westward error on a north-moving vehicle.

Suppose, however, that a clockwise torque equal to Hv/R were applied about the vertical axis of the gyrocompass. This would precess the gyro about the tilt axis at exactly the right rate to keep the spin axis tangent to the surface of the earth at all times as the vehicle proceeds northward. The gyrocompass would, therefore, remain on the meridian. Another way of viewing this method of correction is to consider the vertical torque as being equal and opposite to the "directive effort" which is attempting to urge the compass from the true meridian to the false (sometimes called *virtual*) meridian.

On courses other than north it is the north component of vehicle speed which must be considered. This is equal to $v \cos C$, where C is the course angle. Therefore, the correction torque actually employed is equal to

$$T_V = \frac{Hv \cos C}{R} \tag{5-28}$$

A voltage proportional to this value is continually applied to the torquer on the azimuth axis of the gyro. The electrical analog computer for obtaining this voltage is extremely simple. A linear potentiometer, with a shaft rotation proportional to v, is excited by a fixed voltage. The output of this potentiometer is passed through an electrical resolver, geared one-to-one, to the azimuth gimbal of the compass. The output of the cosine coil of the resolver is then proportional to $v \cos C$, and this voltage is fed to the vertical torquer, properly scaled for the constant H/R.

Suppose it is desired to test the accuracy of such a correction system on a compass located in a test laboratory. Assume that the instrument is mounted on a turntable, so that it may be oriented in any direction. Let the laboratory be located at a latitude of 40°. The turntable is set on, say, a 30° heading, and a speed value of 120 knots is inserted into the correction computer. Now, if the compass were actually in an aircraft proceeding at 120 knots (203 ft/sec) on a 30° course at the same latitude, Eq. (5-27) tells us that, if no correction were applied, the gyro would settle west of the meridian at an angle of

$$\begin{aligned} \epsilon &= \tan^{-1} \frac{203 \times 0.866}{20.9 \times 10^6 \times 72.9 \times 10^{-6} \times 0.766 + 203 \times 0.500} \\ &= 7.9° \end{aligned}$$

Therefore, it might be assumed offhand that the compass on the test floor would settle with an *eastward* error of the same amount, that is, on a heading of 22.1° (30 − 7.9). However, this assumption is not correct.

When the compass is actually on the moving aircraft, the rotor of the electrical resolver in the analog computer is offset from the stator by an angle of 30°, thus producing a correction voltage proportional to $v \cos 30°$. The resulting torque is just enough to cause the compass to settle 7.9° east of the virtual meridian or, in other words, on the *true* meridian. If the compass in the test laboratory were settled 7.9° east of the true meridian, then the angle between the rotor and the stator of the resolver would be the turntable heading (30°) less 7.9°, or 22.1°, which would give a larger voltage than a 30° angle at the output of the resolver. The resolver output voltage is actually proportional to $v \cos (C - \epsilon')$, where C is the turntable setting and ϵ' the settling-point error of the compass. The value of ϵ' may be computed by calculating the settling-point error which the torque coming out of the analog computer will produce.

$$\frac{Hv \cos (C - \epsilon')}{R} = H\omega_E \cos \lambda \sin \epsilon'$$

$$v \cos C \cos \epsilon' + v \sin C \sin \epsilon' = R\omega_E \cos \lambda \sin \epsilon'$$

Dividing both sides by $\cos \epsilon'$, we have

$$v \cos C + v \sin C \tan \epsilon' = R\omega_E \cos \lambda \tan \epsilon'$$

$$\epsilon' = \tan^{-1} \frac{v \cos C}{R\omega_E \cos \lambda - v \sin C} \tag{5-29}$$

This is similar to Eq. (5-27), except for the minus sign in the denominator. The settling-point error in the test laboratory is then

$$\epsilon' = \tan^{-1} \frac{203 \times 0.866}{20.9 \times 10^6 \times 72.9 \times 10^{-6} \times 0.766 - 203 \times 0.500}$$
$$= 9.4^\circ$$

The compass card will therefore read 20.6° in the laboratory under the speed, latitude, and course conditions assumed. The above analysis applies only to compasses employing the vertical-torque method of correcting the north velocity error. On instruments where the dial is offset by the angle ϵ and where the gyro is settled on the virtual meridian when the vehicle is moving, a slightly different result is obtained on a turntable test.

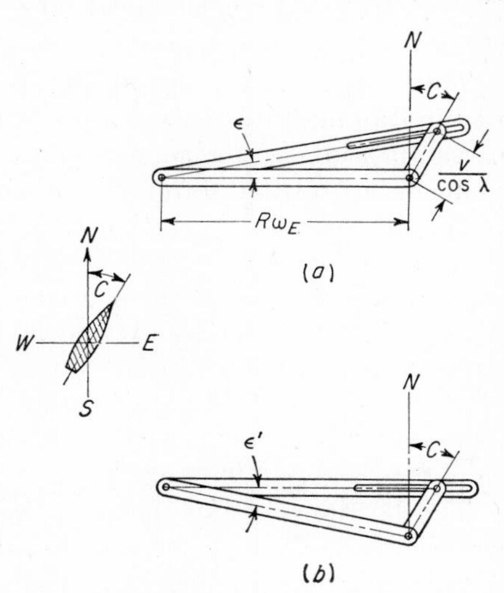

FIG. 5-15. Analog linkage for correcting north velocity error.

A typical mechanical analog computer used for obtaining ϵ is shown in Fig. 5-15 at (*a*). The lower link is made proportional to $R\omega_E$. (The quantity $R\omega_E$ is the surface speed of the earth at the equator with respect to inertial space. It is sometimes designated as E and has a value of 902.464 knots.) This link is oriented east-west by the shaft carrying the compass card. Strictly speaking, the link is parallel to a line passing through the 270 and 90° markings on the card and is east-west when the compass card reads correctly. The right-hand link is maintained parallel to the fore-and-aft line of the vehicle, and its length is adjusted to be proportional to $v/\cos\lambda$. The third sliding link then makes an angle ϵ with the first one, since the mechanism exactly reproduces Eq. (5-27). The motion of the pivot joining the first and third links is fed into a mechanical differential, inserted between the azimuth gimbal and the compass card, thus rotating the card the angle ϵ with respect to the gimbal.

On the test floor the azimuth gimbal will be on north, and the dial will be some angle ϵ' from north. Therefore, the $R\omega_E$ link will lie at the angle ϵ' from east-west. Since the pivot motion between the first and the third links is also ϵ', the third link must now be exactly east-west. The linkage, therefore, assumes the position shown at (*b*) in Fig. 5-15. From this configuration, it can be seen that

$$\epsilon' = \sin^{-1}\frac{v\cos C}{R\omega_E\cos\lambda} \tag{5-30}$$

With the same test conditions ($v = 203$ ft/sec, $C = 30°$, $\lambda = 40°$), the card error would be

$$\begin{aligned}\epsilon' &= \sin^{-1}\frac{203 \times 0.866}{20.9 \times 10^6 \times 72.9 \times 10^{-6} \times 0.766}\\ &= 8.7°\end{aligned}$$

The compass card would read 30 − 8.7 or 21.3°, compared to 20.6° for the other type of corrector.

This type of computer, unlike the one actuating the vertical torquer, requires an input of latitude. It will give the same value of ϵ' regardless of the latitude of the place of test. Therefore, in Eq. (5-30) λ is the value of latitude fed into the computer and is not necessarily the latitude of the test location.

On slow-speed ships the value of v may be set manually. However, on vessels equipped with an underwater log the setting may be made automatically. On a land vehicle the speed input is usually obtained from the speedometer drive system. On aircraft a Doppler radar provides an accurate source of ground speed. Airspeed is, of course, not sufficiently accurate, particularly at high altitudes where jet-stream winds sometimes exceed 200 knots.

The latitude setting is usually made manually, except on the more sophisticated military navigation systems, which have instruments that continuously compute the latitude and longitude of the vehicle.

5-18. East Velocity Error

In Sec. 5-6 it was explained that a horizontal torque equal to $H\omega_E\sin\lambda$ was applied to the compass gyro in order to compensate for the vertical component of earth's rotation. Suppose that the compass is mounted on a vehicle which has a velocity v and is on a course C at a latitude of λ. The velocity v may be broken up into north and east components. These are $v \cos C$ and $v \sin C$, respectively. The action of the first component has been discussed in Sec. 5-17. The eastward component has the effect of increasing the rate of the earth's rotation. Referring to Fig. 5-16, this increase in angular velocity is equal to $v \sin C/R \cos \lambda$. The vertical component is

$$\frac{v \sin C \sin \lambda}{R \cos \lambda} = \frac{v \sin C \tan \lambda}{R}$$

This is the amount by which the vertical component of the earth's rotation is increased. Therefore, the total horizontal torque applied to the gyro should be

$$T_H = H\omega_E \sin \lambda + \frac{Hv \sin C \tan \lambda}{R} \tag{5-31}$$

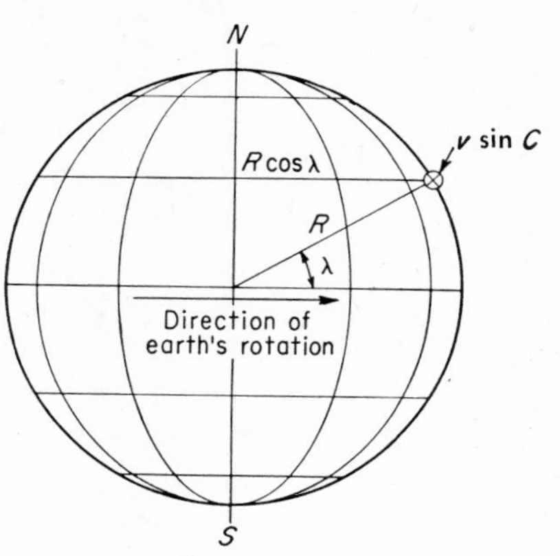

FIG. 5-16. Effect of eastward component of vehicle velocity.

On many gyrocompasses the second term correction is neglected. On these instruments the gyro tilts until the pendulous righting moment puts in a torque just equal to the right-hand term. The action is exactly the same as when a steady spurious horizontal torque exists [see Eq. (5-24)].

With horizontal damping no steady-state error results. However, changes in heading or speed cause small transient errors until the gyro settles to a new tilt.

A steady-state settling-point error, as well as a transient error, exists on compasses with vertical damping. This steady-state error can be calculated from Eq. (5-25).

$$\phi = \frac{M_D T_H}{M_P H \omega_E \cos \lambda} = \frac{M_D}{M_P H \omega_E \cos \lambda} \frac{Hv \sin C \tan \lambda}{R}$$
$$= \frac{M_D v \sin C \tan \lambda}{M_P R \omega_E \cos \lambda}$$

On shipboard applications, where v is low, the error is small. Consider the case of a ship going east at 20 knots (33.8 ft/sec) at a latitude of 40°. Assume that the ratio of $M_D/M_P = 0.0375$. Then

$$\phi = \frac{0.0375 \times 33.8 \times 1 \times 0.839}{20.9 \times 10^6 \times 72.9 \times 10^{-6} \times 0.766}$$
$$= 0.000912 \text{ radian} = 0.052°$$

On high-precision compasses, such as those employed for Navy fire control purposes, or on gyrocompasses used in aircraft, this error should not be neglected. The correction may be obtained readily from a simple analog computer.

It might be thought that in the case of a high-speed aircraft, whose westward component of speed is equal to the eastward surface speed of the earth, the north-seeking action of the compass would be completely nullified. Conversely, on an airplane going east the north-seeking effect might be expected to increase. However, when the complete situation is analyzed, it will be found that the east-west component of aircraft speed has no effect whatsoever on the directive effort of the compass, provided that the proper vertical torque is applied to compensate for the north velocity effect. This analysis does not apply to gyrocompasses where the north velocity error is corrected by an offset of the dial or the dial index. However, for reasons which are explained in the next section, this method of correction is not suitable for gyrocompasses on high-speed vehicles.

In the previous section it was shown [Eq. (5-28)] that the vertical-axis torque required for compensation of the north velocity error is equal to

$$T_V = \frac{Hv \cos C}{R} \tag{5-32}$$

where H = angular momentum
v = vehicle velocity
C = vehicle course
R = radius of earth

This has the effect of precessing the gyro in tilt at a rate equal to

$$\frac{d\theta}{dt} = -\frac{v \cos C}{R} \tag{5-33}$$

(The minus sign indicates that the north end of the gyro is precessed downward when $\cos C$ is positive.)

The tilt rate with respect to the earth when the gyro is off the meridian by an angle ϕ is given by Eq. (5-4).

$$\frac{d\theta}{dt} = \omega_E \cos \lambda \sin \phi \tag{5-34}$$

where ω_E is the angular velocity of the earth and λ the latitude. It has been shown previously that the north-seeking effect of the compass is dependent upon this tilt rate. Equation (5-34) was originally derived on the assumption that the compass was mounted on a stationary base. However, it will now be shown that this equation still applies, regardless of vehicle speed, if the proper north-velocity correction torque is applied about the vertical axis.

At any latitude the eastward surface speed of the earth is

$$v_E = R\omega_E \cos \lambda$$

For example, at 40° latitude v_E is 691 knots, which may easily be exceeded by a modern fighter aircraft.

In order to "stop the earth" an airplane proceeding west ($C = 270°$) must have a ground speed such that

$$v = R\omega_E \cos \lambda$$

Suppose this to be the case. Then, the gyro tilt rate is certainly zero, since the complete equation (see Fig. 5-16) for the combined effect of earth's rotation and the east-west component of aircraft velocity is

$$\frac{d\theta}{dt} = \left(\omega_E + \frac{v \sin C}{R \cos \lambda}\right) \cos \lambda \sin \phi \tag{5-35}$$

However, if the gyro goes off the meridian by an angle ϕ, it will still exhibit a tilt rate exactly equal to that shown by Eq. (5-34) because of the effect of the north velocity correction given in Eq. (5-32). The reason is as follows.

The quantity $\cos C$ in Eq. (5-32) is computed by a resolver whose shaft rotation is equal to the angle between the *gyro spin axis* and the direction of the aircraft. Note that this angle is equal to C only when the gyro is on true north; *the analog computer cannot tell when the gyro is off north.* To illustrate, assume that the gyro has an eastward error of ϕ and that the aircraft is proceeding true west (270°). Instead of applying zero correction, as would be the case if the gyro were on true north, we have the same correction as for a course of $270° - \phi$. Hence, substituting in Eq. (5-33) the values $v = R\omega_E \cos \lambda$ and $C = 270° - \phi$, we obtain

$$\frac{d\theta}{dt} = \frac{-R\omega_E \cos \lambda \cos (270° - \phi)}{R}$$

Since $\cos (270° - \phi) = -\sin \phi$,

$$\frac{d\theta}{dt} = \omega_E \cos \lambda \sin \phi$$

The magnitude and direction of the tilt rate are precisely the same as obtained on a stationary vehicle because of the earth's rotation. Suppose that, with the same compass error ϕ, the aircraft goes west at twice the earth's speed, or

$$v = 2R\omega_E \cos \lambda$$

The speed correction, being twice as great, will result in $d\theta/dt$ [Eq. (5-33)] being doubled. However, Eq. (5-35) shows that this is opposed by a rate of $-d\theta/dt$ one-half as great, since, in effect, the earth's rotation has been reversed. Hence, the net tilt rate is still $\omega_E \cos \lambda \sin \phi$. Or assume that, with the same compass error, the aircraft is proceeding east (90°) at $v = R\omega_E \cos \lambda$. Then, substituting in Eq. (5-33), we have

$$\frac{d\theta}{dt} = \frac{-R\omega_E \cos \lambda \cos (90° - \phi)}{R}$$

Since $\cos (90° - \phi) = \sin \phi$,

$$\frac{d\theta}{dt} = \omega_E \cos \lambda \sin \phi$$

However, a positive $d\theta/dt$ of $2\omega_E \cos \lambda \sin \phi$ [see Eq. (5-35)] results from the earth's rotation rate being effectively doubled, so the net tilt rate is unchanged.

Another interesting case is that in which the aircraft is proceeding at a velocity of $v = R\omega_E \cos \lambda$ on a 270° course *as indicated by a gyrocompass having an error of* ϕ. The true course is actually $270° + \phi$. The north velocity correction mechanism gives zero output in this instance, since the direction of the aircraft is exactly 90° from the gyro spin axis. However, the aircraft now has a north component of speed equal to $v \sin \phi$, or an angular rate in the north-south plane of $v \sin \phi/R$. Since $v = R\omega_E \cos \lambda$, the tilt rate is

$$\frac{d\theta}{dt} = \frac{R\omega_E \cos \lambda \sin \phi}{R} = \omega_E \cos \lambda \sin \phi$$

The general equation, considering all factors, is as follows:

$$\frac{d\theta}{dt} = \left(\omega_E + \frac{v \sin C}{R \cos \lambda}\right) \cos \lambda \sin \phi - \frac{v \cos (C - \phi)}{R} + \frac{v \cos C \cos \phi}{R} \tag{5-36}$$

The first term represents the tilt rate caused by the rotation of the earth plus the amount added to the earth's rotation by the east-west component of aircraft speed. The second term is the tilt rate put in by the north velocity corrector. The third term is the tilt rate caused by the north component of aircraft speed.

Expanding Eq. (5-36) gives

$$\begin{aligned}\frac{d\theta}{dt} &= \omega_E \cos \lambda \sin \phi + \frac{v \sin C \cos \lambda \sin \phi}{R \cos \lambda} - \frac{v \cos C \cos \phi}{R} \\ &\qquad - \frac{v \sin C \sin \phi}{R} + \frac{v \cos C \cos \phi}{R} \\ &= \omega_E \cos \lambda \sin \phi\end{aligned}$$

The above analysis shows that, as long as the velocity corrector is supplied with the proper input of ground speed, the north-seeking effect of a gyrocompass is completely independent of aircraft speed, even when it equals or exceeds the surface speed of the earth.

5-19. Ballistic Deflection Error

When a gyrocompass is carried on a vehicle undergoing a change in course or speed, any component of acceleration along the spin axis acts upon the pendulous element to create a torque about the gyro tilt axis, causing an azimuth precession. The same action results whether the gyro is actually pendulous or nonpendulous and electrically torqued by means of a pendulum.

This azimuth motion is known as the *ballistic deflection error.* It may result from turns as well as from changes in speed, since there will be a component of centrifugal force along the gyro spin axis during a turn. The direction of the azimuth motion is such that the gyro is precessed westward (counterclockwise) by a northward acceleration.

It may be recalled that this is the same direction as the north velocity error when the vehicle has a northern velocity component. The north velocity error increases as the vehicle accelerates to higher and higher speeds. Since both errors increase in the same direction, it would appear that a ratio of angular momentum to pendulous factor could be selected such that both errors would increase at exactly the same rate. Then, the accumulated ballistic deflection error would always equal the north velocity error. Such a gyrocompass would read properly at all times, provided that a card correction were continually made for the north velocity error. Unless the two error rates were exactly matched, the ballistic deflection would overshoot or undershoot the final settling point (the virtual meridian), and considerable time would then have to be allowed for the disturbance to damp out following a speed or course change.

A rigorous analysis indicates that the two error rates cannot be made to "track" exactly. However, for slow-speed vehicles such as ships, where the magnitude of the north velocity correction is small, the error rates can be made substantially equal.

The north velocity error is given by Eq. (5-27).

$$\epsilon = \tan^{-1} \frac{v \cos C}{R\omega_E \cos \lambda + v \sin C} \qquad (5\text{-}27)$$

where v = vehicle velocity
C = course
R = radius of earth
ω_E = angular velocity of earth
λ = latitude

Now, if v is small compared to $R\omega_E$, ϵ can be expressed closely by

$$\epsilon = \frac{v \cos C}{R\omega_E \cos \lambda}$$

The rate of change of ϵ is proportional to the rate of change of v, or to a, the acceleration.

$$\frac{d\epsilon}{dt} = \frac{a \cos C}{R\omega_E \cos \lambda}$$

The ballistic deflection rate is proportional to the component of vehicle acceleration acting along the spin axis (see Fig. 5-17). Assume that the ballistic deflection angle is ϕ at the moment in question. The component of acceleration along the spin axis is $a \cos (C + \phi)$. The couple produced about the horizontal axis, assuming a pendulous factor of M_P, is $M_P a \cos (C + \phi)/g$, where g is the acceleration of gravity. The resulting azimuth precession rate is then

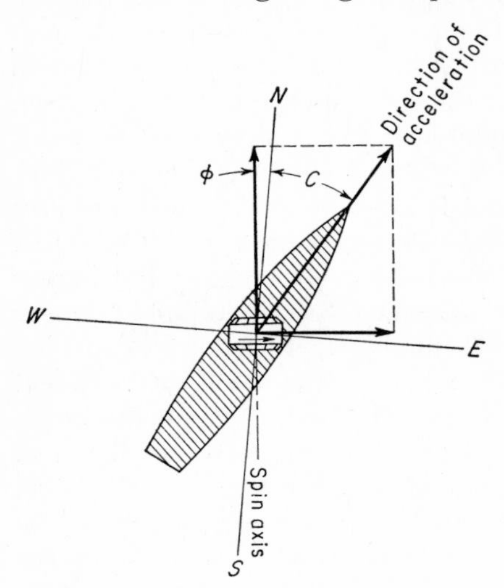

FIG. 5-17. Ballistic deflection error.

$$\frac{d\phi}{dt} = \frac{M_P a \cos (C + \phi)}{Hg} \tag{5-37}$$

When ϕ is small, as on a low-speed vehicle, the rate is substantially

$$\frac{d\phi}{dt} = \frac{M_P a \cos C}{Hg}$$

In order for the two rates to match, $d\phi/dt$ must equal $d\epsilon/dt$, or

$$\frac{M_P a \cos C}{Hg} = \frac{a \cos C}{R\omega_E \cos \lambda}$$

For this condition

$$\frac{H}{M_P} = \frac{R\omega_E \cos \lambda}{g} \tag{5-38}$$

The ratio of H/M_P determines the undamped period of the gyrocompass, as shown by Eq. (5-13).

$$T = 2\pi \left(\frac{H}{M_P \omega_E \cos \lambda} \right)^{1/2} \tag{5-13}$$

Substituting Eq. (5-38) for H/M_P we get

$$T = 2\pi \left(\frac{1}{\omega_E \cos \lambda} \times \frac{R\omega_E \cos \lambda}{g} \right)^{1/2}$$
$$= 2\pi \left(\frac{R}{g} \right)^{1/2}$$

Since $R = 20.9 \times 10^6$ ft, and $g = 32.2$ ft/sec^2,

$$T = 2\pi \times 10^3 \left(\frac{20.9}{32.2} \right)^{1/2}$$
$$= 5{,}060 \text{ sec or } 84.4 \text{ min}$$

A gyrocompass with an 84.4 min undamped period is said to be Schuler tuned.* It will exhibit no acceleration error, provided the range of north-south velocity is relatively small and the compass is operated undamped during changes in speed and course. It should be noted that the value of H/M_P must be changed with latitude in order to maintain the period at 84.4 min [see Eq. (5-13)]. The customary procedure is to maintain the angular momentum proportional to the cosine of the latitude by changing the gyro rotational speed. This is more feasible than altering the pendulous factor on a running compass.

However, reducing the angular momentum with increasing latitude does have the disadvantage of causing a greater than normal deterioration of accuracy at high latitudes.

The assumption that ϕ is small cannot be made in the case of a high-speed vehicle such as a jet aircraft. For example, consider a 600-knot airplane at a latitude of 40°, making a 180° turn from a north to a south heading. The total change in speed in the north-south plane is 1,200 knots. When headed north, the north velocity error [from Eq. (5-27)] is

$$\epsilon = \tan^{-1} \frac{600}{902.4 \times 0.766}$$
$$= \tan^{-1} 0.868 = 41.0°$$

The total ballistic deflection should therefore be twice this, or 82.0°, during the maneuver. Solving the exact ballistic equation (5-37), the value of ϕ can be expressed in the form

$$\phi = \sin^{-1} \left(\frac{e^{2M_P v/Hg} - 1}{e^{2M_P v/Hg} + 1} \right) - C$$

* For a further discussion of Schuler tuning as applied to inertial navigation systems, see Chaps. 7 and 8.

Since with Schuler tuning Eq. (5-38) must hold,

$$\phi = \sin^{-1}\left(\frac{e^{2v/R\omega_E \cos\lambda} - 1}{e^{2v/R\omega_E \cos\lambda} + 1}\right) - C \tag{5-39}$$

An aircraft heading north, accelerating from a standstill to 600 knots, at 40° latitude would cause a ballistic deflection of

$$\begin{aligned}\phi &= \sin^{-1}\left(\frac{e^{(2\times 600)/(902.4\times 0.766)} - 1}{e^{(2\times 600)/(902.4\times 0.766)} + 1}\right)\\ &= \sin^{-1} 0.700 = 44.4^\circ\end{aligned}$$

The total ballistic deflection for the 180° turn would then be 88.8°, or 6.8° more than the change in north velocity error. Such an error cannot, of course, be tolerated.

On the other hand, consider the same maneuver executed by a 30-knot ship. The total change in north velocity error would be

$$\begin{aligned}2\epsilon &= 2\tan^{-1}\frac{30}{902.4 \times 0.766}\\ &= 2\tan^{-1} 0.0434 = 4.97^\circ\end{aligned}$$

The total ballistic deflection is

$$\begin{aligned}2\phi &= 2\sin^{-1}\left(\frac{\exp\,(2\times 30)/(902.4\times 0.766) - 1}{\exp\,(2\times 30)/(902.4\times 0.766) + 1}\right)\\ &= 2\sin^{-1} 0.0434 = 4.97^\circ\end{aligned}$$

The two errors match within 0.01°, so the Schuler tuning is entirely feasible for such low-speed applications.

There are some practical limitations to this technique. One is that the compass should be undamped during the entire maneuver. Unless this situation exists, a so-called "ballistic damping error" occurs. This error will be discussed in the next section. Of course, the compass cannot be left undamped continually, even when settled on the meridian, since the least disturbance would set up oscillations. The method frequently employed is to remove damping automatically whenever accelerations exceed a certain threshold. For example, damping might be cut out whenever an acceleration of over 2 knots/min occurs or if the turning rate exceeds 40°/min. In order to prevent yawing of the ship from operating the rate-of-turn cutout, the additional requirement that the turn must exceed a certain magnitude, say 5 or 10°, is sometimes imposed. The important limitation to all these techniques is that the early part of the maneuver, which is below the acceleration cutout threshold, takes place in a *damped* condition. Some slight ballistic damping error is inevitable.

Another limitation is that the Schuler-tuned compensation is not correct unless the period is exactly right and the north velocity corrector has no error. The compass constants can never be perfectly adjusted. On shipboard, inputs of speed and latitude will invariably have some error. This is particularly true of the speed input which is usually obtained from a device that indicates water speed rather than ground speed. Ocean currents and tides may cause errors of several knots.

The net result of all these factors is that in practice the two error rates are almost never precisely matched on instruments employing Schuler tuning, and heading errors as large as 1° often occur during a series of erratic maneuvers, even on the highest-grade Navy gyrocompasses. On simpler compasses, with manual inputs of speed and manual damping cutout, much larger errors are experienced during prolonged turns and speed changes. These errors do not vanish until a considerable time after the ship has been restored to a constant speed and course.

Fortunately, on modern electrically torqued gyrocompasses, better methods of combating the ballistic deflection error are available. On instruments of this type, where the north velocity error is prevented by applying a vertical torque to the gyro, compensation by means of Schuler tuning is not possible anyway.

The most accurate technique employed is to apply a force to the gravity reference pendulum bob proportional to the linear accelerations acting in the north-south plane. If the vehicle is undergoing a velocity change while on a heading of C, the component of acceleration in the north-south plane is

$$a_{NS} = \frac{dv}{dt} \cos C$$

Therefore, if M is the mass of the pendulum bob, an acceleration force is acting on the bob equal to

$$F = M \frac{dv}{dt} \cos C \tag{5-40}$$

In order to nullify this effect an equal and opposite force is computed and imparted to the pendulum bob. Thus if the vehicle is increasing its velocity, the correction force is applied in the forward direction. The correction is just enough to overcome the acceleration force; the pendulum is still free to respond to any tilt.

An electric "force motor" is used to impart the force to the pendulum. This device can be made very linear, so that the force on the pendulum bob is almost exactly proportional to the voltage in the force-motor control winding. The quantity dv/dt is computed by differentiating the vehicle velocity. For example, if a speedometer type of indication is available, where velocity is measured as a shaft rotation, a tachometer generator geared to this shaft will develop an output voltage proportional to acceleration. The quantity $\cos C$ is readily obtained from an electrical resolver driven by the azimuth gimbal.

The pendulum must also be corrected for the centrifugal force resulting from a turn. This force may be expressed in several ways:

$$F_C = Mr\left(\frac{dC}{dt}\right)^2 = \frac{Mv^2}{r} = Mv\frac{dC}{dt}$$

The radius of turn r is not readily available, so the third form is the most convenient for computing purposes. The rate of turn dC/dt may be obtained from a tachometer generator driven by the azimuth gimbal. A voltage proportional to the velocity v can be taken from a potentiometer positioned by a shaft whose rotation is proportional to vehicle speed.

The total force applied to the pendulum bob to compensate for ballistic deflections caused by changes in both speed and course is, therefore,

$$F = M\left(\frac{dv}{dt}\cos C + v\frac{dC}{dt}\sin C\right) \tag{5-41}$$

Correcting the gravity reference pendulum for ballistic forces is more accurate than Schuler tuning for several reasons:

1. It is theoretically correct for any speed. Schuler tuning is practicable only at low velocities, such as encountered on shipboard applications.
2. The undamped period of the compass may be any value desired.
3. The compass constants need not be changed with latitude.
4. A small error in the speed input does not show up as an immediate heading error. Due to the loose coupling between the pendulum and the gyro, the error builds up very slowly and will probably not become significant before the vehicle maneuver is completed. Tides and ocean currents, which remain constant, have no effect on the correction for vehicle speed changes.

Another method of correcting the pendulum for acceleration effects is to apply a "blinding" voltage, proportional to acceleration, to the pendulum output signal. The pendulum is then allowed to align itself with the virtual vertical. Although this technique avoids the need for an electric force motor, it has two disadvantages. First, the pendulum output must be linear over the entire acceleration range. This is not necessary in the case of a pendulum equipped with a force motor and is somewhat difficult to accomplish. Secondly, because of the viscous damping customarily used on the pendulum for the purpose of preventing response to short-term accelerations, the pendulum error does not build up as soon as an acceleration is applied. The correction, on the other hand, is instantaneous. Hence, the pendulum is overcorrected during the initial stages of an acceleration and is undercorrected immediately following an acceleration. This arrangement is sometimes used because of its simplicity, but it is not as accurate as the force-motor correction method, which does not permit the pendulum to move from its zero position, unless, of course, a gyro tilt should occur.

An acceleration correction technique which has been successfully employed on moderate-accuracy compasses on vehicles going as fast as 60 knots is to equip the damped pendulum with limit stops. This sets a "ceiling" on the ballistic deflection rate. In order to keep this rate low (say in the order of $\frac{1}{2}$°/min) the period of the compass is made quite long—in some cases over 2 hours. This is an extremely simple instrumentation.

A somewhat more refined method is to have the pendulum cut itself off when it reaches the limit stops. The gyro is then cast loose during accelerations instead of being precessed off at a low rate. This method is practicable for aircraft having speeds below about 200 miles/hr. The correction torques for north and east components of velocity and for earth rotation are maintained during the cutout phase. On high-speed aircraft the wind speed changes so rapidly that, even with constant air speed, linear accelerations are so frequent that the gyro would be cut off from the pendulum too great a percentage of the time. Applying correction forces directly to the pendulum is the only feasible method on such aircraft.

5-20. Ballistic Damping Error

This error exists on both vertically and horizontally damped gyrocompasses.

On a vertically damped compass a tilt of the gyro (and, therefore, a horizontal acceleration in the spin-axis plane) always results in a vertical torque being applied to the gyro. Following an acceleration the gyro will be left with a tilt, which causes a precession in azimuth.

On Schuler-tuned compasses this error is avoided by cutting out damping during changes in speed and course. In cases where an electrical pendulum is used as a gravity reference, the methods of combating ballistic deflection error described in the previous section are equally effective in eliminating ballistic damping error.

On horizontally damped instruments, where a thermal time-lag device is employed, the pendulum corrections for accelerations will again prevent ballistic damping errors. Where liquid damping is used, a magnetically actuated valve in the pipe between the liquid vessels is closed during periods of acceleration. It should be noted that, without these corrections, a horizontally damped compass starts precessing in azimuth as soon as the acceleration is applied along the spin axis, whereas a vertically damped instrument first develops a tilt of the gyro.

5-21. Centrifugal and Coriolis Errors

On high-speed vehicles having a velocity component in the east-west plane, significant north-south accelerations exist which affect the gravity reference of a gyrocompass. These accelerations result from the curved path of the vehicle over the spherical surface of the earth and from the combined effect of vehicle velocity and earth rotation.

Consider a vehicle with an east-west component of ground speed equal to v_E at a latitude λ. Its radius from the earth's axis is $R \cos \lambda$, where R is the radius of the earth. The surface speed of the earth at that point with respect to inertial space is then $R\omega_E \cos \lambda$, ω_E being the sidereal angular velocity of the earth. The east-west tangential velocity of the vehicle with respect to inertial space is therefore $v_E + R\omega_E \cos \lambda$. The centripetal acceleration, which is normal to the earth's axis, is this total tangential velocity squared, divided by the radius from the earth's axis, or

$$\begin{aligned} a &= \frac{(v_E + R\omega_E \cos \lambda)^2}{R \cos \lambda} \\ &= \frac{v_E{}^2 + 2R\omega_E v_E \cos \lambda + R^2\omega_E{}^2 \cos^2 \lambda}{R \cos \lambda} \\ &= \frac{v_E{}^2}{R \cos \lambda} + 2\omega_E v_E + R\omega_E{}^2 \cos \lambda \end{aligned} \tag{5-42}$$

The first term is the centripetal acceleration which would result from the vehicle moving over a stationary earth. $2\omega_E v_E$ represents a Coriolis term. The third term is the acceleration felt by a body fixed with respect to the earth. A plumb line carried on a moving vehicle would have to be corrected for the horizontal components of the first two terms but not for the third term. The third term enters into our everyday definition of the vertical and accounts for the elliptical shape of the earth and the change in the value of g with latitude.

In order to obtain the horizontal components of the terms in Eq. (5-42), it is necessary to multiply them by $\sin \lambda$. Also, if v is the ground speed of the vehicle and C the course, $v_E = v \sin C$. Assuming the mass of the gravity reference pendulum bob to be M, we see that the total correction force (directed in the horizontal plane toward the nearest earth's pole) is

$$\begin{aligned} F &= \frac{M(v \sin C)^2 \sin \lambda}{R \cos \lambda} + 2M\omega_E v \sin C \sin \lambda \\ &= \frac{Mv^2 \sin^2 C \tan \lambda}{R} + 2M\omega_E v \sin C \sin \lambda \end{aligned}$$

Neglecting these corrections would not result in any steady-state error of the gyrocompass, since the gyro would settle with a tilt such that its spin axis was perpendicular to the virtual vertical. However, any change in course or speed would result in a transient azimuth error of several times the change in the virtual vertical. It is exactly the same error which would result from a suddenly applied tilt equal to the change in the virtual vertical. This error would be dependent upon the major-to-minor axis ratio of the ellipse traced by the spin axis as the compass settles.

The correction may be completely neglected on a slow-speed vehicle. Assume the case of a ship proceeding east at 40° latitude at a speed of 30 knots (50.7 ft/sec). The angle between the true and the virtual verticals is then

$$\begin{aligned}\theta &= \frac{v^2 \sin^2 C \tan \lambda}{Rg} + \frac{2\omega_E v \sin C \sin \lambda}{g} \\ &= \frac{(50.7)^2 \times 0.839}{20.9 \times 10^6 \times 32.2} + \frac{2 \times 72.9 \times 10^{-6} \times 50.7 \times 0.643}{32.2} \\ &= 3.20 \times 10^{-6} + 147.5 \times 10^{-6} \\ &= 150.7 \times 10^{-6} \text{ radian or } 0.0086^\circ\end{aligned}$$

If the ship should suddenly change from an east to a west course, the virtual vertical would shift twice this amount. However, the resulting azimuth excursion would still be small, probably in the order of 0.2°.

On a 600-knot jet aircraft the centripetal term would be multiplied by a factor of $(600/30)^2$, and the Coriolis term would be 20 times greater. The shift in the virtual vertical would then be

$$400 \times 3.20 \times 10^{-6} + 20 \times 147.5 \times 10^{-6} = 4{,}230 \times 10^{-6} \text{ radian or } 0.242^\circ$$

If the 600-knot aircraft executed the 180° turn, the azimuth excursion of the compass would be several degrees. The centripetal error increases rapidly as the pole is approached owing to the $\tan \lambda$ term. At 80° latitude the effect would be nearly seven times greater than at 40°.

The correction may be generated in an analog computer. The term $v^2 \sin^2 C$ can be computed by exciting a squaring potentiometer with a voltage proportional to $v \sin C$. An averaged linear correction may serve if v is not too large. Such an approximation would result in overcorrection at low speeds and undercorrection at high speeds. The straight line should, of course, match the squared curve most closely at the high-speed end.

Whether or not the centrifugal and Coriolis corrections should be made depends upon the compass accuracy desired, the vehicle speed, and the latitude range. It will probably be found unnecessary on ships or land vehicles. On low-speed aircraft it may turn out that only the Coriolis term need be considered. On high-speed jet aircraft both corrections will be required.

5-22. Gimbaling Error

The card on a gyrocompass should indicate the *heading* of the vehicle in which it is installed. Heading is defined as the angle measured clockwise, *in the horizontal plane,* between the north-south plane and the vertical plane passing through the fore-and-aft axis of the vehicle. A gyrocompass gimbaled as shown in Fig. 5-4 will not show heading correctly unless the vehicle is on a cardinal course (north, east, south, or west) or has no roll or pitch.

The card of the compass shown in Fig. 5-4 measures angles in the "deck" plane and not in the horizontal plane. Although this gimbal geometry is used very frequently, particularly on aircraft directional gyros, it does not measure heading exactly except under the conditions stated above.

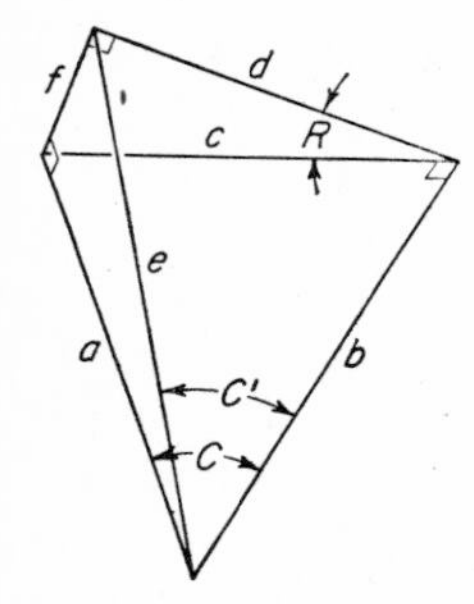

FIG. 5-18. Computation of gimbaling error.

Consider the case of a ship on a heading C and with a roll angle R. In Fig. 5-18, line a represents the gyro spin axis, which is horizontal and lies in the north-south plane. Line b is the fore-and-aft axis of the ship. This line is also horizontal, since in this instance the vessel is considered to be rolling without any accompanying pitch. Hence, triangle abc is in the horizontal plane, and angle C represents the heading of the ship. Triangle bde is in the deck plane; triangle cdf lies in the vertical plane. Line e passes through the 0 and 180° markings on the compass card. The card index is along line b. Therefore, angle C' represents the card reading. When R is zero, C' is always equal to C. Angle C' for any other value of R is calculated as follows:

$$c = b \tan C$$
$$d = c \cos R = b \tan C \cos R$$
$$\tan C' = \frac{d}{b} = \tan C \cos R \tag{5-43}$$

Figure 5-19 shows the gimbaling error $C' - C$ for various combinations of C and R. Several important facts are illustrated by these curves.

1. The gimbaling error reaches a maximum at approximately intercardinal headings, that is, headings of about 45, 135, 225, and 315°. It vanishes on cardinal headings.

2. The error increases approximately as the square of the roll angle.

3. Symmetrical rolling of the vehicle does *not* average out the error. For example, on a 45° heading the dial reads approximately 4° low on both the right and the left extremes of a ±30° roll. If the vehicle is assumed to be rolling with simple harmonic motion, the integrated average error would be about 2½° for this condition.

Pitching of a vehicle produces a somewhat similar effect. Depending upon the phase relationship between pitch and roll, the instantaneous

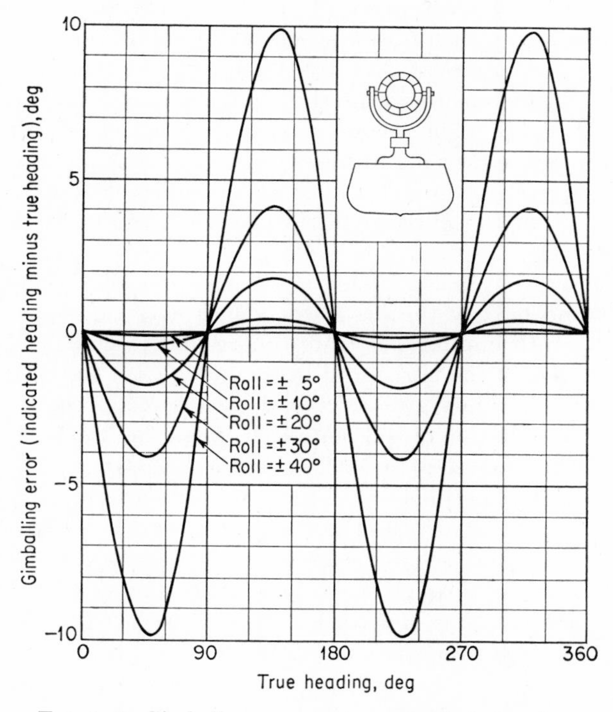

FIG. 5-19. Gimbaling-error in two-axis gimbal system.

errors from the two motions acting simultaneously may either add or subtract. In general, pitch angles are smaller than roll angles and are a less important source of gimbaling error.

On a gyrocompass of moderate accuracy, employed only as a steering reference, the error encountered with the type of gimbal geometry shown in Fig. 5-4 can be disregarded. A ±10° roll is fairly severe for a ship. Yet even on the worst headings, the average gimbaling error under this condition is less than 0.3°. Even on an aircraft banking at 45°, it is not particularly important to the pilot steering it, if, during the course of a turn, the heading is momentarily off by nearly 10°. As the aircraft approaches the new desired heading, the bank angle is progressively reduced, and the craft "homes in" on the final course with the wings level and, therefore, with no gimbaling error.

The gimbaling error is important on high-precision stabilization or navigation systems where the gyrocompass is used for the azimuth stabilization of devices such as guns, optics, or radar antennas or where the vehicle heading is fed to a navigational computer, along with distance traveled, to establish the coordinates of present vehicle position. Another gimbal configuration must be used under such circumstances. To avoid gimbaling error it is first necessary to isolate the azimuth gimbal axis from vehicle motion so that it remains vertical regardless of rolling and pitching. This ensures that the compass card measures angles in the horizontal plane. The second requirement is that the dial index be carried by a member that maintains it in the horizontal plane. Thirdly, the member supporting the index must never change its angle (in the horizontal plane) from the vertical plane passing through the fore-and-aft axis of the vehicle.

The gimbal system in Fig. 5-20*a* meets all three requirements. That in Fig. 5-20*b* meets only the first two. Both configurations completely isolate the azimuth gimbal axis from rolling and pitching. Both maintain the dial index in the horizontal plane, along with the card, by virtue of the fact that the inner gimbal is made pendulous. On system (*a*) no matter what combination of roll and pitch exists, the pitch pivots PP are always in the horizontal plane 90° from the roll pivots RR. The roll pivots are, of course, parallel to the fore-and-aft centerline of the vehicle. Therefore, any object, such as the dial index, which is attached to the pitch gimbal maintains a fixed angle (in the horizontal plane) from the vertical plane passing through the vehicle's fore-and-aft centerline. The third requirement for a system with no gimbaling error is thereby satisfied. The motion of azimuth gimbal pivot C is a measure of the true heading of the vehicle, provided that the gyro spin axis is maintained in the north-south plane. It also works out that the motions of pivots RR and PP measure the roll and pitch, respectively, of the vehicle. Roll is defined as the angle about the "deck plane" fore-and-aft axis, while pitch is the angle about a horizontal axis normal to the vertical plane containing the vehicle's fore-and-aft axis. Hence, the roll axis is horizontal only when no pitch exists.

In system (*b*) first consider the vehicle with roll alone. Pitch pivots $P'P'$ are in a tilted plane. Now, if the vehicle pitches, roll pivots $R'R'$ move in a plane perpendicular to the "deck" plane and not in the vertical plane. A vertical plane through the geometric center of the gimbal system and the dial index will not coincide with the vertical plane through the vehicle's fore-and-aft axis when there is simultaneous roll and pitch.

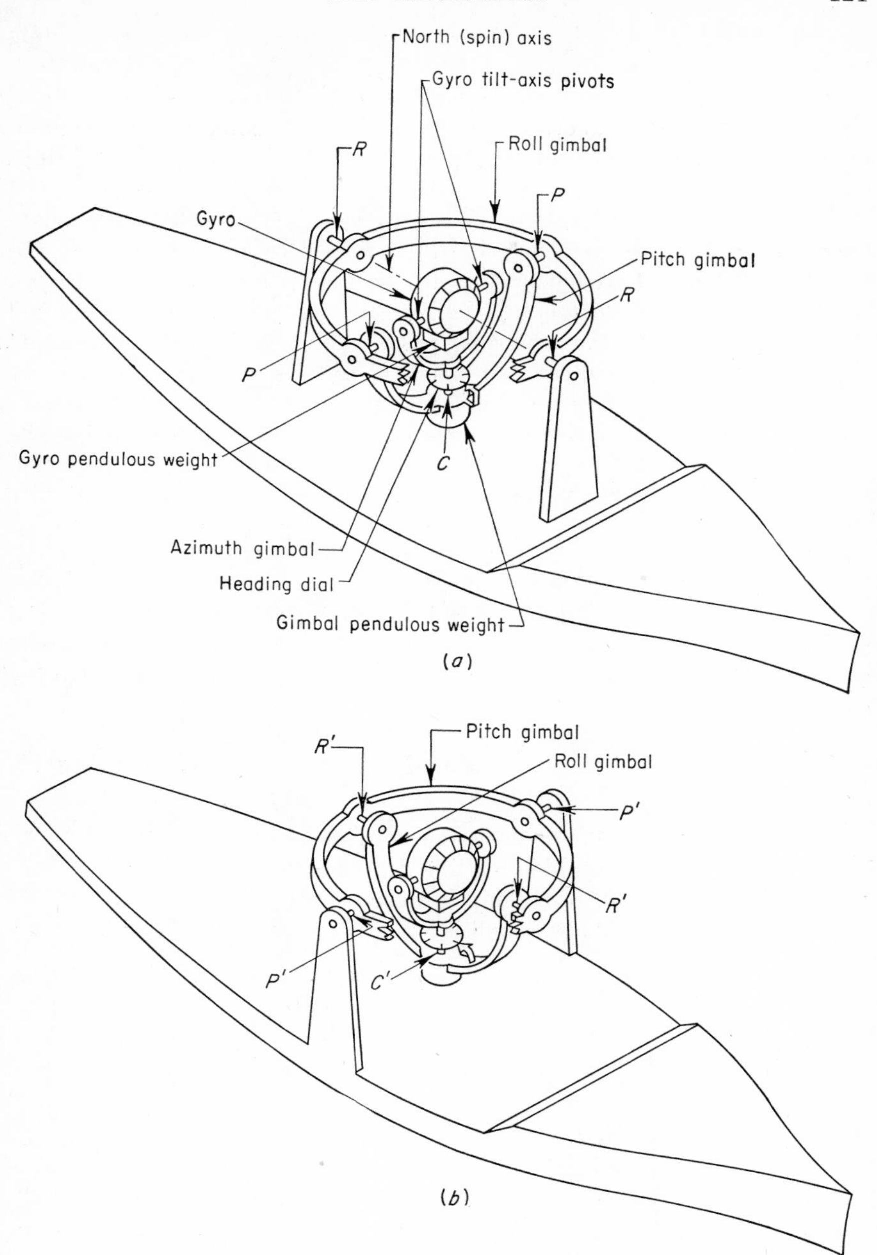

Fig. 5-20. Roll-and-pitch gimbal configurations.

Hence, the dial index will rotate in azimuth, giving an incorrect heading reading.

It is necessary that the *roll* gimbal be the one pivoted to the frame of the vehicle for no gimbal error. The same gimbal geometry must be used on repeater compasses mounted in pelorus stands for taking true bearings of distant objects.

A pendulous gimbal system, such as shown in Fig. 5-20*a*, will create gimbaling errors if subjected to horizontal accelerations which cause the azimuth gimbal axis to depart from the vertical. For example, during a coordinated turn in an aircraft, the resultant of gravity and centrifugal force acts normal to the wings. Under such conditions the roll pivots would be "frozen" in their zero position, and a serious gimbaling error would result. This may be avoided by adding another two-degree-of-freedom gyro (or two single-degree-of-freedom gyros) to stabilize the system in roll and pitch. On shipboard a well-damped pendulous system is reasonably satisfactory because horizontal accelerations are usually small.

5-23. Intercardinal Rolling Error

The torque tending to right a ship is approximately proportional to the angle of roll. Since the ship possesses moment of inertia about the roll axis, the motion may be considered a simple harmonic oscillation having an amplitude of

$$R = R_0 \sin \frac{2\pi t}{T}$$

where R = roll angle
R_0 = amplitude of oscillation either side of vertical
T = period of complete oscillation
t = time ($t = 0$ when ship is level)

The angular velocity of the roll is

$$\frac{dR}{dt} = \frac{2\pi}{T} R_0 \cos \frac{2\pi t}{T}$$

This has a maximum value of

$$\dot{R}_{\text{max}} = \frac{2\pi R_0}{T}$$

The maximum angular velocity occurs as the ship passes through the level position.

The angular acceleration of the roll is

$$\frac{d^2R}{dt^2} = -\frac{4\pi^2 R_0}{T^2} \sin \frac{2\pi t}{T}$$

This has a maximum value of

$$\ddot{R}_{max} = \frac{4\pi^2 R_0}{T^2}$$

The maximum angular acceleration occurs at the ends of the roll.

Suppose the ship's gyrocompass to be mounted a distance h above the center of roll. As the direction of roll reverses, the compass is subjected to a linear acceleration equal to

$$a_{max} = \frac{4\pi^2 R_0 h}{T^2}$$

Assume that $h = 10$ ft, $R_0 = 10°$ ($\pi/18$ radians), and $T = 8$ sec:

$$a_{max} = \frac{4\pi^2 \times \pi \times 10}{18 \times 8^2} = 1.076 \text{ ft/sec}^2$$

This is an acceleration of $0.0334g$. If the ship is on an east or a west heading, the gyro spin axis lies in the roll plane. Because it is pendulous, the gyro at each end of the roll experiences a torque of

$$T_{max} = \frac{M_P a_{max}}{g}$$

where M_P is the gyro pendulous factor.

The resulting precession rate in azimuth is

$$\dot{\phi}_{max} = \frac{T_{max}}{H} = \frac{M_P a_{max}}{Hg}$$

If $M_P = 80{,}000$ dyne-cm, $a_{max} = 0.0334g$, and $H = 4 \times 10^6$ g-cm²/sec, then $\dot{\phi}_{max}$ in degrees per second is

$$\dot{\phi}_{max} = \frac{80{,}000 \times 0.0334}{4 \times 10^6} \times 57.3 = 0.0382°/\text{sec}$$

Since the acceleration force varies harmonically, the azimuth motion is also a harmonic oscillation, and

$$\dot{\phi}_{max} = \frac{2\pi\phi_0}{T}$$

$$\phi_0 = \frac{T\dot{\phi}_{max}}{2} = \frac{8 \times 0.0382}{2}$$

$$= \pm 0.0487°$$

This type of azimuth oscillation will be experienced by any pendulous gyrocompass subjected to rolling in the north-south plane, unless the gyro tilt axis coincides with the center of roll. This ideal situation is never exactly realized in practice because, on an actual ship, the instantaneous center of roll shifts its position continually. Since the long-term average azimuth error is zero, this type of compass disturbance is of little consequence when the instrument is used for navigational purposes only. However, if it is employed for azimuth stabilization of such devices as guns or radar antennas, the error could present a problem. It should be noted that the azimuth oscillation is 90° out of phase with the ship's rolling motion. The azimuth error reaches a maximum as the vessel passes through the level position.

Now, assume that the rolling ship is on a north or a south heading. If the compass has a pendulous gimbal system with the geometry shown in Fig. 5-20*a*, the gimbals will oscillate in the east-west plane, causing the gyro to rotate back and forth about the spin axis (see Fig. 5-21). Since

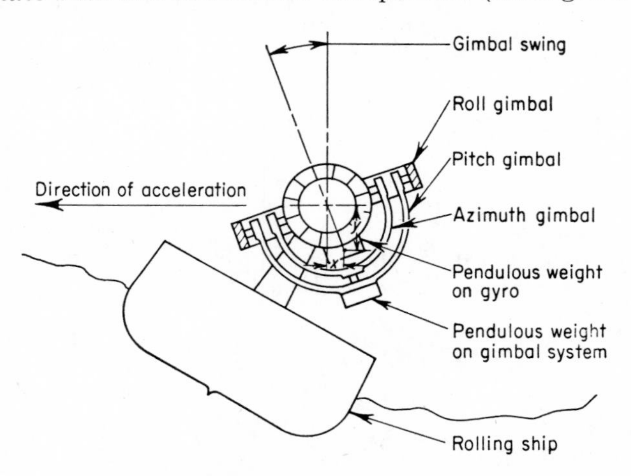

FIG. 5-21. Gimbal swing caused by rolling ship.

the acceleration forces have no north-south component, no precession of the gyro takes place. Also, there is no gimbaling error because the vessel is on a cardinal heading.

Since no long-term compass error results from roll accelerations taking place in the north-south or east-west planes alone, it might be concluded that rolling in any intercardinal plane would also have no harmful effect. After all, such accelerations may be divided into north-south and east-west components. However, this is not the case. With simultaneous accelerations acting both along and normal to the gyro spin axis, a net vertical-axis torque is produced on the gyro which results in a settling-point error.

The reason for this is that the pendulous weight on the gyro is swung a distance x to one side of the vertical axis by the east-west component of acceleration, as shown in Fig. 5-21. Now, any north-south component of acceleration acting on the offset weight produces both a vertical-axis torque proportional to x and a horizontal-axis torque proportional to y.

Assume that the ship is proceeding on a northeast heading. On the right half of the roll the horizontal acceleration force (assuming the compass is above the center of roll) acts in a southeast direction. Its spin-axis component is toward the south while the component normal to the spin axis acts east. With a pendulous gimbal system of the type shown in Fig. 5-21, the gyro pendulous weight moves toward the east, and the south component of acceleration then produces a clockwise (viewed from above) vertical torque and a clockwise (looking west) tilt torque.

On the left half of the roll the horizontal acceleration force reverses, and its components act north and west. The gimbal system is, therefore, swung in the opposite direction. The north component again produces a clockwise vertical torque on the gyro, but the tilt torque is counterclockwise. The vertical-axis torques are additive, while the horizontal axis ones cancel out over the roll cycle.

The additive effect of the vertical-axis "kicks" can make an uncompensated compass completely useless on shipboard, as a simple example will show. In order to facilitate computing the error, the not-unwarranted assumption is made that the period of oscillation of the pendulous gimbal system is short compared with the ship's roll period and that the damping is light enough so that the attitude of the gimbals substantially follows the instantaneous virtual vertical. In a previous example the maximum acceleration in the roll plane was found to be $0.0334g$ when the ship rolled $\pm 10°$, with an 8-sec period, and the point considered was 10 ft above the center of roll. On a northeast heading both north-south and east-west components of acceleration are then 0.707×0.0334, or $0.0236g$. At the end of the roll the east-west component will cause the gyro to tilt about the spin axis by an angle equal to $\tan^{-1} 0.0236$, or 1.35°. Over the entire half cycle the *average* east-west tilt (assuming harmonic motion) is $2/\pi$ times this, or 0.86°. In a similar manner, the *average* north-south acceleration is $0.0236 \times 2/\pi$ or $0.0150g$. Hence, the average torque over the half cycle is

$$T_{\text{avg}} = 0.0150 M_P \sin 0.86°$$

where M_P is the pendulous factor of the gyro. Assume this to be 80,000 dyne-cm. Then

$$T_{\text{avg}} = 0.0150 \times 80{,}000 \times 0.0150 = 18.0 \text{ dyne-cm}$$

If, as in the previous example, an angular momentum of 4,000,000 g-cm²/sec is assumed, the resulting settling-point error at 40° latitude is [from Eq. (5-23)]

$$\begin{aligned}\phi &= \frac{T_{\text{avg}}}{H\omega_E \cos\lambda} \\ &= \frac{18.0}{4 \times 10^6 \times 72.9 \times 10^{-6} \times 0.766} \\ &= 0.0807 \text{ radian or } 4.62^\circ\end{aligned}$$

It will be noted that this error increases as the square of the roll angle. Hence, in the above example, if the angle of roll had been 20° instead of 10°, the compass error would have been about 18.5°. Some method of compensating the intercardinal rolling error must be provided on gyrocompasses installed aboard a ship.

A nonpendulous gyro, controlled by electrical torquing, is still subject to the same intercardinal rolling error if the controlling gravity reference pendulum is undamped and has no limit stops. The vertical torque on the gyro in this case results from the fact that the axis of the electrical torquer is tilted from its normal horizontal position by the east-west component of rolling acceleration. Then, when a torque signal comes from the pendulum as a result of the north-south acceleration component, the torque applied to the gyro has both a vertical and a horizontal component. Again, the vertical components add, and the horizontal components subtract, on opposite halves of the roll.

Two basic methods have been successfully employed for compensating the intercardinal rolling error. The first is to stabilize the compass about the east-west axis by means of another gyro. This reduces the distance x (see Fig. 5-21) to zero, and the north-south component of acceleration then produces no torque about the vertical axis. This technique has been extensively employed and works very well in practice. On the most modern high-accuracy compasses horizontal-axis stabilization is provided in order to prevent gimbaling errors, and this automatically eliminates the intercardinal rolling error as well.

The second method involves the introduction of viscous damping into the gravity couple system. This has two beneficial effects. First, the effective pendulousness of the gyro is reduced during harmonic accelerations whose period is short compared with the time constant of the viscous system. But what is even more important, this harmonic pendulous couple lags the acceleration force by a phase angle of nearly 90°. This means that the gimbal swing about the north-south axis is nearly in quadrature to the north-south acceleration forces. Since the intercardinal error torque is proportional to the product of the gimbal swing and the north-south acceleration forces, a 90° phase lag between the two would result in a net zero torque over the roll cycle. The action is similar to the relationship between the voltage and the current in a purely reactive circuit. The current is 90° out of phase with the voltage, and the integrated product of the voltage and current over the cycle is zero, so no power is consumed.

Several methods have been employed for obtaining viscous damping in the gravity couple system. In electrically torqued compasses damping the gravity reference pendulum with a viscous fluid is all that is necessary.

In many Sperry compasses a device called a *mercury ballistic*, invented by Harrison and Rawlings,[3] is employed in place of a pendulous weight. Two containers of mercury, connected by a small-bore pipe, are mounted so as to tilt with the gyro. These are somewhat similar to the tanks of viscous fluid sometimes used for horizontal damping (see Fig. 5-11). The tanks of mercury act like an *inverted* pendulum, since a tilt of the

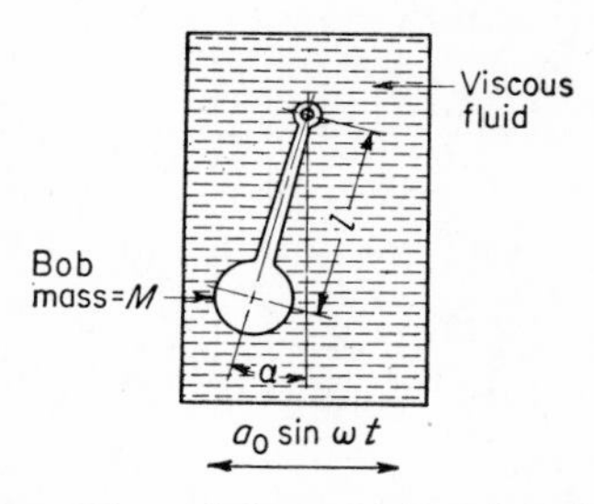

FIG. 5-22. Viscously damped pendulum subjected to horizontal acceleration.

gyro axle causes an upsetting couple rather than a righting one as in a conventional pendulous gyrocompass. However, the gyro is made north-seeking simply by spinning it in the opposite direction to that normally employed. Now, if the time constant of the mercury flow is short compared to the settling period of the compass and long compared to the period of roll, the compass will still settle normally but will have practically no intercardinal rolling error.

In the Brown gyrocompass[3,4] a similar pair of fluid containers is employed. Here, however, the fluid is pumped "uphill" by air pressure whenever the gyro tilts, and the compass has, in effect, a pendulous gyro.

An electrically torqued compass with a viscously damped pendulum is representative of all types employing this kind of compensation and is the simplest case for deriving the equation of motion. The pendulum shown in Fig. 5-22 is enclosed in a container of viscous fluid. The container is subjected to a horizontal linear acceleration of $a = a_0 \sin \omega t$ acting in the plane of the paper. Assume that, at a given instant, the pendulum has an angle of α from the vertical. Calling the mass of the pendulum M and the length l, we have an acceleration producing a torque of $Mal \cos \alpha$. This torque is opposed by three other torques:

1. The gravity couple:

$$Mgl \sin \alpha$$

2. The damping couple:

$$c \frac{d\alpha}{dt}$$

where c is the damping coefficient (the torque per unit of pendulum angular velocity).

3. The angular acceleration couple:

$$Ml^2 \frac{d^2\alpha}{dt^2}$$

The differential equation may now be written

$$Ml^2 \frac{d^2\alpha}{dt^2} + c\frac{d\alpha}{dt} + Mgl \sin \alpha = Mal \cos \alpha$$

If α is small, $\sin \alpha \approx \alpha$ and $\cos \alpha \approx 1$.

$$Ml^2 \frac{d^2\alpha}{dt^2} + c\frac{d\alpha}{dt} + Mgl\alpha = Mal$$

Substituting the operator s for d/dt and dividing both sides by Mgl, we have

$$\frac{a}{g} = \left(\frac{l}{g} s^2 + \frac{c}{Mgl} s + 1\right) \alpha$$

The physical significance of the terms now becomes apparent. a/g is the angle of the virtual vertical due to the applied acceleration. l/g is $\omega_N{}^2$, where ω_N is the undamped natural frequency of the pendulum. c/Mgl is τ, the time constant of the pendulum damping. Therefore,

$$\frac{\alpha}{a/g} = \frac{1}{s^2/\omega_N{}^2 + \tau s + 1}$$

Since a/g is a simple harmonic motion of frequency ω, $j\omega$ may be substituted for s.

$$\frac{\alpha}{a/g} = \frac{1}{1 - \omega^2/\omega_N{}^2 + j\omega\tau}$$

In a practical case, ω will be much smaller than ω_N. For example, a typical compass pendulum might have an undamped period of about 0.4 sec, while the period of the applied acceleration (ship's roll period) would be in the order of 8 sec. Then $\omega^2/\omega_N{}^2$ would be only 0.0025. This term may accordingly be neglected. Therefore, the ratio k between the maximum pendulum deflection and the maximum deflection of the virtual vertical is

$$k = \frac{1}{(1 - \omega^2\tau^2)^{1/2}}$$

The phase angle between the pendulum and the applied acceleration is

$$\gamma = \tan^{-1}(\omega\tau)$$

The intercardinal error is attenuated by the factor $k \cos \gamma$. In a previous calculation it was shown that, when the compass was located 10 ft above the center of roll and the ship was rolling $\pm 20°$ with a period of 8 sec, an intercardinal rolling error of 18.5° would occur on a northeast heading. Now, if the compass pendulum is viscously damped with a time constant of 60 sec,

$$k = \frac{1}{[1 + (2\pi/8 \times 60)^2]^{1/2}} = 0.0212$$

$$\gamma = \tan^{-1} \frac{2\pi}{8} \times 60$$

$$= \tan^{-1} 47.2 = 88.8°$$

Intercardinal error will be reduced to

$$18.5 \times 0.0212 \cos 88.8° = 0.008°$$

The effectiveness of this method of compensation is readily apparent. The 60-sec pendulum time constant has a completely negligible effect upon the settling characteristics of the compass, since it is less than 1 per cent of the compass period.

The horizontal torque applied to the gyro as a result of the rolling acceleration component in the north-south plane is reduced by the factor k when the gravity couple is viscously damped. It should be noted that gimbal stabilization alone, although it isolates the gyro from vertical torques, does not reduce the small oscillation in azimuth caused by horizontal torques resulting from rolling.

PROBLEMS

5-1. A gyrocompass at 40° latitude has an angular momentum of 3,000,000 g-cm²/sec. If a spurious torque of 10 dyne-cm is applied continually about the vertical axis, how far off the meridian will the compass settle?

5-2. Assume that the compass in Prob. 5-1 has a pendulous factor of 40,000 dyne-cm and that it is vertically damped, the damping couple for a given tilt being 1/30 of the pendulous couple. With no torque about the vertical axis but with a steady torque of 100 dyne-cm about the horizontal axis, how much will the spin axis be tilted? How far off the meridian will the compass settle?

5-3. A ship is proceeding at 20 knots on a 45° course at 40° north latitude. Assume that the ship's gyrocompass has no north velocity correction applied. What will the compass reading be?

5-4. A gyrocompass, on a 25-knot ship sailing on a 30° course at 40° north latitude, has an angular momentum of 10,000,000 g-cm^2/sec. What is the correction torque (in dyne-centimeters) necessary about the vertical axis to overcome the north velocity error? What is the total correction torque about the horizontal axis required to compensate the earth rotation and east velocity errors?

5-5. On a 600-knot aircraft, flying on a 50° rhumb-line course at 75° north latitude, the pendulum controlling the gyrocompass has a bob weighing 0.05 lb. What total force must be applied to the bob to overcome Coriolis and centrifugal accelerations?

BIBLIOGRAPHY

1. Military Specification MIL-G-17012A, Gyrocompass, Stabilized.

2. Atwood, D. J., and F. A. Best: Airborne Earth Rate Directional Heading Reference, Proceedings of the IRE National Conference on Aeronautical Electronics, 1958.

3. Rawlings, A. L.: "The Theory of the Gyroscopic Compass and Its Deviations," The Macmillan Company, New York, 1944.

4. Ferry, E. S.: "Applied Gyrodynamics," rev. ed., John Wiley & Sons, Inc., New York, 1933.

CHAPTER 6

THE GYRO VERTICAL

By Charles T. Davenport

Nomenclature

a = acceleration
C = vehicle course
e = base of natural logarithms (2.718282...)
F = force
F_{CE} = east component of Coriolis force
F_{CS} = south component of Coriolis force
F_{CT} = total Coriolis force
F_E = east component of force
F_R = roll component of force
F_S = south component of force
g = acceleration of gravity
H = angular momentum
K = erection constant $1/\tau$
k = pendulum damping ratio
M = mass of pendulum bob
R = earth's radius (20.9×10^6 ft)
T = period
T_H = horizontal-axis torque
T_P = pitch-axis torque
T_R = roll-axis torque
t = time
v = velocity
v_E = east component of velocity
v_N = north component of velocity
θ = spin-axis angle from vertical
λ = latitude
τ = time constant
ω = angular velocity of roll
ω_E = earth's angular velocity (72.9211×10^{-6} radian/sec)

6-1. Definition and Applications

One of the most important applications of the gyroscope is to establish a vertical reference aboard a moving vehicle. A typical gyro vertical is a pitch and roll indicator used aboard aircraft to enable the pilot to maintain level flight under blind flying conditions. Autopilots, which are employed for automatic stabilization of aircraft, also utilize a gyro vertical as a reference. Monorail vehicles and ships use gyro verticals for stabilization. Modern ship stabilizers employ aileron-type fins which are gyro controlled.

Some of the most accurate gyro verticals are used aboard Navy combat vessels for the stabilization of guns, optical devices, radar antennas, and searchlights. Such instruments are quite sophisticated and are compensated for a variety of errors caused by ship motions and the rotation of the earth.

The high speeds of modern jet airplanes have necessitated consideration of errors which heretofore have been negligible on slower-speed earthbound vehicles. Precision bombing and navigation systems on military aircraft demand air-borne gyro verticals of high accuracy.

6-2. Principle of Operation

When hung from a stationary support, a plumb line accurately indicates the local vertical. The same plumb line mounted on a vehicle which subjects the support to horizontal accelerations is no longer considered a reliable vertical reference. Such accelerations occur, for example, whenever the vehicle rolls or pitches or changes speed or bearing.

Except for certain Coriolis and centrifugal errors, however, the long-term average position of a plumb line on a maneuvering vehicle is the true vertical. In the course of time positive and negative acceleration impulses tend to cancel one another. The gyro vertical utilizes a gyroscope as an integrating device to obtain the average position of a pendulous gravity reference. The coupling between the gyro and the gravity reference is relatively "loose," so that the short-term oscillations of the pendulums are effectively filtered by the gyro. Long-term accelerations may require additional corrections to the gravity reference.

The most common type of gyro vertical employs a vertical-shaft gyroscope in a two-degree-of-freedom gimbal system (see Fig. 6-1). This gimbal configuration isolates the gyro from the rolling and pitching of the vehicle.

In practice a number of different forms of gravity reference are used. The type shown in Fig. 6-1 is frequently employed and involves two pendulums mounted so as to indicate pitch and roll components of gyro tilt. These pendulums generate output voltages proportional to their deflections. The voltage of each pendulum is amplified and applied to a torquer on the appropriate gimbal pivot so as to precess the gyro spin axis in the direction tending toward alignment with the pendulum. The pendulum-torquer combination is known as an *erector,* since it urges the gyro into a vertical position. Many different types of erectors have been devised, and the most widely used are described in Secs. 6-6 to 6-9. The

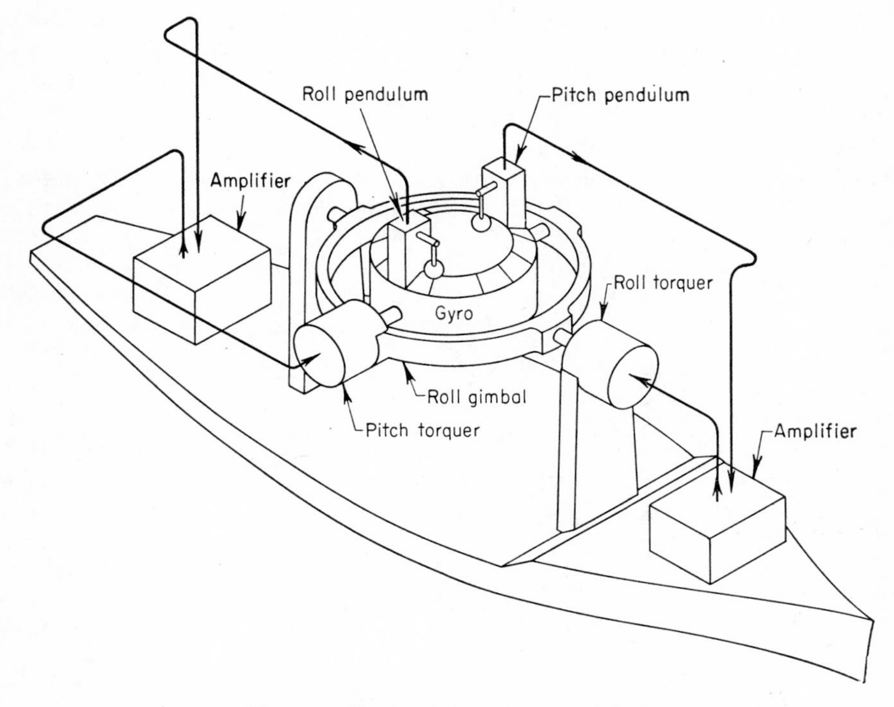

Fig. 6-1. Configuration of gyro vertical.

basic requirement of an erector is that it apply a torque to the gyro about an axis 90° from the tilt axis. For example, if the gyro tilts about the roll axis, the roll pendulum develops a voltage. In order to precess the gyro back toward the vertical a torque must be applied about the pitch axis. Hence, the roll pendulum must be connected to the pitch torquer and the pitch pendulum to the roll torquer.

6-3. Erection Equations

The erector shown in Fig. 6-1 is a proportional type. That is, the gyro erection rate is directly proportional to the gyro tilt. Calling the gyro tilt θ, the following equation applies.

$$\frac{d\theta}{dt} + K\theta = 0$$

Solving,

$$\theta = C_1 e^{-Kt}$$

At time $t = 0$, let the tilt be θ_0. It will also be noted that the constant K is equal to $1/\tau$, where τ is the time constant of the erection system. Then, at any time t

$$\theta = \theta_0 e^{-t/\tau} \tag{6-1}$$

Also, the erection rate is

$$\frac{d\theta}{dt} = -\frac{\theta}{\tau} \tag{6-2}$$

For example, assume that an erector has a time constant of 100 sec and that the gyro is 5° off the vertical. What is the erection rate under these circumstances, and how long will it take the gyro to come within 3′ of the vertical?

The erection rate is in absolute value

$$\frac{d\theta}{dt} = \frac{5 \times 60}{100} = 3' \text{ of arc/sec}$$

The time to erect to within 3′ is

$$3 = 5 \times 60 e^{-t/100}$$
$$t = 461 \text{ sec} = 7.68 \text{ min}$$

6-4. Effect of Earth Rotation

The spin axis of a gyroscope will maintain a fixed orientation in inertial space if no torques act upon it. Unless the spin axis is aligned with the earth's axis, the gyro will tilt relative to the earth because of the earth's rotation.

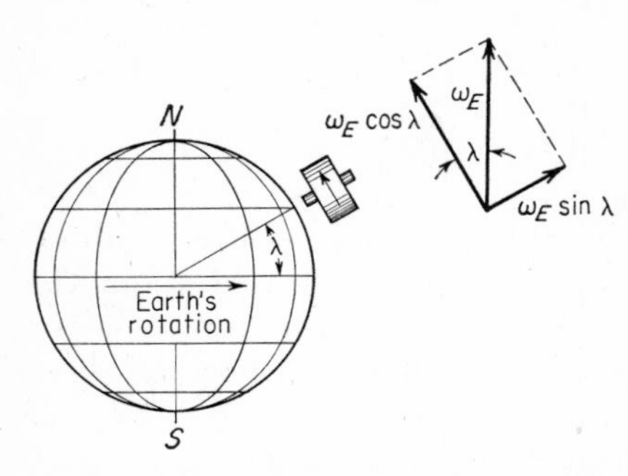

FIG. 6-2. Effect of earth's rotation on vertical gyro.

A vertical-shaft gyro, shown in Fig. 6-2, is located on the earth at a latitude λ. The sidereal angular velocity of the earth is designated by ω_E. (ω_E has a value of 72.9211×10^{-6} radian/sec, or 15.0411°/hr.) Except at the equator or poles, both horizontal and vertical components of earth rotation exist. These are, respectively, $\omega_E \cos \lambda$ and $\omega_E \sin \lambda$. The horizontal component causes an apparent toppling of the gyro toward the west. If the rotor is spinning clockwise, as shown, the vertical component subtracts a minute amount from the angular momentum of the gyro. Since this latter effect usually amounts to only a few parts in a billion, it is customary to neglect it.

In a gyro vertical the erection system combats the westward tilting of the gyro caused by the horizontal component of the earth's rotation. The gyro will seek a position, listed toward the west, such that the erection rate equals the horizontal component of earth rate. Then

$$\omega_E \cos \lambda = -\frac{d\theta}{dt} = \frac{\theta}{\tau}$$

$$\theta = \tau \omega_E \cos \lambda \tag{6-3}$$

Hence, if the time constant is 100 sec, the westward list at 40° latitude would be

$$\begin{aligned}\theta &= 100 \times 72.9 \times 10^{-6} \times 0.766 \\ &= 0.00558 \text{ radian or } 19.2' \text{ of arc}\end{aligned}$$

This is too large an error to be tolerated in many applications. Reducing the erector time constant to 30 sec would cut the error to 5.8′, but this is undesirable in that it makes the gyro more susceptible to short-term acceleration disturbances. However, on many moderate-accuracy gyro verticals, such as aircraft pitch and roll indicators, a value of erector time constant is selected which is a compromise between acceleration errors and earth rotation errors. The list caused by earth rotation is frequently called the *latitude error.*

More sophisticated gyro verticals eliminate the latitude error by applying a correction torque about the horizontal north-south axis of the gyro. The value of this torque must, of course, be $H\omega_E \cos \lambda$, where H is the angular momentum of the gyro. This correction is readily obtained from a simple analog computer which applies appropriate voltages to the roll and pitch pivot torquers. If the vehicle has a heading C (the angle measured clockwise from north to the roll axis), the roll and pitch torques are, respectively,

$$\begin{aligned}T_R &= H\omega_E \cos \lambda \sin C \\ T_P &= H\omega_E \cos \lambda \cos C\end{aligned} \tag{6-4}$$

The analog computer may obtain $\sin C$ and $\cos C$ from an electrical resolver driven by the vehicle's heading reference.

6-5. Effect of Spurious Horizontal Torques

A steady horizontal torque causes a gyro vertical to develop a list about an axis 90° from the torque axis. Consider the case of a gyro which is unbalanced about the pitch axis. The unbalance torque causes a precession rate about the roll axis. The roll erection system now comes into play and provides an ever-increasing torque about the pitch axis. The tilting of the gyro continues until the erection torque balances the torque producing the precession. Let the spurious torque be T_H. Then

$$\frac{T_H}{H} = \frac{\theta}{\tau}$$

$$\theta = \frac{T_H \tau}{H} \tag{6-5}$$

Suppose that a gyro vertical has a gyro, weighing 5 lb, which has an angular momentum of 50,000,000 g-cm²/sec and that the center of gravity is horizontally displaced from the pitch axis by 0.001 in. If the erection-system time constant is 100 sec, what will be the steady-state roll error?

$$T_H = 5 \times 0.001 = 0.005 \text{ lb-in.} = 5{,}650 \text{ dyne-cm}$$

$$\theta = \frac{5{,}650 \times 100}{50 \times 10^6} = 0.0113 \text{ radian} = 38.8' \text{ of arc}$$

The importance of keeping gyro center-of-mass shifts to a minimum is apparent. Other sources of spurious horizontal torques are the gimbal pivot bearings and the slip rings or flexes employed to conduct electric power to the gyro and torquers.

Due to creep of materials, center-of-mass shifts may develop slowly over a long period. These may be compensated by manually set potentiometers which apply appropriate bias voltages to the roll and pitch pendulums. Spirit levels on the gyro may be used to determine whether the instrument has settled with a list. Of course, such readings must be taken when the vehicle in which the gyro vertical is mounted is at rest. Another method of detecting an error in the vertical is to monitor the pendulum output voltages. If the long-term average output of the pendulums is not zero, a verticality error is indicated.

The correction bias may be applied to the pendulums automatically by means of electromechanical integrators. Such an integrator may take the form of an electric motor designed so that its rotational speed is directly proportional to the voltage applied to it and whose direction of rotation is dependent upon the phase of the signal. The output of each pendulum is amplified and fed to a separate motor of this type. Each motor drives a pendulum-biasing potentiometer through a gear train that provides a very large reduction ratio. The time constant of the integrator is made much longer than that of the erection system, so that the normal vertical-seeking action of the gyro is not significantly affected. However, any long-term pendulum output in one direction will slowly be biased out, and the integrators do not come to rest until both pendulums are nulled, showing that the gyro is vertical.

The integrators will also eliminate the list due to earth rotation. However, if the heading of the vehicle is suddenly changed, the integrators, being relatively sluggish, will not be able to accommodate themselves immediately, and a transient error will result. On some three-axis platforms the erection pendulums are oriented north-south and east-west rather than in the roll and pitch planes, and on such instruments one integrator only is affected by the earth's rotation. No other earth rotation correction is required in this instance, unless the vehicle north-south velocity is so great that the integrator cannot keep up with the rate of change of latitude [see Eq. (6-3)].

6-6. Electrolytic-level Erector

The pendulum-torquer type of erector is extensively employed on gyro verticals. A variation of this design utilizes electrolytic levels in lieu of pendulums. These are glass vials partially filled with a conducting fluid. Three electrodes are provided, one at each end of the vial and another in the center. When the level is horizontal, the electric resistance between the center electrode and those on each end is the same. However, when the device is tilted, more fluid runs toward the low end, and the resistance decreases in this half and increases in the other. The electrolytic level is therefore electrically equivalent to a potentiometer, the center electrode corresponding to the rotor arm. By properly connecting it to the torquer, the device can be made to erect the gyro.

This type of erector is not as linear as a pendulum. However, this is not too important as long as the device is symmetrical on both sides of zero. If an erector is not symmetrical and is subjected to a periodically reversing acceleration, the average output will not occur at the electrical zero, and the gyro will settle off the true vertical.

Mercury switches are sometimes used for erectors. These are strictly ON-OFF devices and give a constant erection rate, regardless of the tilt of the gyro. As a result, the gyro is more readily disturbed when the erector is exposed to small accelerations.

6-7. Eddy-current Erector

Eddy-current erectors are often used on gyro verticals. One type is shown in Fig. 6-3*a*. A permanent magnet is suspended beneath the gyro on a separate pendulous roll and pitch gimbal system. A mushroom-shaped disk of copper is fastened to an extension of the gyro shaft and rotates close to the magnet. When the gyro is vertical, the magnet is directly below the center of the disk (assuming no horizontal accelerations are acting on the magnet gimbal system). However, if the gyro tilts, as shown at (*b*), the magnet is no longer centered over the spin axis of the disk, and the motion of the disk over the magnet results in eddy currents in the disk which produce a drag force in the direction shown. This force is in the correct orientation to precess the gyro back toward the vertical. Note that the disk must rotate in the same direction as the gyro for the precession to be correct. Because of their simplicity, eddy-current erectors are extensively employed on aircraft gyro verticals such as pitch and roll indicators.

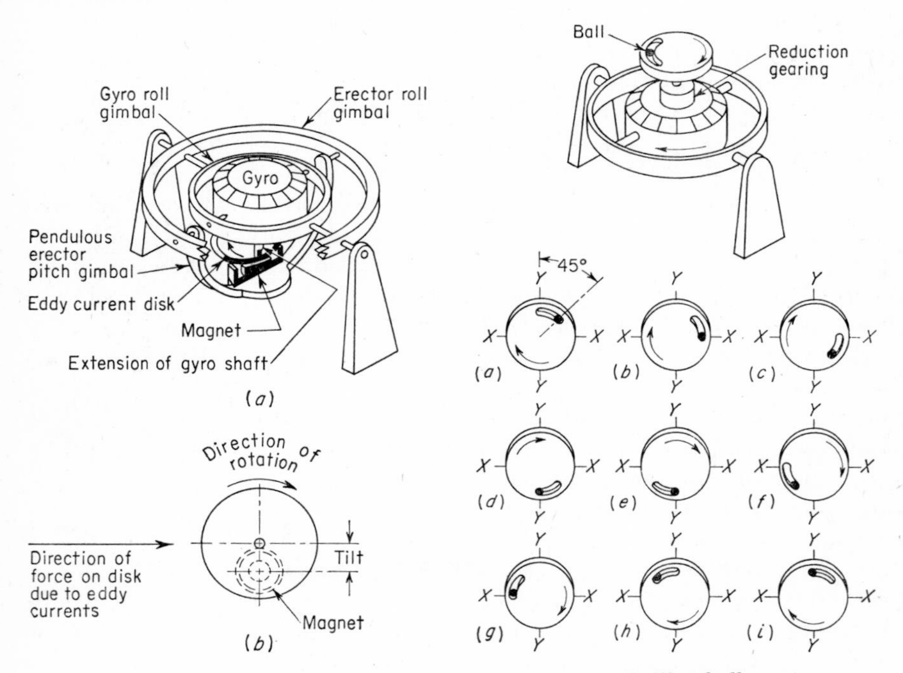

FIG. 6-3. Eddy-currect erector.

FIG. 6-4. Rolling-ball erector.

6-8. Rolling-ball Erector

Rolling-ball erectors are frequently used on gyro verticals of moderate accuracy. Figure 6-4 shows the principle on which they operate. A steel ball rolls freely in a banana-shaped slot in a revolving disk which is fastened to the gyro and driven by the gyro rotor. Although it turns in the same direction, the rotational speed of the disk is far slower than that of the gyro. In some designs it is driven through reduction gearing; in others it is turned by an eddy-current coupling in conjunction with an escapement mechanism which keeps the rotational speed constant. The ball slot is concentric with the axis of rotation so that centrifugal force does not tend to give the ball a preferred position in the slot.

Drawings (*a*) to (*i*) are plan views showing the position of the ball in the slot for every 45° of disk rotation when the gyro is tilted as shown.

Views (i) and (a) show the disk in the same position, it being assumed that the ball rolls instantaneously from one end of the slot to the other as it is carried over the high point of the tilt.

It is apparent that the ball spends a longer period of time to the left of line YY than to the right. For the case shown, where the slot permits the ball to move over a 45° arc, the ball is on the left side during 180° of disk rotation and on the right side for only 135°. Hence, there is a net torque about line YY, tending to push the top of the gyro to the left. Such a torque precesses the gyro toward the vertical.

Unfortunately, the gyro does not erect in a straight path. Note that the ball spends more time below line XX than above (225° compared to 135°). Hence, the gyro is precessed so that the top goes both upward and toward the left. The result is that the gyro erects in a spiral path.

Actually, on small tilts the ball does not roll over the entire length of the slot. Therefore, a proportional erection action is obtained, unless the tilt reaches the point where the ball travels from one end of the slot to the other. The erector then "saturates," and the erection rate is substantially constant from that point on. Because the torque due to the ball's changing position is not uniform, the precession caused by a rolling-ball erector has a characteristic pulsing motion.

6-9. Mercury Erector

Mercury erection systems have been employed on many Navy precision gyro verticals (called *stable elements*). These are extremely accurate instruments used for stabilization of the fire control system on combat vessels. The mercury erector has virtually no dead space and responds to the most minute tilts.

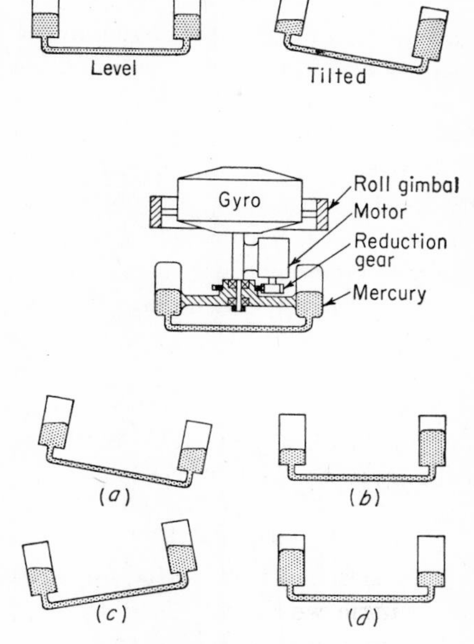

FIG. 6-5. Mercury erector.

Figure 6-5 shows a mercury erector. It consists of two tanks partially filled with the heavy liquid metal and connected by a small-bore pipe. If the system is tilted, the mercury runs toward the lower tank, thus causing a shift in the center of gravity of the device toward the low side. This shift is proportional to the tilt angle and is a function of the tank area and tank spacing.

The flow of mercury is not completed at the instant the tilt is applied, since the liquid has inertia. The force producing the flow is directly proportional to the difference in the head between the two liquid columns. It will be seen that, if disturbed, the mercury in the tanks will oscillate back and forth with simple harmonic motion, since this represents a system having constant inertia and a restoring force proportional to deflection. If such a system is excited at its resonant frequency, it will lag 90° out of phase with respect to the applied force. This principle is utilized in the mercury erector.

The tanks are mounted on the gyro and revolved at the same rate as the natural frequency of the mercury in the system. If the gyro tilts, the mercury is subjected to components of gravity which vary harmonically. The liquid will behave as shown in views (*a*), (*b*), (*c*), and (*d*) of Fig. 6-5. When the tilt is a maximum (both tanks in the plane of the tilt), the liquid is the same depth in both tanks, as at (*a*) and (*c*), and no torque is applied to the gyro. However, when the tanks are level 90° earlier or later, as at (*b*) or (*d*), the maximum difference in depth occurs. The gyro is, therefore, subjected to the greatest torque when the tanks are in a plane at right angles to the tilt plane. If the tanks revolve in the same direction as gyro rotor, an erecting action then takes place.

In practice, the natural period of the mercury in the tanks is made in the order of 2 or 3 sec. Thus, if the period were 2 sec, the tanks would be rotated at 30 rpm. Since the viscosity of the mercury produces considerable damping, the phase angle does not change very rapidly near resonance, so the speed of rotation is not extremely critical. The small-bore pipe connecting the tanks effectively increases the inertia of the system and slows down the period. Too rapid a period would necessitate such a high rotational speed that centrifugal force would completely empty the connecting pipe.

In some designs the entire gyro is rotated along with the tanks. Then, any horizontal unbalance of the gyro assembly is rotated in space so that the gyro does not develop a list. Actually, the gyro would then have a conical wobble of negligible magnitude, since the precession caused by the unbalance continually changes its direction. On such instruments the earth rotation correction is applied by means of a small adjustable eccentric weight which is driven backward, with respect to the gyro, at the same rate as the erector. The weight, therefore, can be maintained properly oriented in the north-south plane as the gyro rotates.

6-10. Single-degree-of-freedom Gyro Vertical

A gyro vertical employing single-degree-of-freedom units requires two gyros.[1,*] In addition, the gimbals must always be servo-driven.

* Superscript numbers indicate references listed in the Bibliography at end of the chapter.

Some two-degree-of-freedom gyro verticals also have servo-driven gimbal systems. However, servos are not employed unless a high-torque output is needed for some reason such as for stabilizing a heavy load or for operating certain types of electric transmitters. Another reason for using servos on two-degree-of-freedom designs is that some of the more refined gyro suspensions, such as those employing fluid flotation or torsional members, need a servoed "phantom" element. Simple gyro verticals, such as those used for aircraft attitude indication, invariably have two-degree-of-freedom gyros.

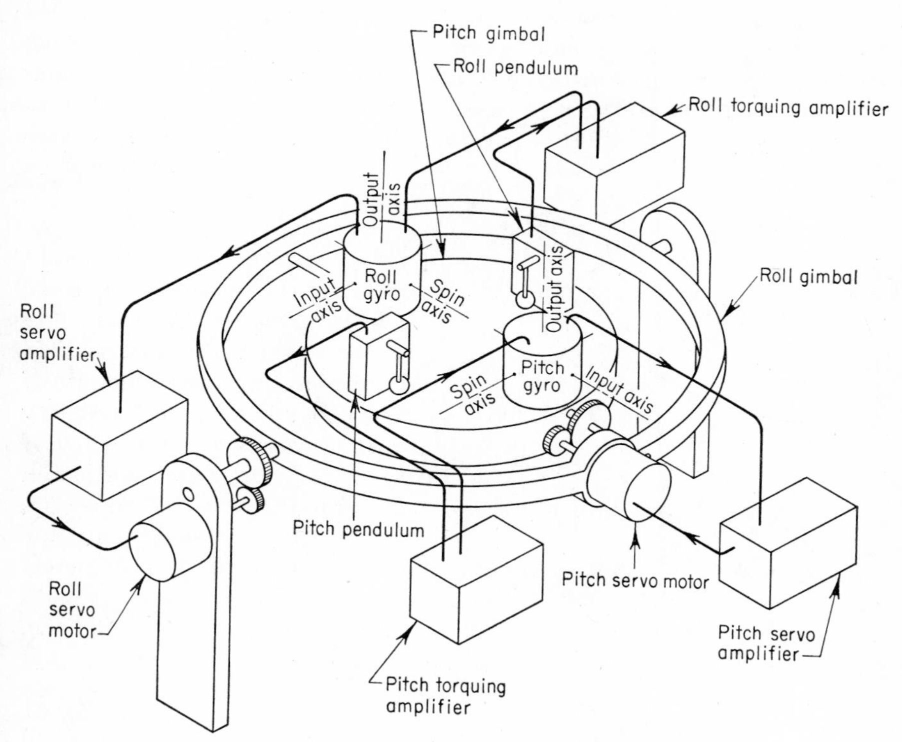

FIG. 6-6. Single-degree-of-freedom gyro vertical.

A typical single-degree-of-freedom gyro vertical is shown in Fig. 6-6. The rate-integrating gyros are mounted on the pitch gimbal with their input axes perpendicular and in the horizontal plane. If packaging considerations permit, the output axis should be vertical so as to eliminate torques about that axis due to possible unbalances being acted upon by gravity. The platform is erected by applying amplified pendulum signals to the gyro torquers located on the gyro output axes. The resulting output axis deflection operates the gyro pickoff. The pickoff signal is then amplified and applied to the proper gimbal servomotor to drive the gyro about the input axis at the rate which will produce a precession torque about the output axis equal and opposite to the one resulting from the pendulum signal.

If the vehicle on which the system is mounted rolls or pitches, an output axis precession results, and the pickoff signal causes the servomotor to drive at the rate necessary to keep the pickoff nulled, thus space-stabilizing the gyro about its input axis. Under very high roll or pitch rates a single-degree-of-freedom platform may exhibit slightly higher dynamic errors than a two-degree one because the single-axis gyros experience a time lag in developing a pickoff signal. This is caused by the combined effects of the viscous damping between float and case and the moment of inertia of the output axis member. A two-axis gyro, on the other hand, does not have to be precessed to generate a pickoff signal, and a servomotor voltage is produced the instant the gimbal system starts to move with respect to the inertially fixed gyro.

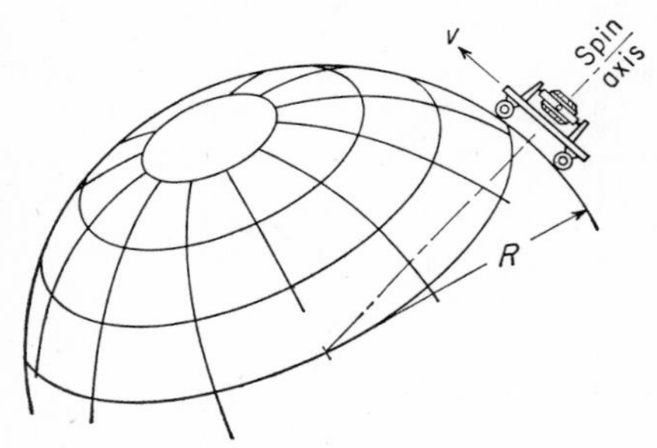

FIG. 6-7. Velocity error.

6-11. Velocity Error

Because the earth is spherical, a vehicle traveling over its surface pitches forward with respect to inertial space at an angular rate of v/R, where v is the vehicle velocity and R the earth's radius (20.9×10^6 ft). A vertical gyro carried on a moving vehicle (see Fig. 6-7) therefore tends to tilt aft at the same rate.

If the gyro is equipped with an erection system, it will tilt until the erector puts in a precession rate of v/R. Since, from Eq. (6-2), the erection rate is equal to θ/τ, the list due to the vehicle velocity is calculated as follows:

$$\frac{\theta}{\tau} = \frac{v}{R}$$

$$\theta = \frac{\tau v}{R} \tag{6-6}$$

Assume that $\tau = 100$ sec and $v = 300$ knots (507 ft/sec). Then

$$\theta = \frac{100 \times 507}{20.9 \times 10^6} = 0.00242 \text{ radian} = 8.3' \text{ of arc}$$

The velocity error is avoided by applying a torque about the roll axis equal to Hv/R. This correction usually may be neglected on slow-speed vehicles, unless the erector time constant is very large. The correction torque is readily generated in a simple analog computer.

6-12. Acceleration Error

Changes in the speed of a vehicle cause the erection system to attempt to bring the gyro spin axis into alignment with the virtual vertical. Thus, a prolonged acceleration of a would eventually result in a verticality error of

$$\theta = \tan^{-1} \frac{a}{g}$$

The method of correction depends upon the type of erector employed. If pendulums are used, a force equal to Ma may be applied to the pitch pendulum bob, where M is the bob mass. If this force exactly balances the acceleration force, the pendulum is still free to respond to any tilts. Another method is to permit the pendulum to align itself with the virtual vertical and then to oppose the output with a bucking voltage just equal to the pendulum signal at the angle θ. Although this technique avoids the complication of a pendulum force motor, it has two disadvantages. First, the pendulum output must be linear over the entire range of acceleration so that the bucking voltage may be readily computed. This condition is somewhat difficult to achieve in practice. The second objection is that the pendulum is usually viscously damped with respect to its case in order to reduce short-term acceleration errors. As a result, the correction is applied before the error builds up to its final value and is removed before the error disappears.

On moderate-accuracy gyro verticals employing pendulums, two other acceleration correction methods are frequently used. The simplest one is to provide stops on the pendulum so as to set a limit on its output. Then, if accelerations do not persist for too long a period, only moderate gyro errors will occur. This technique works well on slow-speed ships and land vehicles. The other method is to provide a so-called "erector cutout." When the pendulum reaches a certain angle, say 1°, it is automatically disconnected from the gyro torquer, and the gyro is left free, except for the earth rotation correction. If its drift rate is low, the gyro will experience only small errors in verticality. This method is used on many aircraft gyro verticals.

Erector cutouts are employed on other types of erector systems. Thus, on the eddy-current type of erector an electromagnet may be used instead of a permanent magnet, and this may be deenergized during speed changes. In the rolling-ball type the ball may be caged automatically. Mercury erectors are usually provided with an electromagnetic shutoff valve in the pipeline so that the flow of mercury from one tank to the other may be prevented during accelerations. Some mercury erectors have an arrangement equivalent to pendulum stops. The device is made to saturate on tilts of over a certain value by reducing the clearance between the tank top and the mercury surface.

Vehicle accelerations may be computed by differentiating the velocity as obtained from a speed indicator. For example, if a shaft rotation proportional to speed is available, a tachometer generator, driven from this shaft through suitable gearing, will give a voltage proportional to dv/dt. Or a centrifugal switch may be employed to actuate erector cutout devices when accelerations are above a certain threshold value.

6-13. Turning Error

When a vehicle carrying a gyro vertical executes a turn, the roll pendulum bob is subjected to a centrifugal force of

$$F = Mv \frac{dC}{dt}$$

where M = mass of bob
v = vehicle velocity
dC/dt = rate of turn

This centrifugal force causes the roll pendulum to swing toward the outside of the turn, and the resulting torque about the pitch axis will precess the top of the gyro toward the center of the turn. Since the line joining the vehicle and the center of the turn is constantly changing its bearing, the gyro spin axis describes a cone around the vertical.

The error may be avoided by applying a force to the roll pendulum equal and opposite to the centrifugal force. A simple analog computer is required for computing the centrifugal force. The velocity may be obtained from the vehicle's speed indicator and used to position the shaft of a potentiometer which is excited by a voltage proportional to dC/dt. The turning rate is readily obtained from the heading reference of the vehicle. Thus, if the heading device is a gyrocompass, a tachometer generator geared to the azimuth gimbal will develop a voltage proportional to dC/dt.

Instead of applying the computed correction voltage to a force motor on the pendulum, it may be used to buck out the pendulum output. (See the previous section for a discussion of the advantages and disadvantages of this technique.)

Pendulum stops and erector cutouts may be employed in exactly the same manner as in compensating for the acceleration error, as previously described. However, in this instance the cutout is actuated by a rate-of-turn or amount-of-turn switch. A low-cost rate gyro is sometimes used.

An ingenious arrangement used extensively on aircraft gyro verticals is to erect the gyro normally with a small forward tilt.[2] It was previously mentioned that, without an erector correction, the gyro would describe a cone during the turn. Now, if the erector has a "ceiling" (pendulum stops, for example), the magnitude of this conical wobble is inversely proportional to the turning rate, provided that the centrifugal force is sufficient to saturate the erector. The turning rate of transport-type aircraft is usually maintained close to a specified value at cruising speed. Suppose that the radius of the conical motion is computed as 1° for this condition. Then, if the initial forward list is 1°, the gyro tilt changes its direction in space at the same rate as the aircraft turns and is always tilted forward 1° relative to the aircraft. For other rates of turn, some error exists, but it is always less than if the initial tilt had not existed. The pitch indication of the instrument is offset by the amount of the gyro tilt, so that it reads zero when the aircraft is level, even though the gyro is tilted forward.

6-14. Centrifugal and Coriolis Errors

A body at the surface of the earth experiences a small centrifugal force due to the earth's rotation. This force acts normal to the earth's axis (see Fig. 6-8). Let ω_E be the earth's sidereal rate, λ the latitude, and R the earth's radius. Then, the centrifugal force exerted on a mass M is

$$F = M\omega_E^2 R \cos\lambda \tag{6-7}$$

If the mass in question is a plumb bob, the horizontal component of F is important. This is

$$F \sin\lambda = M\omega_E^2 R \sin\lambda \cos\lambda$$

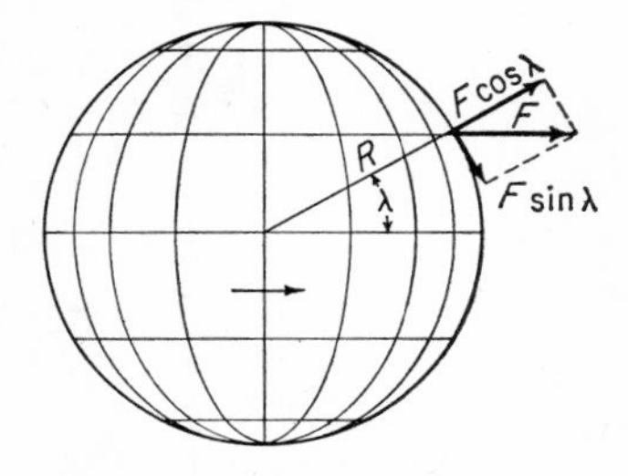

Fig. 6-8. Centrifugal force due to earth's rotation.

By differentiating and equating to zero, we see that this component is a maximum when $\lambda = 45°$. The angle that a plumb line is diverted at 45° latitude is

$$\begin{aligned}\theta &= \tan^{-1}\frac{\omega_E^2 R \sin\lambda \cos\lambda}{g} \\ &= \tan^{-1}\frac{(72.9)^2 \times 10^{-12} \times 20.9 \times 10^6 \times 0.707 \times 0.707}{32.2} \\ &= \tan^{-1} 0.001725 = 5.9' \text{ of arc}\end{aligned}$$

Since the local vertical is defined as the direction of a plumb line, this error is accepted in our everyday life, and no correction is required for it on a gyro vertical. However, if the instrument is mounted on a moving vehicle that has an east-west component of velocity, the earth's rotation is, in effect, altered, and the erection system will no longer bring the gyro into alignment with the local vertical.

A vehicle steered with reference to a true heading device, such as a gyrocompass, follows a so-called "rhumb-line" course. A true heading indicator shows the angle between the fore-and-aft line of a vehicle and the north-south plane. Hence, all longitude lines are crossed at a constant angle (see Fig. 6-9). This results in a spiral path called the *rhumb line*. Eventually, a rhumb-line course would lead to one pole or the other, except for the special case of an east or a west heading. If a great-circle course is desired, it is negotiated as a series of rhumb-line "flats," the heading being altered slightly at regular intervals.

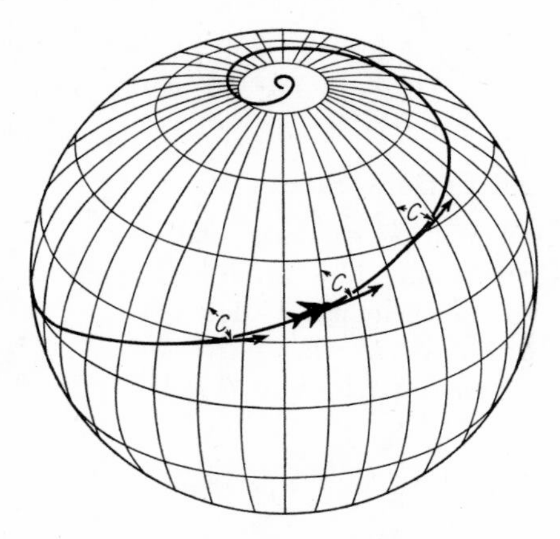

FIG. 6-9. Rhumb-line course.

Assume the vehicle is on a rhumb-line course of C. Then, the velocity v may be broken up into north and east components v_N and v_E, where

$$v_N = v \cos C$$
$$v_E = v \sin C$$

The east component v_E adds directly to the earth's rotation, and the change in centrifugal force may be found by computing the total force and subtracting Eq. (6-7). The total angular velocity about the earth's axis with respect to inertial space is $\omega_E + \dfrac{v_E}{R \cos \lambda}$. The centrifugal force is, therefore,

$$F = M\left(\omega_E + \frac{v_E}{R \cos \lambda}\right)^2 R \cos \lambda$$
$$= M\omega_E^2 R \cos \lambda + 2M\omega_E v_E + \frac{Mv_E^2}{R \cos \lambda}$$

The first term is the same as Eq. (6-7) and can be disregarded. The second is a Coriolis term, which will be considered later. The third term is equal to the centrifugal force that would result from the vehicle velocity if the earth were not rotating. The horizontal component, which affects the local vertical, is

$$F_S = \frac{Mv_E^2}{R \cos \lambda} \sin \lambda = \frac{Mv_E^2 \tan \lambda}{R} \tag{6-8}$$

This force will cause a plumb line on a moving vehicle to develop a southward error in north latitudes.

There is also an eastward component of centrifugal force acting in the horizontal plane. The reason for this, as shown in Fig. 6-10, is that the

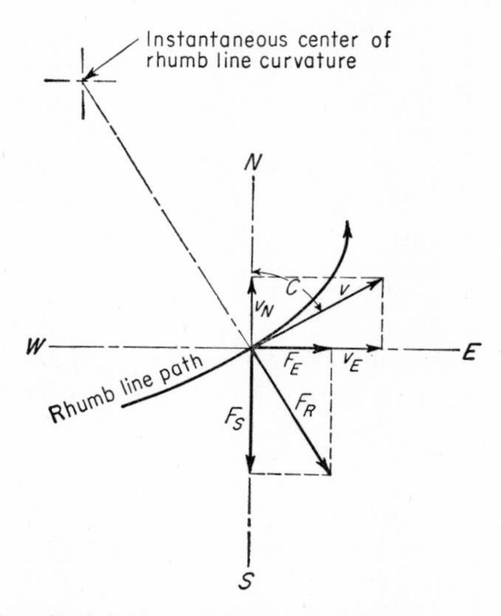

FIG. 6-10. Centrifugal-force components due to rhumb-line course.

instantaneous center of the rhumb-line curvature is not at the earth's center, that is, normal to the tangent to the rhumb line at the point in question. F_S is therefore only the southward component of the total force F_R which acts in the roll plane. The values of F_R and F_E (the eastward component) are easily calculated as follows:

$$\frac{F_R}{F_S} = \frac{v}{v_E}$$

Since

$$F_S = \frac{Mv_E^2 \tan \lambda}{R}$$

$$F_R = \frac{Mvv_E \tan \lambda}{R}$$

But

$$v_E = v \sin C$$

$$F_R = \frac{Mv^2 \sin C \tan \lambda}{R} \tag{6-9}$$

$$\frac{F_E}{F_S} = \frac{v_N}{v_E}$$

$$F_E = \frac{Mv_N v_E \tan \lambda}{R}$$

Since

$$v_N = v \cos C$$

$$F_E = \frac{Mv^2 \sin C \cos C \tan \lambda}{R} \tag{6-10}$$

It is obvious from Fig. 6-10 that no component of F_R exists in the pitch plane. Hence, no pitch pendulum correction is needed for centrifugal force. The roll pendulum is corrected by applying a force to the bob equal and opposite to that given in Eq. (6-9).

If the erector pendulums are oriented north-south and east-west, as on some three-axis platforms, corrections equal and opposite to F_S and F_E must be applied. By substituting $v_E = v \sin C$ in Eq. (6-8), the expression for F_S becomes

$$F_S = \frac{Mv^2 \sin^2 C \tan \lambda}{R} \tag{6-11}$$

The centrifugal correction becomes important on high-speed vehicles at high latitudes. For example, on a 600-knot (1,013 ft/sec) aircraft going east at 80° latitude, the error due to neglecting F_R would be

$$\begin{aligned} \theta &= \tan^{-1} \frac{v^2 \sin C \tan \lambda}{Rg} \\ &= \tan^{-1} \frac{(1{,}013)^2 \times 1 \times 5.67}{20.9 \times 10^6 \times 32.2} \\ &= \tan^{-1} 0.00863 = 29.7' \text{ of arc} \end{aligned}$$

On a 20-knot ship, at the same heading and latitude, the error would be only about 2″ of arc, which would be negligible in most applications.

Navigation computers are available which automatically steer a vehicle on a great-circle course. A great-circle course is also obtained if the vehicle follows a constant directional gyro heading. Directional gyros indicate grid heading rather than true heading. On a great-circle course no horizontal component of centrifugal force exists. Since the great circle is in a plane passing through the earth's center, the centrifugal force is wholly in the vertical plane.

If the gyro vertical has a computer to correct for the rhumb-line force F_R on the roll pendulum [see Eq. (6-9)], the computer has no way of knowing whether the vehicle is actually on a rhumb-line or a great-circle course and will continue to apply a force to the pendulum which is simply a function of heading, velocity, and latitude. On a great-circle course no correction should be made.

However, in order to maintain a great-circle path it is necessary for the true heading to change continually. The turning-error corrector (see Sec. 6-13), which applies a force to the roll pendulum proportional to dC/dt, then comes into play and provides a signal which exactly nullifies the one coming from the rhumb-line corrector.

A Coriolis term, equal to $2M\omega_E v_E$, exists in the expression for the total centrifugal force due to the eastward component of vehicle velocity. The horizontal component, which is directed south, is

$$F_{CS} = 2M\omega_E v_E \sin \lambda$$

Another Coriolis force exists owing to the north component of vehicle speed, since there is a component of motion normal to the earth's axis. This radial velocity is $v_N \sin \lambda$. Since the earth is rotating at an angular velocity of ω_E, an eastward Coriolis force occurs equal to

$$F_{CE} = 2M\omega_E v_N \sin \lambda$$

The total Coriolis force is the vector sum of F_{CS} and F_{CE}.

$$F_{CT} = (F_{CS}^2 + F_{CE}^2)^{1/2}$$

Since $v_N = v \cos C$ and $v_E = v \sin C$,

$$\begin{aligned} F_{CT} &= (4M^2\omega_E^2v^2 \sin^2 C \sin^2 \lambda + 4M^2\omega_E^2v^2 \cos^2 C \sin^2 \lambda)^{1/2} \\ &= 2M\omega_E v \sin \lambda \end{aligned} \tag{6-12}$$

Since a Coriolis force always acts normal to the direction of motion of a particle, it must occur in the roll plane. It tends to swing the roll pendulum to the right of vertical. In the case of the 600-knot aircraft at 80° latitude, the Coriolis error, if uncorrected, would be

$$\begin{aligned} \theta &= \tan^{-1} \frac{2\omega_E v \sin \lambda}{g} \\ &= \tan^{-1} \frac{2 \times 72.9 \times 10^{-6} \times 1{,}013 \times 0.985}{32.2} \\ &= \tan^{-1} 0.00452 = 15.5' \text{ of arc} \end{aligned}$$

The error in the vertical is avoided by applying a force to the roll pendulum bob equal and opposite to that given by Eq. (6-12).

6-15. Rolling Error

The loose coupling between the erector and the gyro greatly attenuates the effect of short-term periodic accelerations such as those caused by the rolling of a ship. However, if a low "ceiling" is placed on the erector so as to reduce the error due to prolonged accelerations in one direction, there is danger that the erector will saturate on both halves of the roll.

This has the effect of destroying the erector integrating action, and the gyro would then drift in an uncontrolled manner.

This difficulty is easily avoided by adding damping to the erector. For example, if a pendulous type is used, the bob may be arranged to run in a viscous fluid.

In Chap. 5 an equation was derived for the ratio k between the maximum pendulum deflection and the maximum virtual vertical for a viscously damped pendulum. The equation is

$$k = \frac{1}{(1 - \omega^2\tau^2)^{1/2}}$$

where ω is $2\pi/T$, T being the period of the disturbing acceleration, and τ is the pendulum damping time constant.

The value of τ is made large enough so that the erector does not saturate during any anticipated roll condition. τ should not be made any larger than necessary, since excessive erector damping causes the gyro to overshoot the vertical during erection.

PROBLEMS

6-1. The erector of a certain gyro vertical precesses the gyro at a rate directly proportional to its angle from the vertical. When the gyro is tilted 2°, it erects at the rate of 1°/min. Assume that the instrument is mounted on a stationary base located at 40° latitude and that no earth rate correction is applied. At what angle from the vertical will the gyro settle?

6-2. On a gyro vertical, having an angular momentum of 4,000,000 g-cm^2/sec, what verticality error will be caused by a spurious horizontal torque of 500 dyne-cm, if the erector time constant is 60 sec?

6-3. What velocity correction torque (in dyne-centimeters) must be applied about the roll axis of a gyro vertical carried on a 1,000-knot aircraft, if the gyro has an angular momentum of 1,000,000 g-cm^2/sec? If the erector time constant is 120 sec, what verticality error would exist without the correction torque?

6-4. The roll pendulum bob in the erection system of a gyro vertical weighs 0.06 lb. What force must be applied to the bob to overcome turning error if the instrument is mounted in a 300-knot aircraft turning at the rate of 3°/sec?

6-5. A 500-knot aircraft is operating at 60° north latitude on a 30° rhumb-line course. Assume that the roll pendulum bob in the gyro vertical weighs 0.04 lb. What total force must be applied to the bob to correct for centrifugal and Coriolis effects? What verticality error would exist without these corrections?

BIBLIOGRAPHY

1. Draper, C. S., W. Wrigley, and L. R. Grohe: The Floating Integrating Gyro and Its Application to Geometrical Stabilization Problems on Moving Bases, Institute of the Aeronautical Sciences, S.M.F. Fund Paper FF-13, January, 1955.

2. Davidson, Martin: The Gyroscope and Its Applications, Hutchinson & Co. (Publishers), Ltd., London, 1946.

CHAPTER 7

INERTIAL NAVIGATION—PART 1

By Theodore J. Newman

Nomenclature

$\bar{r}$ = position vector
$\bar{a}$ = acceleration
$\bar{v}$ = velocity
0 (subscript) = initial value, e.g., at time $t = 0$
m = mass
c = damping constant
k = restoring or spring constant
x_i, x_o = notations explained in Fig. 7-3
T_i, T_o = torque
V = voltage
θ = angle of rotor with fixed reference
H = angular momentum
I = moment of inertia
K_G = scaling constant
G = constant of gravity
T = period (of Schuler pendulum)

7-1. Introduction

Recent activity in the field of guided missile development has underlined the importance of self-contained automatic navigation systems. In addition, anticipated increases in the speed of manned aircraft and spacecraft indicate the desirability of automatic navigation techniques for these applications as well. Systems which are in use or under development range from simple dead-reckoning devices, utilizing magnetic heading and airspeed data as inputs, to more sophisticated systems, employing Doppler radar, automatic star trackers, radio aids (loran, etc.), and inertial navigation techniques. Of these, only inertial navigation is free from enemy interference, the necessity for cooperative ground stations, and the vagaries of the weather. This is a result of the inherent self-contained nature of this type of navigation system, which arises from the character of its input data.

Fundamentally an inertial navigation system is a *dead-reckoning system* with a very significant characteristic which differentiates it from more conventional dead-reckoning equipment. In the usual type of dead reckoning direct measurements are made of the vehicle heading and velocity magnitude. Vehicle position is then determined from a single integration of the measured velocity vector. In inertial navigation, however, direct measurements are made of the vehicle's *acceleration* rather than its velocity. The vehicle is then navigated by a double integration of directly measured acceleration. Now, a direct measurement of velocity for "conventional" dead reckoning requires data from external observations, e.g., airspeed indication, Doppler radar velocity data, etc., while an inertial system internally determines vehicle acceleration by measuring reaction forces sensed entirely within the airframe.* This property of acceleration, i.e., its direct proportionality to reaction forces, as enunciated by Newton in his second law, is the fundamental principle which lends to inertial systems their ability to navigate "inside a box," so to speak, with no inputs of energy from external sources (e.g., infrared, sonar, radar, etc.). Of course, this method of navigation requires extremely accurate data-sensing components, since a constant error in acceleration results in a positional error which varies as the square of time (for short mission times), while a constant velocity error (such as might occur in a conventional dead-reckoning system) causes positional errors which are only proportional to the first power of time. The adequate solution of this component accuracy problem has been the most important development in recent years in transforming inertial navigation from a theoretically interesting idea into a practical method of determining vehicle position and velocity.

It should be noted that, in practice, inertial navigation systems assume many different configurations. In order to focus our attention on fundamental concepts the discussion in this chapter will be limited to a single configuration. In the following chapter alternative system configurations will be discussed.

7-2. Theoretical Basis

Let us assume that, relative to an appropriately chosen system of coordinates, the position of a vehicle be given by a position vector $\bar{r}$.

* The determination of vehicle acceleration by measurement of reaction forces does not include the gravitational accelerations to which the vehicle is subjected. Special methods (see Sec. 7-7 of this chapter) are necessary for gravity acceleration determination, but these methods do not interfere with the self-contained nature of inertial navigators.

Assume further that the velocity and acceleration of the vehicle be given by the vectors $\bar{v}$ and $\bar{a}$, respectively. From the definitions of velocity and acceleration, we have

$$\bar{a} = \frac{d\bar{v}}{dt} \tag{7-1}$$

$$\bar{v} = \frac{d\bar{r}}{dt} \tag{7-2}$$

Integrating these two expressions

$$\bar{v} = \int_0^t \bar{a}\, dt + \bar{v}_0 \tag{7-3}$$

$$\bar{r} = \int_0^t \bar{v}\, dt + \bar{r}_0 \tag{7-4}$$

where $\bar{v}_0$ and $\bar{r}_0$ are the velocity and position vectors, respectively, when time is zero.

Before proceeding further, a few words should be said about the choice of the coordinate system. One of several possible types may be selected in the design of a particular inertial navigation system. This choice is important, since the physical characteristics of the system are significantly affected by the type of coordinates used. A judicious choice can result in considerable simplification of the equipment. Later in the discussion we shall consider the question of coordinate systems in greater detail. However, our immediate purpose, which is to discuss the fundamental principles of inertial navigation, will be best served by choosing a simple coordinate system. For the present, therefore, let us select a system of rectangular coordinates. In addition, our coordinate frame must be an *inertial* system. An inertial coordinate system is defined as one in which the laws of physics, based on Newtonian mechanics, are valid. Such a system may be considered to be either at rest or in motion of translation with constant velocity relative to the "fixed" stars. The choice of a coordinate system which is inertial is very advantageous, since Newton's second law ($F = ma$) is valid *only* in inertial coordinate systems. Thus the measurement (via accelerometers) of reaction forces can be interpreted directly as vehicle accelerations only relative to an inertial coordinate system.

Written explicitly in terms of rectangular components (x,y,z), Eq. (7-3) becomes

$$\begin{aligned} v_x &= \int_0^t a_x\, dt + v_{0x} \\ v_y &= \int_0^t a_y\, dt + v_{0y} \\ v_z &= \int_0^t a_z\, dt + v_{0z} \end{aligned} \tag{7-5}$$

and, similarly, Eq. (7-4) provides

$$\begin{aligned} x &= \int_0^t v_x\,dt + x_0 \\ y &= \int_0^t v_y\,dt + y_0 \\ z &= \int_0^t v_z\,dt + z_0 \end{aligned} \tag{7-6}$$

Equations (7-5) and (7-6) form the *mathematical basis* of inertial navigation systems. Figure 7-1 shows a basic block diagram of an inertial navigation scheme, indicating the operations which must be performed in solving Eqs. (7-5) and (7-6) to arrive at the vehicle position coordinates

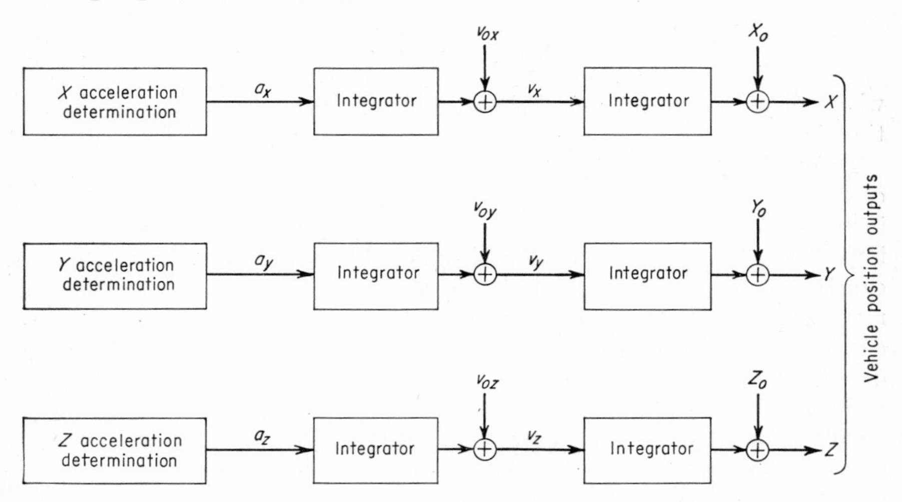

FIG. 7-1. Basic operations performed in an inertial navigation system.

x, y, z. Although this diagram is highly simplified, it points out some of the problems which must be solved in designing an inertial navigation system. The following are some of the more significant areas.

Acceleration Determination. Devices known as *accelerometers* must be devised for determining accelerations by accurate measurement of reaction forces. As will be explained later in this chapter, *accelerometers are incapable of sensing vehicle accelerations which result from the gravitational pull of the earth or any of the heavenly bodies.* Therefore, vehicle accelerations due to gravity must be determined indirectly by using computational methods. In Fig. 7-1, the boxes marked "acceleration determination" should be considered as including the direct measurement of nongravitational accelerations by accelerometers as well as the indirect determination of gravitational accelerations by appropriate computational techniques.

Physical Realization of Inertial Coordinate Axes. The three accelerometers used to measure nongravitational accelerations must be aligned, one each with the x, y, and z coordinate axes of an appropriate inertial reference frame. In order to maintain this alignment at all times, in spite of changes in angular orientation of the vehicle, it is necessary to mount these components on a gyroscopically stabilized gimbaled platform known as an *inertial platform*.

Integration. Figure 7-1 indicates the prominence of integrators in the data processing which occurs in a basic inertial navigation system. The precision of the navigational data obtained from the system is intimately related to the precision of the system's integrators. Hence, for good inertial navigation, these components should be of the greatest possible accuracy. Both analog and digital integrators are commonly used.

Determination of Initial Conditions. It is clear from Eqs. 7-5 and 7-6 and also from Fig. 7-1 that the three components of initial velocity, v_{0x}, v_{0y}, v_{0z}, and the three initial position components, x_0, y_0, z_0, must be separately determined and set into the system at the start of navigation. Since the entire inertial navigation process is usually carried out in a nonrotating "inertial" coordinate system, the initial velocity must include the linear velocity due to the rotation of the earth (approximately 1,000 mph at the equator). The initial position is determined from a precise knowledge (from maps, etc.) of the location of the point of departure of the vehicle.

Conversion from Inertial Coordinates to Earth-referenced Coordinates. Although the inertial navigation process is carried out with respect to a nonrotating coordinate system, for practical purposes it is often required to determine navigational position with respect to a rotating coordinate system fixed to the earth. Hence, the conversion from inertial to earth-fixed coordinates is also performed in the inertial navigation system. The earth-fixed coordinate system commonly employed is the usual latitude-longitude grid.

In the remainder of this chapter we shall discuss in greater detail some of the areas mentioned above.

7-3. Accelerometers

Let us consider the characteristics of some typical accelerometers. In order to illustrate the basic principle of the accelerometer, examine the rocket shown in Fig. 7-2.

The thrust exerted by the rocket engine accelerates only those parts of the missile which are rigidly connected to the engine. Thus, if there is a free "test mass" in the missile, it will not be accelerated. If, however, we *force* the test mass to accelerate together with the missile, e.g., by attaching it thereto with a spring, then when equilibrium is reached, the force required to hold the test mass stationary relative to the accelerating missile is a measure of the acceleration of both the missile and the test mass. In the case shown in Fig. 7-2, the force on the test mass (and hence the acceleration of the missile) is measured by the extension of the spring. Of course, in the device pictured damping of the test mass is

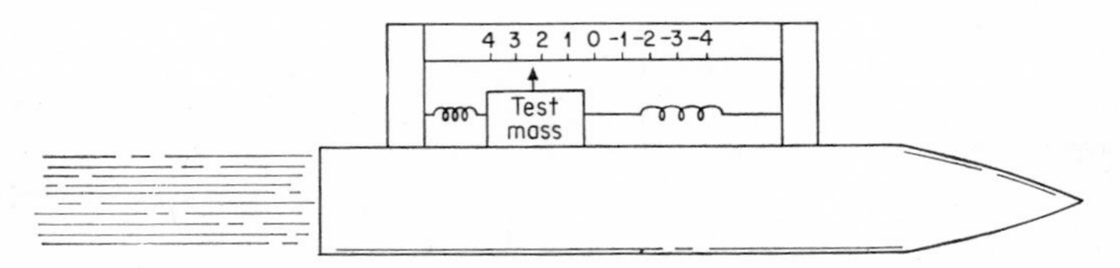

FIG. 7-2. Method of measuring acceleration due to nongravitational forces.

required in order that it settle at the equilibrium position. Devices of this type fall in the general category of accelerometers. Although accelerometers utilize a wide variety of physical phenomena—the stretching of a spring, the precession of an unbalanced gyro, the passage of current through the winding of an electromagnet, etc.—they all employ the fundamental principle of coercing a test mass to remain at rest relative to the accelerating vehicle through the action of a calibrated, measurable force. This force (by virtue of Newton's second law) is used as a measure of the acceleration of the test mass and more important, of course, of the vehicle in which the accelerometer is mounted.

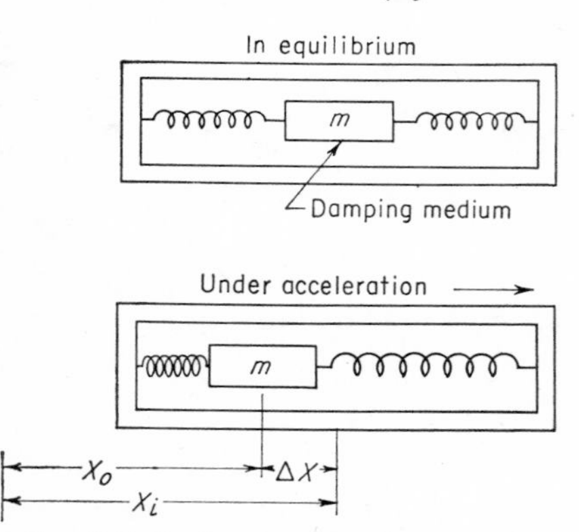

FIG. 7-3. Spring-mass accelerometer.

It is appropriate to examine in slightly greater detail a spring-mass accelerometer of the type discussed above. Figure 7-3 shows such an accelerometer. The equation of motion of the test mass is

$$m\ddot{x}_0 = K\,\Delta x + c\,\Delta\dot{x} \tag{7-7}$$

where K is the spring constant and c is the damping constant. Remembering that $x_0 = x_i - \Delta x$, as shown in Fig. 7-3, we obtain

$$m\ddot{x}_i = m\,\Delta\ddot{x} + c\,\Delta\dot{x} + K\,\Delta x$$

which can be used to derive the transfer function

$$\frac{\Delta x}{s^2 x_i} = \frac{1}{s^2 + (c/m)s + K/m} \tag{7-8}$$

where s denotes the differential operator d/dt.

From this transfer function it can be seen that at low excitation frequencies (s close to zero) the displacement Δx of the test mass is proportional to the acceleration s^2x_i of the accelerometer case. It is clear from Eq. (7-8) that such an accelerometer deteriorates in sensitivity and perhaps in accuracy as the exciting frequency increases, indicating the importance of selecting the instrument's constants (m,c,K) so that accuracy will be optimized in the dynamic frequency region of greatest interest for a particular application. It should be noted that, in practice, accelerometers of this simple type are not capable of great precision. Therefore, they are not generally used in precision inertial navigation systems, their application usually being limited to crude acceleration

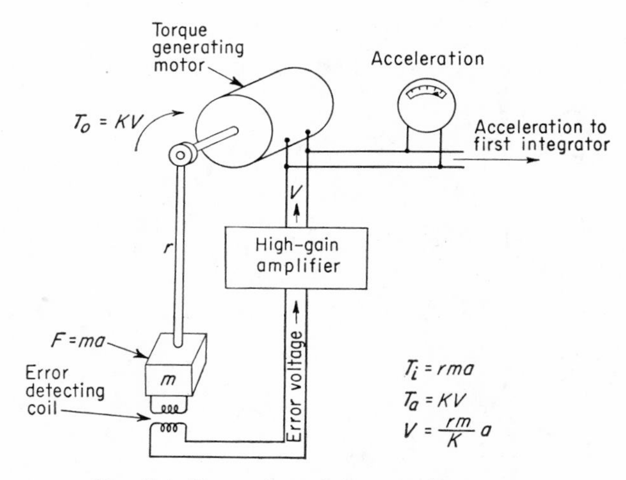

FIG. 7-4. Torqued-pendulum accelerometer.

measurements, e.g., testing vibration environments. The remainder of the accelerometers considered in this section are actually employed in inertial navigation systems.

A second physical principle used in accelerometers is shown in Fig. 7-4. This is the *torqued pendulum*. Let us assume that the vehicle in which the accelerometer is mounted undergoes an acceleration a perpendicular to r. The sensitive mass m then experiences a force $F = ma$. Therefore, the torque about the pivot is

$$T_i = rma \tag{7-9}$$

When this torque is applied, the pendulum tends to swing off the vertical. The error-detecting coil is designed so that when such a misalignment occurs a voltage proportional to the angular misalignment appears across the terminals of the secondary coil. This error voltage is amplified to the value V in a high-gain amplifier, and the voltage V is applied to the terminals of a torque-generating motor which is designed so that the torque output T_o is

$$T_o = K_1 V \tag{7-10}$$

where K_1 is a constant characteristic of the motor.

As the pendulum swings off the vertical, the error voltage increases, causing the motor to generate an increasingly large T_o. When the motor torque T_o equals the acceleration-induced torque T_i, the system reaches equilibrium, and the pendulum departs no further from the vertical. When this equilibrium condition has been reached, we have from Eqs. (7-9) and (7-10)

$$rma = K_1 V \tag{7-11}$$

except for a small additional term, inversely proportional to the gain of the amplifier. Therefore,

$$V = \frac{rm}{K_1} a \tag{7-12}$$

from which it appears that the voltage V is proportional to the vehicle acceleration a. This voltage is used as one of the inputs to the first set of integrators shown in Fig. 7-1. It is clear that the primary factor limiting the precision of this device is the uncertainty in the torque generator's electromechanical constant of proportionality K_1. The quantities r and m are controlled by good mechanical tolerances applied in manufacture and assembly.

In the two accelerometers described thus far (spring-mass and torqued-pendulum types) the output is the acceleration itself, which then must be integrated once to obtain velocity and integrated again to secure position. A very interesting class of accelerometers, known as *integrating accelerometers*, perform internally the operations of sensing acceleration and carrying out one integration, so that the accelerometer yields velocity directly and must therefore be followed by only a single integrator to obtain position. An important accelerometer of this type is the *unbalanced gyro accelerometer*, shown schematically in Fig. 7-5. The heart of this device is a single-degree-of-freedom integrating gyro. The usual single-degree-of-freedom integrating gyro is balanced as accurately as possible about its output axis. When used as an integrating accelerometer, however, it is deliberately unbalanced about the output axis by a mass m offset by a distance r. In addition, the unbalanced gyro is mounted on the shaft of a motor (output axis of the accelerometer) so that the entire unbalanced gyro unit may be driven about this axis perpendicular to both the gyro spin axis and the gyro output axis. Let us assume that the vehicle in which the unit is mounted is subjected to an acceleration a, assumed upward in Fig. 7-5. Because of the reaction force ma acting on the sensitive mass, the gimbal is subjected to a torque T_i, given by

$$T_i = rma \tag{7-13}$$

This torque T_i causes the gimbal to start rotating about the gyro output axis. The rotation results in an output shaft error angle E. The error pickoff (usually a component known by the trade name *microsyn*) is an angle-to-voltage transducer which produces a voltage proportional to the error angle E. This error voltage is fed through a high-gain amplifier whose output drives the motor upon which the unbalanced gyro unit is mounted. As the unit is driven by the motor, a gyro precessional torque T_o is generated, which under a steady-state condition, and neglecting the very small motion of the end point of the spin axis parallel to the acceleration vector, is given by

$$T_o = H \frac{d\theta}{dt} \tag{7-14}$$

where H is the angular momentum of the gyrowheel and θ is the angle through which the motor drives the unit. The unit is so designed that the gyro precessional torque T_o is in a direction opposite to the acceleration produced torque T_i. Therefore, the motor continues to speed up until $T_o = T_i$. When this condition is reached the net torque tending to increase the error angle E is zero. Therefore, the motor has no further tendency to increase its speed. Under these *equilibrium* circumstances we have, from Eqs. (7-13) and (7-14),

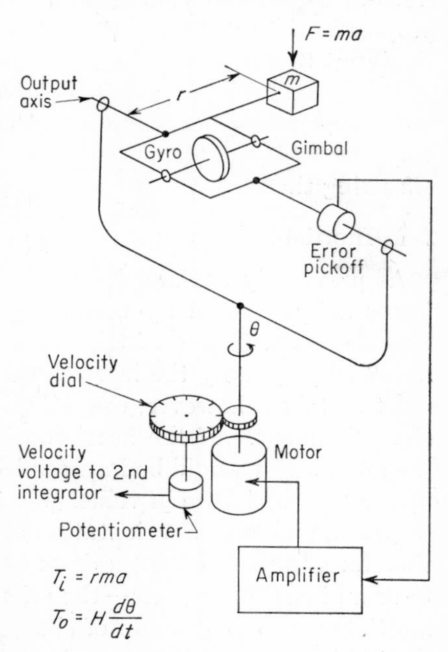

FIG. 7-5. Unbalanced gyro integrating accelerometer.

$$rma = H \frac{d\theta}{dt} \tag{7-15}$$

$$d\theta = \frac{rm}{H} a\, dt \tag{7-16}$$

But $a\, dt$ is the increment of velocity dv occurring in time dt. Therefore,

Eq. (7-16) can be written

$$d\theta = \frac{rm}{H}\, dv \tag{7-17}$$

which upon integration yields

$$\theta = \frac{rm}{H}\,(v - v_o) \tag{7-18}$$

This states the extremely important result that the shaft angle θ is directly proportional to the acquired vehicle velocity v. This velocity can be read directly from the dial shown in Fig. 7-5. In addition, a resistance potentiometer geared to the θ shaft might deliver a voltage proportional to θ (hence proportional to velocity) which can be used as the input to a second integrator to compute vehicle position. Referring again to Fig. 7-1, we see that the unbalanced gyro accelerometer performs both the acceleration measurement and the first integration to determine vehicle velocity. The insertion of the initial velocity is accomplished by offsetting the motor shaft position prior to the start of navigation.

7-4. Inertial Platforms

As previously explained, vehicle accelerations due to nongravitational forces are measured by accelerometers, each of which has its sensitive axis aligned with one of the coordinate axes of the particular reference frame employed by the inertial navigation system. Special precautions must be taken, however, to maintain continuously the proper accelerometer alignment. If the accelerometers were to be rigidly connected to the airframe, it would be impossible to maintain continuous proper alignment, since a change in vehicle heading or attitude would produce a corresponding change in orientation of the accelerometers. It is necessary, therefore, to mount the accelerometers on a gimbaled platform—referred to as an inertial platform—the orientation of which remains stabilized in inertial space independent of changes in orientation of the vehicle. Figure 7-6 is a schematic impression of a simplified inertial platform for the idealized case in which the vehicle is confined to motion in a single plane (say the XY plane) and in which it can only rotate about the Z axis. A real inertial platform would have three axes of rotation, since a vehicle is capable of roll, pitch, and yaw. In our simplified example, however, one axis is sufficient, since we have limited the vehicle to motion in a single plane. The component that is the basic sensing element for maintaining proper platform orientation is the gyroscope. A basic principle of mechanics states that, in any mechanical system, the rate of change of angular momentum is equal to the external torque applied. A gyro may be considered to be a system possessing an angular momentum $\bar{H} = I\bar{\omega}$, since it contains a wheel with moment of inertia I which spins with an angular velocity $\bar{\omega}$, where $\bar{\omega}$ is a vector directed along the wheel's spin axis and equal in magnitude to the spin rate. Special precautions are taken in building a gyro to ensure that no undesired torques are exerted on the gyrowheel assembly. These precautions include (as pointed out in previous chapters) careful balancing of the assembly, elimination of as much friction as possible from the gimbal assembly suspension, etc. Thus, in accordance with the above principle of mechanics, the angular-momentum vector of the gyrowheel remains constant in inertial space, i.e., in magnitude and—even more important—in direction. Therefore, the gyro spin axis provides a fixed directional reference in inertial space,

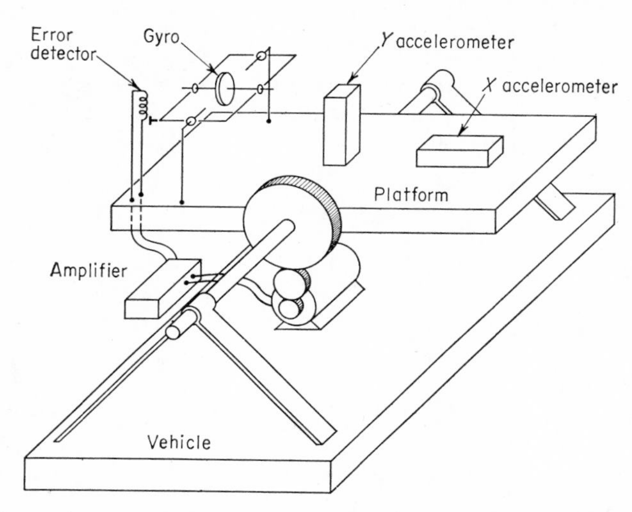

FIG. 7-6. Schematic representation of an inertial platform for a vehicle which remains in a single plane.

regardless of the motion of the vehicle. The platform can be forced to maintain alignment with this fixed reference, thus maintaining proper alignment of the accelerometers with the fixed coordinate system employed. The manner in which the platform is forced to remain aligned with the gyro directional reference is explained with the aid of Fig. 7-6 as follows. Suppose there is a tendency for the platform to develop an angular alignment error with the gyro spin axis. (This tendency might develop, for example, because of a pitching motion of the vehicle.) The gyro assembly incorporates an error-sensing device which yields an electric signal proportional to the angular misalignment developed by the platform. This error signal, after amplification, is applied to a servomotor coupled to the platform in a manner such that the error signal returns the platform to alignment with the gyro spin axis. The transient misalignment of the accelerometers during the corrective process is held to a minimum by employing a high-gain amplifier, so that only a very small misalignment error is required to set the servomotor in motion.

Thus far in the discussion of inertial platforms we have, for simplicity, confined ourselves to a consideration of the motion of a vehicle in a single plane. Obviously, any practical system must be capable of navigating in three dimensions. In such a system the inertial platform (see Fig. 7-7) must comprise three mutually orthogonal accelerometers and must be

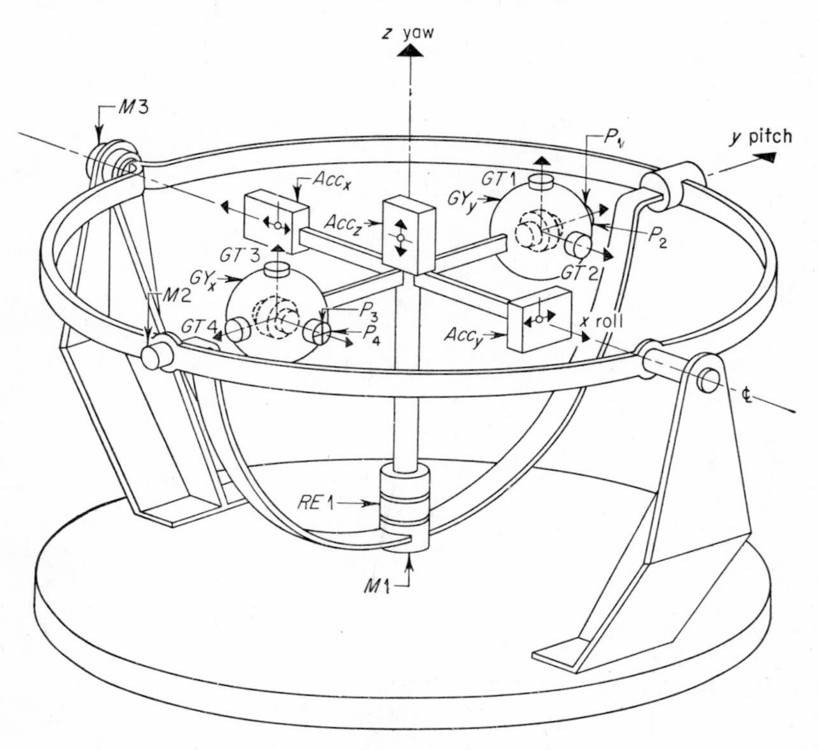

FIG. 7-7. Three-axis inertial platform.

gyro-stabilized about the roll, pitch, and yaw axes by the action of three separate servos. A typical gyro which might be used in such a platform is shown in Fig. 7-8. This is a "two-degree-of-freedom" gyro which can sense angular motion of the platform about two axes simultaneously. Thus only two gyros of this type are required to stabilize an inertial platform about all three axes. The great importance of preventing spurious torques (unbalance, friction, etc.) from acting on a gyro was mentioned previously. In the gyro illustrated these spurious torques are minimized by mounting the gyro in a spherical shell which is floated in *neutral buoyancy* within a ball-shaped tank which is rigidly connected to the platform. The shell can then be supported by very thin wires which have extremely low torsional stiffness, thus eliminating the friction which arises from normal bearing suspension.

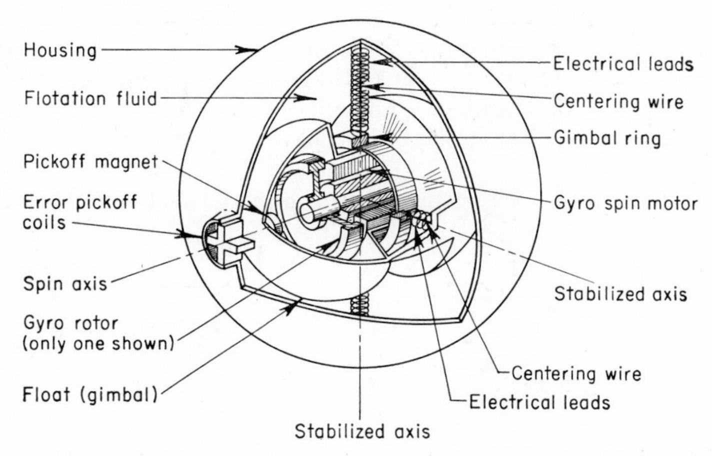

FIG. 7-8. Two-degree-of-freedom gyro typical of those used in inertial platforms.

7-5. Integrators

It has already been mentioned that precise integration is essential to accurate inertial navigation. We shall consider the methods of integration in greater detail.

In digital systems the integration is performed by counting pulses in a digital counter. In analog systems a number of integration principles are employed. The following are some typical examples:

Electrical Integrators. A typical purely electrical integrator employs d-c voltage as input and consists of a high-gain amplifier with capacitive feedback.

Mechanical Integrators. A common purely mechanical integrator is the disk-roller type. In this unit a disk is driven by a constant-speed motor. A roller perpendicular to the plane of the disk is driven through friction by the disk. The quantity to be integrated positions the roller mechanically at a proportional distance from the center of rotation of the disk. Hence, the speed of the roller is proportional to the quantity to be integrated. Consequently, the total angle generated by the roller is the desired integral.

Electromechanical Integrators. Since this is one of the most commonly employed types of integrator, we shall consider it in more detail. A typical electromechanical integrator is shown schematically in Fig. 7-9. The quantity to be integrated must be furnished to this unit in the form of an electric voltage. In an inertial navigation system this input voltage might, for example, be derived from an accelerometer such as the torqued-pendulum unit shown in Fig. 7-4.

As shown in Fig. 7-9, the input voltage V_1 to be integrated is fed to a high-gain amplifier whose output drives a motor. The angular position of the motor shaft is designated θ. A generator is mechanically coupled to the motor. The output voltage of the generator is subtracted from the input voltage to be integrated. The operation of this unit is as follows: When an input voltage is applied, the motor builds up speed, causing the generator voltage to increase. The motor speed continues to increase until the output voltage of the generator matches the input voltage.

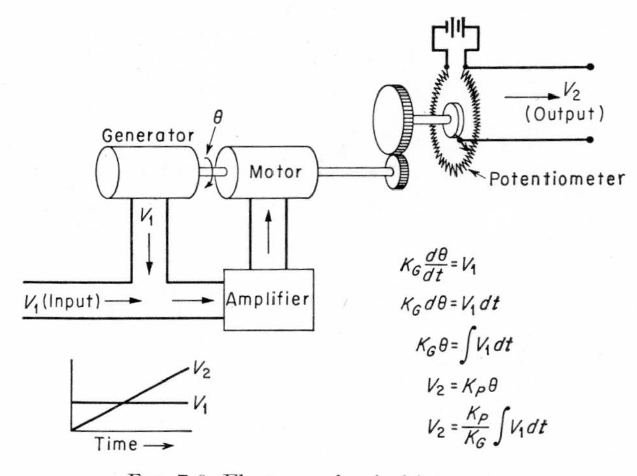

FIG. 7-9. Electromechanical integrator.

When this condition is reached, the motor continues to run at constant speed. (NOTE: Actually, at equilibrium the generator voltage is slightly less than the input voltage, since some small difference voltage is required to keep the motor rotating. However, by using an amplifier of sufficiently high gain this error voltage is very small, so that, to a good degree of approximation, we can consider the generator output voltage as equal to the input voltage.) The generator is designed so that its output voltage is accurately proportional to the shaft speed. Therefore, at equilibrium

$$K_g \frac{d\theta}{dt} = V_1 \tag{7-19}$$

where K_g is the scaling constant of the generator. Equation (7-19) can be integrated to yield

$$\theta = \frac{1}{K_g} \int_0^t V_1 \, dt \tag{7-20}$$

Thus we see that the angle θ turned by the motor is proportional to the integral of the input voltage V_1. Should the output integral be required as a voltage, a resistance potentiometer is geared to the motor. The output voltage V_2 of the potentiometer is proportional to the motor shaft angle.

$$V_2 = K_p\theta \tag{7-21}$$

From Eqs. 7-20 and 7-21

$$V_2 = \frac{K_p}{K_g}\int_0^t V_1\,dt \tag{7-22}$$

and thus we see finally that the output voltage V_2 is proportional to the integral of the input voltage V_1.

7-6. Summary to This Point

Before proceeding with our consideration of inertial navigation, it is appropriate to review briefly the conclusions which have been reached thus far.

1. Inertial navigation is a means for continuously determining the position of a vehicle by double integration of the vehicle accelerations.
2. In the case of nongravitational accelerations, such as those produced by engine thrust, the accelerations are measured by accelerometers. These components operate by coercing a test mass to remain at rest relative to the vehicle. The force required to maintain this condition is measured and taken as a quantitative indication of vehicle acceleration.
3. The sensitive axis of the accelerometers must be maintained aligned with the appropriate coordinate axes in inertial space. In order to maintain this alignment in spite of changes in orientation of the vehicle, the accelerometers must be mounted on an inertial platform, which is a gimbaled, gyro-stabilized platform.
4. The integrators used in inertial navigation systems are of both the digital and the analog types. Analog integrators are electrical, mechanical, and electromechanical.

7-7. Inclusion of Gravitational Accelerations

It is important to point out the basic characteristic of gravitational fields that the acceleration of an object in such a field is independent of its mass. This can be illustrated for a simple case as follows. Suppose we consider a mass m at a constant distance r from the center of the earth. Then the force acting on this object is

$$F = \frac{GMm}{r^2} \tag{7-23}$$

Equation (7-23) is a statement of the universal law of gravitation, first formulated by Newton. In this expression, G is the universal gravitational constant and M is the mass of the earth. By Newton's second law of motion, the acceleration a of the object is given by

$$a = \frac{F}{m} \tag{7-24}$$

From Eqs. (7-23) and (7-24) we find the acceleration

$$a = \frac{GM}{r^2} \tag{7-25}$$

entirely independent of the mass m of the object. This principle, i.e., that the acceleration of an object in a gravitational field is independent of its mass, is known as the *principle of the equivalence of gravitational and inertial mass* or more simply as the principle of equivalence. This principle was first demonstrated by Galileo in his famous leaning tower of Pisa experiment, in which he showed that two unequal masses released simultaneously struck the ground apparently at the same instant. The principle of equivalence is of critical importance in our analysis of inertial navigation.

The fundamental properties of inertial navigation systems can be further clarified by trying to answer the following question: Is it possible to design an inertial navigation system which would incorporate a device to *measure directly* the gravitational acceleration acting on the vehicle? We state that this direct-measurement scheme would be impossible in an inertial space, because of its conflict with the principle of equivalence. This can be shown as follows: Any device for measuring the acceleration of a vehicle does so by measuring the force exerted, e.g., by a spring, to maintain an *otherwise isolated* "test mass" at rest relative to the accelerated vehicle. Under these conditions the acceleration of the test mass (which is determined through Newton's second law by measuring the force exerted on it) is equal to the acceleration of the vehicle. As discussed above, however, in a vehicle which is acted upon only by gravitational forces the principle of equivalence requires that every element of mass in the vehicle experience the *same* acceleration. Therefore, if an accelerometer test mass is coupled to the vehicle with a device such as a spring, it is impossible to "otherwise isolate" the test mass (since the gravity field acts on the test mass as well as on the vehicle), and hence the spring would experience no change in tension with changes in gravitational field strength. A direct measurement of the gravitational field in a vehicle *such as an orbiting earth satellite* would require that the test mass of the measuring system be made of the science fictioneer's "antigrav" material. The force required to keep this element in the orbit with the rest of the vehicle would then be a measure of vehicle acceleration due to the gravitational field. The discovery of such a material (which must be considered extremely unlikely) would necessitate discarding the principle of equivalence, together with all its other logical consequences. While the tidal action of the moon on the earth might appear to be an observable effect of purely gravitational forces, it must be remembered that the earth is sufficiently large so that the moon's gravitation field varies noticeably over the surface of the earth. It is this *differential* gravitational effect, rather than the over-all gravity field of the moon itself, which gives rise to tides. Any man-made vehicle, however, is small enough so that the gravitational field is essentially constant at all points of the vehicle, and therefore detection of a gravitational field in such a vehicle is impossible.

On the basis of these considerations, we conclude that the gravitational acceleration inputs as required for inertial navigation must be determined by indirect computation rather than by direct measurement. As will be explained, this computation is based on a prior knowledge of the gravitational field as a function of present vehicle position.

As an example of the indirect method which must be used for determining vehicle accelerations due to gravity, let us consider an inertial navigator for a vehicle which is acted upon only by gravitational forces. An examination of this case will illustrate several concepts of importance in inertial navigation. An example of such a vehicle is a freely orbiting space station which is outside the earth's atmosphere (thus free of aerodynamic forces) and which also does not exert any thrust through rocket engines. Nongravitation forces (such as aerodynamic and thrust forces) have been temporarily excluded for simplicity. The method of including such nongravitational accelerations through the use of accelerometers has already been discussed.

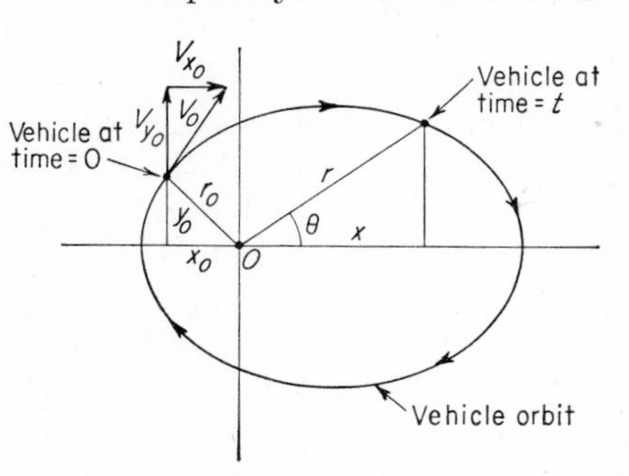

FIG. 7-10. Path of a freely orbiting space platform.

Figure 7-10 is a geometry diagram which is applicable to this problem. Point O is the center of gravitational attraction, i.e., the center of the earth. It can be seen that the orbit assumes the elliptical shape typical of keplerian motion. At time zero we are given the required initial velocity $\bar{v}_0$, resolved into its components v_{x0} and v_{y0}, and also the required initial position $\bar{r}_0$, resolved into components x_0 and y_0. (The determination of these initial conditions in a space platform poses some practical difficulties which the reader may imagine solved by celestial fixes, radar tracking from the earth's surface, or some equivalent method.)

Let us consider an inertial navigator which continuously yields the satellite vehicle's position in cartesian coordinates x, y, and also in polar coordinates r, θ. Figure 7-11 shows, in block form, an inertial navigator for this application. The primary purpose of this diagram is to emphasize the operations which must be performed rather than the physical hardware employed. In an actual physical realization of this system the operations could be carried out by digital or analog computations or by a combination of these.

Equations (7-5) and (7-6), the fundamental equations of inertial navigation, may be written for the case under consideration as

$$\begin{aligned} v_x &= \int_0^t a_x\,dt + v_{x0} \\ v_y &= \int_0^t a_y\,dt + v_{y0} \end{aligned} \tag{7-26}$$

$$\begin{aligned} x &= \int_0^t v_x\,dt + x_0 \\ y &= \int_0^t v_y\,dt + y_0 \end{aligned} \tag{7-27}$$

(NOTE: We have selected our coordinate system so that the XY plane coincides with the plane of vehicle motion. Therefore, the Z component of motion is zero and may be ignored.) The integrators and "adders" of box I of Fig. 7-11 carry out the operations required by Eqs. (7-26) and (7-27). The output of this box is a continuous indication of the vehicle position in terms of rectangular coordinates X and Y. These quantities might appear as voltages, for example, which are schematically shown displayed on meters in the output display unit (box IV).

As previously explained, box I must be furnished with inputs of initial velocity, initial position, and vehicle acceleration. Since the initial velocity and position data are constants, they need no longer concern us once they have been determined and fed in. However, since the acceleration is a variable input, it is necessary to consider in greater detail the method used for its determination. Now the entire force acting on the freely orbiting vehicle under consideration is caused by the gravitational field of the earth. In a case such as this, the force acting on the vehicle at a particular instant can be completely specified in direction and magnitude if the location of the vehicle is known. Thus, in general terms, we can use the vehicle position output of box I to compute the acceleration caused by the gravitational field, and this result can in turn be used as an input to box I. It is evident that we have described a feedback path resulting in a closed loop around box I. It will be seen that this closed-loop characteristic appears in one form or another in all inertial navigation systems.

Let us trace out in greater detail this computation of acceleration due

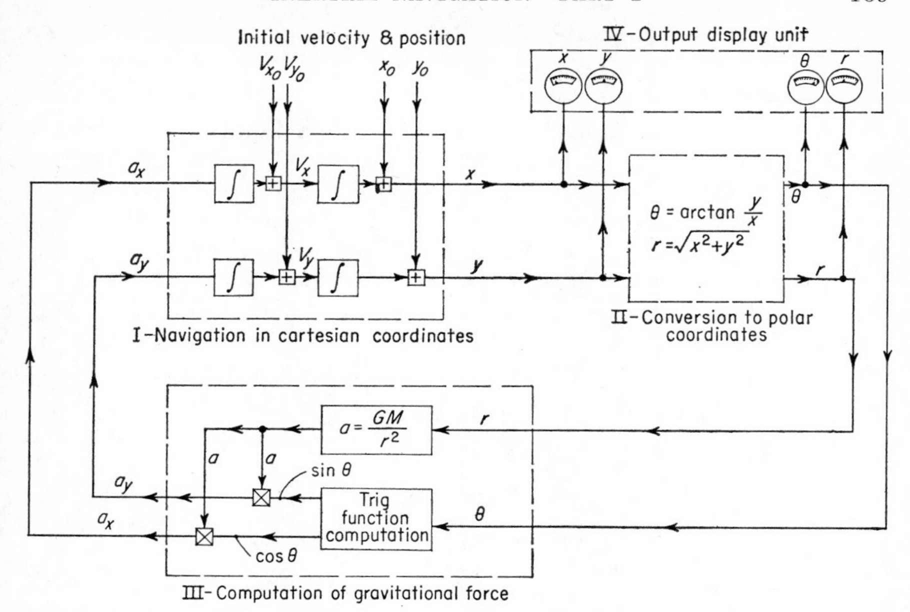

FIG. 7-11. Inertial navigator for freely orbiting space platform. (I) Navigation in cartesian coordinates; (II) conversion to polar coordinates; (III) computation of gravitational force; (IV) output display unit.

to gravitational forces. We note first that the force on the vehicle is directed toward the center of the earth, and its magnitude is given by the previously mentioned universal law of gravitation as

$$F = \frac{GMm}{r^2} \tag{7-28}$$

where G = universal gravitational constant
M = mass of earth
m = mass of vehicle
r = distance from earth's center to vehicle

As previously explained, we require the acceleration a, which, by Newton's second law and the universal law of gravitation, is given by

$$a = \frac{F}{m} = \frac{GM}{r^2} \tag{7-29}$$

Resolution into X and Y components leads to

$$a_x = -a \cos \theta = \frac{-GM \cos \theta}{r^2} \tag{7-30}$$

$$a_y = -a \sin \theta = \frac{-GM \sin \theta}{r^2} \tag{7-31}$$

The computation of these acceleration components is carried out in box III, with the inputs r and θ obtained from x and y in box II, which converts cartesian to polar coordinates.

It is interesting to note that the acceleration inputs to the inertial navigation computation [see Eq. (7-8)] depend only on vehicle location and not at all on vehicle mass. This leads to the conclusion that the orbit of a space platform is completely determined by its initial position and velocity and is not affected by its mass. This behavior is a consequence of the previously mentioned *principle of equivalence.*

It is revealing to examine some of the dynamic characteristics of the inertial navigator of Fig. 7-11. This examination will help to demonstrate some of the important properties of inertial navigators in general. For simplicity, we consider the case of a vehicle in a circular orbit of constant radius r_0. First of all, note that the inertial navigation equations (7-26) and (7-27) are actually equivalent to

$$\frac{d^2x}{dt^2} = a_x \qquad \frac{d^2y}{dt^2} = a_y \tag{7-32}$$

which for *the circular orbit case* can be combined with Eqs. (7-30) and (7-31) resulting in

$$\frac{d^2x}{dt^2} = -\frac{GM}{r_0^2}\cos\theta = -\frac{GM}{r_0^3}x \qquad \frac{d^2y}{dt^2} = -\frac{GM}{r_0^2}\sin\theta = -\frac{GM}{r_0^3}y \tag{7-33}$$

since $\cos\theta = x/r$ and $\sin\theta = y/r$ (see Fig. 7-10). Equations (7-33) have oscillatory solutions of the form

$$x = r_0 \sin\sqrt{\frac{GM}{r_0^3}}\,t \qquad y = r_0 \cos\sqrt{\frac{GM}{r_0^3}}\,t \tag{7-34}$$

Hence, we reach the conclusion that the inertial navigation system of Fig. 7-11 is capable of sustained oscillations. These are the well-known *Schuler* oscillations, which actually occur in any mathematically correct inertial navigation system. From Eqs. (7-34) it appears that the period of oscillation is $T = 2\pi\sqrt{r_0^3/GM}$. Now g_0, the acceleration of gravity at distance r_0 from the earth's center, is given by $g_0 = GM/r_0^2$, and hence the period of the Schuler oscillation can be expressed as $T = 2\pi\sqrt{r_0/g_0}$, which at the surface of the earth ($r = 3{,}963 \times 5{,}280$ ft, $g = 32.2$ ft/sec^2)

has the value $T = 84.4$ min, a "magic number" to those engaged in the study of inertial navigation. It is of basic interest to note that the period of the Schuler oscillation of an inertial navigator at a given altitude is identical with the period of revolution of an earth satellite at the same altitude.

7-8. Inertial Navigation in the Presence of Both Nongravitational and Gravitational Accelerations

So far we have considered the means for inertially navigating in the presence of nongravitational accelerations and have regarded gravitational accelerations as separate problems. However, these were simple

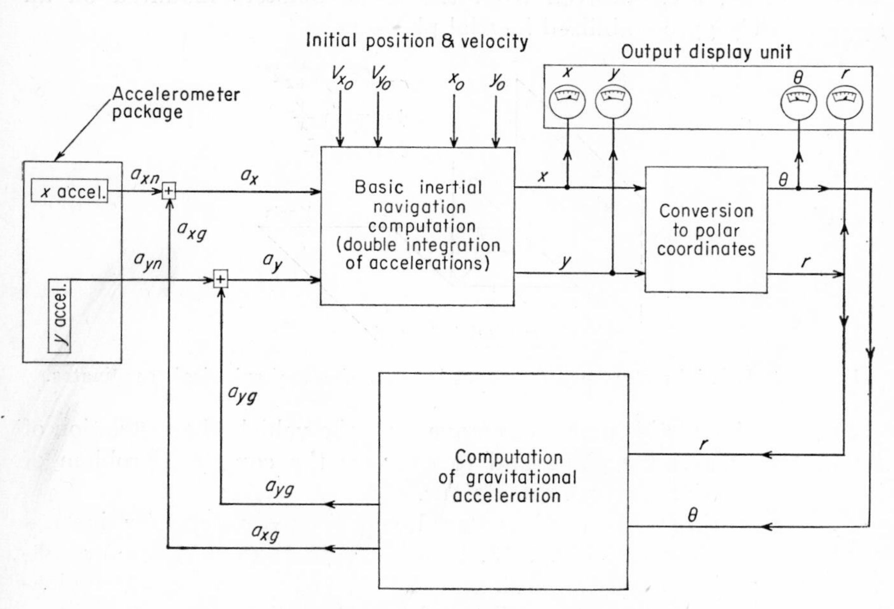

FIG. 7-12. Inertial navigator for vehicle which moves in a single plane.

idealizations made for ease of explanation. It is now necessary to consider a situation of greater practical interest. Figure 7-12 shows an inertial navigation system which is usable in a vehicle subject to both gravitational and nongravitational forces, such as a ballistic missile during its powered flight. In this system accelerometers, which are mounted so that they are mutually perpendicular and aligned with the appropriate axis, are used to detect the components of nongravitational vehicle acceleration. For simplicity, we temporarily retain the assumption of plane motion in this portion of the discussion; thus we require only x and y accelerometers. This is clearly an idealization, since it obviously lies within the capability of a vehicle in powered flight to depart from a single plane of motion. All the remarks which were previously made concerning an inertial navigator for a satellite are also valid in the present case of powered flight, except that now the vehicle's acceleration components a_x, a_y are given by

$$\begin{aligned} a_x &= a_{xg} + a_{xn} \\ a_y &= a_{yg} + a_{yn} \end{aligned} \tag{7-35}$$

where a_{xg} and a_{yg} are the components of gravitational acceleration derived from the Schuler-loop feedback computations based on present vehicle position, while a_{xn} and a_{yn} are the components of nongravitational acceleration (thrust, etc.) derived from the accelerometers mounted on an appropriately gyro-stabilized inertial platform.

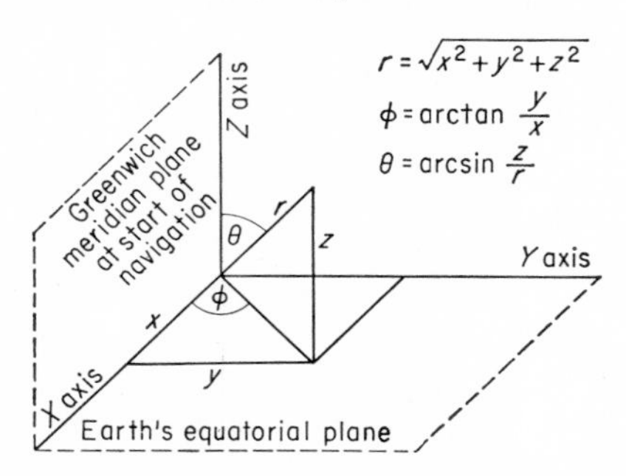

FIG. 7-13. Inertial reference system showing cartesian and spherical coordinates.

It is suitable at this point to remove from the vehicle the restriction of remaining in a single plane and to consider the complete problem of inertial navigation in three dimensions.

A typical three-axis earth-centered coordinate system for inertial navigation is shown in Fig. 7-13, together with the equations for converting from the cartesian coordinates x, y, z (in which the inertial navigation computations are performed) to spherical coordinates r, ϕ, θ. Figure 7-14 shows how the two-accelerometer simplified system discussed previously must be generalized to solve the three-dimensional inertial navigation problem.

Although the generalization to three dimensions is quite clear, a few comments should be made concerning the conversion to earth-fixed latitude-longitude-altitude coordinates. Up to this point all the inertial navigation computations have been performed in a coordinate system which is nonrotating in inertial space. However, in most practical navigation problems we desired the position of the vehicle relative to a coordinate system fixed with respect to the rotating earth. The most common choice of earth-fixed coordinates is the latitude-longitude-altitude system. In Fig. 7-14 the conversion from inertial spherical coordinates r, ϕ, θ to earth-fixed coordinates is shown as the final operation of the system. It is assumed here that the cartesian inertial system satisfies the following conditions:

1. The XY plane coincides with the earth's equatorial plane.
2. The XZ plane coincides with the Greenwich meridian plane at the time of the start of inertial navigation.

These conditions are satisfied by proper alignment of the inertial platform prior to takeoff or missile launch. This alignment, incidentally, constitutes one of the difficult problems which must be solved in any actual

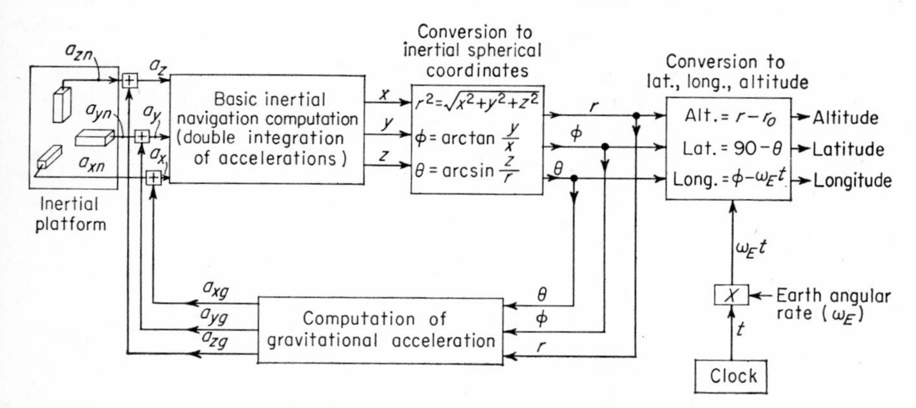

FIG. 7-14. A complete three-axis inertial navigator for determination of earth-referenced latitude, longitude, and altitude.

inertial navigation system. Alternate choices of inertial coordinate systems are possible, but the selection made here will suffice to illustrate the principles involved.

The equation for altitude

$$\text{Altitude} = r - r_0$$

(r_0 = earth's radius) is obviously true. The relation for latitude

$$\text{Latitude} = 90° - \theta$$

is evident from the geometry of Fig. 7-13. The equation for longitude

$$\text{Longitude} = \phi - \omega_E t$$

(ω_E = earth's angular rate) requires that the inertial azimuthal angle ϕ be corrected by an amount equal to the angular rotation of the earth measured from the instant inertial navigation is started. A sidereal clock provides the necessary data for this longitude correction.

PROBLEM

Suppose the inertial navigation system of Fig. 7-12 is placed at the North Pole with the inertial platform perfectly aligned so that the y-accelerometer-sensitive axis is along the earth's axis and the x-accelerometer-sensitive axis is horizontal. The proper initial conditions are inserted into the system, i.e.,

$$\begin{aligned} v_{x0} &= 0 \\ v_{y0} &= 0 \\ x_0 &= 0 \\ y_0 &= 4{,}000 \text{ miles (earth's radius)} \end{aligned}$$

(*a*) Show analytically that, if all equipment components are perfect, the y output of the system remains constant at 4,000 miles even though the output of the y accelerometer is 32.2 ft/sec².

(*b*) Analyze what happens to the y output if, due to an equipment error, the y accelerometer output is in error by a small amount e so that its output is $(32.2 + e)$ ft/sec² instead of 32.2 ft/sec².

(*c*) Suppose at $t = 0$ the platform is suddenly tipped through a small angle Δ ($\sin \Delta \approx \Delta$, $\cos \Delta \approx 1$). Find the x output of the inertial navigation system as a function of time.

HINT:

$$a_{xg} = -\frac{GM}{r^2}\frac{x}{r}$$

$$a_{xn} = \begin{cases} 0 & (t \leqq 0) \\ \dfrac{GM}{r^2}\Delta & (t > 0) \end{cases}$$

BIBLIOGRAPHY

1. Schuler, Max: Die Storüng von Pendul- und Kreiselapparaten durch die Beschleunigung des Fahrzeuges, *Physik. Z.*, vol. 24, p. 344, 1923.
2. Wrigley, W.: Schuler Tuning Characteristics in Navigational Instruments, *J. Inst. Navigation,* vol. 3, December, 1950.
3. Sommer, A. V.: Missile Guidance. . . . Why So Little Progress, *Aviation Age,* vol. 22, August, 1954.
4. Statsinger, J.: Absolute Guidance for Airborne Vehicles, *Aviation Age,* vol. 22, September, 1954.
5. Bishop, R. L.: Inertial System Components Are Here, *Aviation Age,* vol. 22, October, 1954.
6. Klass, P. J.: Inertial Navigation: Out of the Laboratory into Missile Systems, *Aviation Week,* vol. 64, Jan. 2, 1956.
7. Slater, J. M.: Choice of Coordinate Systems in Inertial Navigation, *J. Inst. Navigation,* vol. 9, June, 1956.
8. Draper, C. S., W. Wrigley, and L. R. Grohe: The Floating Integrating Gyro and Its Application to Geometrical Stabilization Problems on Moving Bases, Institute of the Aeronautical Sciences, S.M.F. Fund Paper FF-13, 1955.
9. Wrigley, W., R. B. Woodbury, and J. Hovorka: Inertial Guidance, Institute of the Aeronautical Sciences, S.M.F. Fund Paper FF-16, 1957.
10. Duncan, D. B., and J. M. Slater: Inertial Navigation, *Aeronaut. Eng. Rev.,* vol. 15, no. 1, p. 50, January, 1956.

11. Mundo, C. J.: Aided Inertial Systems, *Arma Engineering*, vol. 2, no. 2, November, 1958.

12. Duncan, D. B.: Analysis of an Inertial Guidance System, *J. Am. Rocket Soc.*, vol. 28, no. 2, pp. 111–116, February, 1958.

13. Mundo, C. J.: Three Approaches to the Design of Inertial Systems, *Aviation Age*, November, 1959.

14. J. Hovorka et al.: Recent Advances in Inertial Guidance, *J. Am. Rocket Soc.*, vol. 29, no. 12, December, 1959.

15. Ishlinsky, A. Y.: Equations of Problems Concerning the Determination of Moving Object Position by Means of Gyros and Accelerometers, *Prikladnaya Matematika i Mekhanica*, vol. 21, pp. 725–739, 1956.

16. Bodnev, Z. A., Z. P. Seleznev, and V. E. Ovcharov: Contribution to the Theory of Inertial Damped Systems with Arbitrary Period, Invariant with Respect to the Maneuvering of Object, *Ozvestia Akad. Nauk S.S.S.R.*, no. 3, pp. 11–18, 1959.

17. McClure, C. L.: "Theory of Inertial Guidance," Prentice-Hall, Inc., Englewood Cliffs, N.J., 1960.

18. Savant, C. J., Jr., R. C. Howard, C. B. Solloway, and C. A. Savant: "Principles of Inertial Navigation," McGraw-Hill Book Company, Inc., New York, 1961.

CHAPTER 8

INERTIAL NAVIGATION—PART 2

By Charles J. Mundo, Jr.

Nomenclature

x = displacement along track
$\ddot{x}_A$ = geometric acceleration, x direction
$\ddot{x}_m$ = measured acceleration, x direction
x_c = computed position, x direction
y = displacement, crosstrack
z = displacement, heading direction
$\ddot{z}_A$ = geometric acceleration, z direction
$\ddot{z}_m$ = measured acceleration, z direction
z_c = computed position, z direction
v_x = velocity, x direction
v_y = velocity, y direction
A_I = indicated acceleration
A_T = true (geometric) acceleration
R = radius of earth
g_{0x}, g_{0y}, g_{0z} = gravitational acceleration at the surface of earth
ω = Schuler circular frequency
ω' = Schuler circular frequency, detuned
λ = latitude
$\dot{L}$ = longitude rate upon pseudosphere (inertial space)
θ = angle of traverse of local vertical
ψ_x, ψ_y, ψ_z = angle of traverse of platform
ϕ_x, ϕ_y, ϕ_z = error in platform orientation
ω_p = turning rate of platform (space coordinates)
ω_p' = turning rate of platform (own coordinates)
τ = duration of unpowered flight
T = duration of acceleration impulse
ϵ, ϵ_p = gyro drift rate

8-1. Introduction

In summarizing essentials inertial navigation is based upon sensing thrust accelerations. These serve as basic data necessary for computing a vehicle's change of position in inertial space. In addition to the thrust-sensing accelerometers an inertial navigator requires some device of spatial rigidity in inertial orientation, such as a gyroscopic reference system, to prevent the accelerometers from forcefully following the transporting vehicle's angular gyrations in space. In this chapter our attention will be focused upon how these elements are combined for navigation, what kinds of errors such a system will entail, and what can be done to overcome, or at least to attenuate, these errors.

8-2. Gravity-free-space Inertial Navigation

As seen in Chap. 7, inertial navigation in a gravity-free space is based on relatively simple principles. Gyroscopic references actuate servos which maintain three accelerometers aligned with three fixed coordinate directions in space, and these accelerometers sense the components of imparted accelerations of the vehicle along said coordinate axes. The outputs of the accelerometers are doubly integrated to yield velocity, after a first integration, and vehicle position, after another integration. Obviously, such a configuration provides only changes in velocity and position, so that initial conditions in vehicle velocity and position have to be introduced at the outset of the problem. The inertial system then computes changes with respect to these initial conditions.

8-3. Gravity Problem

When gravity is present, as in the case of navigating upon the earth, the picture is somewhat more involved. Again, the same elements, i.e., accelerometers and coordinate reference gyros, are the core of the system. However, in this case a major problem arises because vehicle-mounted accelerometers cannot actually measure accelerations resulting from gravitational fields, although these fields do cause the vehicle to accelerate as viewed from the earth. In order to understand the full meaning of this physical fact, consider Fig. 8-1. The accelerometers, as explained in Chap. 7, consist of a proof mass attached through a sensing constraint to the reference frame. When a thrust is applied to the vehicle and thus to the accelerometer frame, the latter is caused to accelerate with the vehicle. However, the only force which acts upon the proof mass is applied through the constraint structure as it is made to follow the vehicle. This force, simultaneously exerted and measured by the constraint, is proportional to the acceleration (Fig. 8-1*a*). However, an acceleration resulting from gravitational forces acts (equally) upon both the proof mass and the frame of the accelerometer, causing them to be accelerated together, and consequently no force is apparent across the constraint (Fig. 8-1*b*). Thus the vehicle is accelerated while the accelerometer reads zero. Also, and obviously again, when a vehicle is constrained from falling in a gravity field, the accelerometer does not indicate its true acceleration. Such a vehicle could be said to have a force equal to its weight preventing it from falling. However, the proof mass of the accelerometer in this case is acted upon by the gravitational forces. A force must be exerted by the constraint to prevent it from accelerating with gravity and thus causing the constraint to indicate that the vehicle is being accelerated upward when it is stationary in the particular frame of reference fixed with respect to the earth (Fig. 8-1*c*).

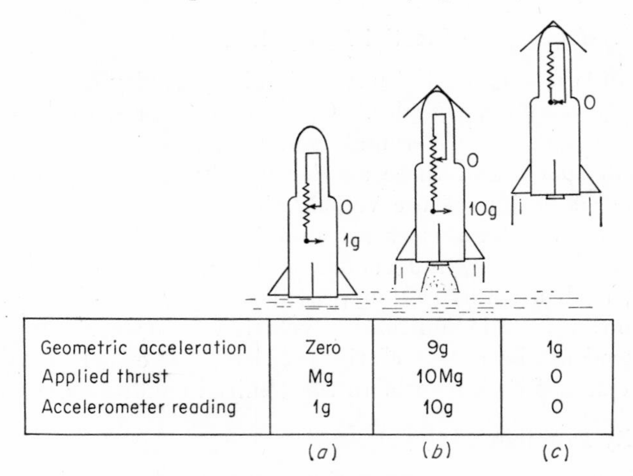

	(*a*)	(*b*)	(*c*)
Geometric acceleration	Zero	9g	1g
Applied thrust	Mg	10Mg	0
Accelerometer reading	1g	10g	0

FIG. 8-1. Principle of accelerometer.

The inability of the accelerometer to sense gravity accelerations directly is a serious problem when using a system (based upon inertial sensing elements) to navigate over areas such as the surface of the earth, where the gravitational accelerations are large compared with those encountered in the dynamics of the vehicle. However, when the proper design configuration is realized, a phenomenon known as *Schuler tuning* (which enables the system to isolate purely dynamic forces) takes place and lends a particular performance to terrestrial inertial navigators, in certain respects superior to that which might be expected in free space.

Schuler tuning necessarily arises when an attempt is made to compensate completely for the (unmeasurable) gravitational accelerations acting upon a body. As will be seen later, it also reduces the rate of divergence of navigation errors. For example, an acceleration error which normally would be expected to contribute to the computed position error at a rate proportional to the square of time merely causes an oscillating bias error.

In the matter of actual instrumentation, there are two basic approaches which might be followed in introducing Schuler tuning, thus eliminating what is known as the gravity problem. The first, called the *analytic approach*, calls for mathematically dubbing the gravity into the computation. The second method is based upon maintaining the accelerometers perpendicular to the gravity field when navigating upon the earth so that no compensation is required. The semianalytic and geometric systems described in more detail later in this chapter operate in the latter manner.

8-4. Analytic Inertial Navigator

In the analytic approach to inertial guidance (Fig. 8-2) the platform has three mutually orthogonal accelerometers fixed in inertial space by a platform which is servoed to follow untorqued gyroscopic references.

The accelerometer senses the net thrust acceleration $\ddot{x}_m$ applied to the vehicle, such as from engine thrust or aerodynamic lift force, thus indicating the combination of actual geometric acceleration $\ddot{x}_A$ plus the outward acceleration g_{0x} which prevents the vehicle from falling into the center of the earth. The net thrust acceleration in an ideal accelerometer is therefore

$$\ddot{x}_m = \ddot{x}_A + g_{0x} \tag{8-1}$$

If the vehicle were maintained geometrically fixed in the earth's field, the geometric acceleration representing a true physical motion would be $\ddot{x}_m = 0$. However, the accelerometer would measure the force maintaining the vehicle fixed in space with respect to the earth; therefore, $\ddot{x}_m = g_{0x}$. This value of g_{0x} is dependent only on the position of the vehicle with respect to the earth; and the latter in turn is computed by doubly integrating the output of the accelerometer. Thus, if the accelerometer is to be corrected to account for its inability to sense separately gravitational accelerations (if the navigation takes place upon the surface of the earth), a correction must be derived from the doubly integrated output of the accelerometer itself, thus closing the computation loop. Such closed-loop systems containing two integrations are generally oscillatory. They have an 84.4-min period upon the earth, which is known as the *Schuler period* of the system.

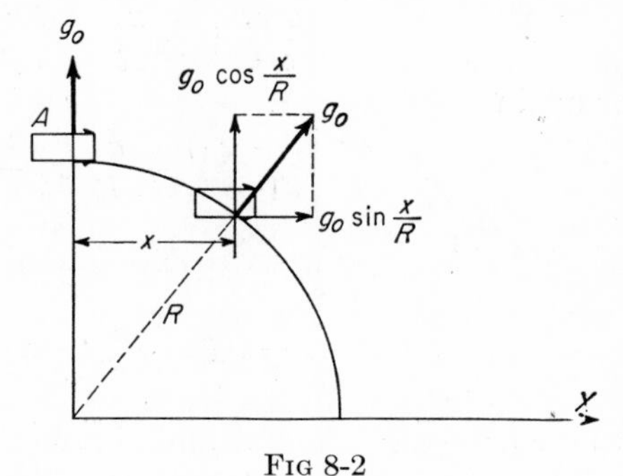

FIG 8-2

In order to illustrate the foregoing analytically, let the accelerometer A in Fig. 8-2 (which is maintained parallel to the x coordinate axis at all times) sense the horizontal acceleration of a vehicle moving over the surface of the earth. This accelerometer is aligned with the surface of the earth at $x = 0$ and sees no component of gravity initially; but as the vehicle proceeds away from $x = 0$, a component of gravity g_{0x}, proportional to the displacement, becomes apparent to the accelerometer.

If the position of the vehicle is to be computed from the output of the accelerometer, it must be corrected for the particular component of acceleration which is seen as a result of the accelerometer being displaced from $x = 0$. Thus after double integration

$$x_c = \int_0^t \int_0^t (\ddot{x}_m - g_{0x})\, dt^2 \tag{8-2}$$

where x_c = computed position
$\ddot{x}_m$ = acceleration measured by the accelerometer
g_{0x} = component of gravity seen by the x accelerometer

It is apparent from Fig. 8-2 that g_{0x} is a function of position. Since the only indication of position is a computed one, we have

$$g_{0x} = g_0 \sin \frac{x_c}{R} \approx g_0 \frac{x_c}{R} \tag{8-3}$$

Now let us look at the behavior of an error which is propagated in the computation if it is assumed that a steady bias error a_{0x} exists in the accelerometer. Remembering that the measured acceleration of the vehicle is the true acceleration $\ddot{x}_A$ less the gravity component $-g_0x_A/R$ or, explicitly, $\ddot{x}_m = \ddot{x}_A + x_z g_0/R$, and substituting in Eq. (8-2), we get the computed position x_c as given by

$$x_c = \int_0^t \int_0^t \left[\left(\ddot{x}_A + a_{0x} + g_0 \frac{x_A}{R}\right) - g_0 \frac{x_c}{R}\right] dt\, d\tau \tag{8-4}$$

Since x_c also occurs under the integral sign, a rearrangement is necessary; this provides

$$\frac{d^2x_c}{dt^2} + g_0 \frac{x_c}{R} = \frac{d^2x_A}{dt^2} + g_0 \frac{x_A}{R} + a_{0x} \tag{8-5}$$

or again

$$\frac{d^2(x_c - x_A)}{dt^2} + \frac{g_0}{R}(x_c - x_A) = a_{0x} = \text{const} \tag{8-6}$$

The difference between the computed and the true position becomes

$$x_c - x_A = \frac{a_{0x}}{\omega^2} + A \cos \omega t + B \sin \omega t \tag{8-7}$$

where $\omega^2 = g_0/R$ and A and B are constants of integration.

Thus, it is apparent that the system is capable of computing from sensed accelerations $\ddot{x}_m$ the true position of the vehicle. Furthermore, it appears that the errors in the computation, which arise from imperfections in the components, are *oscillatory* in nature and have a characteristic circular frequency of $2\pi/84.4$ min. This is commonly known as closing a Schuler loop or carrying out a Schuler tuning of the system. It is of great importance to state that an accelerometer nonlinearity which in a gravity-free space would diverge as the square of time, as far as position accuracy is concerned, is no longer divergent but, as appears from Eq. (8-7), creates a bias error $(R/g_0)a_{0x}$ plus an oscillatory component with a period of 84.4 min.

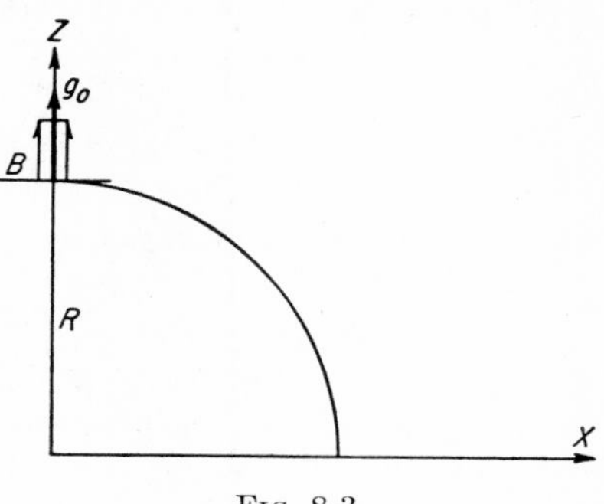

FIG. 8-3

For an analytic system, it should be pointed out that, while navigation within the earth's surface is stable, particular problems arise in the vertical direction unless means are provided to prevent divergent oscillations in this direction. The origin of these oscillations can be seen if the equation for vertical motion of the vehicle is more closely examined. We have

$$z_c = \int_0^t \int_0^t [\ddot{z}_m - (g_{0z})_c]\, dt^2 \tag{8-8}$$

where $\ddot{z}_m$ = vertical acceleration measured by accelerometer
z_c = computed vertical position
$(g_{0z})_c$ = computed component of gravity in vertical direction

In this case, the accelerometer B which is aligned parallel to the z axis sees the principal component of gravity. As the altitude of the vehicle changes, the required gravity compensation varies as the square of the distance from the center of the earth. Since $|z| \ll R$, we have approximately

$$\begin{aligned} (g_{0z})_c &\approx g_0\left(1 - \frac{2z_c}{R}\right) \\ (g_{0z})_A &\approx g_0\left(1 - \frac{2z_A}{R}\right) \end{aligned} \tag{8-9}$$

where $(g_{0z})_A$ = true component of gravity in vertical direction

Remembering, on the other hand, that

$$\ddot{z}_A = \ddot{z}_m - a_{0z} - (g_{0z})_A \tag{8-10}$$

where $\ddot{z}_A$ = geometric vertical acceleration, we have, by elimination of $\ddot{z}_m$ from Eqs. (8-8) to (8-10),

$$\ddot{z}_c = \ddot{z}_A - g_0\left(1 - \frac{2z_c}{R}\right) + g_0\left(1 - \frac{2z_A}{R}\right) + a_{0z} \tag{8-11}$$

Therefore,
$$z_c = z_A + \frac{a_{0z}}{s^2 - g_0/R} \tag{8-12}$$

As revealed by Eq. (8-12), an accelerometer bias error will create an exponentially increasing position error. Unless some secondary means of measuring altitude is provided, the system becomes useless. Fortunately, it is possible to incorporate an altimeter in the system and practically eliminate this difficulty entirely.

There are certain advantages claimed by proponents of an analytic inertial system. The first is that the coordinate system is fixed in space and no compensations such as those pertaining to Coriolis accelerations are required to compensate for the use of a rotating coordinate system. The second is that the coordinate system is rectangular cartesian, and hence there are no singular points such as the poles of the earth to complicate the computation. Indeed, these singular points would require infinite angular rates to be made good in navigation and must therefore be avoided, or possibly special local coordinates used, when crossing these regions. The third advantage is that the gyros remain fixed in inertial space and thus are not subject to uncertainties in torquing, although the system does suffer from the problem that the principal acceleration vector changes in orientation with respect to the spin axis of the gyro.

In general, it is found that, owing to the vertical divergence of errors and computing accuracy requirements, the analytic system has been most successfully used in guidance applications where the control time is short, such as in ballistic missiles and short-range cruise missiles. Some thought has been given to using it for extended-time applications also, but there seems to be a question as to whether round-off errors or gravity-function expansion would not lead to an excessive complexity of design.

8-5. Semianalytic Inertial Navigator

In the second approach to inertial navigation, the gravity problem is overcome by maintaining the accelerometers oriented tangentially to an isogalic surface, so that gravity does not present an explicit problem. Obviously, then, the position of a vehicle in this (isogalic) surface can be computed by doubly integrating the uncompensated output of the accelerometer; thus one derives the progress of the vehicle (over the isogalic surface) just as is done in free space. Since the vehicle moves at an essentially constant distance from the center of the earth, navigation in the radial direction is not necessary. In this case, the Schuler tuning does not come into being through computing a local position but through maintaining the accelerometers aligned with an isogalic surface, that is to say, maintaining the platform erect. Indeed, the key to the understanding of how a semianalytic inertial navigator works is based precisely upon the method which is satisfactorily used in maintaining the accelerometers aligned with the isogalic surface. Common to all of the methods to be considered is a *vertical gyro*, which physically establishes the isogalic tangent plane.

There are a number of different erection signals which might be used to maintain the vertical gyro. The simplest one uses a signal directly proportional to the output of the accelerometer, fed into the torquer of the gyro, as shown in Fig. 8-4. In order to describe the operation of the system, let us denote the following:

x_c = computed position of vehicle
v = velocity of vehicle upon earth
ϕ = tilt of platform relative to local vertical
ψ = angle of turn of platform in inertial space

Using operational notations and neglecting initial conditions, the accelerometer would see a vehicle acceleration of $sv(s)$ if the platform were erect. However, because of a tilt $\phi(s)$ of the platform the acceleration sensed will appear as $sv(s) - g\phi(s)$, assuming that $\phi(s)$ is small enough to replace $\sin \phi(s)$ by $\phi(s)$. Since considerations of geometry reveal that

$$\psi(s) = \phi(s) + \frac{v(s)}{Rs}$$

and since torquing results in a precession of the platform expressed in terms of a time derivative of $\psi(s)$, we have (if damping is neglected)

$$K[sv(s) - g\phi(s)] = s\phi(s) + \frac{v(s)}{R}$$

$$\text{or} \quad \phi(s) = \frac{Ks - 1/R}{s + Kg} v(s) \qquad (8\text{-}13)$$

where K is an appropriately selected scale factor, appearing as the gain in the feedback instrumentation.

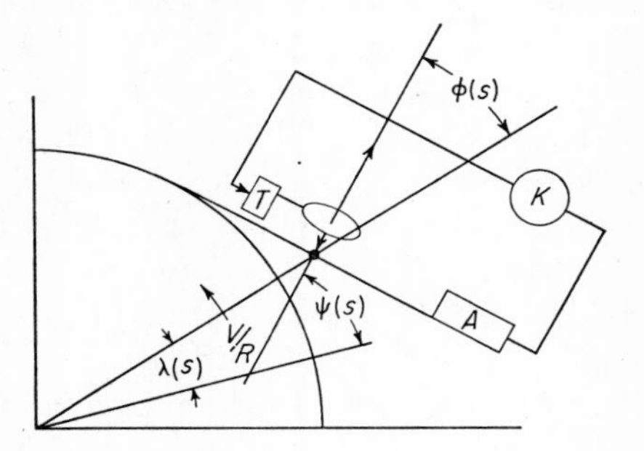

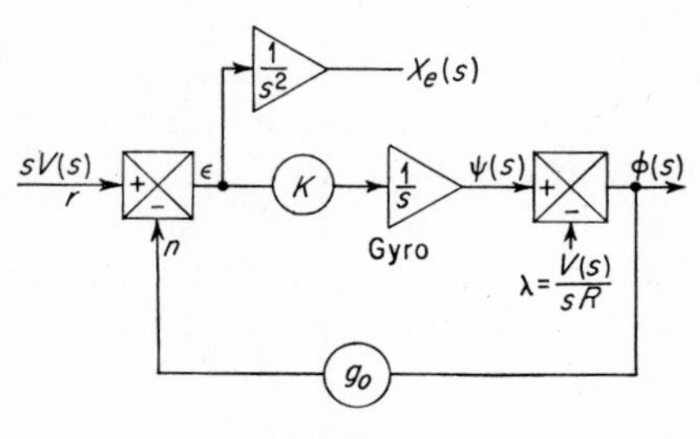

FIG. 8-4

This equation shows that in a steady-state condition [limit of $s\phi(s)$ for $s = 0$; $v(s) = v_0(s)$] a residual tilt of

$$\phi_0 = \frac{v_0}{KgR}$$

prevails, which is a characteristic property of the system described.

With this steady tilt taken into consideration, an acceleration bias error

$$g\phi_0 = -\frac{v_0}{KR}$$

is introduced into the computation loop, which results in an over-all absolute position error becoming of the order

$$\frac{v_0}{2KR}t^2$$

in addition to the transient errors which result from the actual solution of Eq. (8-13). Denoting by δx the position error caused by the platform tilt just mentioned, and remembering the Schuler frequency $\omega = (g/R)^{1/2}$, we have

$$\delta x = -\frac{g\phi(s)}{s^2} = \frac{g/R - Kgs}{Kg + s}\frac{v(s)}{s^2} = \frac{\omega^2 - Kgs}{Kg + s}\frac{v(s)}{s^2} \tag{8-14}$$

the solution of which provides the steady-state position error corresponding to a constant platform tilt plus an exponentially decaying relative position error of time constant $1/Kg$, as expected.

In summary, as shown in Fig. 8-4, the accelerometer sees a linear acceleration of the vehicle, combined with the gravity component, resulting from the tilt $\phi(s)$ of the platform as referred to the isogalic plane (input n). These inputs are amplified by K and used to torque the gyro; the latter acts as an integrator in space with respect to time. The gyro itself causes the platform to precess in space through the angle $\psi(s)$. At the same time, due to the progress of the vehicle over the surface of the earth, the local vertical changes with respect to the platform by an angle equal to the angular travel of the vehicle.

The tilt of the platform, then, is the difference between the travel over the surface of the earth and the angle made good by the gyro-controlled platform precession.

In this system, a first-order servo is used for tracking the local vertical. Common to all first-order systems, a *velocity lag error* will prevail, which results from tracking the vertical in the way mentioned. The accelerometers therefore continuously see a component of gravity, which creates an error in position increasing linearly with velocity and as the square of time.

This velocity lag error can be corrected by integrating the sensed acceleration, as shown in Fig. 8-5. The result of this operation is primarily the elimination of the tracking lag error in the steady-state vertical. However, a gain error may still remain, and the vertical might be disturbed when the system accelerates. As a result, an error might still exist in the computation of the distance traveled. Take again the apparent acceleration sensed, including the part of the gravity injected as a result of the platform tilt, and use the first integral of this signal to

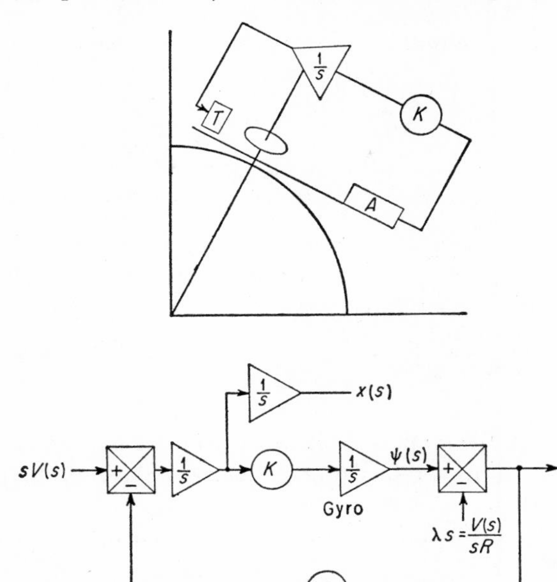

FIG. 8-5

make the platform precess. We have, in a way analogous to the derivation of (8-13),

$$\phi(s) = \frac{1/R - K}{s + Kg/s} v(s) \tag{8-15}$$

If the system accelerates when the gain is too high, i.e., $K > 1/R$, the platform turns faster than the local vertical and thus leads it. If the gain is too low, $K < 1/R$, and the platform turns slower than the local vertical and lags it temporarily. In each case errors in position and velocity are introduced (Fig. 8-6). There is a proper gain between these extremes, however, when a system acceleration introduces no transient error in the local vertical. This occurs when the loop gain is exactly $K = 1/R$, so that the sensed linear acceleration is converted directly into angular acceleration of precession, and there are no transient errors introduced in the vertical. Setting $K = 1/R$ is also the condition for Schuler tuning, for now the characteristic part of the vertical and position equation (8-15) becomes $s^2 + g/R$, offering the classical 84.4-

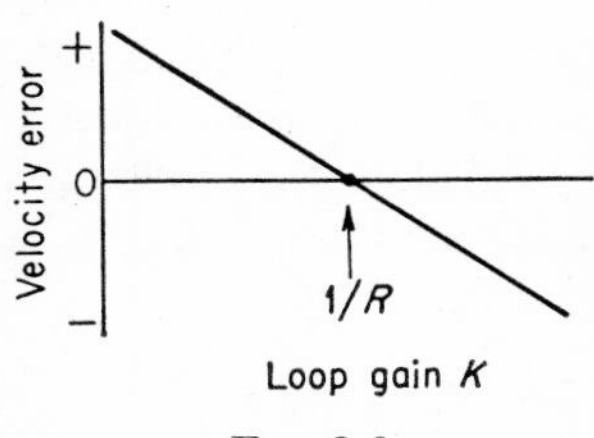

FIG. 8-6

min oscillation of Schuler systems. Let us also mention that, since the steady-state platform tilt error vanishes, the computed position error (in a steady state) increases as the first power of time, as against the second power encountered in the previous system.

The normal to the isogalic plane (the local vertical) turns in space at a rate v/R, i.e., earth's profile. Thus, if the output of the accelerometer used to compute position is integrated and divided by R, the rate v/R is generated (if $K = 1/R$). If this signal is used to torque a vertical gyro, the gyro is caused to precess at the same rate as the local vertical. Thus, the accelerometers slaved to this vertical gyro are maintained gravity-free. Errors which disturb this vertical alignment will tilt the accelerometers out of the isogravity plane, causing them to see the component of the constraining thrust which prevents the vehicle from falling with the gravity field. This thrust is the equivalent of an acceleration in the direction opposite to the tilt of the platform, so the gyro torquing signal returns the platform toward alignment with the isogravity plane. The two integrations in the loop, one in the gyro and the other in the external integrator, give the same oscillatory Schuler oscillation as experienced in the analytic system.

There are certain advantages that are claimed by the proponents of the semianalytic system:

1. The first advantage is that the gyros are maintained at a constant attitude with regard to the major applied thrust vector, so that the drift errors are essentially constant and might readily be predicted or biased out.

2. The second advantage lies in the direct generation of the vertical, which has many uses in navigation problems such as encountered in radar stabilization, instrument vertical reference, astrotracker reference, etc.

3. The system reputedly results in the simplest computer configuration, involving no complex computations for gravity.

4. The system can be built so that no initial scale error is inherent in its application.

The disadvantages of this system are mainly twofold:

1. It is limited in general by torquer linearity.

2. Polar navigation is a difficult problem because of the polar singularity.

8-6. The Geometric Inertial Navigator

The geometric system, like the semianalytic approach, overcomes the gravity problem by maintaining the sensitive axis of the accelerometers in an isogalic plane. However, the gyros, like those of the analytic system, serve as true space references—fixed in inertial space. Thus the gyro package serves as a rigid angular space reference in the same manner as the stars appear in a stellar navigator. The accelerometers are used to locate the local zenith or the local vertical in space. They have a Schuler loop, operating through *integrators which physically orient the accelerometers with respect to the space-fixed gyro base.* The navigation problems in this type of system are solved by the gimbals which interconnect the space-fixed gyro elements to the local vertical-seeking accelerometers (Fig. 8-7). For example, the gimbal freedom axis of this gyro

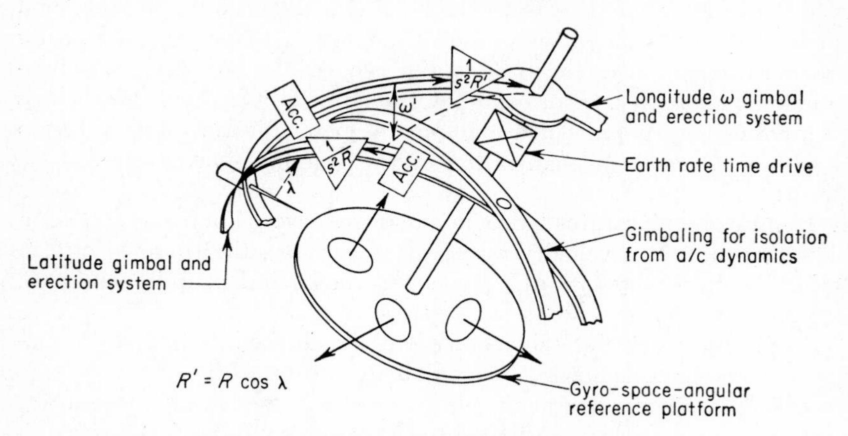

Fig. 8-7. Geometric inertial navigator.

package is specifically aligned with the polar axis of the earth. The drive orders for this axis are derived from the sum of a sidereal-time drive plus the local meridian Schuler erection loop. The bail connecting the most interior gimbal axis to the next gimbal axis mounts the meridian accelerometer. The next gimbal axis that lies in a plane parallel to the equatorial plane will be driven by a Schuler loop in vehicle latitude by an accelerometer mounted on the bail, which connects the inertial navigator to the isolation gimbals. The isolation gimbals free the inertial system from the disturbances in roll, pitch, and heading attitudes of the vehicle. This system is, in effect, a large gimbal computer which measures the angles between an angular coordinate reference fixed with respect to the earth and the local vertical determined by the accelerometers.

The advantages of the geometric system are as follows:

1. No computer external to the platform is required for navigation.

2. Gyros are not torqued, and hence no torquing error is introduced into the system.

3. The position computation is directly closed through the 84.4-min loop; hence, there is no drift due to integrators external to the erection loop.

8-7. The Coordinate Problem

In the semianalytic and geometric systems the coordinate reference used for navigation leads to difficult problems in readout instrumentation. The heart of the difficulty lies in the coordinate convergence at the poles, associated with the curvature of the surface of the earth. Both these systems maintain the accelerometers collinear to the earth's surface, so that the computation of the navigational parameters is performed in this curved two-dimensional space. Such spherical surfaces do not lend themselves easily to the use of a cartesian coordinate system, which either has a coordinate convergence problem or necessitates the use of a coordinate nonorthogonality. For example, the latitude-longitude coordinates have a convergence of the meridians in the polar region. This leads to two problems in the mechanization of the computation of the vehicle position:

1. Infinite angular rates arise in polar regions. For example, as a vehicle traveling at a velocity v passes by the pole, the traverse rate in longitude $\dot{L}$ is given by $\dot{L} = v/R \cos \lambda$. As the latitude λ approaches 90°, $\dot{L}$ becomes infinite.

2. A platform which is inertially stabilized (i.e., unslaved in azimuth) is unable to maintain a fixed relationship with the coordinate reference axis. For example, a platform which is moving around the pseudosphere of the earth, supposed to be stationary in inertial space at a fixed longitude rate $\dot{L}$ at a fixed latitude λ, will appear to turn with respect to the north coordinate at a rate of $\dot{L} \sin \lambda$ while it is actually being turned in space at the erection rate of $\dot{L} \cos \lambda$, as appears in Fig. 8-8.

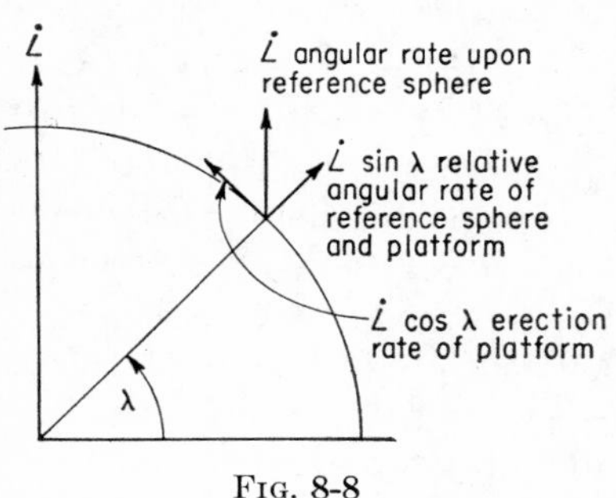

Fig. 8-8

Although there is no approach which leads to a completely general solution to the first of these problems, there are particular fixes which make this type of system suitable for most practical applications in a point-to-point navigation—for example, in a great-circle system, where the region of navigation is suitable for being instrumented in orthogonal coordinates.

The second problem mentioned can be solved by transforming the velocity data generated by the system into the earth's true coordinate system by passing them through a resolver which is turned at the relative angular rate of $\dot{L} \cos \lambda$. This can also be done by slaving the heading gyro north and compensating the accelerometer data for the separately computed Coriolis accelerations.

A secondary result of the heading slaving used by the system appears in the vertical that the inertial system tracks in its steady state. The system in which the heading gyro is unslaved will track a vertical known as the *Newtonian vertical.* The latter is defined as the direction in which a plumb bob would point if it were held stationary in inertial space while the location on the surface of the earth rotated underneath it. This may also be defined as the direction of the mass attraction component of the gravitational acceleration of the earth. However, the north slaved system, with accelerometers compensated for Coriolis effects, will track the plumb bob or geodetic vertical, which is the vertical that a plumb bob would indicate if it were fixed to the surface of the rotating earth and corrections were made for isostasy. Altogether, one would have a vector sum of mass attraction and earth's centrifugal force.

The analytic method, by using a cartesian coordinate system, appears to overcome both of these problems. However, it leads directly to another set of geometry problems associated with accuracies involved in accelerometers which must continuously sense the *full* gravity vector and compute a precise *gravitational* function for adequate compensation. Such a gravity function will, of course, depend upon the precision of navigation required.

8-8. Gyro Torquing versus Gyro Tumbling

Any system configuration has a material effect upon the performance of a gyro in that system. The relative merits of different systems have been inconclusively debated by proponents both of different gyro designs and of different system configurations. In general, it will probably be found that specific system requirements far outweigh these considerations. The argument revolves about whether it is better to tumble the gyro with respect to the gravity vector and suffer a variable drift uncertainty or to live with torquer uncertainties and maintain the gyros fixed with respect to gravity.

In the analytic and geometric systems the gyro remains fixed in space, so that the gravity vector apparently rotates with respect to the gyro as the system travels over the surface of the earth. The unbalance and anisoelastic torque inputs change as a function of travel. Proponents of this school of thought contend that these drifts can be precalibrated and balanced out by small countertorques supplied to the gyro as a function of its traverse along the predicted track. The other school of thought, supported by proponents of the semianalytic approach, maintains that better results might be obtained if the gyros were erected to the local vertical by closing the Schuler loop through torquing the gyro. This group feels that it is easier to design a high-precision torquer than to predict the drift coefficients of a gyro with sufficient accuracy to com-

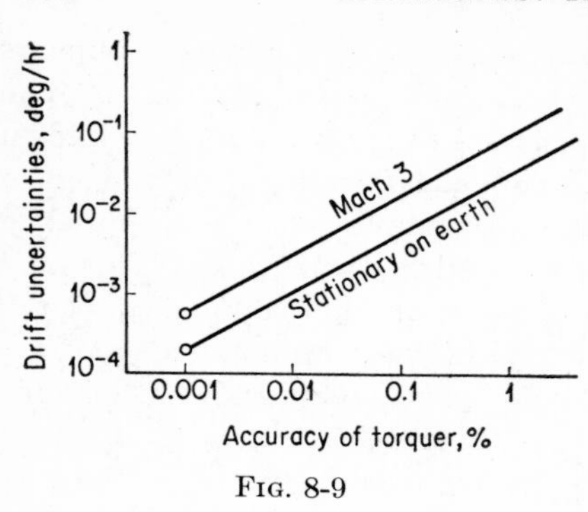

FIG. 8-9

pensate for such drift in a tumbling gravity field. Figure 8-9 shows the trade-off between torquer accuracy and tumbling drift uncertainty for a stationary system or a Mach 3 aircraft.

8-9. The Damping Problem

It is apparent from the previous discussion that the systems analyzed are subject to driving errors. These errors, which generally build up during a mission, originate partly as a result of component imperfections and partly because of the oscillatory nature of the Schuler loop combined with a possible nonlinearity and ensuing rectification of instantaneous conditions. Therefore, in order to build a precise extended-time navigator, some means must be found to damp out these oscillations.

Internal damping of the Schuler loop would be possible if a thorough knowledge of the vehicle's path were at hand. In general, this is not the case, and any damping must be referenced to some externally secured information. A number of these "references" might be considered, depending upon the nature and the mission of the vehicle. For example, Doppler radar, airspeed, water speed, or some form of ground-based aids might be used.

In general, the damping systems take the inertially measured velocity and position and compare them with those corresponding to an outside reference. The error signal thus generated is fed into a computer to derive signals which may provide second-, third-, or fourth-order damping terms in the characteristic equation of the loop to bring the amplitude of oscillations gradually to zero. The specific design of these schemes depends on the particular behavior and error characteristics of the system involved.

8-10. Error Evaluation of Inertial Navigators

The accuracy of inertial navigation lies primarily in the quality of the components used to instrument the system. This differs materially from radio systems where factors such as base line and signal-to-noise ratios play the principal role.

In this section the error equations will be developed for free-space and earth's surface inertial navigators. The fundamental difference between these two systems will become apparent by the particular influence exerted by component errors upon the two sets of error equations. These equations show, among other factors, how initial conditions, alignment, and component errors affect the performance of the system. A great deal of insight into the nature of inertial navigation on the earth's surface might be obtained from an understanding of the major differences which exist between the free-space navigation and navigation over the earth's surface. This is true with respect to both component and system errors, as they influence the performance in the two cases.

Error Analysis of Free-space Systems. Consider in free space three mutually perpendicular accelerometers which sense the acceleration and from this compute vehicle position (Fig. 8-10). These accelerometers are subject to bias errors, scale errors, and nonlinearities and may also exhibit a cross-axis sensitivity. As the first two of these errors dominate in general, they will be the only ones treated here.

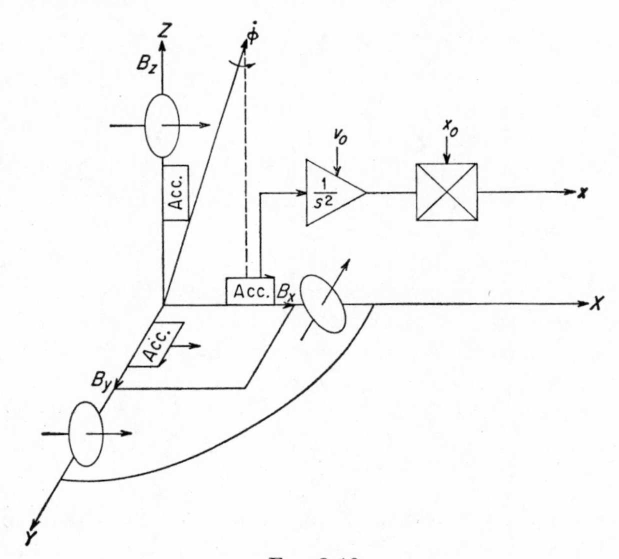

FIG. 8-10

The free-space system shown in Fig. 8-10 has three gyros for coordinate stabilization and three orthogonally mounted accelerometers to measure the acceleration of the platform in inertial space. Both accelerometers and gyros will give rise to errors in the computed position.

The errors within the accelerometer might be expressed by an equation such as the following:

$$\ddot{\epsilon} = A_I - A_T = (a_0 + a_1 A_T) + \text{neglected higher-order terms} \qquad (8\text{-}16)$$

where A_I = indicated acceleration
A_T = true geometric acceleration
a_0 = bias error
a_1 = scale error (dimensionless magnitude)

The higher-order terms arise from nonlinearities and cross-axis sensitivity.

If a position is computed from the accelerometer output, the errors which arise can be broken down into two types: (1) those originated during the acceleration and (2) those created during the unaccelerated motion resulting from velocity errors accumulated in the accelerated portion of the flight. The position error arising from the accelerometer becomes

$$\delta x = (a_0 + a_1 A_T)\left(\frac{T^2}{2} + T\tau\right) + a\frac{\tau^2}{2} \tag{8-17}$$

where T = duration of acceleration impulse
τ = duration of unpowered flight, which follows the period of acceleration impulse

All higher-order nonlinearities will have the same form as the scale error. The bias errors cause an error diverging at a rate proportional to the square of flight time, while scale errors diverge as the square of the duration of the powered flight. After the termination of the latter, however, they diverge linearly with the duration of unpowered flight and are proportional to the velocity error prevailing at the termination of the powered flight, i.e., $K_1 A_T T$.

The gyro does not contribute directly to an error in the output of the system; however, it causes errors by cross-coupling the data between the accelerometer outputs as a result of the drift in orientation in inertial space. As the accelerometers become misaligned with respect to the particular axis, the computer assumes they are aligned, and an acceleration error $\ddot{x}$ results, given approximately by the vector or cross product

$$\bar{\ddot{x}} = \bar{\phi} \times \bar{A}_T \tag{8-18}$$

where $\bar{\phi}$ represents the vector drift rate of the gyros, provided $|\phi|$ is small.

The position error resulting from the cross-coupled accelerometer readings is then given vectorially, in first approximation, by

$$\delta\bar{x} = (\bar{\phi} \times \bar{A}_T)\left(\frac{T^3}{6} + \frac{T^2}{2}\tau\right) \tag{8-19}$$

Thus, during the accelerated flight, an error is introduced as the third power of the time duration of the accelerated flight; but after the termination of the accelerated portion, it increases only linearly with time.

In practice, gyro drift errors are also dependent upon applied thrust, which greatly complicates the problem.

Error Evaluation of Terrestrial Inertial Guidance Systems. The manner in which component errors in the terrestrial case affect the system performance is completely different from that of those encountered in free space. There are two principal factors which create this difference of performance: (1) navigating in a central force field; (2) navigating essentially upon a curved surface of a gravitational equipotential.

Three methods have been described above for instrumenting an inertial navigator for terrestrial navigation. Although the three approaches appear quite different in configuration, in practice the only difference is in the coordinate system in which the problem is solved. For a perfect solution, they all should yield perfect and identical results, with the exception of areas of singularities encountered. With these considerations in mind, the treatment will be limited here to the semianalytic case. In practice, navigation on a great-circle path over a *nonrotating* spherical earth will be treated.

To make an error analysis a triaxial platform is considered (Fig. 8-11). The first axis, which will be referred to as the transport or traverse axis, is aligned with the axial rotation vector ψ_y, representing the progress of the platform along the great-circle path in terms of apparent angular rotation within the plane of travel. The second axis ψ_x will be the cross-track axis of the platform; the third axis ψ_z will be the heading axis of the platform. The primary reason that a triaxial analysis is necessary is the interchange of data between the heading and the cross-axis loops as the platform is transported over the track.

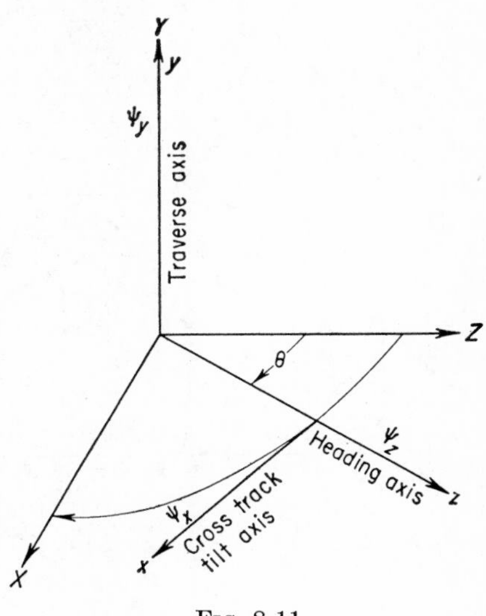

Fig. 8-11

The transport axis dynamics can be examined independently of the other two axes. The loop in Fig. 8-12 represents the erection and navigation loop for this axis.

The motion of the vehicle is the input to the loop. It enters as an input in two places: (1) directly as the acceleration seen by the accelerometer and (2) as the motion of the local vertical with respect to space as the platform is transported over the surface of the earth. It enters the loop as $v(s)/sR$. The accelerometer signal $sv(s)$ is integrated and then used to torque the gyro, which performs a space integration. If the output of the gyro is perfect, the platform should coincide with the local vertical. If not, the platform will have a tilt error $\phi_y(s)$. This will couple back into the accelerometer, since the latter also sees a component $g_x(s) = g_0\phi_y(s)$, as is shown in the feedback part of the loop. In addition to the erection function, a second output of the loop provides the present position, which is obtained by doubly integrating the output of the accelerometer, once within the loop and once external to it, as shown by the block diagram in Fig. 8-12.

There are a number of factors shown in this figure which may cause a deterioration of performance of the loop, specifically the following: Scaling error of accelerometer a_{1x} (dimensionless); bias error of accelerometer a_{0x}; initial velocity error v_{0x}; initial position error x_0; initial platform tilt error ϕ_{0y}; and gyro drift rate $\epsilon_y(t)$.

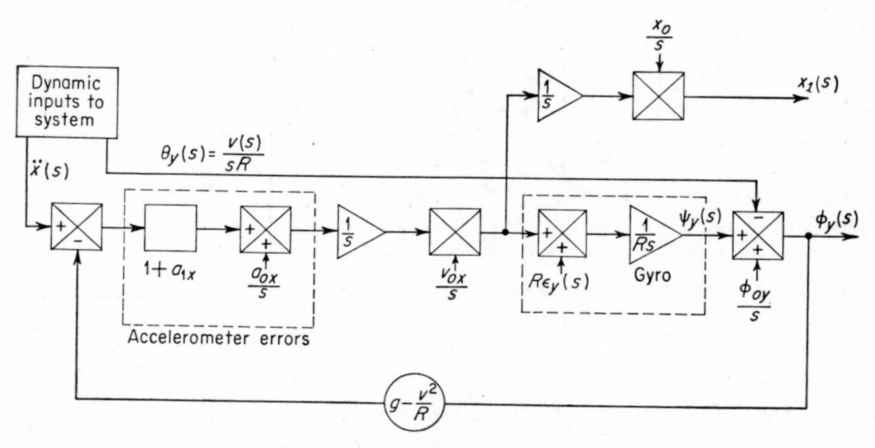

FIG. 8-12. Block diagram of track inertial navigator, showing dynamic inputs and computational function of loop.

The manner in which these factors contribute to the error in verticality and in computed position can be derived by a closed-loop servo input-output analysis. Table 8-1 shows the position errors that arise from erroneous inputs to the system as a result of either initial conditions or gyro drifts. In preparing this table, we assumed that $g \gg v^2/R$, $a_{1x} = k^2 - 1$, $\omega^2 = g/R$, and $\omega' = k\omega$.

In addition, if the scale of the accelerometer $k^2 \neq 1$, the traverse over the surface of the earth contributes to a position error, which can be determined by subtracting the true traverse θ from the outputs computed by the system. Thus

$$\delta[x(s)]_{\text{scale}} = \frac{(k^2/s)\ddot{x}(s)}{[1 + (k^2/s)(g/sR)]s} + \frac{(k^2g/s)[v_x(s)/sR]}{[1 + (k^2/s)(g/sR)]s} - x(s) \quad (8\text{-}20)$$

where the first term is the output resulting from the sensed acceleration, the second term is the output resulting from the change of the local vertical as the inertial system is moved over the surface of the earth, and the third is the actual traverse of the vehicle. Expressing all the inputs

TABLE 8-1

Source of input error	Input error	Loop gain	Loop gain	Schuler loop transfer function	External integration	Output position error
Initial position constant....	$\frac{x_0}{s}$	...	...	....	...	$\frac{x_0}{s}$
Initial velocity constant....	$\frac{v_{0x}}{s}$	1	$\frac{k^2g}{Rs^2}$	$\frac{s^2}{s^2 + \omega'^2}$	$\frac{1}{s}$	$\frac{v_{0x}}{s^2 + \omega'^2}$
Accelerometer bias.........	$\frac{a_{0x}}{s}$	$\frac{1}{s}$	$\frac{k^2g}{Rs}$	$\frac{s}{s^2 + \omega'^2}$	$\frac{1}{s}$	$\frac{a_{0x}}{s(s^2 + \omega'^2)}$
Gyro drift.................	$R\epsilon_y(s)$	$\frac{k^2g}{Rs^2}$	1	$\frac{\omega'^2}{s^2 + \omega'^2}$	$\frac{1}{s}$	$\frac{R\omega'^2\epsilon_y(s)}{s(s^2 + \omega'^2)}$
Initial vertical offset constant	$\frac{\phi_{0y}}{s}$	$\frac{k^2g}{s}$	$\frac{1}{Rs}$	$\frac{s\omega'^2}{s^2 + \omega'^2}$	$\frac{1}{s}$	$\frac{\phi_{0y}\omega'^2}{s(s^2 + \omega'^2)}$

in terms of $v_x(s)$, i.e., $\ddot{x} = sv_x(s)$ and $x(s) = v_x(s)/s$, Eq. (8-20) becomes

$$\delta[x(s)]_{\text{scale}} = \frac{sk^2v_x(s) + \omega'^2v_x(s)/s}{s^2 + \omega'^2} - \frac{v_x(s)}{s} \tag{8-21}$$

Substituting for k^2 the expression

$$k^2 = a_{1x} - 1 = \frac{a_{1x}sv_x(s)}{s^2 + \omega'^2}$$

in Eq. (8-21) one gets

$$\delta x(s) = \frac{x_0}{s} + \frac{v_{0x}}{s^2 + \omega'^2} + \frac{a_{0x}}{s(s^2 + \omega'^2)} - \frac{R\omega'^2\epsilon_y(s)}{s(s^2 + \omega'^2)} + \frac{\omega'^2\phi_{0y}}{s(s^2 + \omega'^2)} + \frac{a_{1x}sv_x(s)}{s^2 + \omega'^2} \tag{8-22}$$

This can be expressed easily in the time plane, if it is assumed that the gyro drift is a constant and the vehicle is traveling at constant velocity v_{1x} so that $\epsilon_y(s) = \epsilon_{1y}/s$ and $v_x(s) = v_{1x}/s$.

$$\delta x(t)_{\text{total}} = x_0 + \frac{v_{0x}}{\omega'}\sin\omega't + \frac{a_{0x}}{\omega'^2}(1 - \cos\omega't) - R\epsilon_{1y}\left(t - \frac{1}{\omega'}\sin\omega't\right) - R\phi_{0y}(1 - \cos\omega't) + \frac{a_{1x}}{\omega'}v_{1x}\sin\omega't \tag{8-23}$$

All the error and alignment inputs shown in Eq. (8-23), with the exception of the initial position, result in an 84.4-min oscillation, characteristic of Schuler-tuned systems. The initial position error does not show this oscillation because it is not enclosed within the loop, but it is the same as an arbitrary change in the reference-position coordinates, which obviously would not be detectable by the system.

The difference in the way the equivalent errors appear in free space and upon the great-circle course is of particular interest. A bias of the accelerometer a_{0x} (term 3), for example, results in a biased oscillatory error in great-circle navigation over the surface of the earth; however, er free space the error diverges as the square of time. The accelerometof linearity errors (term 6) result in a simple oscillation on the surface in the earth, while during the unaccelerated period in space a linear divergence with time is created. Gyro drift (term 4) gives an error equal to the accumulated drift angle of the gyro plus an oscillatory term and is not directly dependent upon the acceleration profile of the system.

In free space the picture is completely different. The only effect gyro drift has is that the accumulated drift results in misaligning the accelerometers, thus coupling these outputs erroneously into the computer. These variations in error dependence clearly demonstrate the difference in the nature of the two systems. Indeed, in free space the accelerometers are the prime sensing elements while the gyros are essentially a source of coordinate reference, whereas on the surface of the earth the gyros, coupled with the accelerometers, do the sensing. What is actually sensed in the latter case is the rate of precession of the gyro in inertial space as it follows the local vertical. The accelerometer and Schuler loop merely provide the instrumentation with which the vertical is tracked.

An even greater difference in the performance between free-space and terrestrial navigation is noted in the case where a constant acceleration is maintained throughout the flight. In terrestrial navigation only the nonlinearity terms alter its output in the system by changes from an oscillation to a biased oscillation. In free space the position error due to a linearity error in the accelerometer will increase as the square of time, while the contribution of the gyro drift, as combined with other disturbances, causes an error amplification as the cube of time.

Returning to the second output of the terrestrial navigator, the indicated local vertical has a particular interest from the point of view of its use in aided inertial systems. The error in this indicated local vertical can be derived in the same manner as the position error and is given by Eq. (8-24) in the Laplace transform or s plane.

$$\phi_y(s) = \frac{s\phi_{0y}}{s^2 + \omega'^2} + \frac{v_{0x}/R}{s^2 + \omega'^2} + \frac{s\epsilon_y(s)}{s^2 + \omega'^2} + \frac{a_{0x}/R}{s(s^2 + \omega'^2)} + \frac{sa_{1x}v_x(s)/R}{s^2 + \omega'^2} \qquad (8\text{-}24)$$

The corresponding error in the local vertical can be transformed into the time plane if it is assumed that gyro drift rate is equal to a constant, or $\epsilon_y(s) = \epsilon_{1y}/s$, and that the vehicle is traveling at a constant velocity $v_x(s) = v_{1x}/s$. Thus

$$\phi_y(t) = \phi_{0y} \cos \omega' t + \frac{v_{0x}}{R\omega'} \sin \omega' t + \frac{\epsilon_{1y}}{R\omega'} \sin \omega' t + \frac{a_{0x}}{R\omega'^2} (1 - \cos \omega' t) + \frac{a_{1x}v_x}{R\omega'} \sin \omega' t \quad (8\text{-}25)$$

The error in the determination of the local vertical in space by the platform fortunately has no divergent errors. Except for accelerometer bias errors, all the other error sources result in a simple oscillation about the local vertical. The accelerometer bias errors result in an average constant offset plus an oscillatory component. This is of great importance when space-reference aids such as astrotrackers are used, for then the system can determine the position of the vehicle within the small bounds set by oscillations of the vertical.

The errors in position computation that the system incurs in the crosstrack loop arise from two factors. The first is internal to the computation loop, comes from initial conditions and mechanization errors, and occurs in the track loop. The second, and a more subtle source of error input, is that stemming from the history of misalignment of the platform coordinates. To clarify this point let us look at the transfer of an initial heading error into a crosstrack displacement error as the vehicle travels over the surface of the earth. Assume initially that the system is on track; there is a heading error so that the x axis of the platform is not aligned with the direction that the vehicle is flying. Now the platform is turned by the x accelerometer, torquing the ψ_y' gyro about the ψ_y' axial direction vector. This ψ_y' vector is perpendicular to the x axis and the heading axis ψ_z' of the platform. If the vehicle travels 90° along its path, the platform is caused to turn 90° about the ψ_y' axis. This is the same as traveling south from the North Pole along two meridians. If at the North Pole there is a difference in path directions, at the equator the two paths are parallel but displaced one from the other. In this case the initial heading error of the platform ϕ_{0z} is transformed into a crosstrack displacement y.

Let us now develop these errors in analytic terms. The motions of the platform, i.e., gyro drift, gyro torquing, and precession, are known in the platform coordinate system. To be useful they must be described as motions of the platform in space. Therefore, a set of transformation equations will be developed which describe the motion of the platform in space. The space coordinates are defined by the local vertical which is referred to as the unit $\bar{k}$ direction vector; the tangent of the great circle on which the vehicle is traveling defines the unit vector in the $\bar{\imath}$ direction; and the perpendicular to these two vectors defines the $\bar{\jmath}$ direction unit vector (Fig. 8-13).

On the other hand, the platform has imbedded in itself its own coordinate system $\bar{\imath}'$, $\bar{\jmath}'$, and $\bar{k}'$, corresponding to the three perpendicular sensitive axes of the gyros mounted upon the platform. An angular misorientation of the platform $\bar{\imath}'$, $\bar{\jmath}'$, $\bar{k}'$ axes from the corresponding axes in space may be represented as ϕ_x, ϕ_y, and ϕ_z. Magnitude ϕ_y is the great-circle tilt of the platform with respect to the local vertical, which has

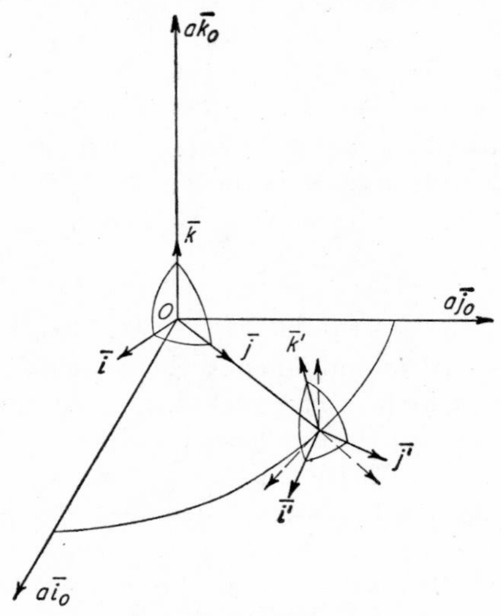

Fig. 8-13

already been examined. The other two error angles introduce cross-axis errors in the determination of position; since they are in error, they result directly (or indirectly) in the cross-axis accelerometer sensing a component of g. ϕ_x is introduced directly, as it is the cross-axis tilt, and ϕ_z indirectly, as it is the heading error which results in a cross-axis tilt as a function of vehicle traverse.

Now let us determine the equation of motion of the platform in terms of its deviations from ideal conditions. One can determine relatively simple error equations for the cross-axis inertial system. In terms of platform coordinates, the platform will be making good a turning rate $\omega_p(\bar{\imath}',\bar{\jmath}',\bar{k}')$, expressed by

$$\omega_p(\bar{\imath}',\bar{\jmath}',\bar{k}') = \bar{\imath}'\epsilon_x + \bar{\jmath}'(\epsilon_y + \dot{\theta} + \Delta\dot{\theta}) + \bar{k}'\epsilon_z \tag{8-26}$$

where $\dot{\theta} = v_x/R$ or platform traverse. The platform is torqued about the $\bar{\jmath}'$ axis to follow the motion of the local vertical. In addition to this desired torque, it is turned in space by gyro drifts ϵ_x, ϵ_y, and ϵ_z, respectively. On the other hand, the space turning rate of the platform can be expressed directly as turning rates in the local coordinate system $(\bar{\imath},\bar{\jmath},\bar{k})$ by the equation

$$\omega_p(\bar{\imath},\bar{\jmath},\bar{k}) = \bar{\imath}\phi_x + \bar{\jmath}\phi_y + \bar{k}\phi_z \tag{8-26a}$$

If the platform turning rate $\omega_p(\bar{\imath}',\bar{\jmath}',\bar{k}')$ [Eq. (8-26)] is transformed into great-circle local vertical coordinates in space $(\bar{\imath},\bar{\jmath},\bar{k})$ and equated to the space platform turning rate $\omega_p(\bar{\imath},\bar{\jmath},\bar{k})$, we get

$$\omega_p(\bar{\imath},\bar{\jmath},\bar{k}) = \begin{vmatrix} 1 & \phi_z & -\phi_y \\ -\phi_z & 1 & \phi_x \\ \phi_y & -\phi_x & 1 \end{vmatrix} \omega_p(\bar{\imath}',\bar{\jmath}',\bar{k}') \tag{8-27}$$

The three components of $\omega_p(\bar{\imath},\bar{\jmath},\bar{k})$ provide three equations describing the error expressions of the platform, viz.,

$$\begin{aligned} \dot{\phi}_x &= \epsilon_x + \phi_z(\epsilon_y + \dot{\theta} + \Delta\dot{\theta}) - \phi_y\epsilon_z \\ \dot{\phi}_y &= (\epsilon_y + \dot{\theta} + \Delta\dot{\theta}) + \phi_x\epsilon_z - \phi_z\epsilon_x \\ \dot{\phi}_z &= \epsilon_z + \phi_y\epsilon_x - \phi_x(\epsilon_y + \dot{\theta} + \Delta\dot{\theta}) \end{aligned} \tag{8-28}$$

These equations can be simplified by neglecting second-order terms which are small, i.e., the $\phi_y\epsilon_z$, $\phi_x\epsilon_z$, $\phi_z\epsilon_x$, $\phi_y\epsilon_x$, and $\Delta\dot{\theta}$ terms. Performing this simplification, we get

$$\begin{aligned} \dot{\phi}_x - \dot{\theta}\phi_z &= \epsilon_x \\ \dot{\phi}_y &= \dot{\theta} \\ \dot{\phi}_z + \dot{\theta}\phi_x &= \epsilon_z \end{aligned} \tag{8-29}$$

Transforming these equations into the s plane, assuming that $\dot{\theta} = v_{0x}/R$, we have

$$s\phi_x(s) - \phi_{0x} - \frac{v_{0x}}{R}\phi_z(s) = \epsilon_x(s)$$

$$s\phi_y(s) - \phi_{0y} = \frac{v_{0x}}{R}$$

$$s\phi_z(s) - \phi_{0z} + \frac{v_{0x}}{R}\phi_x(s) = \epsilon_z(s)$$

These equations can be easily solved for $\phi_x(s)$, $\phi_y(s)$, and $\phi_z(s)$. This operation yields explicitly

$$\phi_x(s) = \frac{s\phi_{0x}}{s^2 + (v_{0x}/R)^2} + \frac{(v_{0x}/R)\phi_{0z}}{s^2 + (v_{0x}/R)^2} + \frac{s\epsilon_x(s)}{s^2 + (v_{0x}/R)^2} + \frac{(v_{0x}/R)\epsilon_z(s)}{s^2 + (v_{0x}/R)^2} \tag{8-30}$$

$$\phi_z(s) = \frac{s\phi_{0z}}{s^2 + (v_{0x}/R)^2} - \frac{(v_{0x}/R)\phi_{0x}}{s^2 + (v_{0x}/R)^2} + \frac{s\epsilon_z(s)}{s^2 + (v_{0x}/R)^2} - \frac{(v_{0x}/R)\epsilon_x(s)}{s^2 + (v_{0x}/R)^2} \tag{8-31}$$

These equations can be transformed back again into the time domain to describe the platform motion explicitly as a function of time. If it is assumed, for the sake of simplicity, that $\epsilon_x(s) = \epsilon_{0x}/s$ and $\epsilon_z = \epsilon_{0z}/s$, we get

$$\phi_x(t) = \phi_{0x} \cos \frac{v_{0x}}{R} t + \phi_{0z} \sin \frac{v_{0x}}{R} t + \frac{R}{v_{0x}} \epsilon_{0x} \sin \frac{v_{0x}}{R} t + \frac{R}{v_{0x}} \epsilon_{0z} \left(1 - \cos \frac{v_{0x}}{R} t\right) \tag{8-32}$$

and

$$\phi_z(t) = \phi_{0z} \cos \frac{v_{0x}}{R} t - \phi_{0x} \sin \frac{v_{0x}}{R} t - \frac{R}{v_{0x}} \epsilon_{0x} \left(1 - \cos \frac{v_{0x}}{R} t\right) + \frac{R}{v_{0x}} \epsilon_{0z} \sin \frac{v_{0x}}{R} t \tag{8-33}$$

The crosstrack tilt of the platform ϕ_x may now be used to derive the crosstrack error in measurement of position. This can be done in the

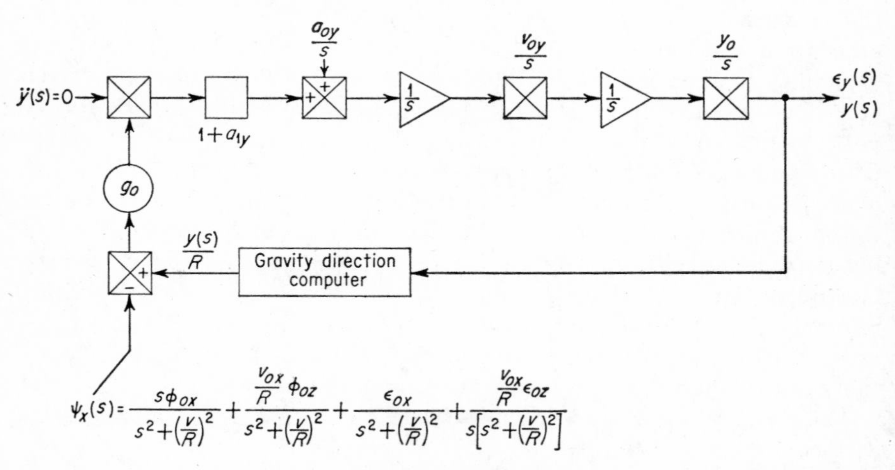

FIG. 8-14. Block diagram of crosstrack inertial navigator, showing both dynamic inputs and computational function of the system.

same manner as the path errors were determined. Figure 8-14 shows a block diagram of the system, incorporating both the dynamic inputs resulting from the motion of the platform and the error introduced within the computing loop itself.

The crosstrack loop which has been studied in this case is an analytic system; however, similar examination of a semianalytic system in this loop will yield essentially the same results. Applying a Laplace transform analysis to the loop shown in Fig. 8-14, the following expression for the error in position computation is derived:

$$\delta y(s) = \frac{a_{0y}}{s(s^2 + \omega'^2)} + \frac{v_{0y}}{s^2 + \omega'^2} + \frac{sy_0}{s^2 + \omega'^2} + \frac{sR\omega'^2\phi_{0x}}{(s^2 + \omega'^2)[s^2 + (v_{0x}/R)^2]} + \frac{\omega'^2 v_{0x}\phi_{0z}}{s(s^2 + \omega'^2)[s^2 + (v_{0x}/R)^2]} \tag{8-34}$$

Assuming that this can be transformed into the time plane and remembering that $v_{0x}/R \ll \omega'$, we get

$$\delta y(t) = y_0 \cos \omega' t + \frac{v_{0y}}{\omega'} \sin \omega' t + \frac{a_{0y}}{\omega'^2} (1 - \cos \omega' t) + R\phi_{0x} \left(\cos \frac{v_{0x}}{R} t - \cos \omega' t \right) + R\phi_{0z} \sin \frac{v_{0x}}{R} t + \frac{R^2}{v_{0x}} \epsilon_{0x} \sin \frac{v_{0x}}{R} t - \frac{R^2}{v_{0x}} \epsilon_{0z} \left(1 - \cos \frac{v_{0x}}{R} t \right) \tag{8-35}$$

Several interesting facts about inertial systems become apparent from the crosstrack error question. First, the errors in inertial navigators arise from the limited quality of components and from our imperfect capability to align the system initially. Second, different from the track equations, gyro drift does not cause a continuously diverging error in position but an oscillatory error, which is dependent upon the Schuler period and a second period (v_{0x}/R) arising from the travel of the vehicle over the surface of the earth. This phenomenon leads to the reason for the convergence of gyrocompass systems and their capability of establishing north reference and latitude data—a capability which also exists in inertial systems if they are appropriately damped to the earth coordinate reference system by some position or velocity reference, such as Doppler radar. However, the computation loop is not closed in a meridian position, and this must be supplied from an external source.

The convergence of error brought about by the curvature of the earth's surface obviously has no counterpart in free space.

Although the treatment of errors was made for a particular formulation of an inertial navigator, essentially similar results might be demonstrated for all three of the principal types of inertial navigation systems—analytic, geometric, and semianalytic.

PROBLEMS

8-1. What is the period of an inertial navigator flying about Mars at a radius of 9.2×10^3 km at low velocities?

8-2. Suppose that an inertial navigator is used for navigation over the surface of a planet where the total mass is three times that of the earth and the radius is 40 per cent less. What would be the ratio of the amplitude of these errors to those experienced on the earth if the system components had the following characteristics:

$$\epsilon_x = \epsilon_y = 0.01°/\text{hr} \times g$$
$$\epsilon_z = 0.03°/\text{hr} \times g$$
$$a_{0x} = a_{0y} = 10^{-3}\ \text{ft/sec}^2$$
$$v_x = v_{0x} = 880\ \text{ft/sec}$$

8-3. Derive the error equations in the time plane for an inertial navigator which is

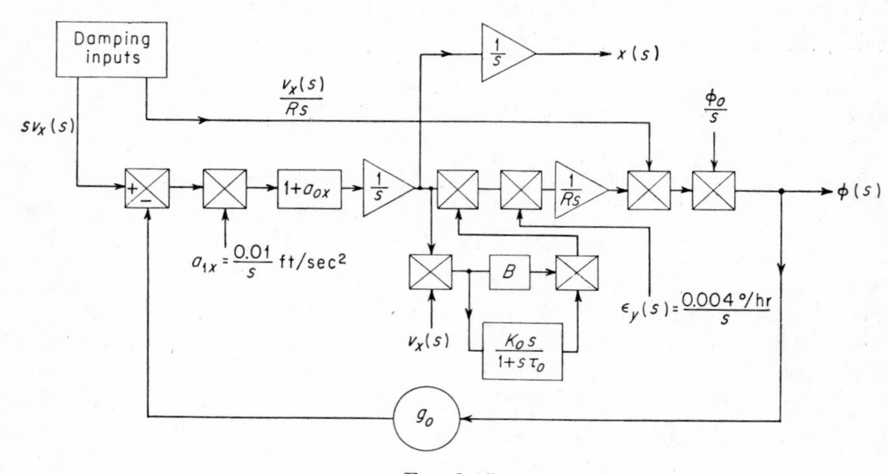

Fig. 8-15

damped to a velocity reference v_{Rx} as shown in Fig. 8-15. Take the particular case of

$$v_{Rx} = \frac{v_{0x}}{s+b} + \frac{0.1\ \text{ft/sec}}{s} + \frac{0.002\ \text{ft/sec}^2}{s^2+l^2}$$

where $b = 0.037/\text{min}$
$l = 0.1/\text{min}$

BIBLIOGRAPHY

1. Schuler, Max: Die Storüng von Pendul- und Kreiselapparaten durch die Beschleunigung des Fahrzeuges, *Physik. Z.*, vol. 24, p. 344, 1923.
2. Wrigley, W.: Schuler Tuning Characteristics in Navigational Instruments, *J. Inst. Navigation*, vol. 3, December, 1950.
3. Sommer, A. V.: Missile Guidance. . . . Why So Little Progress, *Aviation Age*, vol. 22, August, 1954.
4. Statsinger, J.: Absolute Guidance for Airborne Vehicles, *Aviation Age*, vol. 22, September, 1954.
5. Bishop, R. L.: Inertial System Components Are Here, *Aviation Age*, vol. 22, October, 1954.
6. Klass, P. J.: Inertial Navigation: Out of the Laboratory into Missile Systems, *Aviation Week*, vol. 64, Jan. 2, 1956.
7. Slater, J. M.: Choice of Coordinate Systems in Inertial Navigation, *J. Inst. Navigation*, vol. 9, June, 1956.

8. Draper, C. S., W. Wrigley, and L. R. Grohe: The Floating Integrating Gyro and Its Application to Geometrical Stabilization Problems on Moving Bases, Institute of the Aeronautical Sciences, S.M.F. Fund Paper FF-13, 1955.

9. Wrigley, W., R. B. Woodbury, and J. Hovorka: Inertial Guidance, Institute of the Aeronautical Sciences, S.M.F. Fund Paper FF-16, 1957.

10. Duncan, D. B., and J. M. Slater: Inertial Navigation, *Aeronaut. Eng. Rev.*, vol. 15, no. 1, p. 50, January, 1956.

11. Mundo, C. J.: Aided Inertial Systems, *Arma Engineering*, vol. 2, no. 2, November, 1958.

12. Duncan, D. B.: Analysis of an Inertial Guidance System, *J. Am. Rocket Soc.*, vol. 28, no. 2, pp. 111–116, February, 1958.

13. Mundo, C. J.: Three Approaches to the Design of Inertial Systems, *Aviation Age*, November, 1959.

14. J. Hovorka et al.: Recent Advances in Inertial Guidance, *J. Am. Rocket Soc.*, vol. 29, no. 12, December, 1959.

15. Ishlinsky, A. Y.: Equations of Problems Concerning the Determination of Moving Object Position by Means of Gyros and Accelerometers, *Prikladnaya Matematika i Mekhanica*, vol. 21, pp. 725–739, 1956.

16. Bodnev, Z. A., Z. P. Seleznev, and V. E. Ovcharov: Contribution to the Theory of Inertial Damped Systems with Arbitrary Period, Invariant with Respect to the Maneuvering of Object, *Ozvestia Akad. Nauk S.S.S.R.*, no. 3, pp. 11–18, 1959.

17. McClure, C. L.: "Theory of Inertial Guidance," Prentice-Hall, Inc., Englewood Cliffs, N.J., 1960.

CHAPTER 9

FUNDAMENTALS OF GYRO DESIGN

By Marvin Taylor

Nomenclature

ω_s = rotor spin speed, radians/sec
α = volumetric coefficient of thermal expansion of the gimbal structure, $cm^3/(cm^3)(°C)$
ρ = mass density of suspension fluid at neutral buoyant temperature, g/cm^3
β = volumetric coefficient of thermal expansion of fluid, $cm^3/(cm^3)(°C)$
Θ_{0A} = output axis response, radians
Θ = drift angle, radians
$\dot{\Theta}$ = drift rate, radians/sec
δ = mass density of balance weight, g/cm^3
Ω = thermal coefficient of expansion of rim material, cm/(cm)(°C)
Ω' = thermal coefficient of all remaining rotor and gimbal parts, cm/(cm)(°C)
ϵ = distance shifted by gimbal element, cm

9-1. Introduction

In previous chapters fundamental physical concepts were presented, and from these, theoretical relations were developed to describe gyroscopic phenomena. The practical application of these concepts in a compass, vertical reference, or stabilized platform requires a "gyro component" integrated into an instrument structure containing servos, optics, and moving gimbals. The design discussions in this chapter will be limited to the gyro component only.

In the course of its application into many different kinds of equipment, the gyro component has taken a very wide variety of forms. Complete coverage of all types and their associated design details is beyond the scope of this chapter. Furthermore, the multitude of considerations and compromises that govern the design of a gyro component make it impractical to attempt to classify design concepts to the extent that a "handbook" approach is utilized to find the right combination for a particular application. This chapter will, therefore, cover fundamental relations between gyro performance characteristics and their design influence factors. It is felt that this approach will most efficiently equip the gyro designer with the necessary tools for determining optimum design for a given application.

Accuracy requirements are significant factors governing gyro design. In the interest of rigor and utility the material presented will be directed for the most part toward gyros of high precision. Those of lower-performance levels permit compromises which can be best exploited by a designer armed strongly with knowledge of both gyro fundamentals (as they apply in units of ultimate capability) and their specific applications.

The major design problems are concerned with the elimination of spurious torques acting on the gyro rotor. In recognition of this paramount fact the introduction of design features will be developed within the framework of these torques or error-producing effects. Further detailed discussion of design considerations will be presented in Chaps. 10 and 11.

9-2. Major Gyroscopic Elements

At first glance, a gyro might appear to be a deceptively simple device—a spinning wheel freely suspended. Our design problems are created by

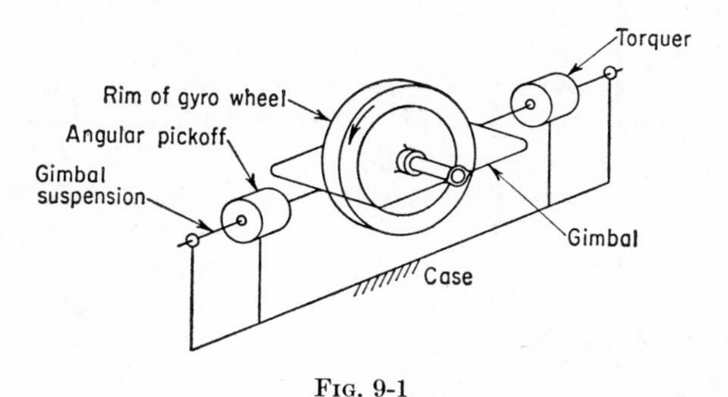

FIG. 9-1

the demand for certain control and information functions coupled with a high degree of performance, all within a unit of smallest possible size.

For the sake of the discussion which is to follow, the gyro component can be divided into six major elements, as shown schematically in Fig. 9-1.

Rim. The primary element is the rotating mass defining the angular-momentum vector. The rotating parts consist of the rim, web, bearings, shaft, and rotor portion of the motor. However, the rim normally supplies the predominant portion of the angular momentum. Some designs contain two wheels mounted at the ends of a rotating shaft, and in this case the sum of the angular momenta of both wheels is utilized by the gyro.

Gimbal. The gimbal within the gyro is the structure which carries the rotating mass. In addition to this main function, it normally provides the following:

1. Motor or other means for driving the rotating parts.
2. Spin bearings.
3. Inner terminus of an over-all gimbal suspension system.
4. Portions of information-sensing and control transducer devices.
5. Structure for maintaining a fixed spatial relation between the rim(s) and the information-sensing and control systems. It is important to recognize that this structural linkage contains the web of the wheel, spin bearings, and shaft in addition to the gimbal structure.

Gimbal Suspension. The gimbal suspension is the low-friction mechanism by which the gimbal is carried within its supporting case. The level of gyro performance obtained from a given unit depends to a large measure on the degree to which suspension torques can be eliminated. This area of gyro construction more than any other has in recent years commanded the most ingenious efforts of gyro designers. A variety of techniques have been devised for units of different levels of performance and application.

To achieve maximum performance levels many suspension systems have been designed in which the mechanism for supporting the gimbal has been separated from that for centering the latter within its supporting case. A prime example is floating the gimbal in neutral buoyancy for support and utilizing tensioned wires or jeweled pivots for centering. These principles have been applied to both single- and two-degree-of-freedom units.

A major consideration in the design of a gimbal suspension system is the requirement that electric power leads be provided for energizing the spin motor and the information-sensing and control transducers.

Supporting Case. The supporting case is the outer enclosure of the gyro component. Its fundamental requirements are as follows:

1. To provide the outer terminus of the gimbal suspension system
2. To carry the information-sensing and control transducer parts acting with corresponding parts on the gimbal
3. To provide a mounting arrangement for the gyro
4. To provide structural rigidity between items 1 and 2

It must also provide for temperature control (heaters, sensors) and hermetic closure for fluid suspensions.

Angular Pickoff. Information sensing is provided by transducers which detect relative angular displacements between the gyro gimbal and the supporting case. Normally, for each degree of freedom there are two sets of pickoff elements in the system, one on the gimbal and the other corresponding part on the supporting case.

Torquer. For control purposes most applications require that a torquing system be provided. This enables compensation for certain types of errors, the use of a single-degree-of-freedom gyro as a rate-sensing device, and primarily the capacity for precessing the gyro at desired rates in inertial space.

In most gyros this function is supplied by an electric transducer having elements on the gimbal and supporting case. In addition elastic and viscous restraints might be utilized to perform a control torquing function.

9-3. Construction Features

An example of contemporary construction of a single-degree-of-freedom rate gyro is shown in Fig. 9-2. A hysteresis synchronous motor

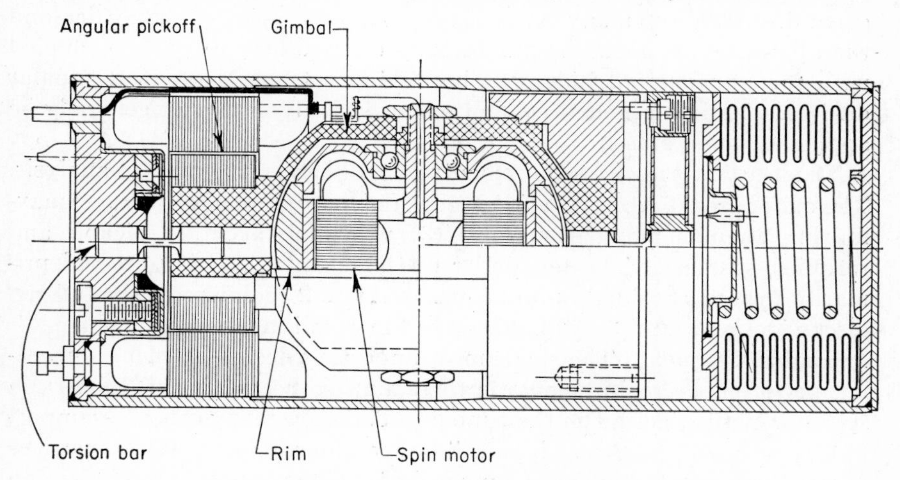

FIG. 9-2. (*Courtesy of U.S. Time Corporation.*)

and outer-race rotation are utilized to drive the rotor at 24,000 rpm within a hermetically sealed gimbal. Silicone fluid is used to provide damping and to assist in supporting the weight of the gimbal. Damping control at different temperatures is obtained by using a cylindrical nylon section joined to the gimbal. Expansion of this cylinder reduces the fluid gap, thus compensating for a diminishing fluid viscosity resulting from an increase in ambient temperature, and vice versa.

A set of torsion bars centers the gimbal and provides an elastic restraint, while a rotary differential transformer is utilized as a pickoff.

9-4. Design Goals

The art of gyro design has taxed the ingenuity of many skilled scientists and engineers. A multitude of considerations with complex interrelations demands both a complete understanding of the dynamic principles involved and a refined sense of compromise.

Requirements. The designs of all precision devices have certain common requirements:

1. Performance—meeting specifications covering function, accuracy, and environmental conditions
2. Producibility—capable of being produced within certain cost and time limitations
3. Reliability—ability to maintain operational capability within performance specifications after exposure to various conditions of handling, test, service use, and storage

The principles governing design for producibility and reliability are, in general, common to many types of precision instruments. They demand the application of rather standard rules of good design practice coupled with some specialized judgment born of direct experience with similar devices. Rigid mathematical and scientific analyses cannot generally be applied in these areas.

To meet performance requirements gyro design is amenable to analysis. The major areas of consideration are (1) reducing gimbal torques, (2) maximizing angular momentum, and (3) providing accurate pickoff and torquing systems. The remainder of this chapter will be directed primarily toward consideration of item 1. Item 2 requires relatively brief discussion, and item 3 will be discussed in detail in Chap. 11.

Gimbal Torques. The single most important design problem in meeting performance requirements is to minimize the magnitude of certain spurious torques acting on the gimbal. There are many other less important functional problems which will be mentioned below. However, the overriding consideration with a myriad of complex inputs is the reduction and elimination of these torques acting on the gimbal.

There are two classes of gimbal torques: (1) systematic and (2) random. Such classification of an error-producing effect can generally be applied to most measuring or sensing devices. A meter, for example, is periodically calibrated; i.e., its error is measured and a correction curve established. This measured error is a systematic one. If the systematic error never changes, the meter, together with the correction curve, represents a perfect measuring device. Any changes in meter characteristics during the period between calibration measurements introduce random errors which actually establish the useful accuracy level of the device.

A systematic torque can be defined as a torque which can be measured and whose characteristics can be correlated with some parameter. It is theoretically possible to compensate either directly or indirectly for the errors produced by systematic torques. This compensation is often based on a predicted knowledge of operating conditions, such as acceleration, temperature, or vibration. Random or unpredicted variations in these conditions will introduce uncompensated errors which must be charged to the gyro. It is therefore best practice to minimize systematic torques, thus in turn minimizing the degree of compensation required and reducing performance sensitivity to operating variables.

The difference between the total systematic torque predicted for a given situation and the total gimbal torque measured is composed of random torques, which can be considered as spurious changes in the systematic torques, plus other unpredictable inputs. The magnitudes of the random torques establish the level of uncertainty in gyro performance. Their reduction and elimination are a major target of the gyro designer.

For the purpose of discussion, these two classes of torques can be further categorized as follows:

A. Systematic torques
  1. Nonacceleration-sensitive
     a. Elastic
     b. Viscous coupling
     c. Magnetic
     d. Torque due to nonorthogonality of suspension axes
  2. Acceleration-sensitive
     a. Unbalance
     b. Compliance
     c. Temperature error
     d. Fluid torques

B. Random torques
  1. Friction
  2. Balance instability of gimbal assembly
  3. Hysteresis or instability in elastic coupling
  4. Suspension fluid

The design process by which all of these torques are reduced is an art demanding the application of accumulated experience, observation, ingenuity, judgment, and intuition.

Angular Momentum. There are two basic ways in which we can minimize gyro precession. One way is to reduce gimbal torques, as mentioned above, and the other is to increase the angular momentum of the gyro. Gyro drift rate is defined by

$$\text{Drift rate} = \frac{\text{gimbal torque}}{\text{angular momentum}} \tag{9-1}$$

Hence, we see that maximization of angular momentum is equally as effective in this equation as reduction of gimbal torques in reducing gyro drift. The angular momentum of the rotor is given by

$$H = \omega_s M k^2 \tag{9-2}$$

where H = angular momentum, g-cm²/sec
ω_s = rotor spin speed, radians/sec
M = mass of rotor, g
k = radius of gyration of rotor, cm

The maximum angular momentum that can be obtained for given design must be compromised with a number of physical and functional limitations. This can best be understood by examining the factors involved in maximizing each of the parameters in Eq. (9-2).

Rotor Spin Speed ω_s. Increasing rotor spin speed is one method of increasing angular momentum. However, as spin speed is increased, the power required to overcome windage and bearing friction rises sharply. A larger motor is necessary, and increased heating effects are produced. In addition, spin-bearing life is sharply reduced at higher operating speeds.

Rotor Mass M. Rotor mass can be increased by using a rim of larger volume or by using materials of higher density. In either case larger spin bearings with higher preloads may be required to support the rotor. This results in increased bearing friction torque, leading to demands for a larger motor with increased power and heating. The total weight of the gimbal rises together with increased (potential) gimbal torques, which may seriously reduce the effectiveness of the higher angular momentum.

In gyros utilizing fluid suspension (Sec. 9-5) a fixed *total* gimbal assembly weight must be obtained for neutral buoyancy. The designer must strive to have all nonrotating gimbal parts as light as possible in order to leave maximum remaining weight for incorporation into the rotor with a view to increasing the angular momentum.

Radius of Gyration k. Increases in the diameter of the rotor are limited by the over-all physical dimensions specified for the gyro. Within this package the largest possible rotor should be used. Also, if a given weight is permitted for the rotor, it should be distributed so that a minimum is spent in the web and hub regions and a maximum is left for the region of most effectivity at the rim. However, sufficient material must be used in the web to ensure adequate stiffness in supporting the rim.

Pickoff. The pickoff device should provide usable, accurate information describing the relative angular position between the gimbal and the supporting case without introducing spurious torques. Furthermore, the gimbal structural rigidity should be sufficient to prevent any angular motion between the spin axis and the pickoff element on the gimbal.

Torquer. The torquer should provide the capability for exerting torques of the exact magnitude and direction required for any compensation or control purpose. Its operation should not in any way affect the pickoff system.

9-5. Fluid Suspension

Before continuing with a more detailed discussion of torque characteristics and the attainment of gyro design goals, the concept of fluid suspension will be introduced.

The majority of contemporary precision gyros utilize the buoyant force of displaced fluid to assist in supporting the gyro gimbal. This has been done both to reduce loading on the suspension bearing or elastic centering means and to provide viscous coupling characteristics as required for either damping or integration, as shown in Chap. 4.

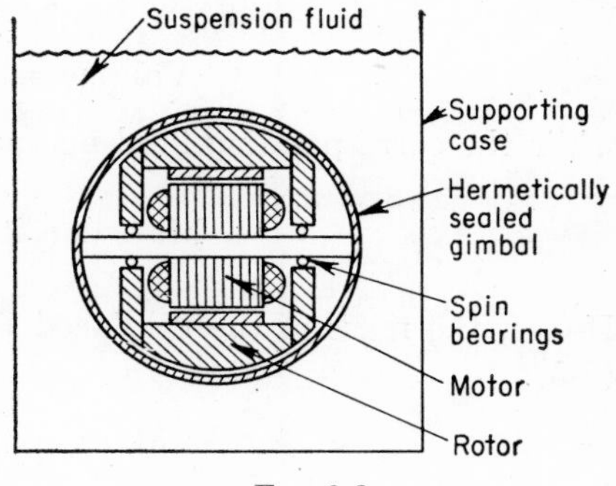

FIG. 9-3

Consider the gyro shown within a hermetically sealed gimbal container in Fig. 9-3. The gyro rotor is supported by spin bearings and driven by an electric motor within the gimbal. In this idealized picture, no power leads are shown for conducting motor power into the gimbal. If the gimbal assembly were neutrally buoyant, i.e., equal in weight to the displaced fluid, there would be no tendency on the part of the gimbal to translate with respect to the sides of the fluid-containing supporting case under the influence of gravity or imparted accelerations.

Centering Force. In actual practice, perfect neutral buoyancy is virtually impossible to achieve because of the temperature sensitivity of both the fluid density and the volume displaced. As a result, the gimbal will tend to translate through the suspension fluid under the influence of gravity or accelerations. The centering force required to keep the gimbal from translating under these conditions can be readily calculated. Let

V = volume of gimbal at neutrally buoyant temperature, cm^3

α = volumetric coefficient of thermal expansion of gimbal structure, $cm^3/(cm^3)(°C)$

ρ = mass density of suspension fluid at neutral buoyant temperature, g/cm^3
β = volumetric coefficient of thermal expansion of fluid, $cm^3/(cm^3)(°C)$
Δt = temperature error off neutral buoyancy, °C
F = centering force required to offset lack of neutral buoyancy, dynes
M = mass of gimbal, g
a = acceleration of supporting case, cm/sec^2

At neutral buoyancy, the mass of the gimbal is exactly equal to the mass of the displaced fluid.

$$M = V\rho \tag{9-3}$$

At any temperature other than that for neutral buoyancy, the gimbal volume or displaced fluid volume will be

$$\text{Volume} = V(1 + \alpha\,\Delta t) \tag{9-4}$$

while the corresponding fluid mass density becomes

$$\text{Mass density} = \frac{\rho}{1 + \beta\,\Delta t} \tag{9-5}$$

Hence, the mass of the displaced fluid will be the product of (9-4) and (9-5).

$$\text{Mass} = V\rho\,\frac{1 + \alpha\,\Delta t}{1 + \beta\,\Delta t} \tag{9-6}$$

However, the mass of the gimbal has not changed from the value shown in (9-3), leaving as the net force due to lack of neutral buoyancy the difference between (9-3) and (9-6) multiplied by the acceleration a, i.e.,

$$F = V\rho a\left(1 - \frac{1 + \alpha\,\Delta t}{1 + \beta\,\Delta t}\right)$$

or, after elimination of second-order terms and substituting $M = \rho V$,

$$F = Ma(\beta - \alpha)\,\Delta t \qquad \text{approx} \tag{9-7}$$

To examine the magnitude of this centering force, let us use some representative values of Δt, β, and α.

$$\Delta t = 0.5°\text{C}$$
$$\beta = 800 \times 10^{-6}/°\text{C}$$
$$\alpha = 72 \times 10^{-6}/°\text{C}$$

Therefore,

$$\Delta t\,(\beta - \alpha) = 0.5(800 - 72)10^{-6} = \frac{1}{2{,}750}$$

This means that if bearings, pivots, or elastic devices are used to center the gimbal within its supporting case, the maximum load on the centering means will be 1/2,750 of the value it would have been had there been no fluid present. This virtual elimination of load permits the use of extremely fine centering devices with commensurate reduction in angular coupling between the gimbal and the supporting case.

It should be clear for any analyses that follow that the total supporting force on the gimbal is always the resultant of the buoyant force and the centering force.

Single-degree-of-freedom Gyros. In single-degree-of-freedom floated gyros the floatation fluid may, in addition to supporting the gimbal, play an important role as a damping medium (see Chap. 4). Also the fluid coupling about both the input and the output axes can act to protect the pivots from excessive loading during the operation of the gyro. This situation is not related to the previous discussion of buoyant forces and their support of gimbal weight but to gyroscopic torques and viscous coupling.

Output Axis Damping. The fundamental performance of a single-degree-of-freedom gyro requires an output axis response Θ_{OA} to an input axis displacement. Neglecting inertia terms, we can write an expression for the resulting input axis torque T_{IA} on the gimbal: $T_{IA} = H\dot{\Theta}_{OA}$. Fluid damping due to the viscosity of the suspension fluid and the small gap between gimbal and supporting case sharply reduces $\dot{\Theta}_{OA}$ and hence the input axis torque T_{IA}.

Input Axis Coupling. The reduced input axis torque T_{IA}, described above, must be exerted on the gimbal. If no fluid were present, the pivot loads required to exert this torque might be excessive for precision applications. Fortunately, the viscous characteristics of the suspension fluid can be exploited to protect the pivots. Figure 9-4 shows a typical cylindrical gimbal used in single-degree-of-freedom gyros. If the supporting case suddenly starts to rotate in a clockwise direction, as shown, the small gap between the gimbal and the case will start to close at b and c and open at a and d. There are small clearances between the gimbal pivot and the jewel bearing in the case, so that minute relative angular motions between the gimbal and the case can occur about the input axis. However, any tendency for this angular displacement to occur requires a flow of fluid from b to a and from c to d. By utilizing small gaps and viscous fluids, the resulting fluid

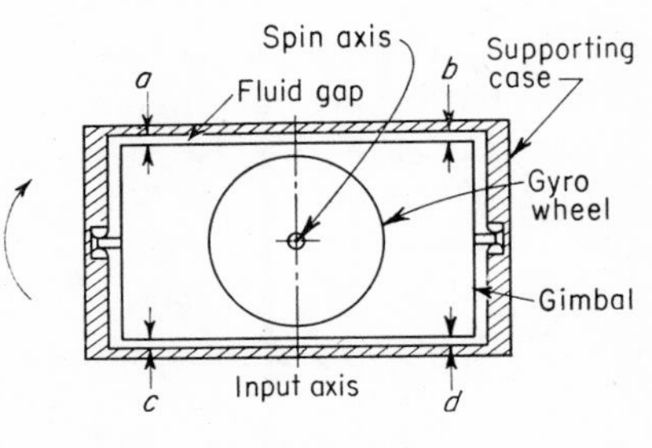

FIG. 9-4

coupling between the gimbal and the case about the input axis can be made very stiff, thereby protecting the pivots from excessive loading.

9-6. Elastic Torques—Systematic; Nonacceleration-sensitive

Elastic torques are those restraining torques which are directly proportional to gimbal angular displacement from a null or centered position with respect to the case. They are primarily due to mechanical spring connections between gimbal and case. In addition there can be magnetic or electromagnetic torques which are also directly proportional to gimbal displacement from a null position with respect to the case.

The sum of all mechanical and magnetic elastic restraints on the gimbal can be represented as a coupling (dyne-centimeters per radian). Let the angular displacement between gimbal and case be Θ (radians); the elastic torque T_e will be given by

$$T_e = K\Theta \tag{9-8}$$

This torque is systematic, since it can be related to a measurable displacement between gimbal and case. Utilization of a pickoff signal to indicate this displacement makes possible the application of an equal and opposite torque through the gyro torquing system. There are practical limitations to the degree of compensation which can be obtained. For example, any electrical compensation will vary with power-supply fluctuations, while the mechanical torque it is bucking does not vary.

It should be clear that elastic torques are not sensitive to acceleration or vibration but only to the angular displacement, as described by Eq. (9-8).

In rate gyros and in certain two-degree-of-freedom applications, the elastic coupling is a functional requirement. Control torques may then be exerted by introducing an angular offset between the gimbal and the supporting case.

Elastic Suspensions. The fundamental requirement of a suspension system is to position the gimbal with a maximum of translational rigidity. Low angular rigidity is required about each suspension axis, except when a definite coupling is required for torquing, as in a rate gyro. Some designers have resorted to elastic suspensions with low torsional gradients to avoid the random friction characteristics of systems utilizing bearings or pivots. This requires a servo follow-up system to keep the operating angular displacement between gimbal and case down to acceptable low limits. In addition, translational and angular stops are required between gimbal and case to protect the elastic members from being overstressed.

An example of an elastic suspension is shown in Fig. 9-5. A symmetrical assembly of three tapes in tension at each end of the gimbal supplies translation rigidity perpendicular to axis xx. Axial rigidity along

xx is supplied by fine wires at both ends of the gimbal. Springs for preloading the tapes and wires are required, but to simplify the diagram they have not been shown. The tapes are fastened to the gimbal close to axis xx to minimize their angular coupling about xx. The total elastic coupling is the sum of the restraints due to the bending of the tapes and the twisting of the wires.

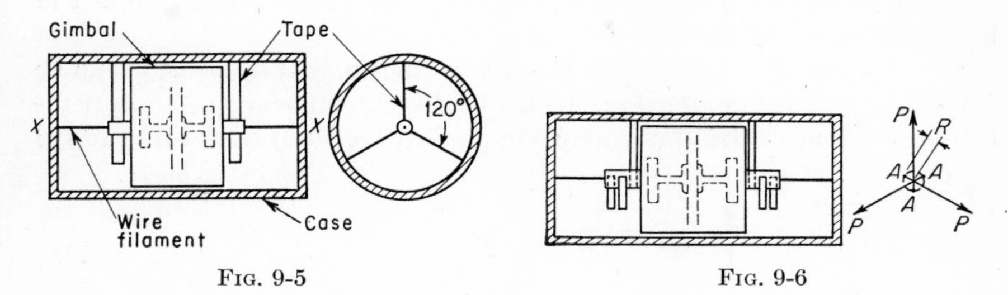

FIG. 9-5 FIG. 9-6

It is of interest to point out a variation of the arrangement shown above in which the elastic coupling is theoretically zero for small angular displacements. This is illustrated in Fig. 9-6.

In this suspension the tapes are attached to the gimbal "past the center," i.e., the tension force P exerted by each tape is acting from the point of attachment A on the gimbal toward the center. This creates a negative or upsetting torque due to the tension P when the gimbal rotates from a null position. This can be seen by examining Fig. 9-7 for one tape. The upsetting torque for each tape will be $T_u = RP\Theta$. By proper adjustment of R and P it is theoretically possible to compensate for the positive elastic coupling due to bending of the tapes and twisting of the wires.

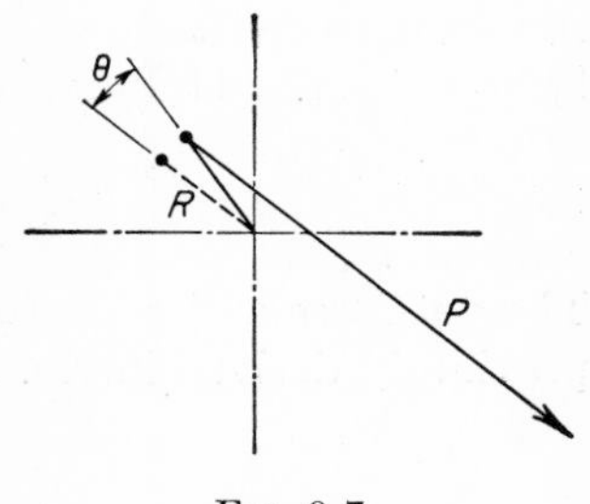

FIG. 9-7

In Fig. 9-6, it should be noted that the three tapes in each set must be offset from each other axially to permit the "over-center" arrangement.

Elastic Centering. In precision gyro applications fluid suspension (Sec. 9-5) serves to support the gimbal weight. The minute centering forces required to correct for deviations from perfect neutral buoyancy can be supplied by small bearings, pivots, or elastic devices. Simple arrangements of extremely fine tapes and wire filaments with very low torsional gradients can be successfully utilized both for centering and for conducting electric power into the gimbal.

In a gyro utilizing the buoyant force of displaced fluid, the type of elastic suspension shown in Fig. 9-5 can be simplified to that shown in

Fig. 9-8. A diaphragm preload spring is shown in Fig. 9-8 as a means for applying a given tension P through the wire filaments at each end of the gimbal. The elimination of the tapes becomes possible in the fluid suspension, since the tension in the filaments, together with the supporting buoyant force of the fluid, is sufficient to provide adequate stiffness radial to axis xx.

The stiffness of a simple filament suspension will now be examined in both translation and rotation.

Translational Stiffness. The stiffness of the filament suspension can be determined by examining Fig. 9-8b. Under the influence of a temperature error from neutral buoyancy, coupled with acceleration (or gravity)

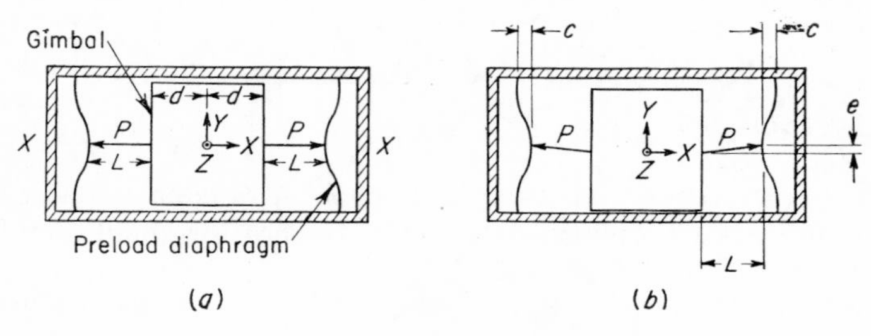

Fig. 9-8

in the y direction, the gimbal will tend to translate from its centered position (Fig. 9-8a) to an offset e (Fig. 9-8b). The filaments will provide a centering force F_y due to the y component of tension which is developed by the offset. The sum for the two filaments will be

$$F_y = 2P\frac{e}{L} \tag{9-9}$$

The net force acting on the gimbal due to lack of neutral buoyancy was previously derived in Eq. (9-7).

$$F = Ma(\beta - \alpha)\,\Delta t$$

In the steady state Eqs. (9-9) and (9-7) must be equal. Therefore,

$$2P\frac{e}{L} = Ma(\beta - \alpha)\,\Delta t$$

$$e = \frac{L}{2P}Ma(\beta - \alpha)\,\Delta t \tag{9-10}$$

To examine this quantitatively consider the representative parameters given in the section on Centering Force, viz.,

$$(\beta - \alpha)\,\Delta t = \frac{1}{2{,}750}$$

and additional representative values, such as

$$\begin{aligned} L &= 2 \text{ cm} \\ P &= 200{,}000 \text{ dynes} \\ M &= 600 \text{ g} \\ a &= 980 \text{ cm/sec}^2 \end{aligned}$$

We can write

$$\begin{aligned} e &= \frac{2}{2 \times 200{,}000} \times 600 \times 980 \times \frac{1}{2{,}750} \\ &= 0.001 \text{ cm} \end{aligned}$$

From Eq. (9-9) the total suspension system stiffness in the y direction can be expressed as

$$K_y = \frac{F_y}{e} = \frac{2P}{L} \tag{9-11}$$

Let us consider the system stiffness K_x in the x direction and compare it to K_y. First let us introduce two definitions:

K_s = stiffness of each preload diaphragm spring in the x direction, dynes/cm
c = nominal deflection of each preload spring when tension in filament is P, cm

We can write

$$P = cK_s \tag{9-12}$$

The total suspension system stiffness K_x in the x direction is

$$K_x = 2K_s \tag{9-13}$$

Substitution of (9-12) into (9-11) provides

$$K_y = \frac{2cK_s}{L} \tag{9-14}$$

and, from (9-13) and (9-14),

$$\frac{K_x}{K_y} = \frac{L}{c} \tag{9-15}$$

Normally $L \gg c$, so that the system is stiffer along the filament axis than it is along a lateral axis.

Angular Coupling. To examine the angular coupling between gimbal and housing, let $(T/\Theta)_x$ = torsional gradient of one filament about its centroidal (x) axis (dyne-centimeters per radian). Since there are two filaments in parallel, the total coupling about the x axis will be $2(T/\Theta)_x$. This number is primarily a function of the filament cross section, and in most units, where it is not used for control torquing, it must be low to ensure high levels of gyro performance.

There is also elastic coupling about the Z axis which, for a symmetrical situation, is the same as that about the Y axis. In this case the gradient is primarily a function of the tension in the filaments rather than their cross section. Let Θ_z = angle of rotation of the gimbal about the Z axis (radians). Consider the diagram of forces in Fig. 9-9 when Θ_z is small. The torque about the Z axis is

$$T_z = 2\left[P\left(\frac{\Theta_z d}{L}\right)d + P\Theta_z d\right]$$

or

$$T_z = 2P\Theta_z d\left(\frac{d}{L} + 1\right)$$

The coupling gradient about the Z (and the Y) axis will be

$$\left(\frac{T}{\Theta}\right)_z = \left(\frac{T}{\Theta}\right)_y = 2Pd\left(\frac{d}{L} + 1\right) \tag{9-16}$$

It is desirable that this number have a high value. Assuming that the spin axis of the gyro is parallel to the Z axis, as in Fig. 9-9, we see that

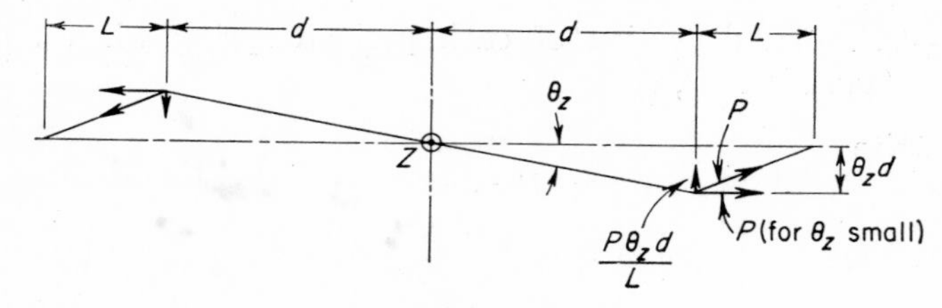

FIG. 9-9

axis Y becomes an input axis. High $(T/\Theta)_y$ coupling is desirable to assist the fluid forces in exerting inputs to the gimbal. High $(T/\Theta)_z$ coupling maintains gimbal rigidity about the Z axis in opposition to coercive torques due to any change in rotor speed resulting from power-supply fluctuations. This action can be explained with the aid of the picture of the idealized gyro shown in Fig. 9-3. In the steady-state condition the rotor is spinning at constant speed; therefore, the net torque on the rotor must be zero. At this time there are three torques acting on the gimbal:

T_M = motor reaction torque
T_W = windage drag torque
T_B = bearing friction drag torque

By definition, in the steady state

$$T_M + T_W + T_B = 0 \tag{9-17}$$

Fluctuations in the power supply will cause T_M to vary. However, over small speed changes both T_W and T_B will remain essentially fixed. Thus the equality of Eq. (9-17) will be disturbed. A net torque will act on the rotor to change its speed and react on the gimbal to cause it to rotate about axis Z. A high value of $(T/\Theta)_z$ coupling will keep this gimbal motion to small angles.

Stop System. The design of the elastic suspension or centering system and its protective stop systems are intimately related. In a single-degree-of-freedom gyro the stop system limits the maximum motion between the gimbal and the case. In a two-degree-of-freedom gyro the stop system must limit any motion between the inner and the outer gimbals and between the outer gimbal and the case. This is done for rotation and translation in all directions and is specifically designed to limit the deflection of the elastic system to protect it from being overstressed.

A fundamental compromise must always be made. The stops must allow sufficient motion to avoid premature "caging" or hitting of the stop's surfaces under expected operating extremes of loading. This is necessary to avoid any deterioration in gyro performance during operation. However, they cannot permit too much motion, since this would cause excessive stress levels in the elastic members.

Power Leads. Electric leads must normally be provided to carry power into the gimbal for the spin motor and, in some designs, for the pickoff and torquing systems. Slip rings must be used if continuous rotation is desired. If this motion is limited, as it is in most contemporary gyros, flexible leads can be used between the gimbal and the case. The problem is to provide an arrangement permitting adequate angular freedom with a low torque gradient and freedom from hysteresis.

In a number of fluid-suspended gyros utilizing elastic centering the centering members serve a dual purpose as power leads. This is one of the major advantages of elastic centering as compared to jeweled pivots used for the same purpose.

9-7. Viscous Coupling—Systematic; Nonacceleration-sensitive

The use of fluid as a suspension and damping medium has already been described (Sec. 9-5). There are a number of ways in which the fluid can impose torques on the gimbal, some desirable, as in the case of damping, others undesirable because of a variety of complex effects. One that we shall consider here is viscous coupling resulting from relative angular velocity between the gimbal and the supporting case. This torque is a function of viscosity, fluid gap, and configuration of the gimbal and supporting case.

In two-degree-of-freedom gyros viscous coupling plays one minor beneficial role in damping nutation oscillations. However, there is sensitivity to rectification of oscillatory inputs and possible servo instability if the coupling is excessive. In the latter case consider a two-degree-of-freedom gyro having sensitive axes X and Y. The torque about X, due to viscous coupling, can be expressed as

$$T_x = C_x\dot{\Theta}_x \tag{9-18}$$

where C_x = damping constant about X, dyne-cm/(radian/sec)
$\dot{\Theta}_x$ = relative angular velocity between gimbal and case about X, radians/sec

This torque about the X axis will produce a precessional rate about the Y axis.

$$\dot{\Theta}_y = \frac{C_x\dot{\Theta}_x}{H} \tag{9-19}$$

where $\dot{\Theta}_y$ = precessional rate of gimbal about the Y axis (radians per second) and H = angular momentum (dyne-centimeters per second). Integrating both sides gives

$$\Theta_y = \frac{C_x\Theta_x}{H} \tag{9-20}$$

To ensure servo stability it is desirable that $(C_x/H) \ll 1$.

In single-degree-of-freedom units the maintenance of a stable damping coefficient under a variety of environmental conditions for the life of the gyro is often a fundamental design problem. An important factor in attaining this goal is the selection of a fluid having minimum change in viscosity over the expected operating temperature range. As a result the density requirement for neutral buoyancy must often be compromised with that for certain viscous characteristics.

In some designs compensation for temperature sensitivity of fluid viscosity has been introduced by varying the fluid gap through the use of temperature-sensitive mechanical devices.

9-8. Magnetic Torques—Systematic; Nonacceleration-sensitive

In designing a gyro we must take into consideration magnetic torques which may be exerted on the gimbal. These result from interaction between magnetic fields and materials on the gimbal, case, and surrounding equipment. The torques are usually a function of gimbal orientation with respect to case or external reference and hence are nonacceleration-sensitive and can be theoretically considered as systematic.

This classification is largely academic, since realistically the factors involved, i.e., field strengths and shapes and magnetic retentivity, are complex, sometimes unstable, and difficult to correlate.

Those torques which are proportional to gimbal angular displacement with respect to the case were mentioned (Sec. 9-6) as part of the elastic coupling between gimbal and case. They can all be categorized as torques due to the following effects:

1. External fields acting with the gimbal
2. Internal gimbal fields acting with adjacent parts on case
3. Anomalies in electromagnetic pickup or torquing systems

External Fields. Magnetic fields due to the earth's field combined with that generated by any local electrical equipment in the vicinity of the gyro can react with magnetic material or with magnetic fields on the gimbal to produce spurious torques. Two fundamental ways in which the designer can overcome this problem are elimination of magnetic materials on the gimbal or use of high-permeability magnetic shielding around the gyro.

Elimination of magnetic material from the gimbal is difficult to accomplish, since this material is necessary in the spin motor, many pickoff and torquer designs, and most gyro spin bearings. Furthermore, in designing a precision gyro care must be taken to match the thermal coefficients of expansion of the various structural materials used in the gimbal. Until the very recent advent of beryllium as a material of gyro construction, the major suitable materials having coefficients matching those of the bearing, motor, and pickoff elements were also magnetic. Some designers chose to limit the use of magnetic materials to the vital elements mentioned and were then faced with the problem of joining with microstability parts having dissimilar coefficients of expansion.

The alternate approach has been more liberal in the use of magnetic materials to obtain closer matching of coefficients.

Generally, larger gimbal torques will result if the magnetic material tends to line up in a straight line or bar rather than in a ball or spherical relation. When these torques are excessive, effective reduction can be accomplished by using a high-permeability magnetic shield to "short circuit" the external field, sharply weakening the field left passing through the gimbal.

A torque may also result from the reaction of an external field with one internal to the gimbal and having directional properties. For the most part the fields internally generated are circular in nature and do not contribute in this manner to the production of major torques.

Internal Fields. There are magnetic fields on the gimbal which are associated with the spin motor and pickup and torquing devices. These fields can react with adjacent magnetic mat rials on the supporting case. It is important to determine where these field strengths are concentrated in order to avoid magnetic materials on the case in these regions. This is normally not as difficult a problem as the elimination of magnetic materials from the gimbal.

Anomalies in Pickup and Torquer. The use of electromagnetic devices in pickups and torquers is common and is conducive to the generation of magnetic coupling. In the case of pickups the coupling is undesirable. The design approaches necessary to avoid this condition will be covered in Chap. 11.

Undesirable magnetic coupling can occur as a result of an error in the alignment of the torquing system. Hence, incorrect torque components might be applied to the gimbal.

9-9. Nonorthogonality of Suspension Axes—Systematic; Nonacceleration-sensitive

In the section on Elastic Centering a brief discussion of internal gimbal torques was introduced to demonstrate the desirability of having high angular coupling about the spin axis between the gimbal and the supporting case. During periods of power-supply fluctuations inequality between the motor-drive torque and the sum of bearing and windage drag torques must be offset by a torque about the spin axis exerted on the gimbal. Lack of orthogonality between a suspension (or centering) axis and the spin axis will then result in a drift-producing torque exerted on the gimbal.

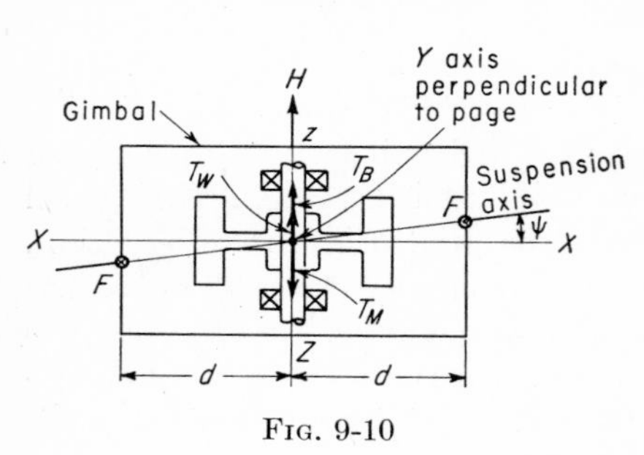

FIG. 9-10

Consider the diagram shown in Fig. 9-10, in which the suspension axis is not orthogonal to the spin axis. Let

T_B = bearing drag torque on gimbal
T_W = windage drag torque on gimbal
T_M = motor reaction torque on gimbal
ψ = orthogonality error in suspension
F = force exerted on gimbal
J = polar moment of inertia of rotor
H = angular momentum of rotor
ω_1 = initial rotor spin speed
ω_2 = final rotor spin speed
Θ_y = angular displacement about Y axis
t = time

During periods of rotor speed change

$$T_M + T_B + T_W \neq 0 \tag{9-21}$$

A slight motion of the gimbal about the spin axis will take place until forces F are developed at the points of connection of the suspension or centering axis. The following equality results:

$$2Fd + T_M + T_B + T_W = 0 \tag{9-22}$$

Due to lack of orthogonality in the suspension, the forces F will be applied at a moment arm ψd about sensitive axis X, with a resulting drift-producing torque $2F\psi d$ being applied to the gimbal. This will establish a drift rate about the Y axis.

$$\dot{\Theta}_y = \frac{2F\psi d}{H} \tag{9-23}$$

The rotor spin speed change taking place because of power-supply variation will be $\omega_2 - \omega_1$, and the average wheel acceleration will be $(\omega_2 - \omega_1)/t$. Now, with the gimbal in equilibrium about the spin axis, the external torque $2Fd$ about the spin axis must be equal in magnitude to that being applied to the rotor. Hence,

$$2Fd = J\,\frac{\omega_2 - \omega_1}{t} \tag{9-24}$$

Substitution of (9-24) into (9-23) provides

$$\dot{\Theta}_y = J\,\frac{\omega_2 - \omega_1}{t} \cdot \frac{\psi}{H} \tag{9-25}$$

For small changes in spin speed, the angular momentum will remain essentially constant at $H = J\omega_1$; therefore,

$$\Theta_y = \dot{\Theta}_y t = \frac{\omega_2 - \omega_1}{\omega_1}\,\psi \tag{9-26}$$

The design approaches in minimizing this error are obviously reduction in nonorthogonality of suspension and use of a motor and supply having stable speed characteristics.

9-10. Unbalance Torques—Systematic; Acceleration-sensitive

Torques due to unbalance result from a displacement between the resultant vector of all gimbal supporting forces and the center of mass of the gimbal. The supporting force is proportional to acceleration, and hence the unbalance torque is acceleration-sensitive and systematic.

Balance can be trimmed by adjusting either the points of application of the supporting forces or the center of mass of the gimbal. The latter technique is usually much simpler for making final fine adjustments and is achieved by the use of adjustable balance weights.

Gimbal parts should be designed to obtain a normally balanced assembly, i.e., one in which the resultant supporting force vector will pass through the center of mass. Surfaces which serve to locate the heaviest parts in the assembly should have tight tolerances to avoid a wide range of unbalance. Similarly, weight-control specifications should be imposed on the fabrication of these parts.

If convenient, the center of support should be made adjustable so that it can be moved during early balancing operations.

The net result of the procedures mentioned above will be to reduce the burden on the balance-weight adjustment system. Less capacity will be

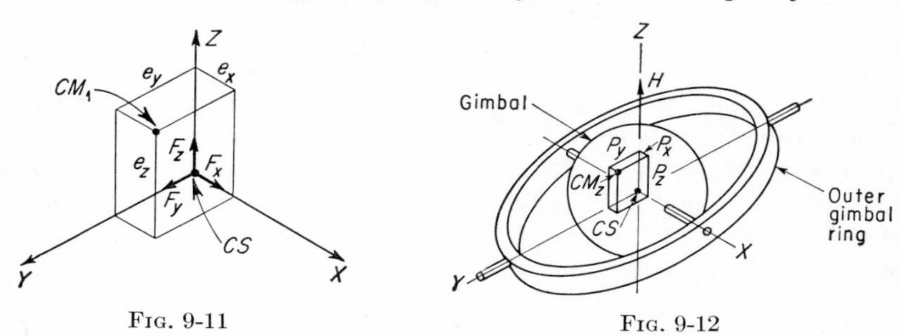

FIG. 9-11

FIG. 9-12

required, small weights will be practical, and greater sensitivity will be possible.

Torque Analysis. To examine the magnitudes of the unbalance torques, consider the generalized three-axis presentation in Fig. 9-11. Let

M_1 = mass of gimbal
A_x, A_y, A_z = components of acceleration
F_x, F_y, F_z = components of supporting force
e_x, e_y, e_z = components of displacement between center of mass CM_1 and center of support CS
T_x, T_y, T_z = components of unbalance torque

We have

$$F_x = M_1 A_x \qquad F_y = M_1 A_y \qquad F_z = M_1 A_z \tag{9-27}$$

The torque components about the center of mass will be

$$T_x = F_z e_y - F_y e_z \tag{9-28}$$
$$T_y = F_x e_z - F_z e_x \tag{9-29}$$
$$T_z = F_y e_x - F_x e_y \tag{9-30}$$

The spin axis and angular-moment vector are shown along the Z axis. Therefore, T_z in Eq. (9-30) will not produce a precession rate but will only have the secondary effect of loading the gimbal centering members. The torques of major importance are T_x and T_y.

In a two-degree-of-freedom gyro the effect of unbalance of the outer gimbal will also cause gyro drift. Consider Fig. 9-12, in which an outer gimbal has been added to the scheme in Fig. 9-11. Let

M_2 = mass of outer gimbal

P_x, P_y, P_z = components of displacement between CM_2 and CS

The outer gimbal has only one degree of freedom, about axis Y. It cannot impose any unbalance torques on the inner gimbal about the X axis, since the outer axis support would take up this torque. Hence, it can only affect the gyro torque situation about axis Y as follows:

$$T_y = A_x(M_1e_z + M_2P_z) - A_z(M_1e_x + M_2P_x) \qquad (9\text{-}31)$$

Examining Eqs. (9-28) and (9-31), we see that e_x appears in Eq. 9-31 only. This means that for balance ($T_x = T_y = 0$), e_x need not be equal to zero, providing that $M_1e_x + M_2P_x = 0$. In other words, the inner gimbal can be unbalanced along the X axis to compensate for outer gimbal unbalance along the X axis.

The Z axis situation does not permit similar compensation of M_2P_z by adjusting M_1e_x. If this were attempted, then for $M_1e_z = -M_2P_z$ in Eq. (9-31), the inner gimbal would have to be purposely unbalanced in such a way that

$$e_z = -P_z(M_2/M_1) \qquad (9\text{-}32)$$

But as shown in Eq. (9-28), this would create X axis unbalance torques due to F_y.

Unbalance is normally considered as a function of the parameters measured at $1g$. For different accelerations the values of e and P may change, as well as the magnitudes of the forces involved. Any deviation of unbalance torque from direct proportionality with respect to acceleration due to changes in e and P as a function of acceleration will be treated separately in Sec. 9-11 as compliance torques.

Balance-adjustment Weights. The use of small balance weights is a convenient technique for adjusting the position of centers of mass of the inner and outer gimbals to achieve a balanced condition. The fundamental design problems are (1) adequate capacity to compensate for maximum expected unbalance; (2) adequate sensitivity so that minimum reasonable adjusting motion will correspond to desired level of balance adjustment; (3) locking means to prevent motion of balance weights during vibration and operation; (4) access to balance weights, preferably after the gyro is assembled and initially tested. Let

M_x, M_y, M_z = masses of respective balance weights on inner gimbal which can be adjusted in a direction parallel to the subscript axis

l_x, l_y, l_z = respective adjustment of each balance weight required to achieve a balanced gyro

For achieving balance, we should have

$$l_y = \frac{M_1 e_y}{M_y} \tag{9-33}$$

$$l_z = \frac{M_1 e_z}{M_z} \tag{9-34}$$

$$l_x = \frac{M_1 e_x + M_2 P_x}{M_x} \tag{9-35}$$

Space limitations are often a serious problem in designing a balance-weight system, since this is the design feature which is usually added after the design of the major basic parts has been established. It is often necessary to maximize the capacity of a weight scheme under these circumstances. Referring to Fig. 9-13, we have a typical situation where a given tapped opening of length a is available for threaded balance-adjustment weights. To find the balance-weight length b producing maximum capacity, let

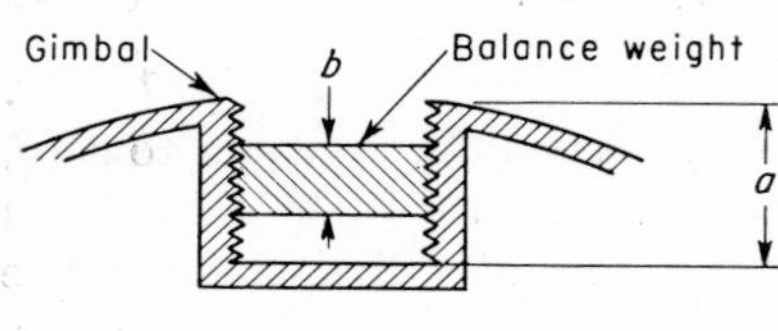

FIG. 9-13

K_1 = weight per unit length of balance weight
W = total weight of balance weight
c = total available travel of balance weight inside of tapped hole
T_B = balance torque capacity

Now,

$$c = a - b \tag{9-36}$$

$$W = bK_1 \tag{9-37}$$

$$T_B = cW \tag{9-38}$$

Putting (9-36) and (9-37) into (9-38), we get

$$T_B = (a - b)bK_1 \tag{9-39}$$

To maximize, first differentiate with respect to b:

$$\frac{dT_B}{db} = aK_1 - 2bK_1 \tag{9-40}$$

Setting this equal to zero and solving for b,

$$b = \frac{a}{2} \tag{9-41}$$

Combining (9-39) and (9-41) for maximum capacity,

$$T_B = \left(\frac{a}{2}\right)^2 K_1 \tag{9-42}$$

Balance in a Flotation Fluid. For a gimbal suspended in a flotation fluid the resultant of all the fluid buoyant forces is combined with the forces exerted at the centering members to define the location of the center of support. In the case of a gimbal at neutral buoyancy no forces are required at the centering members, and the effective center of support is at the center of buoyancy of the displaced fluid.

Final balancing takes place in the fluid; hence, balance weights attached to the gimbal must be moved through the fluid. The motion of the balance weights affects not only the center of mass of the gimbal but also the location of the center of buoyancy (or support for the case of neutral buoyancy).

Consider a gyro float at neutral buoyancy (Fig. 9-14). The buoyant supporting force F_s is equal to the weight of the gimbal assembly. In an

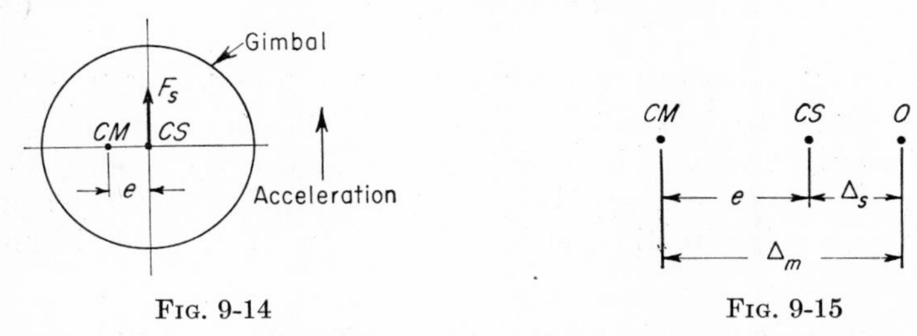

FIG. 9-14

FIG. 9-15

unbalanced condition there will be displacement e between CM, the center of mass, and CS, the center of support, which in this case is the center of buoyancy of the displaced fluid. As a result of the externally applied supporting force F_s not passing through the center of mass, an unbalance torque $T = eF_s$ will be exerted on the gimbal.

How far must a balance weight be moved to achieve coincidence between CM and CS?

Recalling that both the center of buoyant support and the center of mass would be affected by the motion of the balance weight, we see in Fig. 9-15 that a balance will be achieved when CM has moved Δm and CS has moved Δs until they coincide at some point O.

This occurs when

$$\Delta m - \Delta s = e \tag{9-43}$$

In order to calculate the balance-weight motion required, let

ρ = fluid mass density
δ = mass density of balance weight
V = volume of gimbal
v = volume of balance weight
Δs = motion of center of buoyancy of gimbal assembly due to motion of balance weight
Δm = motion of center of mass of gimbal assembly due to motion of balance weight
l = motion of balance weight

Considering linear motions of l, Δm, and Δs in one direction only, we get

$$\Delta s = \frac{v}{V} l \tag{9-44}$$

$$\Delta m = \frac{v\delta l}{V\rho} \tag{9-45}$$

Combining Eqs. (9-43) to (9-45), we have

$$\frac{v\delta l}{V\rho} - \frac{v}{V} l = e$$

or

$$l = \frac{V}{v} \frac{\rho}{\delta - \rho} e \tag{9-46}$$

Thus the effectiveness of a balance weight is a function of its relative volume compared to the gimbal and its relative density compared to the fluid. If a weight were to have the same density as the fluid, both the center of mass and the center of buoyancy of the gimbal would be equally affected by the weight motion, with the result that there would be no net change in balance.

9-11. Compliance Torques—Systematic; Acceleration-sensitive

As previously described, unbalance torques result from a displacement between the center of mass and the resultant gimbal supporting force vector. Under dynamic conditions of shock, vibration, and varying acceleration, the gyro structural members within the gimbal and external to it will deflect to some small degree. Some of this deflection or compliance may contribute to a change in this displacement. Torques resulting from this change are called *compliance torques.* They are systematic since they can be related to acceleration.

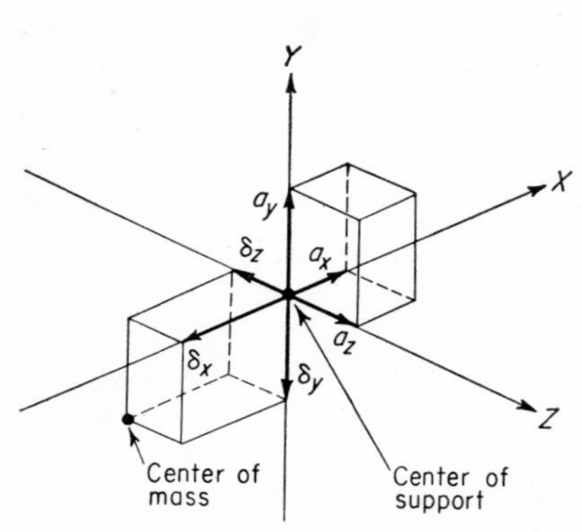

FIG. 9-16

Torque Analysis. Consider a balanced gimbal in which the centers of mass and support are coincident in a zero acceleration field. Under the influence of forces applied at the center of support, the gimbal will experience an acceleration, and the various gimbal parts will yield. Let us establish an orthogonal coordinate system in Fig. 9-16, with the Z axis along the spin axis and the X and Y axes along the gyro-sensitive axes. Assume linear compliances and the origin of the coordinate system at the center of support. Let

a_x, a_y, a_z = coordinates of acceleration, cm/sec^2
C_x, C_y, C_z = coordinates of equivalent compliance of gimbal mass center, cm/dyne
M = mass of gimbal assembly, g
$\delta x, \delta y, \delta z$ = coordinates of compliant motion of mass center with respect to center of support, cm

Torques about the Z axis are not of fundamental interest, since they do not produce any gyro drift.

Now
$$T_x = M(a_y\delta_z - a_z\delta_y) \quad (9\text{-}47)$$
$$T_y = M(-a_x\delta_z + a_z\delta_x) \quad (9\text{-}48)$$

But
$$\begin{aligned} \delta x &= Ma_xC_x \\ \delta y &= Ma_yC_y \\ \delta z &= Ma_zC_z \end{aligned} \quad (9\text{-}49)$$

Substituting (9-49) in (9-47) and (9-48), we get

$$T_x = M^2a_ya_z(C_z - C_y) \quad (9\text{-}50)$$
$$T_y = M^2a_za_x(C_x - C_z) \quad (9\text{-}51)$$

Let l, m, and n be the direction cosines of the acceleration field A. Then

$$\begin{aligned} a_x &= lA \\ a_y &= mA \\ a_z &= nA \end{aligned}$$

and substituting into (9-50) and (9-51),

$$T_x = M^2A^2mn(C_z - C_y) \quad (9\text{-}52)$$
$$T_y = M^2A^2ln(C_x - C_z) \quad (9\text{-}53)$$

Examining these equations we see that this torque is proportional to the squares of both gimbal mass and acceleration. It is a direct function of the differences in compliance rates along each principal axis, reducing to zero for both axes when we have an isoelastic condition, i.e., the compliance rates in all directions are equal.

The direction of the acceleration vector with respect to the principal axes is also a factor. If the acceleration vector is parallel to a principal axis, the other two direction cosines are zero, and no torques result. The maximum condition for either of the two torques arises when A is perpendicular to the particular axis and 45° from each of the other two axes.

If a gyro is subjected to a sinusoidal vibration at a frequency well below the natural frequency of any of the structural parts, there is, unfortunately, a rectifying torque effect due to compliance. This is seen by letting

$$A = A_0 \sin \omega t \tag{9-54}$$

and by substituting in Eqs. (9-52) and (9-53), which provides

$$T_x = M^2 A_0^2 \sin^2 \omega t \cdot mn(C_z - C_y)$$
$$T_y = M^2 A_0^2 \sin^2 \omega t \cdot ln(C_x - C_z)$$

yielding average values

$$T_x = \tfrac{1}{2} M^2 A_0^2 mn(C_z - C_y) \tag{9-55}$$
$$T_y = \tfrac{1}{2} M^2 A_0^2 ln(C_x - C_z) \tag{9-56}$$

Summing up, the safest approach in designing for low compliance torques is to use a very stiff structure to minimize the values of C_x, C_y, and C_z. The next step is to attempt to achieve the condition where $C_x = C_y = C_z$. The more rigid the structure, the larger can be the relative differences between the compliance constants for achieving low torque levels. In most cases the largest factor in the determination of the compliance constants is the yield rate of the rotor spin bearings. Isoelastic bearings having equal axial and radial yield rates are therefore utilized in high-precision gyros.

Equivalent Compliance. *Definition.* In gyro design the equivalent compliance is the shift in the center of mass of the complete gyro with respect to the resultant supporting force vector per unit of supporting force (in inches per pound or centimeters per dyne). All gyros are composite structures with distributed masses and compliances, but for practical purposes these structures may be considered as a finite number of point masses and springs. These masses and springs may be in series and/or in parallel, depending on the particular configuration of the gyro.

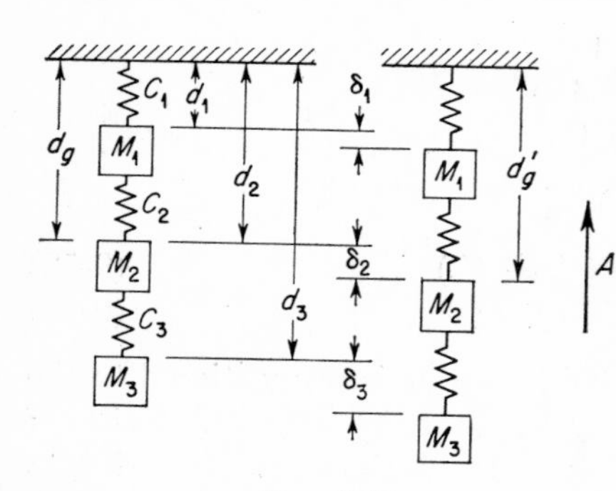

FIG. 9-17

Series Compliances. Consider the example of Fig. 9-17, with masses M_1, M_2, M_3 and compliances C_1, C_2, C_3. Determine the shift in the center of gravity of the system when subjected to a vertical acceleration A. It is obvious that

$$\delta_1 = A(M_1 + M_2 + M_3)C_1 \tag{9-57}$$

$$\delta_2 = \delta_1 + A(M_2 + M_3)C_2$$
$$= A[(M_1 + M_2 + M_3)C_1 + (M_2 + M_3)C_2] \tag{9-58}$$

$$\delta_3 = \delta_2 + M_3 C_3$$
$$= A[(M_1 + M_2 + M_3)C_1 + (M_2 + M_3)C_2 + M_3 C_3] \tag{9-59}$$

If d_1, d_2, and d_3 are the distances to the centers of mass of the three masses with respect to the reference support when in a zero acceleration field, the distance to the center of mass of the system is initially

$$d_g = \frac{M_1 d_1 + M_2 d_2 + M_3 d_3}{M_1 + M_2 + M_3} \tag{9-60}$$

Due to the acceleration A, the center of mass shifts to a new position, defined by

$$d'_g = \frac{M_1(d_1 + \delta_1) + M_2(d_2 + \delta_2) + M_3(d_3 + \delta_3)}{M_1 + M_2 + M_3} \tag{9-61}$$

Therefore, the shift in the center of gravity is

$$\delta_g = d'_g - d_g = \frac{M_1\delta_1 + M_2\delta_2 + M_3\delta_3}{M_1 + M_2 + M_3} \tag{9-62}$$

Substituting Eqs. (9-57) to (9-59) in (9-62) and collecting terms, we get

$$\delta_g = (M_1 + M_2 + M_3)AC_1 + \frac{(M_2 + M_3)^2}{M_1 + M_2 + M_3} AC_2 + \frac{M_3{}^2}{M_1 + M_2 + M_3} AC_3 \tag{9-63}$$

The equivalent compliance is therefore

$$C' = \frac{\delta_g}{A} \frac{1}{M_1 + M_2 + M_3} = C_1 + \left(\frac{M_2 + M_3}{M_1 + M_2 + M_3}\right)^2 C_2 + \left(\frac{M_3}{M_1 + M_2 + M_3}\right)^2 C_3 \tag{9-64}$$

This analysis can be easily extended to include a larger number of masses on series springs. Thus for four masses in series, the equivalent compliance is

$$C' = C_1 + \left(\frac{M_2 + M_3 + M_4}{M_T}\right)^2 C_2 + \left(\frac{M_3 + M_4}{M_T}\right)^2 C_3 + \left(\frac{M_4}{M_T}\right)^2 C_4 \tag{9-65}$$

where $M_T = M_1 + M_2 + M_3 + M_4$.

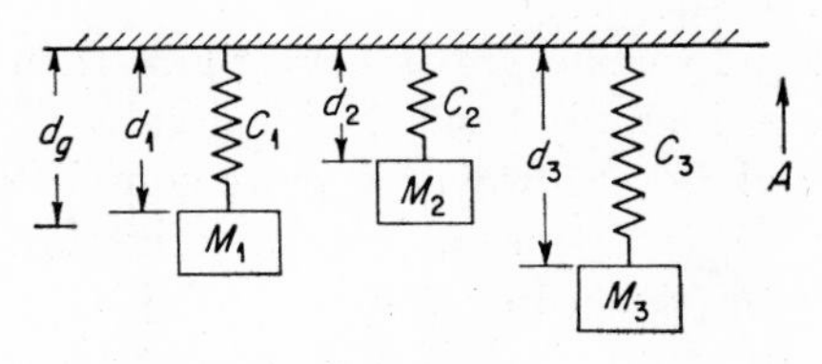

FIG. 9-18

Parallel Compliances. Given the point masses M_1, M_2, M_3 of Fig. 9-18 and using the same notation as in the previous section, we find that

$$\delta_1 = M_1AC_1 \tag{9-66}$$
$$\delta_2 = M_2AC_2 \tag{9-67}$$
$$\delta_3 = M_3AC_3 \tag{9-68}$$
$$d_g = \frac{M_1d_1 + M_2d_2 + M_3d_3}{M_1 + M_2 + M_3} \tag{9-69}$$
$$d'_g = \frac{M_1(d_1 + \delta_1) + M_2(d_2 + \delta_2) + M_3(d_3 + \delta_3)}{M_1 + M_2 + M_3} \tag{9-70}$$
$$\delta_g = d'_g - d_g + \frac{M_1\delta_1 + M_2\delta_2 + M_3\delta_3}{M_1 + M_2 + M_3} = A\,\frac{M_1^2C_1 + M_2^2C_2 + M_3^2C_3}{M_1 + M_2 + M_3} \tag{9-71}$$

The equivalent compliance is

$$C' = \frac{\delta_g}{AM_0} = \left(\frac{M_1}{M_0}\right)^2 C_1 + \left(\frac{M_2}{M_0}\right)^2 C_2 + \left(\frac{M_3}{M_0}\right)^2 C_3 \tag{9-72}$$

where $M_0 = M_1 + M_2 + M_3$.

Parallel Series Compliances. If the structure contains both series and parallel compliances, as in Fig. 9-19, let us reduce the series compliances C_2 and C_3 to an equivalent compliance, say C_5, in parallel with C_4. The mass attached to the equivalent spring of course will be equal to $M_2 + M_3$. Next reduce the compliances C_4 and C_5 to an equivalent spring with a compliance C_6 and a suspended mass equal to $M_2 + M_3 + M_4$. The over-all equivalent compliance is found for the two-mass system by the method indicated in the section on Series Compliances.

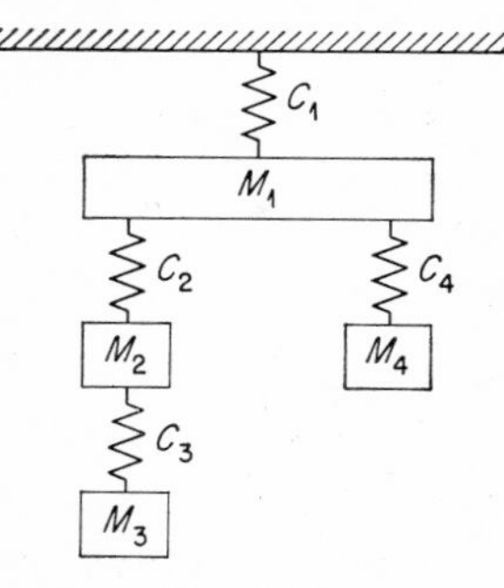

FIG. 9-19

Anisoelastic Compensation. If a gyro structure has the same equivalent compliance in three principal orthogonal directions, it is isoelastic and no torques result due to compliance. If the compliances are not equal in the three orthogonal directions, it is anisoelastic. The elastic ratios C_x/C_y, C_y/C_z, and C_z/C_x are a measure of anisoelasticity; a value of 1 for all three would indicate an isoelastic structure.

If the equivalent gyro structure is very rigid, then even though the elastic ratios differ considerably from the ideal value of 1, the compliance torques may be negligible. However, a more compliant gyro must have its elastic ratios very close to 1 in order to keep the torques to a negligible value. An anisoelastic structure, however, may be made isoelastic by the addition of one or more small masses mounted on soft springs that will increase the equivalent compliances along the more rigid axes.

Let M be the mass of the gyro, except for the compensator, and C_x, C_y, C_z be the equivalent compliances along the three principal axes. Assume that we add a mass m on a member which has compliances c_x, c_y, c_z and that it is in parallel with the main mass M. By the method previously described, the equivalent compliances of the complete system are

$$C'_x = \left(\frac{M}{M+m}\right)^2 C_x + \left(\frac{m}{M+m}\right)^2 c_x \tag{9-73}$$

$$C'_y = \left(\frac{M}{M+m}\right)^2 C_y + \left(\frac{m}{M+m}\right)^2 c_y \tag{9-74}$$

$$C'_z = \left(\frac{M}{M+m}\right)^2 C_z + \left(\frac{m}{M+m}\right)^2 c_z \tag{9-75}$$

If the compensated gyro is to be isoelastic, then

$$C'_x = C'_y = C'_z \tag{9-76}$$

and

$$m^2(c_x - c_y) = M^2(C_y - C_x) \tag{9-77}$$

$$m^2(c_y - c_z) = M^2(C_z - C_y) \tag{9-78}$$

$$m^2(c_z - c_x) = M^2(C_x - C_z) \tag{9-79}$$

These equations may be solved for suitable values of c_x, c_y, and c_z. In an anisoelastic structure at least one of the compliances will be greater, and no additional compliance will be required in that direction. For example, if $C_y < C_z > C_x$, then c_z may be made equal to zero, and

$$c_x = \left(\frac{M}{m}\right)^2 (C_z - C_x) \tag{9-80}$$

$$c_y = \left(\frac{M}{m}\right)^2 (C_z - C_y) \tag{9-81}$$

9-12. Temperature-error Torques—Systematic; Acceleration-sensitive

The relation between the resultant gimbal supporting force vector and the center of mass of the gimbal is of prime importance in any consideration of acceleration-sensitive torques. This has certainly been evident in previous discussions of unbalance and compliance torques. A practical problem in this area is present in gyro "hardware," namely, the sensitivity of this relation to temperature. The location of either the support vector or the center of mass may be sensitive to temperature. The resulting torque is systematic and is both temperature- and acceleration-sensitive.

Mass Location Sensitivity. Temperature sensitivity of the location of the gimbal mass center results from asymmetries in the expansion and contraction of the gimbal structure. These can occur when materials having different thermal expansion rates are not arranged symmetrically.

This can be illustrated by examination of the design configuration shown in Fig. 9-20. Assume the rim of the wheel to be made of a high-density material having a coefficient of expansion which differs from all other

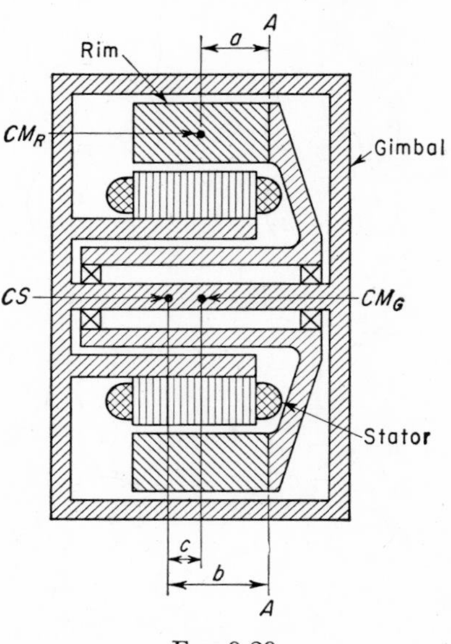

FIG. 9-20

parts on the gimbal. Let

M_R = mass of rim
M_G = mass of remaining gimbal and rotor parts
Ω = thermal coefficient of expansion of rim material
Ω' = thermal coefficient of all remaining rotor and gimbal parts (assume the same)
T_0 = operating temperature
Δt = deviation from operating temperature
CM_R, CM_G, CS = centers of mass and support, as shown
a, b, c = distances shown on diagram (assume all are positive)
A = acceleration perpendicular to plane of page

At operating temperature T_0 let

$a = a_0$
$b = b_0$
$c = c_0$

For a balanced condition at T_0,

$$A[M_R(a_0 - b_0) - M_G c_0] = 0 \tag{9-82}$$

When temperature deviations occur, we have

$$a = a_0(1 + \Omega\,\Delta t)$$
$$b = b_0(1 + \Omega'\,\Delta t)$$
$$c = c_0(1 + \Omega'\,\Delta t)$$

The resulting unbalance torque will be

$$\text{Unbalance torque} = A[M_R(a - b) - M_G c]$$
$$= A[M_R(a_0 - b_0) - M_G c_0 + M_R(a_0\Omega - b_0\Omega')\,\Delta t - M_G c_0 \Omega'\,\Delta t] \quad (9\text{-}83)$$

Combining (9-82) and (9-83) yields

$$\text{Unbalance torque} = A\,\Delta t[M_R(a_0\Omega - b_0\Omega') - M_G c_0 \Omega'] \quad (9\text{-}84)$$

This will reduce to zero for two cases, namely, when

$$\Omega = \Omega' \quad (9\text{-}85)$$

and

$$\Omega = \Omega' \frac{(M_G/M_R)c_0 + b_0}{a_0} \quad (9\text{-}86)$$

This illustrates that to achieve temperature balance insensitivity with an asymmetrical structure, either materials having equal coefficients of expansion should be used or masses should be distributed in a way to achieve compensatory effects. In general it is safest to avoid this problem by the dual approach of symmetrical design of the gimbal rotor structure and use of materials having equal coefficients of expansion.

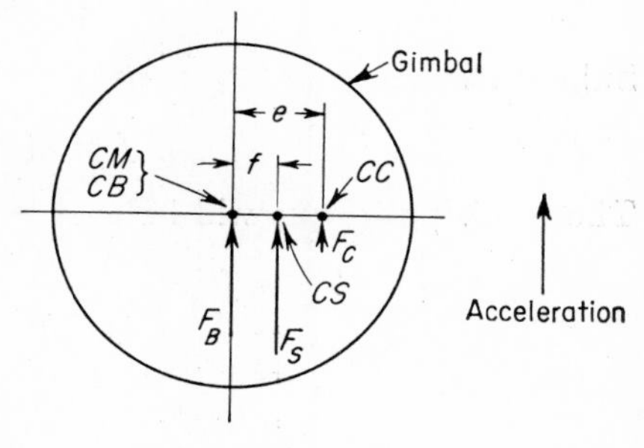

Fig. 9-21

Center of Support Sensitivity. Temperature sensitivity of the location of the center of support is a problem which is most generally associated with gyros utilizing fluid suspension. It occurs as a result of misalignment between the center of buoyancy of the gimbal and the axis of the centering pivots or elastic members. Let us consider a simple single-axis analysis, shown in Fig. 9-21. We denote the following:

CB = center of buoyancy
CM = center of mass (assumed coincident with CB)
CC = center of centering forces
CS = center of all gimbal supporting forces
F_B = buoyant force
F_C = centering force
F_S = total gimbal supporting force
e = alignment error between CB and CC
f = distance between CM and CS

We can write

$$F_S = F_B + F_C \tag{9-87}$$

Taking moments about CB, we get

$$fF_S = eF_C \tag{9-88}$$

Combining (9-87) and (9-88), we have

$$f = e\frac{F_C}{F_B + F_C} \tag{9-89}$$

At perfect neutral buoyancy no centering force is required ($F_C = 0$, hence $f = 0$); no torque will be exerted on the gimbal. As a temperature error develops, a finite value for F_C will be created so that $f \neq 0$ and CS will move away from CB, causing a torque $T_S = fF_S$.

An expression for this effect can be obtained using Eqs. (9-3) and (9-7), from which we can write

$$\begin{aligned} F_B &= Ma \\ F_C &= Ma(\beta - \alpha)\,\Delta t \end{aligned}$$

Substitution into (9-89) gives

$$f = e(\beta - \alpha)\,\Delta t \tag{9-90}$$

The resulting torque will be

$$\begin{aligned} T_S &= fF_S \\ &= f(F_B + F_C) \\ &= e(\beta - \alpha)\,\Delta t[Ma + Ma(\beta - \alpha)\,\Delta t] \\ &\approx e(\beta - \alpha)\,\Delta t Ma \end{aligned} \tag{9-91}$$

The following are the most direct ways of minimizing this effect:

1. Keep e small either by having tight tolerances on alignments or by providing means for adjustment after assembly and test.
2. Keep Δt small by tight temperature control.
3. Minimize $\beta - \alpha$ by selection of fluids and gimbal shell materials having similar coefficients of expansion.

Using the typical values for Δt, β, and α given in Sec. 9-5, we can write

$$T_S = \frac{eMa}{2{,}750}$$

This expression illustrates one of the major advantages of fluid suspension, i.e., the relatively noncritical aspect of the location of the axis of the centering forces in contributing to the very critical location of the equivalent center of support. For the above parameters a shift of the centering axis of 0.00275 in. results in a shift of the center of support of only 0.000001 in.

9-13. Fluid Torques—Systematic; Acceleration-sensitive

Fluid torques which are acceleration-sensitive can be considered systematic in only a limited sense. The relation between the acceleration and these particular fluid effects cannot be stated with the same degree of certainty as can, for example, unbalance or compliance torques. However, the following are two types of fluid torques which can be briefly considered under this category:

1. Translation torques
2. Density-gradient torques

Translation Torques. In fluid-suspended gyroscopes it is possible to encounter a transient torque on the gimbal while it is translating through the fluid. This translation could occur under the combined conditions of deviation from neutral buoyancy and acceleration. The translation motion is extremely small, equal only to the clearance between jewel and pivot in pivot-centered gyros or to the motion required for elastic members to provide centering forces in elastically centered units. In either case a torque can be exerted on the gimbal if it is off center in a direction perpendicular to the translation motion (Fig. 9-22). The gimbal is eccentrically located in the X direction, i.e., gaps a and b are unequal. Any gimbal translation in the Y direction will cause fluid displacement resulting in unequal fluid velocities through gaps a and b. Unequal viscous shear forces will be exerted on either side of the gimbal, resulting in a moment causing precession. For a step input of acceleration this is a transient effect which ceases when translation motion stops and adequate centering forces are exerted by pivots or elastic devices.

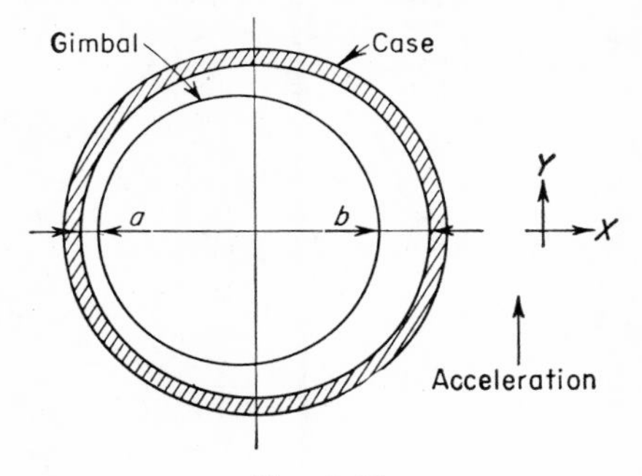

Fig. 9-22

Density-gradient Torques. The power supplied to the gimbal is dissipated at the motor, at the bearings, in windage, and, in some designs, in the pickoff and torquing transducers. Depending on the distribution of these heat sources inside the gimbal, some temperature gradients will exist at the surface of the gimbal and in the adjacent fluid gap. The resulting density gradient encountering discontinuities in the shape of the gimbal can produce a torque (Fig. 9-23). In Fig. 9-23*a*, a section is taken through a gimbal at a point where slots have reduced its cross section to the outline *abcd*. This outline is shown in Fig. 9-23*b* with fluid pressure forces acting on it. Assume that a temperature T_{bc} exists along arc bc and a lower temperature T_{da} along arc da. Also, a uniform temperature gradient $(T_{bo} - T_{da})/l$ prevails along sides ab and cd. As a result a fluid mass density ρ_{bc} will exist along arc bc and a higher density ρ_{da} along arc da, and a uniform fluid mass density gradient $(\rho_{bc} - \rho_{da})/l$

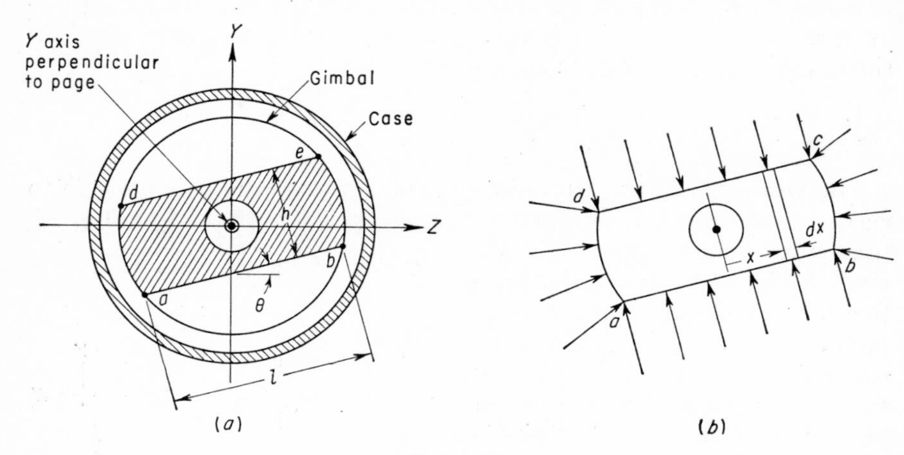

FIG. 9-23

will exist along sides ab and cd. At any distance x from the center the density of the fluid will be

$$\rho_x = \frac{1}{2}(\rho_{bc} + \rho_{da}) + \frac{2x}{e}\frac{1}{2}(\rho_{bc} - \rho_{da}) \tag{9-92}$$

The difference between the fluid pressure against side cd and that against side ab at distance x will be

$$\Delta p_x = \rho_x A_y h \cos\theta$$

where A_y is the y acceleration component. Assuming a unit length of section $abcd$ perpendicular to the plane of the paper, we see that the differential torque about the center of the section (Y axis) due to the forces over a distance dx will be

$$dT_y = x\,\Delta p_x\,dx = x\rho_x A_y h \cos\theta\,dx \tag{9-93}$$

Substitution of (9-92) in (9-93) gives

$$dT_y = A_y h \cos\theta \left[\frac{x}{2}(\rho_{bc} + \rho_{da}) + \frac{x^2}{l}(\rho_{bc} - \rho_{da})\right] dx$$

Integration between $-l/2$ and $+l/2$ yields

$$T_y = \tfrac{1}{12} A_y l^2 (\rho_{bc} - \rho_{da}) h \cos\theta \tag{9-94}$$

The pressure forces against arcs *bc* and *da* pass through the center of the section, and as a result no torques about the center can result from any variation in these forces.

The best design practice is to avoid concentrated heat sources near the fluid region on the gimbal and case and to use relatively massive sections of materials having good thermal conductivity to reduce the gradients. In addition the fluid cavity should be smooth, continuous, and symmetrical to minimize fluid torques.

9-14. Friction Torques—Random

Gimbal bearing or pivot friction has historically been a major problem for the gyro designer. Early units utilized ball bearings to approach a rigid, "frictionless" suspension. More recently the use of fluid displacement for gimbal support has become synonymous with the majority of precision gyros. The use of an air or gas bearing has shown strong promise and is being actively developed by a number of major gyro builders. Other investigations are examining the use of magnetic and electrostatic suspensions to support the gimbal. All these developments have been generated by the inability, until very recently, to obtain ball bearings with static friction uncertainties below 50 dyne-cm.

A very recent major improvement in this area has been the development of "dynamic" bearings in which an oscillation is introduced to break up static friction down to levels of 10 dyne-cm. For a gyro of typical size having an angular momentum of 2×10^6 dyne-cm/sec, a 10-dyne-cm torque would create a precessional drift rate of approximately 1°/hr. This is still excessive for many high-precision applications.

Mechanism and Effect. Friction is a coupling between the gimbal and the supporting case that is due to rubbing, sliding, or rolling action in the gimbal support bearing or pivot. The factors which affect the magnitude of this coupling are (1) size and geometry of the bearing, (2) loading of the bearing, (3) alignment of bearings and mating parts, (4) surface finish of bearing races and balls, (5) cleanliness of the bearing, and (6) materials and lubrication.

Friction, along with balance, is a major fundamental consideration in any discussion of gimbal torques. However, of the two, it is friction which must generally be guarded against with most care because of its random behavior. Friction torques must be accepted as a fundamental limitation on performance, while balance, along with other systematic effects, can be measured and often compensated for.

The mechanism by which friction coupling degrades gyro performance should be clearly understood. For this purpose, let us examine the behavior of the two-degree-of-freedom gimbal system shown in Fig. 9-24. Any slight rotary motion of the supporting case about axis *AA* will carry the outer gimbal ring with it and, through friction in bearings A_1 and A_2, impose a torque on the gimbal. This slight rotation can be the result of vehicle motion, servo inaccuracy, or earth's rotation. Similarly, any slight rotary motion of the supporting case about axis BB will, through friction in bearings B_1 and B_2, impose a torque on the outer gimbal ring which will be directly transmitted to the gimbal. The torques thus imposed would cause the gyro to precess and degrade its accuracy as a space reference.

In an ideal frictionless, unit motion of the supporting case about the gimbal produces no torque and hence no disturbance to the gyro's spatial position.

In the single-degree-of-freedom gyro shown in Fig. 9-25, friction in bearings C_1 and C_2 directly limits its accuracy as a rate-sensing device about the input axis IA. No output axis (OA) response will occur until the input axis rate exceeds a threshold of

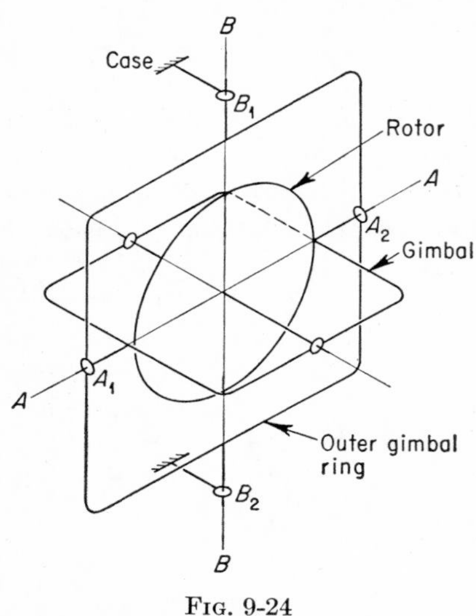

FIG. 9-24

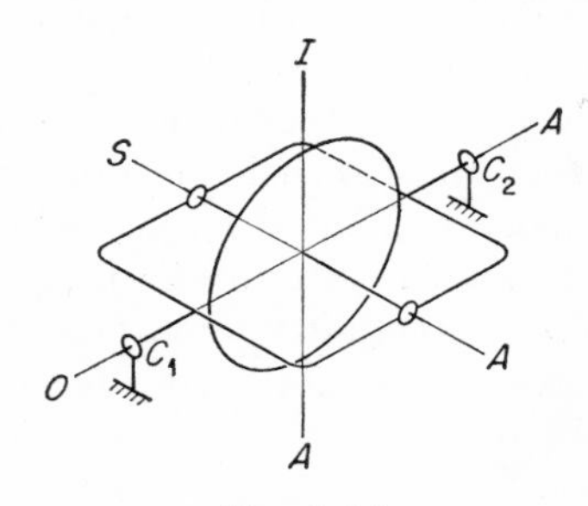

FIG. 9-25

$$\omega_{IA} = \frac{T_F}{H}$$

where ω_{IA} = input axis threshold rate
T_F = friction coupling in bearings C_1 and C_2
H = angular momentum of gyro wheel

Slip Rings. In some gyros the capability for rotation in excess of 360° must exist between gimbal and supporting case. Under these circumstances it is sometimes necessary to use slip rings to conduct electric power into the gimbal. The rubbing between the slip rings and their brushes produces an undesirable static friction coupling which limits this approach to low-accuracy units only.

The use of a servo follow-up system to limit the motion between gimbal and supporting case offers a distinct functional advantage. The slip rings necessary to accommodate complete continuous motion can then be used between servo-driven gimbal rings outside of the supporting case. Their friction load can then be taken up by the servomotors with no deterioration in gyro performance.

9-15. Balance Instability—Random

One of the most difficult problems facing the designer and manufacturer of gyros is the achievement of complete mechanical stability in the finished unit. Instability of gimbal balance can result either from small shifts of gimbal parts, contributing to a displacement of the center of mass of the gimbal assembly, or from shifts in suspension parts, causing a change in the location of the center of support.

In Sec. 9.10 unbalance torques were shown to be both systematic and acceleration-sensitive and hence amenable to compensation. However, any instability in gimbal balance would introduce an error into the compensation based on a previously measured value of unbalance. In gyros of high precision balance stability is required down to levels of a millionth of an inch.

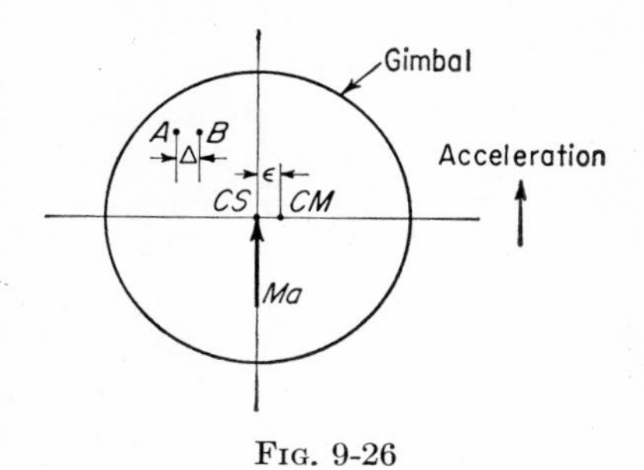

FIG. 9-26

Mass Instability. The gimbal assembly is composed of many parts joined together mechanically. A shift in any of these parts will change the location of the mass center and introduce a balance change. To examine this effect using Fig. 9-26, let

M = total mass of gimbal assembly
m = mass of a particular part on gimbal
Δ = shift of mass m from A to B, perpendicular to acceleration vector
ϵ = resulting change in location of mass center from CS to CM
T = unbalance change resulting from shift of mass m
a = acceleration

Assume an initially balanced condition where the gimbal center of mass CM is coincident with the center of support at CS. Next, consider the effect of a shift of part of the gimbal of mass m from A to B. This will cause the gimbal center of mass CM to shift by an amount in proportion to the mass ratio, which is

$$\epsilon = \Delta \frac{m}{M} \tag{9-95}$$

But

$$T = \epsilon M a$$

hence

$$T = \Delta \frac{m}{M} Ma = \Delta ma \tag{9-96}$$

This shows that the greater the mass of the part which can shift, the greater care must be taken to ensure stability. The major factors affecting mass stability will now be discussed.

Creep. Instability in structural parts of the gimbal assembly can result from creep which is a direct consequence of stress in the part. Very recent precision tests* have indicated a plastic flow at the microinch level in many common metals at stress values far below presently published elastic limits. These low but objectionable stress levels can result from a locked-in stress pattern remaining after fabrication and heat-treatment. In addition loading in the assembly may become excessive in the attempt to achieve secure shrink fits and tight bolting and bearing preloading conditions. A further consideration is the loading imposed by excessive conditions of shock, vibration, and acceleration.

Joining. The various elements comprising the gimbal assembly must be joined with extreme care to minimize the possibility of slippage between parts. Interference and shrink fits, dowel pins, precision-ground faces meeting squarely, and use of high-strength locking adhesives are all vital to the achievement of joints of maximum stability.

Number of Parts. The surest way of joining two parts with greatest stability is to fabricate them as one piece. The reduction in the number of separate parts is an important, sound philosophy to be applied in designing a gimbal assembly. This has received added impetus in recent designs in the area of the rotor spin bearings. An increasing number of precision gyros have eliminated separate bearing rings and have utilized bearing cartridges in which the bearing races are machined directly into the rotor and gimbal parts. In some designs a reduction in the number of parts has resulted from constructing the spin motor squirrel cage of one solid piece rather than as a laminated stack.

As gyros continue to "grow" smaller, the designer will be forced of necessity to combine functions into fewer numbers of parts, with a consequent potential improvement in dimensional stability.

Metallurgical Instability. With the constant demands for improved gyro performance the fundamental metallurgical stability of structural materials must receive greater attention. Lack of such stability can result in a dimensionally unstable part. The major cause of such a condition is an incomplete phase change in which an equilibrium condition is slowly attained. This can result when two metals form a solid solution at an elevated temperature, and as the temperature is lowered, the solubility of one metal decreases, forcing the second to precipitate. This precipitation may not be complete by the time the part is fabricated, resulting in an unstable condition.

* Bruce Chalmers, "The Structure and Mechanical Properties of Metals," Chapman & Hall, London, 1951.

Temperature Effects. The deleterious effect of temperature cycling on mass stability is perhaps the most serious and difficult problem to eliminate. Such cycling can occur while a unit is shut down and exposed to various temperature conditions before returning to normal operation. The resulting instability is random and generally can be explained by a number of phenomena.

1. Joints between materials having dissimilar coefficients of thermal expansion are prime suspects. Consider the series of diagrams in Fig. 9-27, which demonstrate a possible explanation of this type of unstable behavior. In Fig. 9-27*a*, a ring is shown assembled into a housing with an interference fit. Due to slight inaccuracies in the parts, a tighter fit exists at side *B* when compared with side *A*. The housing has a higher coefficient of expansion than the ring. Therefore, as the temperature of the assembly is reduced, the housing shrinks at a faster rate than the ring, resulting in a tendency for a slip to occur at the joint interface between the parts. As a result of the tighter fit on side *B*, slippage would occur at side *A* to the position shown in Fig. 9-27*b*. In addition, the radial stress at the interference fit would increase because of the more rapid shrinkage of the housing. As a result, some local plastic deformation might occur at side *B*, decreasing the fit differential between side *A* and side *B*. When the assembly is reheated to its original temperature, there is no assurance that the cycle of relative slippage will be exactly reversed. If the parts caught, or "hung up," to some extent at side *A*, then a slippage would occur at side *B*, resulting in the final displaced arrangement shown in Fig. 9-27.

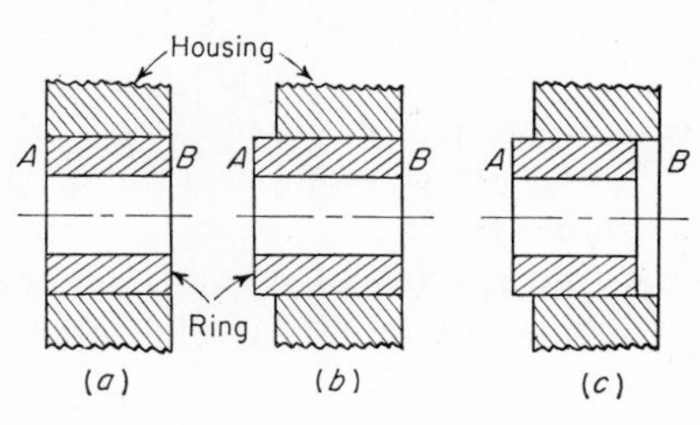

Fig. 9-27

This explanation exaggerates the degree to which this shift could occur. Nevertheless, it is quite probable that some partial behavior of this type does occur, with a resulting shift in the relative location of parts. Even if shift does not take place between parts of different coefficients of expansion, a varying internal stress situation will develop with temperature cycling and with it the possibility of creep.

2. Temperature gradients in the gimbal assembly can produce effects similar to those described above even when the parts being joined have equal coefficients of expansion. In the latter case the parts expand differently because their average temperature is different and not because they have different coefficients of thermal expansion.

3. Temperature cycling "exercises" each part, thus contributing to a relaxation of internal stresses which, in turn, can produce dimensional instability.

Shape of Parts. In general, gimbal parts of simple, massive shapes will offer greater potential for dimensional stability. Unwieldy, flimsy, irregular, or asymmetrical shapes should be avoided since they contain sharp stress concentrations at points of irregularity and are prone to networks of internal stresses resulting from uneven heating and cooling during heat-treatments. Furthermore, residual machining stresses and operating stresses are likely to be higher in such parts.

Spin Bearings. One special set of elements in the gimbal assembly deserves most careful attention in any discussion of mass stability. These are the rotor spin bearings. The functional problems imposed on them are quite formidable. They must support a significant portion of the gimbal weight, permitting it to rotate at very high speed with low friction, and must position it with the same complete stability as a shrink fit or a secured, bolted joint in other parts of the gimbal. Also, there are limitations to the weight of the lubricant that can be used, since this cannot be secured in position and might contribute to mass instability.

To ensure maximum stability, bearings are *preloaded,* constructed of materials having optimum characteristics of wear, hardness, and stability, and they are machined as closely as possible to perfect geometric shapes.

Support Instability. The random shift of the suspension parts which establish the position of the gimbal support vector is equivalent to mass instability in degrading unbalance compensation based on any previously measured data. An example of this would be a shift in the suspension-bearing bracket, shown in Fig. 9-28. Under conditions of shock, vibration, and temperature cycling it is a difficult problem to make such an arrangement stable down to a few millionths of an inch.

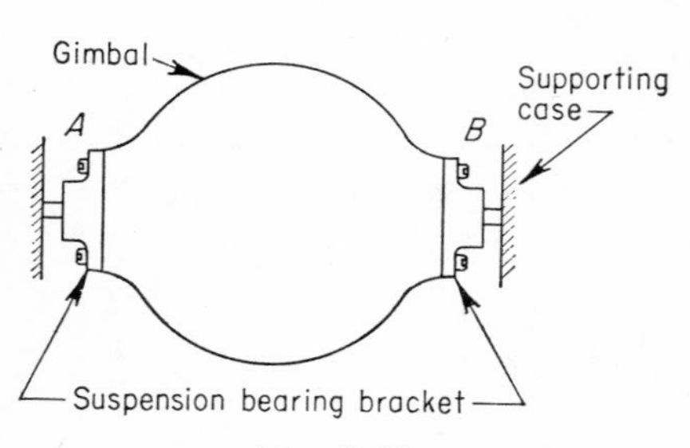

FIG. 9-28

The utilization of fluid suspension (described in Sec. 9-5) offers distinct advantages with regard to stability of the center of support. At neutral buoyancy, fluid forces supply all the supporting forces, and under expected conditions of inaccuracy of temperature control they will still contribute 2,749/2,750 of all supporting forces. The location of the center of support is therefore dependent on the geometry of the displaced fluid. This can be altered only if there is a shift or distortion in part of the gimbal shell. There is no concentration of support force at any one vital point, as in the bearing-supported arrangement in Fig. 9-28. Hence, there is less danger of shift due to shock and vibration loading.

The analysis below shows the unbalance torques resulting from support instability in both types of suspension. In the arrangement shown in Fig. 9-28, assume that the suspension bearings are equidistant from the mass center of the gimbal. If one of the bearing brackets, bracket B, for example, shifts by a small amount ϵ from position 1 to position 2 in a direction perpendicular to the acceleration vector, the resultant supporting force vector will shift by an amount $\epsilon/2$ from position 3 to position 4, as shown in Fig. 9-29. The dash-line vectors represent the position of forces after the shift. The resulting effect on balance stability will be

$$\text{Unbalance torque} = \tfrac{1}{2}\epsilon Ma \tag{9-97}$$

where M is total gimbal mass and a the acceleration.

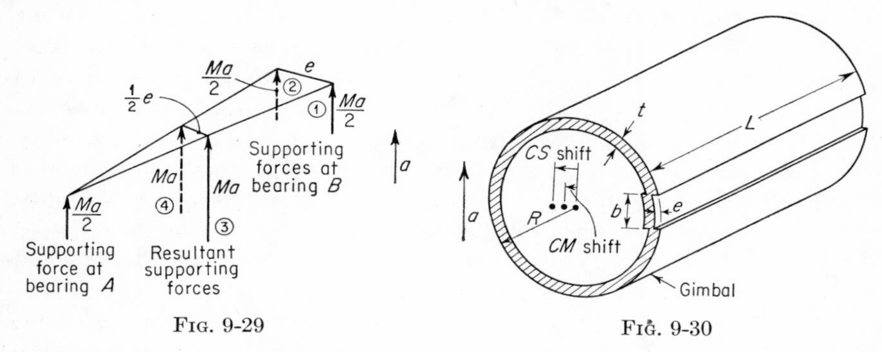

FIG. 9-29

FIG. 9-30

In the case of a fluid-suspended gyro some portion of the gimbal shell must shift in order to produce a shift in the location of the support vector. This could occur as a result of some structural instability or looseness in the shell. For simplicity, this is shown schematically in Fig. 9-30 as a motion of a simple element of a cylindrical gimbal shell in a direction perpendicular to the acceleration vector. Let

b = width of shell element which has shifted
t = thickness of shell
L = length of cylindrical gimbal
ρ_m = mass density of shell material
ρ_f = mass density of suspension fluid
a = acceleration
M = total gimbal mass
ϵ = distance shifted by gimbal element
m = mass of shifted element = $btL\rho_m$
m_f = mass of fluid in shifted volume = $beL\rho_f$
R = radius of gimbal cylinder

The shift in the center of mass of the gimbal will be

$$\text{CM shift} = \epsilon \frac{m}{M} \tag{9-98}$$

A shift in the gimbal center of buoyancy will occur. In a neutrally buoyant gimbal this will be a shift in the center of support.

$$\text{CS shift} = R\frac{m_f}{M} \tag{9-99}$$

The effect on gimbal balance will mean an

$$\text{Unbalance torque} = Ma(\text{CS shift} - \text{CM shift}) \tag{9-100}$$

Combining Eqs. (9-98) to (9-100), we get

$$\text{Unbalance torque} = a(Rm_f - \epsilon m) \tag{9-101}$$

In general the fluid-suspended gyro is less sensitive than the ball-bearing-suspended unit to any shift in center of support due to instability.

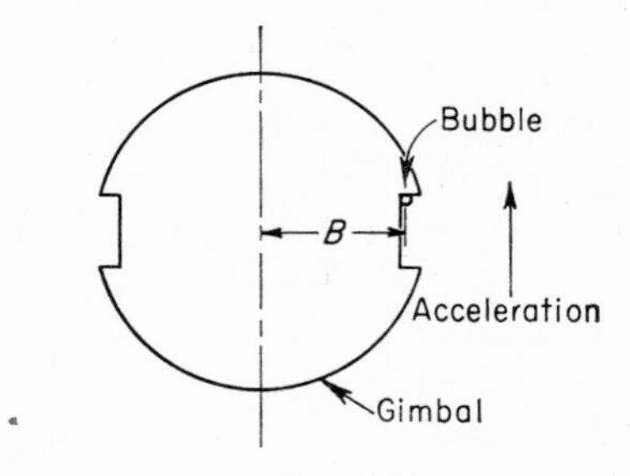

FIG. 9-31

It is, however, prone to the same type of torque from a different cause: bubbles in the suspension fluid. If a bubble is trapped in some gimbal cavity, as shown in Fig. 9-31, it will create an unbalance torque.

$$\text{Unbalance torque} = Bv\rho_f a \tag{9-102}$$

where B = moment arm shown
v = volume of bubble
ρ_f = fluid mass density
a = acceleration

If the bubble moves, the moment arm B will change, and the unbalance torque will change too. It is extremely important that the gyro parts and the fluid be thoroughly degassed before filling the gyro assembly and that perfect hermetic seals be realized to avoid any bubbles in the fluid.

9-16. Instability of Elastic Coupling—Random

As pointed out in Sec. 9-6, elastic coupling results from both mechanical and magnetic restraints. Variations in the value of the coupling gradient or in the location of its null position introduce torques on the gimbal. The mechanical contribution to this coupling is subject to the effects of hysteresis, metallurgical instability, creep, and slippage at holding clamps. The magnetic coupling can change with time and local environment.

Mechanical Coupling. The fundamental mechanical instability problems are similar to those of mass instability discussed previously.

Creep. Microplastic deformation of mechanical members with time and at comparatively low stresses has already been mentioned. The stress can result from loading or internal conditions. In either case a shift in the null position of the mechanical elastic member can occur, producing a torque on the gimbal in its servo-controlled central position with respect to the case.

Metallurgical Instability. The long-term completion of a phase change or any other transient metallurgical condition can lead to a change in shape of the elastic member, resulting in a torque on the gimbal.

Hysteresis. Under stress cycles the null position of an elastic member may change because of hysteresis in the metal.

Joint Instability. The completely stable attachment of an elastic member to the structural body of the gimbal or case can present a problem. Care must be taken to avoid stress concentration which could produce local deformation and the effect of a shift in the null position of the elastic member. Another consideration is slippage, which might occur at a clamp or joint. A sound approach to the problem is to minimize the number of parts and to fabricate part of the clamping arrangement directly into the elastic member.

Shape. Elastic members of simple shape offer greater potential for stability than those that are unwieldy, flimsy, or asymmetrical. They lend themselves to more even response to heat-treatment and symmetrical stress patterns.

In general, with stress factors being equal, greater elastic stability will result with a member having a lower torque gradient. Any random angular offset from a null position will reflect itself as a smaller torque with a lower torque gradient.

Magnetic Coupling. Magnetic coupling between gimbal and case can create a torque similar to that due to mechanical elastic restraints. Any initial compensation for elastic coupling will automatically include some portion to buck out the magnetic torque. Variations in field strengths, permeability, or retained permanent magnetism can alter the magnetic torque and introduce an error into the compensation. Best practice is to minimize the amount of magnetic material on or near the gimbal and to provide adequate shielding against external fields.

9-17. Suspension Fluid Torques—Random

Random suspension fluid torques are generally associated with bubbles, dirt in the fluid, density gradients, non-Newtonian characteristics, and lack of homogeneity. The effect of bubbles has already been discussed.

Dirt in the Fluid. Random torques can result from dirt in the fluid, lodging in small gaps between the gimbal and the case. This is especially important in single-degree-of-freedom units where very small fluid gaps are required to provide adequate damping with high-density flotation fluids. The use of pivot centering also leads to sensitivity to this disturbance, since the small clearance gap between pivot and jewel must be clean to prevent friction. Elastic centering avoids this problem, especially in a two-degree-of-freedom unit where no special damping requirements exist and large fluid gaps are permissible.

Non-Newtonian Characteristics. A fluid having non-Newtonian characteristics will exert torques as a result of a displacement between gimbal and case. This is in addition to viscous torques resulting from relative velocity. Lack of pure Newtonian properties introduces torques of an unpredictable nature which are part way between friction and elastic coupling. This is not normally a major problem, however, since in gyros of highest precision the suspension fluid to be selected is subjected to exhaustive tests to confirm its Newtonian behavior.

Lack of Homogeneity. Any lack of uniformity or homogeneity in the suspension fluid can produce torques due to a variety of phenomena such as density gradients, viscosity gradients, and non-Newtonianism.

These effects can occur as a result of chemical breakdown of the fluid or separation of components during temperature cycling.

PROBLEMS

9-1. In the two-degree-of-freedom gyro in Fig. 9-32 consider two arrangements of the Y-axis torquer acting between

(1) The supporting case and outer gimbal
(2) The supporting case and the inner gimbal

For each of these torquer arrangements, discuss the effect of the axial misalignment of the Y-axis torquer assuming that the latter is

(*a*) In the X-Y plane not perpendicular to the X axis
(*b*) In the Y-Z plane not perpendicular to the Z axis

Which case is most critical? Consider four combinations, i.e., (1)-(*a*), (1)-(*b*), (2)-(*a*), (2)-(*b*).

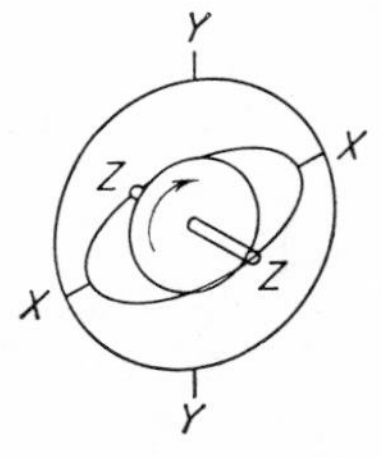

Fig. 9-32

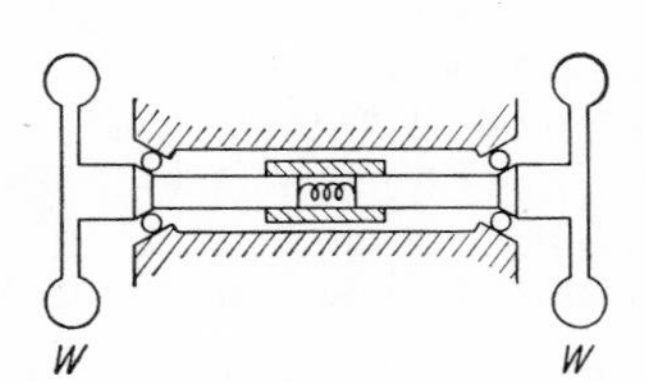

Fig. 9-33

9-2. In the preloaded bearing system shown in Fig. 9-33, discuss the axial compliance characteristics for

$$K_s > K_b$$
$$K_s < K_b$$

where K_b denotes the compliance rate of one bearing (pounds per inch), K_s represents the compliance rate of the center spring (pounds per inch), and P_0 is the initial load (pounds).

9-3. Using the following parameters, calculate the maximum friction torque that could be developed at the pivots of the floated gyro shown in Fig. 9-34:

Temperature error off buoyancy, 1°C
Acceleration, $2g$
Fluid volumetric coefficient of expansion, 800×10^{-6}/°C
Gimbal volumetric coefficient of expansion, 70×10^{-6}/°C
Fluid mass density at buoyancy, 2 g/cm^3
Pivot diameter, 0.05 cm
Pivot-jewel coefficient of friction in fluid, 0.01

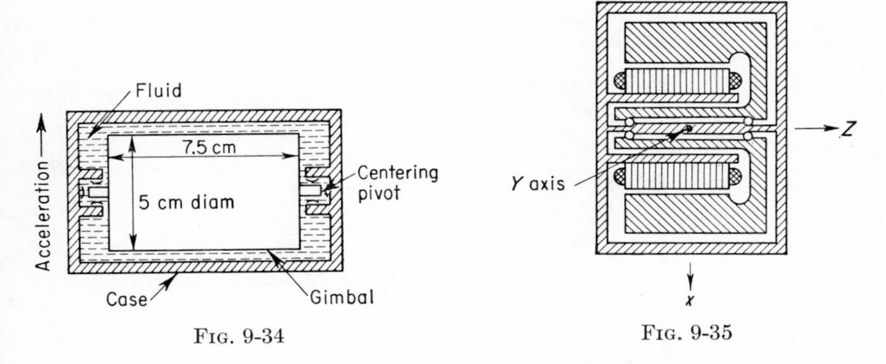

Fig. 9-34

Fig. 9-35

9-4. Consider the gyro shown schematically in Fig. 9-35 and having the following characteristics:

Part	Mass, g	Compliance, cm/dyne		
		C_x	C_y	C_z
Wheel..................	300	0.5×10^{-10}	0.5×10^{-10}	1×10^{-10}
Shaft..................	0	0.5×10^{-10}	0.5×10^{-10}	0
Bearing pair............	0	2.5×10^{-10}	2.5×10^{-10}	2.5×10^{-10}
Stator (and its support)..	75	1×10^{-10}	1×10^{-10}	0

The angular momentum of the gyro is 10^6 dyne-cm/sec. Calculate the compliance torque exerted on the gyro for the following accelerations:

(*a*) $2g$ in the XZ plane at 45° to the two axes
(*b*) $2g$ parallel to the X axis

9-5. Given a gyro with an angular momentum H and a spin velocity ω_s, discuss the effect on gyro precession caused by the following systematic torques, if the density of the wheel material is doubled so that the angular momentum will be $2H$ at a spin velocity of ω_s.

(*a*) Elastic
(*b*) Viscous coupling
(*c*) Magnetic
(*d*) Nonorthogonality of suspension axes
(*e*) Unbalance (Assume that the unbalance torque is proportional to wheel weight.)
(*f*) Compliance (Assume that the mass of the wheel is the only significant mass in the compliant gimbal structure.)
(*g*) Temperature error
(*h*) Fluid

BIBLIOGRAPHY

1. Gray, Andrew: "A Treatise on Gyrostatics and Rotational Motion-theory Applications," St. Martin's Press, New York, 1918.
2. Deimel, R. F.: "Mechanics of the Gyroscope: The Dynamics of Rotation," Dover Publications, New York, 1950.
3. Ferry, E. S.: "Applied Gyrodynamics," rev. ed., John Wiley & Sons, Inc., New York, 1933.

CHAPTER 10

GYROSCOPIC ELEMENTS

By George H. Neugebauer

Nomenclature

a = major axis of ellipse
A = area
b = minor axis of ellipse
B = total bearing curvature
C = bearing compliance
C_A, C_B = elastic constants
C_D = diametral clearance in bearing
D, d = diameter
e = eccentricity
E = modulus of elasticity
f = coefficient of friction
F, P = load
G = shear modulus of elasticity
h = thickness; bearing-groove depth
J = polar moment of inertia
K, k = (spring) constant
K_p = permeation constant
L = moment arm; length
m = conformity factor
M = figure of merit; moment; molecular weight
n = number of balls
p = unit pressure
Q = volume per unit time
R = ratio of axial to radial stiffness of bearing; radius
S = bearing-ring contact stress
T = torque; temperature
V = radial load on bearing
w = width
W = weight
Y = deflection

α = angular acceleration; coefficient of expansion
β = bearing contact angle
δ = deflection
θ = angle
μ = micro . . . (10^{-6}); coefficient of viscosity
ν = Poisson ratio
ρ = mass density
σ = normal stress
τ = shear stress

10-1. Introduction

The design of precision gyroscopes with the low drift rates needed in many modern applications, particularly for inertial navigation, requires both an over-all philosophic approach and a tremendous respect for the usually insignificant details. For inertial navigation, random drift rates in thousandths of a degree per hour are being discussed and measured. A gyro with a steady drift rate of 0.001°/hr would drift only 8.76° in a year, or it would take more than 41 years to make a complete revolution! Every effort should be made to keep all torques acting on a gyro to a minimum, but, theoretically at least, it is possible to compensate for all except random (unpredictable) torques.

Before tackling the problem of designing a gyro, the design engineer must become completely familiar with the over-all requirements of the particular application and be cognizant of all the possible sources of error torques. Table 10-1 indicates typical drift ranges for several applications. The drift rates (degrees per hour) are average in a $1g$ field.

TABLE 10-1. ACCURACY REQUIREMENTS OF GYROSCOPES

Type of gyroscope	*Gyro drift-rate requirements, deg/hr*
Rate gyroscope for fire and flight control	10–150
Directional gyroscope and gyro horizon for flight indication and autopilot applications	1–15
Marine gyro vertical	1–5
Polar (high-altitude) directional gyroscope (compensated for earth rotation; used in traversing polar regions)	0.1–1
Gyrocompass (ship-borne)	0.03–0.4
Gyroscope for aircraft inertial navigator	0.0005–0.1

The sources of error torques are many but may be arbitrarily divided into two classes: (1) acceleration-sensitive torques and (2) nonacceleration-sensitive torques.

The acceleration-sensitive torques include (1) mass unbalance with respect to output axes, (2) center-of-buoyancy unbalances with respect to output axes, (3) compliance torques, (4) unbalance due to bubbles in fluid, and (5) fluid torques due to temperature errors combined with acceleration. Items (2), (4), and (5) would apply only to floated gyros. The degree of balance which can be attained by proper design, fabrication, and adjustments is remarkable, but maintaining this balance over long periods, with and without shutdowns, is very difficult. For high-performance gyroscopes shifts in center of gravity and center of buoyancy must be detected in billionths of an inch. This can be achieved only by having perfectly symmetrical designs, by using stable materials, by avoiding high stresses which may be relieved, by avoiding contacts between materials having different coefficients of expansion, by avoiding temperature gradients, by using structural and other members with maximum rigidity, by using flotation fluids with low coefficients of expansion to avoid density gradients, by designing for isoelasticity, etc. It is impossible to design a gyroscope which would meet all these requirements, and a compromise is always necessary. For example, the coefficients of expansion of the motor laminations and the winding do not match, but the stator may be made comparatively stable by designing for maximum-use factor in the slots, by winding coils tightly by machine, and by impregnating or encapsulating the windings. Bubbles in the fluid can be avoided by adequate degassing and sealing techniques. Fluid torques due to temperature gradients combined with acceleration may be minimized by good temperature control and by the use of high-conductivity materials to avoid temperature gradients.

The nonacceleration-sensitive torques include (1) fixed torques due to centering wires, (2) friction torques at pivots or due to dirt in fluid, (3) fixed torques due to electric flex leads, (4) magnetic torques due to interaction of magnetic material with the earth's field or other stray fields, (5) coercion of pickoffs, and (6) stray torques of electrical torquers. These torques must also be kept to a minimum by proper design and assembly techniques. For example, the torques due to external magnetic fields may be easily reduced to negligible values by shielding and by using nonmagnetic materials where possible.

Design Principles. To summarize, the basic principles listed below should be followed in the design of high-performance gyros.

1. Design for high angular momentum per unit of weight and random torque.
2. Use simple, rigid construction. Avoid compound structures unless joined by brazing, welding, or equivalent bond.
3. Fabricate from stable materials only.
4. Use materials with matched coefficients of expansion, preferably low values.
5. Avoid assembly procedures or processes which will cause instability.

6. Design for symmetry.
7. Design for isoelasticity.
8. Avoid large heat sources that may cause severe temperature gradients.
9. Use high-conductivity materials to avoid temperature gradients.
10. Design at stress levels well below the elastic limit.

In the ensuing sections discussing the elements of the gyroscope, the basic design goals must always be kept in mind and not forgotten in the morass of details. The design of high-precision gyros will be emphasized, since this is a difficult task, whereas practically no effort is required to degrade gyro performance by several orders of magnitude.

10-2. Gyro Spin Bearings

The assembly of precision gyro spin bearings and all subsequent operations on a gyro element with exposed bearings must be performed in a superclean area. Dirty bearings will result in rough operation, random torques, and high rate of wear with consequent weight shifts.

The function of the gyro spin bearings is to provide a stable and rigid axis of rotation for the gyrowheel with low friction and adequate life. Bearings must be stable in order to reduce mass shifts. They should be rigid and have the proper elastic ratios in order to minimize compliance effects. They should have a low friction torque in order to reduce to a minimum the weight of the motor and the effects of temperature gradients due to the power input. Lastly, they must have a life adequate for the particular application.

Although some development work, mostly of a classified nature, is being performed on hydrodynamic (gas) spin bearings, most precision gyroscopes use ball bearings.

Ball bearings have a number of desirable characteristics. They will maintain relatively accurate alignment of parts over long periods of time; they are relatively very rigid; they may take both radial and axial loads; their lubrication is simply accomplished by a supply of oil or grease for the life of the bearing; and they have low starting torque as well as low running torque. Ball-bearing characteristics are well known, based on many years of experience in various applications, and development work is continuing to improve bearing geometry and materials for gyroscopic applications.

In this text the discussion on bearings is not intended to be complete or exhaustive, but the background information should be sufficient to ensure an intelligent selection for most applications. For more detailed information, consult the manufacturers' literature and the references at the end of the chapter. It is assumed that the spin bearings will be at least of ABEC 5 quality and preferably ABEC 7 or better.

The stability of bearing materials is of utmost importance to the stability of the gyro. The most commonly used steels for bearings are the 52100 and 51100 steel alloys, and until recently they have been universally hardened to Rockwell C62 to C65. However, it has been found that at this high hardness there is still considerable retained austenite and that the retained austenite will transform into martensite when subjected to the stress cycling that occurs in a loaded ball bearing. There are also rather high internal stresses which tend to be relieved with time. Both of the above factors result in volumetric changes or in warping. In order to minimize these effects gyro spin bearings are generally drawn to a slightly lower hardness of about C58 to C61 and are temperature-cycled to −100°F before final grinding. This treatment reduces slightly the ultimate tensile strength but optimizes the elastic limit and the dimensional stability (see Table 10-4).

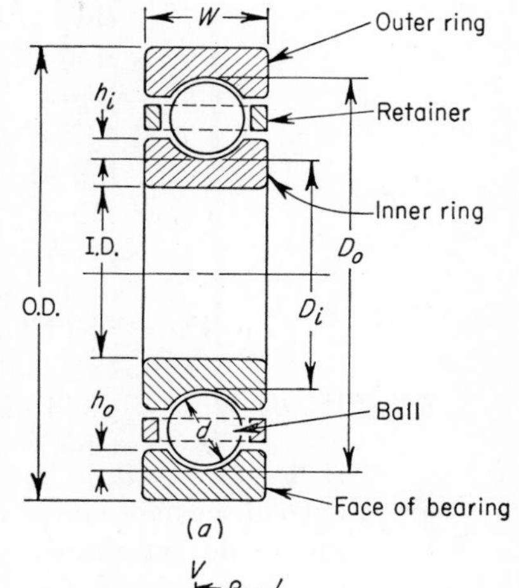

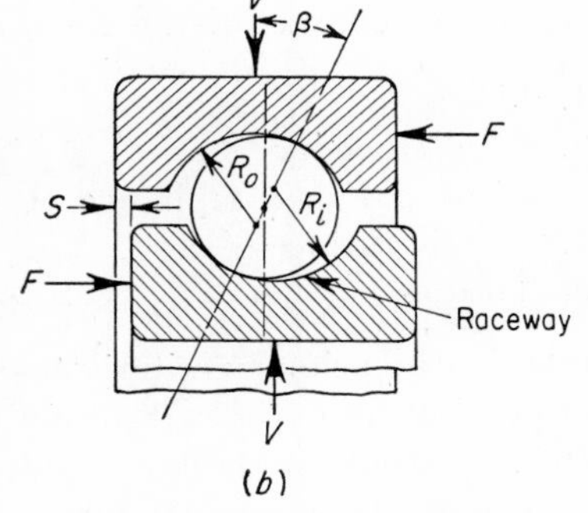

Fig. 10-1

Definition of Terms. A ball bearing consists of four essential parts: (1) the outer ring on which the balls roll; (2) the balls; (3) the inner ring on which the balls roll; and (4) the retainer or separator which maintains a proper angular separation of the balls. The parts of a ring on which the balls roll are called the *raceway* or *race* (see Fig. 10-1).

The following terms are used frequently and should be a familiar part of the vocabulary of every gyro designer. They are illustrated in Fig. 10-1 or derived therefrom.

OD = outside diameter
ID = inner diameter or bore
d = ball diameter
n = number of balls
D_i, D_o = race diameter
W = width of ring (outer and/or inner ring)

R_i, R_o = radius of curvature of raceway

f_i, f_o = race curvature. A measure of conformity of the race to the ball. $f_i = R_i/d$, $f_o = R_o/d$. It is sometimes expressed as a percentage instead of as a decimal

B = total curvature $= f_o + f_i - 1$

V = radial load applied to bearing

F = thrust or axial load applied to bearing

S = ring stickout or offset under a given thrust load

h_i, h_o = race or groove depth

β = Contact angle. Angle between radial line and line through ball contact points

C_D = Diametral clearance or radial play $= D_o - D_i - 2d$. Press fits of the races will reduce the diametral clearance or even make it negative

Y_V, Y_F = yield or deflection, radial or axial, from a zero external load condition

$dY_V/dV, dY_F/dF$ = yield rate or slope of load-deflection curve

R_Y = elastic ratio $= dY_F/dF \div dY_V/dV$

NOTE: The subscripts i and o denote inner and outer race, respectively.

Performance Characteristics. The following are the most important performance characteristics for use as a spin bearing.

1. Life
2. Load capacity
3. Yield rate or compliance
4. Elastic ratio
5. Torque

These are the primary criteria to consider in the successful application of spin bearings in a gyro; all others are secondary.

Life. In general the life of spin bearings is not limited by the fatigue strength of the material; instrument bearings rarely fail by spalling. Most bearing failures are really lubricant failures due to insufficient lubrication or to local overheating. Out-of-round shafts and bearing housings, misalignment of bearings, bearing geometry errors, and instability of materials resulting in dimensional changes contribute to early lubricant failure.

For best results bearings should be fitted on shafts or housings that are round to within 50 μin. The effect of angular misalignment of a pair of bearings will depend on the race curvature and the contact angle; bearings with open curvature and low contact angle can operate with greater misalignment than those with close curvature and high contact angles.

Errors in race roundness, groove profile, ball sphericity, and ball matching are probably the most serious bearing geometry errors. Tolerances on raceways of 50 μin., ball sphericity to 5 μin., and ball matching to 10 μin. are not uncommon.

The effect of contact angle on life is rather complex. The amount of slipping of the balls on the races increases as the contact angle increases, but the resultant load on each ball for a given axial preload is reduced, thus lowering the frictional torque and resultant heating effects. It might be stated that, in general, the life of instrument bearings is not too dependent on the contact angle.

It is generally considered that the life of a bearing varies approximately inversely proportional to the square or cube of the speed. If failures due to fatigue alone are considered, it would be expected that the life is inversely proportional to the speed. There is some evidence that with the higher surface speeds obtained with outer-race rotation, the life may be only two-thirds that obtained with inner-race rotation.

Load Capacity. The maximum load on a bearing is equal to the preload plus the change in load due to acceleration or shock. The maximum load must not exceed the load capacity of the bearing.

The load capacity of a bearing will vary with the size of the bearing, the number of balls, the size of the balls, the contact angle, the race curvature, and the desired life. The axial load capacity for a given size bearing will increase with increased contact angle, since the normal load per ball is $F/n \sin \beta$. The smaller the race curvature, the more closely it will conform to the ball and therefore the greater the load capacity. For gyro stability, the maximum stress on the bearings due to vibration or acceleration should not exceed the elastic limit of the bearing material after initial run-in. For the 52100 or 51100 steels that are most commonly used, the elastic limit is usually considered to be about 150,000 lb/in.^{2}, although a value of about 90,000 lb/in.^{2} is more appropriate where stability is a factor.

Yield Rate or Compliance. In order to reduce compliance torque effects the yield rate for spin bearings should be as low as practicable. Large bearings, heavy preloads, close race curvatures, and use of preloaded pairs rather than spring-loaded pairs all tend to reduce compliance. Most of these factors unfortunately also tend to increase the bearing torque and aggravate the problem of lubrication. Compliance of bearings will be discussed below.

Elastic Ratio. The elastic ratio R_Y of a bearing is the ratio of axial yield rate to radial yield rate. An ideal gyro would have an over-all elastic ratio of 1 in order to eliminate compliance torque effects. Such a gyro is said to be isoelastic. Theoretically it is possible to have an over-all elastic ratio of 1 even though each component (bearings, rotor, motor, etc.) may have an elastic ratio different from 1. In practice, however, it is best to design each component to be isoelastic, since variations due to tolerances will have a less significant effect. It has been determined that isoelasticity of a ball bearing is achieved at a contact angle of about 35°. The effect of contact angle on the elastic ratio is illustrated in Fig. 10-2 for a typical gyro bearing. It is evident that slight errors in preload or contact angle will not affect the elastic ratio as much at the nominal value of 35° as at the lower nominal value of 15°.

Torque. In order to minimize temperature effects and motor size it is desirable to have low bearing friction torque. Small-diameter bearings, high contact angles, low preloads, and open curvature all tend to reduce bearing friction torque. These same factors also affect life, load capacity, compliance, and elastic ratio; therefore, a compromise is necessary and engineering judgment must be used in any particular application. Most designers use isoelastic bearings and consider the stiffness-torque ratio as the most important figure of merit. It has been found that the frictional torque varies approximately as the four-thirds power of the load for any given bearing and speed. The torque is also very dependent on the lubricant, as the viscous drag of the lubricant increases with speed and decreases with a rise in temperature.

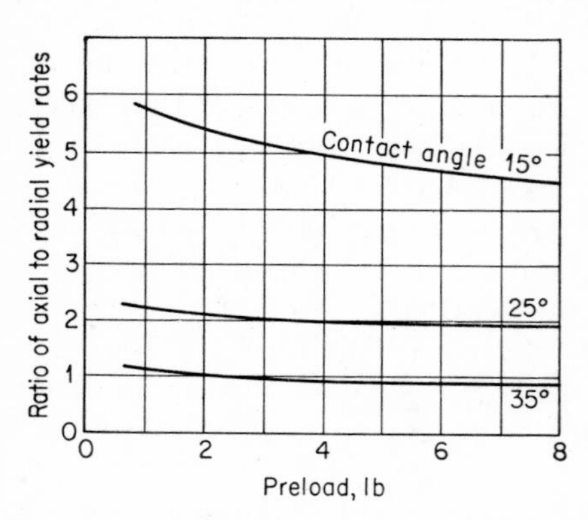

Fig. 10-2. Effect of preload and contact angle on the elastic ratio of a bearing.[5]

Bearing Compliance. In many gyro applications, particularly in missiles subject to high accelerations, anisoelastic torques are very significant, since they vary as the square of acceleration. An anisoelastic compliance torque, which is negligible at an acceleration of $1g$, becomes two orders of magnitude greater at $10g$. The compliance of the bearings is particularly important, since the mass of the wheel and the driving rotor are attached to the bearing and move with it.

It is most convenient to discuss the axial compliance of a bearing and its elastic ratio from which the radial compliance may be derived. Figure 10-3 shows the moment resulting from the center-of-gravity shift of a typical gyro, due to compliance of a preloaded bearing pair under $10g$ loading, as a function of the angle of loading and the initial contact angle.[5,21,*]

* Superscript numbers indicate references listed in the Bibliography at the end of the chapter.

Consider the compliance of a single bearing. According to the Hertz equations,[1,2] the yield of a ball on a grooved plate varies as the two-thirds power of the load, i.e.,

$$Y_F = k(F)^{2/3} \tag{10-1}$$

where k is a constant dependent on ball and plate geometry and materials. Tests with glass balls on flat glass plates have confirmed the theory. However, tests with steel balls on grooved steel plates[3] indicate that the power of F is frequently nearer one-half for these materials and proportions. That is, the load-deflection curve is more nearly parabolic, as expressed by

$$Y_F = k(F)^{1/2} \tag{10-2}$$

The expression for the yield of a bearing is not quite as simple, since in addition to the deflection of ball and races there is also an increase in the contact angle as the load rises.[19,20] There is little change in contact angle with load when the initial contact angle is greater than 25°. The load-deflection curve of the bearing will then be of the type given by Eq. (10-1) or (10-2), where k depends on the geometry of the bearing, the number of balls, and the materials. With low contact angles there may be a considerable change in contact angle with load, and its effect cannot be neglected. A typical yield curve for a single bearing subjected to a thrust load is shown in Fig. 10-4. The slope dY_F/dF is a maximum at no load and quickly drops to a comparatively low value. Thus the slope (compliance) at F_2 is only one-third that at F_1; therefore, when subjected to a small external load, a bearing with a preload of F_2 will have only one-third the compliance it would have if the preload were F_1.

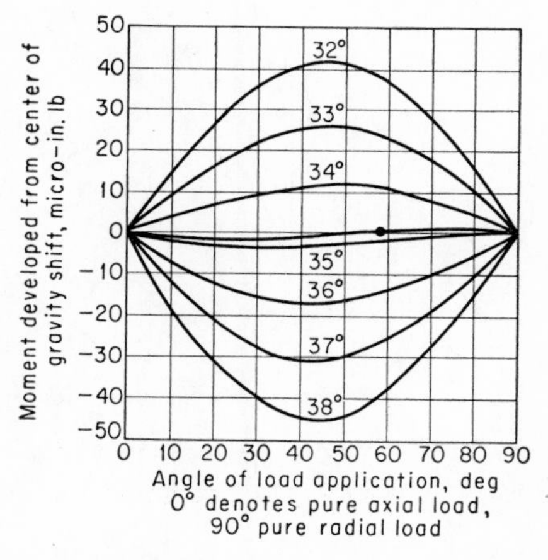

FIG. 10-3. Moment resulting from the center-of-gravity shift as a function of the angle of loading and initial contact angle.[5]

Compliance of Spring-loaded Pairs. If a pair of bearings is mounted on a shaft and internally loaded by a soft spring so that the two bearings are equally but oppositely loaded, this pair is said to be *spring-preloaded.* A pair of bearings J and K, preloaded by a spring to the load (F_e), is shown schematically in Fig. 10-5; the yield curve of each bearing is shown in Fig. 10-4. If the structure is subjected to an acceleration A, the inertia of the shaft and wheels will cause the bearings to deflect, and the shaft will move slightly to the right.

Because of the soft preload spring, the slight deflection will not appreciably relieve the load on bearing J; therefore, the load on bearing J will remain at F_0. On the other hand, bearing K must resist the spring preload plus inertia load (external load) F_e. The total load on bearing K will

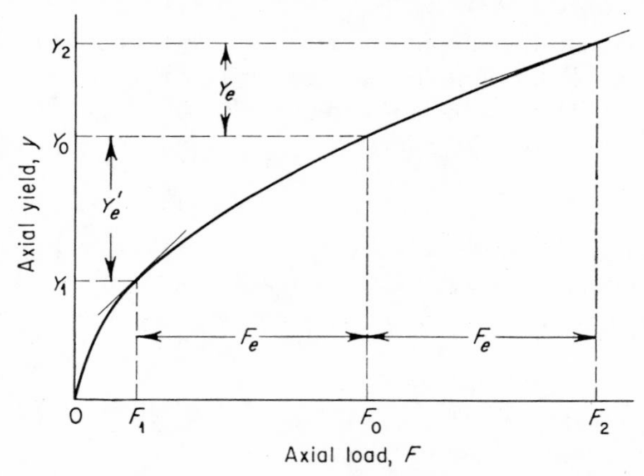

FIG. 10-4. Typical yield curve for a single bearing.

now be F_2, where $F_2 = F_0 + F_e$, and the deflection due to the external load will be $Y_e = Y_2 - Y_0$. The average compliance of the bearing is

$$C = \frac{Y_e}{F_e} = \frac{Y_2 - Y_0}{F_e} \tag{10-3}$$

For a sufficiently high preload, the compliance will be approximately constant.

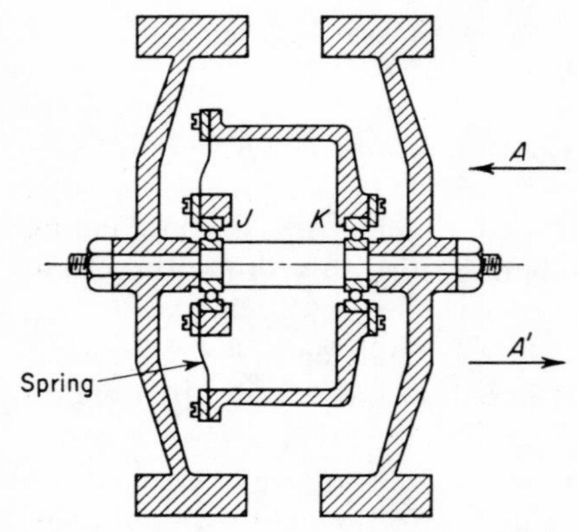

FIG. 10-5. Spring-preloaded gyro bearings.

However, under the acceleration A' acting in the opposite direction, the load on bearing J will still be F_0, but the load on bearing K will drop to F_1, where $F_1 = F_0 - F_e$. The average compliance in this case is

$$C' = \frac{Y_e'}{F_e} = \frac{Y_0 - Y_1}{F_e} \tag{10-4}$$

Depending on the preload and F_e, the compliance C' may be appreciably greater than C, and the action is nonlinear. If $F_e = F_0$, then bearing K is completely relieved of load. For $F_e > F_0$, the preload spring will take the entire load, and the compliance will be that of the preload spring.

The following are the principal advantages of a spring-loaded bearing pair:

1. It has comparative insensitivity to groove wobble and misalignment.
2. The preload is not affected by changes in temperature.
3. The preload is not affected by moderate wear.
4. Looser machining and assembly tolerances are possible.

The principal disadvantages are as follows:

1. The rigidity is reduced by a factor of 2.
2. Expansions due to temperature variations are not, in general, balanced, since one end is fixed while the other is floating. This will cause changes in balance.
3. A radial load can cause an angular rotation of the spin axis, especially with high-contact-angle bearings, because of the rotational compliance of the spring about a radial axis.

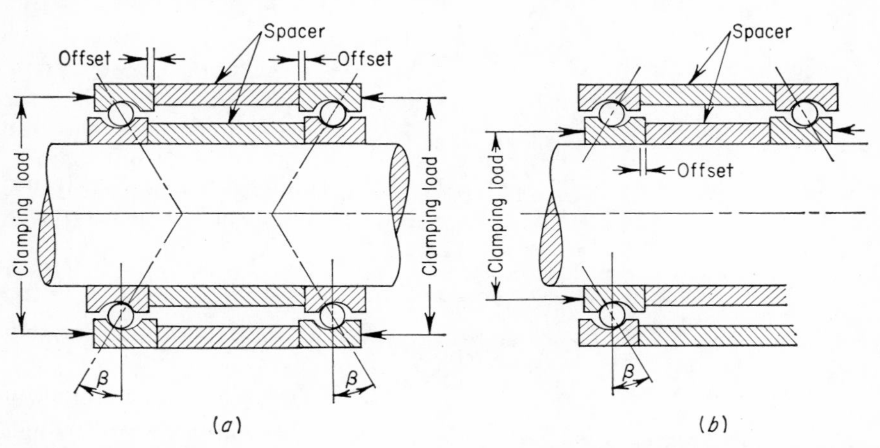

FIG. 10-6. Preloaded pair bearings. (*a*) Preloaded *DF* (face to face); (*b*) preloaded *DB* (back to back).

4. Because of the dissymmetry of axial compliance, the compliance torque constant will vary with the amplitude and direction of the acceleration.
5. A higher preload is required to withstand an equal acceleration in either direction as compared to a preloaded pair described in the next section.

Compliance of Preloaded Pairs. If two bearings are rigidly mounted in opposition, as indicated in Fig. 10-6*a* or *b*, they are called a *preloaded pair*. Before the clamping load is applied, there is an offset between the outer ring and the spacer in Fig. 10-6*a* and an offset between the inner ring and the spacer in Fig. 10-6*b*. This offset is reduced to zero by the clamping and determines the design preload. It is evident that the arrangement of Fig. 10-6*b* is more resistant to a moment about a radial axis, but it is more sensitive to temperature changes (see the following section).

The load-deflection curve of a preloaded pair will now be analyzed. The yield curve of a single bearing of a preloaded pair is shown in Fig. 10-7 as curve 1. Let F_0 be the preload on the pair and Y_0 the corresponding deflection per bearing. Reflect curve 1 about the line $Y = Y_0$ to obtain curve 2.

If an external axial load F_e is applied to the shaft of the preloaded pair, the load on one bearing (bearing 1) will increase, while the other bearing load will be partially relieved. It is evident that the increase in deflection on bearing 1 is exactly equal to the decrease in deflection on bearing 2, provided the deflections of the spacers are negligible, as is usually the case. Referring to Fig. 10-7, the change in deflection Y_e has increased the load on bearing 1 from F_0 to F_1 and decreased the load on bearing 2 from F_0 to F_2. The applied external load

$$F_e = F_1 - F_2 \tag{10-5}$$

and the corresponding deflection is Y_e. Since both bearings are active in a preloaded pair, the compliances of the pair at a given preload are only one-half the compliance of a single bearing at the same preload.

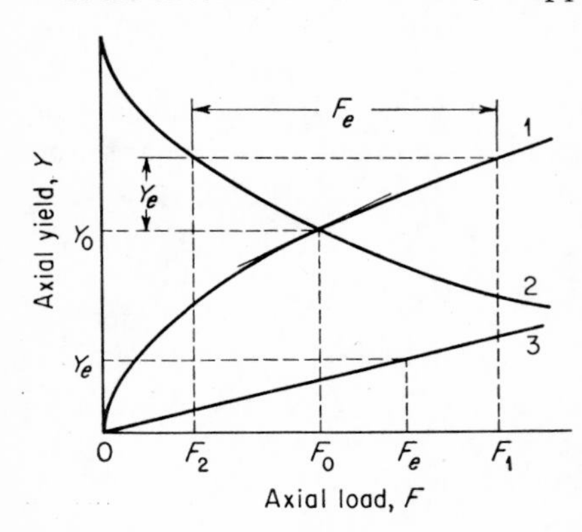

FIG. 10-7. Determination of the axial compliance of a typical preloaded pair bearing. Curve 1 is the load-deflection curve of each bearing of the pair; curve 2 is reflection of curve 1 about line y_0; and curve 3 is the derived load-deflection curve of the preloaded pair.

It can be shown that a preloaded pair with a parabolic deflection curve for each individual bearing [Eq. (10-2)] will result in a linear load-deflection curve for the pair (Fig. 10-7) and that one bearing is completely unloaded when the externally applied load $F_e = 4F_0$.[21] However, the parabolic law only applies for high-contact-angle bearings. For preloaded low-initial-contact-angle bearings, the relief load may be as high as five to seven times the preload, because of the change in angle with load. If the ball deflection follows the Hertzian[20] equation (10-1) rather than (10-2), the load deflection of a preloaded high-contact-angle bearing pair will be nearly linear for external loads up to approximately one and one-half times the preload. One bearing of the pair will be completely relieved by an external load $F_e = 2\sqrt{2}\,F_0$. For low-contact-angle bearings, however, a considerably higher external load will be required for relief of the preload. The maximum load on a bearing should always be smaller than the relief load in order to avoid scuffing and brinelling.

Fits and Temperature Effects. Since contact angle varies with initial internal clearance, any expansion or contraction of the bearing rings due to fits or temperature differentials will change the contact angle and, therefore, the preload. It is important to anticipate these effects during the design stage.

Usually in gyro designs the shaft member tends to run hotter than the outer member. With the preload arrangement illustrated in Fig. 10-6*a*, a relative axial or radial expansion of the shaft member will cause an increase in preload. With the arrangement illustrated in Fig. 10-6*b*, the axial expansion of the shaft member tending to reduce the preload will partially offset the increase in preload due to the radial expansion. If temperature differentials are appreciable, the latter design provides better maintenance of the initial preload.

If materials with different coefficients of expansion are used in the preloading members, considerable difficulty may be encountered. Every effort should be made to use materials with similar coefficients of expansion in all members that may affect the preload.

Bearing Lubrication. The lubrication of gyro spin bearings is a field in which much effort will be required before the art of gyroscopy becomes satisfactory. Proper lubrication is required to obtain low friction torque, long life, and stability. Whether for spin bearings or other applications, the lubricant performs the following functions:

1. Prevents metal-to-metal contact between raceways and balls and reduces sliding friction where true rolling motion is violated. Sliding friction is enhanced by high loads, high contact angles, and close conformity of the raceways.
2. Reduces sliding friction between retainer and balls and between retainer and rings.
3. Protects bearing parts from corrosion.
4. Assists the shields in preventing any harmful foreign matter from entering the bearing.
5. Assists in dissipating heat.

With proper bearing and shield design and proper assembly practices, long life, stability, and low torque have been achieved with grease- or oil-lubricated bearings and with inner- or outer-race rotation.

With outer-race rotation the shields must be carefully gasketed to prevent loss of oil due to centrifugal force. With inner-race rotation slingers should be provided to throw the oil back into the bearing. A conical section on the shaft within the grease cavity is effective, the large end of the cone being next to the bearing, as in Fig. 10-8.

In most gyro applications it is desirable to have as high an angular momentum as practicable; therefore, most gyros operate at speeds in the range of 10,000 to 30,000 rpm. For comparatively low friction torque at these speeds and for minimum weight shift, ball retainers are generally made of phenolic laminate, although porous nylon and other resins have been used.

Grease Lubrication. A grease is a semisolid, composed of a saponified animal or vegetable oil compounded with a natural mineral or synthetic oil. For spin-bearing applications, it must satisfy the following requirements:

1. Yield a supply of free oil in sufficient quantity to satisfy the functions listed above.
2. Remain stable in consistency and chemically neutral within the required life and temperature range. Must not separate into its constituents of oil and soap.
3. Channel properly and not cause weight shifts by mass flow due to a steady acceleration, shock, or vibration within the operating or storage temperature ranges.
4. Have a low vapor pressure, particularly in applications where the gyro is degassed and/or evacuated several times or for prolonged periods during the assembly operations.

For best results, grease cavities should be provided on either side of the bearing. When no more than half filled (to avoid overheating and loss of excess grease), these cavities should contain the minimum quantity of grease required for the desired life of the bearings. This quantity will depend on the particular application and the type of grease and should be determined by test or from previous experience with similar applications. The advice of the bearing manufacturer should be sought whenever possible. Bearings may be obtained with shields and grease grooves from several manufacturers, but the quantity of grease is frequently too limited for very long life, say above 5,000 hr of operation.

The principal advantages of the grease-lubricated bearing are the comparative ease with which sufficient lubricant may be supplied and the protection it provides from contamination during assembly. The principal disadvantages are the long run-in time required for proper channeling (varies from possibly 50 hr or less for some petroleum greases to 100 to 200 hr for some silicone greases) and the possibility of weight shifts in the very low drift rate gyros used in inertial navigation. It should be noted that an initial run-in at low speeds improves bearing performance, probably by improving the conformity of the contact surfaces, and thus prevents local overheating and excessive wear. The initial run-in period should be at least 24 hr, with the speed being increased in several steps from about 200 rpm to full operational speed. If the bearing is disassembled or the preload removed, the run-in procedure should be repeated all over again. A bearing is considered to be properly run-in when the high-speed torque is stabilized.

Oil Lubrication. Many modern gyros are lubricated by oil-impregnated retainers. The retainers are vacuum-impregnated for maximum retention and centrifuged at 400g to remove excess oil that might cause weight shifts. Many designers consider oil-lubricated bearings superior to grease-lubricated bearings, because possible weight shifts are minimized and less run-in time is required. At the present time, however,

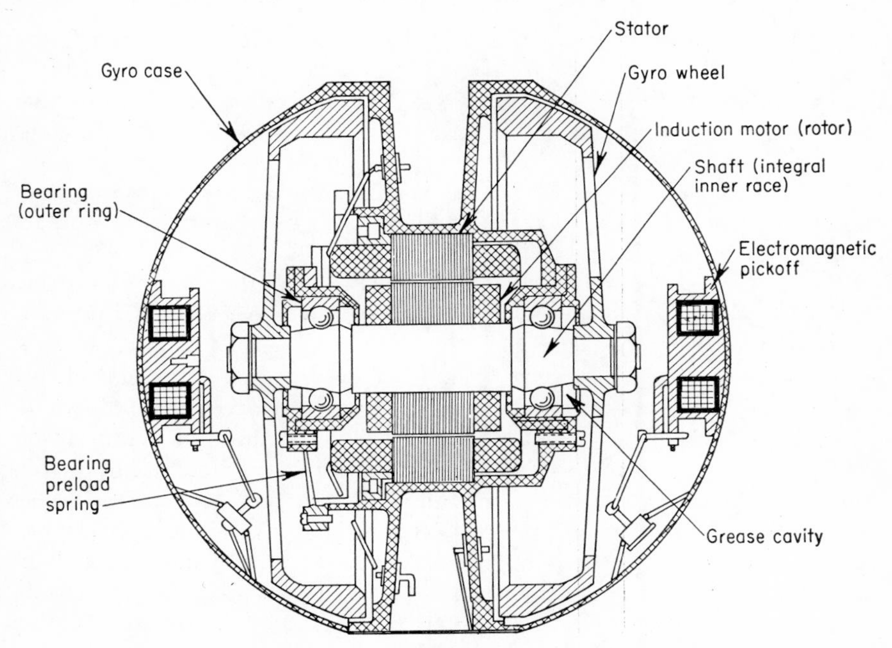

FIG. 10-8. Section of typical two-degree-of-freedom gyro. (*Arma Division, American Bosch Arma Corporation.*)

these advantages are more illusory than real, since properly designed grease cavities with a minimum amount of a stiff grease will result in negligible weight shifts. For best results, all bearings should be run-in for a period of at least 24 hr, starting at a low speed and reaching full speed in several steps; a 50-hr run-in is preferred by the author.

The ideal retainer material should absorb sufficient oil for the life of the bearing and supply that oil at a fairly uniform rate to the bearing surfaces. The rate at which the oil is supplied is a function of the local temperature; therefore, an increase in friction would result in an increased supply of oil as required for stability.

At the present time retainers are being manufactured of phenolic laminates and porous nylons, but other materials are being investigated. The oil absorption of the present materials ranges from 3 to 15 per cent by weight. Results of bearing-life tests with oil-impregnated retainers have been rather spotty; the lives range from only a few to over 10,000 hr. Variations in porosity of various batches of retainer materials and variations in bleed-out rate are contributing factors to these spotty results.

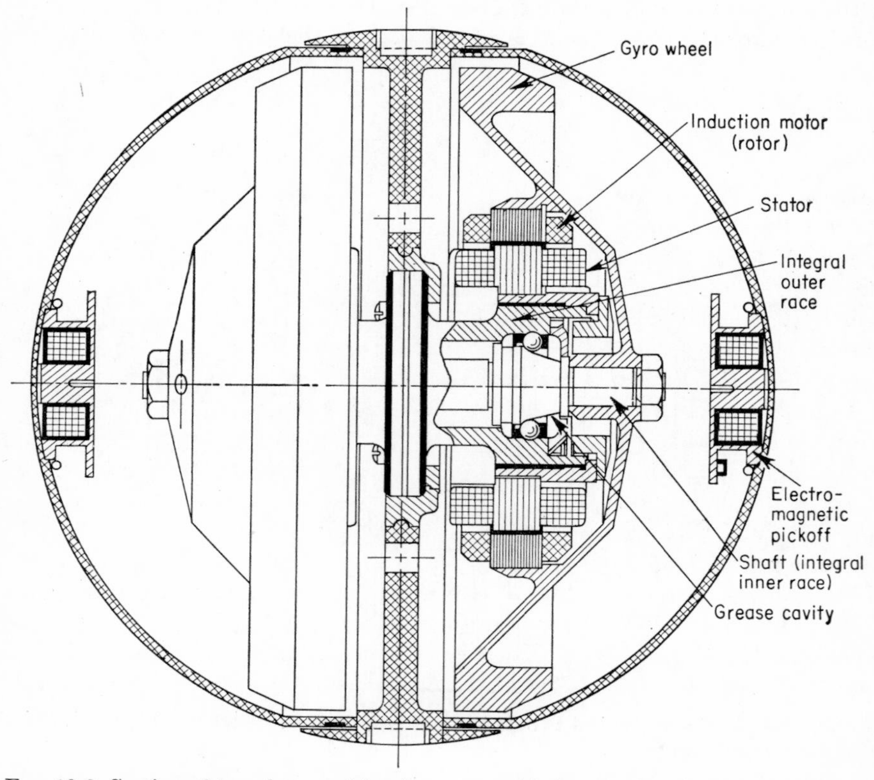

Fig. 10-9. Section of two-degree-of-freedom gyro with integral bearing races. (*Arma Division, American Bosch Arma Corporation.*)

The outlook for impregnated retainers is becoming more optimistic as more causes and effects are uncovered. It can be expected that impregnated retainers will be successfully employed in all precision gyros within the next five years. This will result in simplified designs and will minimize the possibility of weight shifts in the even more precise gyros of the future.

Integral Raceway. There is a very definite trend on the part of most gyro manufacturers to use integral bearing raceways on the rotating member and, less frequently, on the stationary member as well. Typical gyro designs using integral raceways are shown in Figs. 10-8 and 10-9. Figure 10-8 illustrates a gyro with integral inner raceways. The outer rings are separate and attached to the housing. Figure 10-9 illustrates a gyro design with integral inner and outer raceways.

The elimination of separate rings provides a more accurate and rigid structure, eliminates cumulative mounting errors, and reduces the possibility of relative motion due to vibration and thermal expansion. Integral raceways on the rotating element also eliminate the need for rebalance if the rotor is removed and replaced, since there can be no shift in the center of rotation.

10-3. Gyrowheel

Most of the angular momentum of a gyro is contributed by the gyrowheel; it is therefore a very important element. However, it is such a simple element that many designers neglect to give it the attention it deserves and to consider all the design principles outlined previously. The design of the gyrowheel must always be a compromise, since many of the design principles are incompatible with one another. Thus, for a given weight, speed, and diameter, the angular momentum is a maximum with a wide, thin rim of high-density material, such as tungsten, joined to a thin central web of low-density material, such as magnesium. Such a design, however, seriously violates several other basic principles; e.g., it is a soft compound structure, the coefficients of expansion are badly matched, and it would be much more compliant axially than radially. In addition, the increased surface area would increase the windage loss, with resulting increase in temperature gradients and motor size.

Not only is it impossible to optimize all design parameters of a gyrowheel per se; the best designs must often be modified by other considerations. These considerations include the mutual modifying effects of all the gyro elements, manufacturing and assembly problems, reliability, life, appearance, and cost. Thus the wheels shown in Figs. 10-8 to 10-10 are quite different, yet each is a successful design. For instance, the nonsymmetrical wheel of Fig. 10-8 was dictated by the advantage of placing the floated gimbal within the waist of the gyro case; the multipart wheel assembly of Fig. 10-10 was chosen for its isoelasticity.

It is important to remember that it is not the angular momentum alone that determines the accuracy of a gyro, but the ratio of angular momentum to unwanted or random torques. Thus, increasing the weight at the rim of the wheel will increase not only the angular momentum but also the random torques. The increased weight will require an increased bearing preload, which will increase the power loss and result in steeper temperature gradients and variations in temperature gradients that will cause greater random weight shifts and, in the case of floated gyros, greater fluid torques and variations in fluid viscosity. Because the bearing stiffness does not increase linearly with the preload, the residual compliance torques will also increase. The increased preload may also seriously affect the life of the bearing. For those cases where the failure is due to overstress rather than to lubricant failure, this might be offset by increasing the bearing size, but at the price of further increasing the friction torque. The larger bearing, however, would have the advantage of being stiffer. Each case must be studied and tested to determine the optimum design parameters.

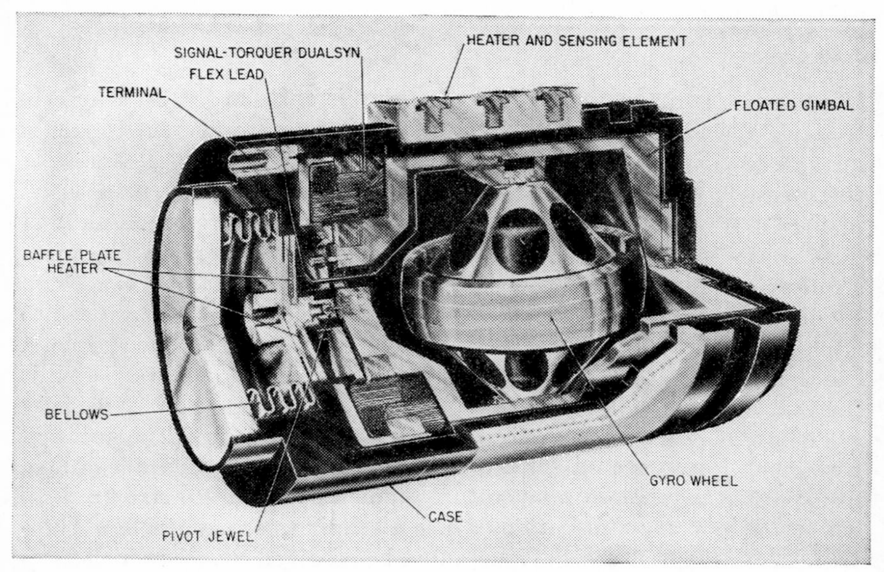

FIG. 10-10. Section of the Miniature Integrating Gyro (MIG). (*Minneapolis-Honeywell Regulator Co.*)

In general it is considered good practice to have a fairly compact rim at the largest radius possible and integral with a stiff symmetrical web. A suggested figure of merit is

$$M = \frac{H^2K}{W^3|R - 1|} \tag{10-6}$$

where H = angular momentum
K = axial stiffness
W = total weight of wheel
R = ratio of axial to radial stiffness

The absolute value of $(R - 1)$ should not be the nominal value but the largest possible considering the effect of manufacturing tolerances, particularly for values of R approaching 1. A tapered web, as in Fig. 10-9, will increase the figure of merit, whereas holes in the web (sometimes used to decrease the web weight) will decrease the figure of merit and should be avoided unless necessary for assembly, inspection, or isoelasticity, as in Fig. 10-10.

The thickness of the web is generally determined by considerations of stiffness and handling in the shop rather than by considerations of stress, particularly for surface velocities under 200 ft/sec. Formulas for stresses and deflection of uniform disks or plates due to centrifugal and axial loads may be found in many texts on strength of materials.[9,10] Stodola[11] indicates the solution for the stresses and deflections of axially loaded plates whose thickness increases exponentially toward the hub. Conway[12,13] has studied plates with linearly varying thickness. Chenea and Naghdi[14] give an approximate solution for a plate with varying thickness by splitting the plate into a series of concentric rings. The latter solution may be applied to a symmetrical web with any arbitrary variation in thickness. The stiffness of conical-shaped webs such as those illustrated in Fig. 10-9 or 10-10 may be solved with the aid of reference 9. Since most gyrowheels do not conform exactly to the idealized solution, it is strongly recommended that the stiffness be checked experimentally. It should be recognized that in general a single symmetrical web will not be isoelastic; however, this is not necessary, provided the stiffness is sufficiently great to reduce the compliance torques to an acceptable level in the particular application.

The gyrowheel should be dynamically balanced in two planes in order to reduce bearing loads and noise. The equivalent static unbalance is usually held to within 0.0003 oz-in. or less, depending on the size of the wheel and the application. Where two wheels are mounted on a single shaft, it is usually sufficient to use one plane in each wheel for dynamic balancing. The theory of balancing and a description of some balancing machines may be found in references 15 and 16. The balancing must be done on a complete assembly, or at least with the rotating members of the spin bearings attached, in order to avoid changes in eccentricity which may affect the balance at final assembly.

Since a shift in the center of gravity of the wheel with respect to the gimbal pivot or suspension is most critical in any gyro, the necessity for fabricating and assembling a stable wheel cannot be overemphasized. The wheel structure should be as simple as possible and fabricated of stable materials. (See Sec. 10-14 for the principal properties of materials currently being used in gyros.) If weight shifts are to be minimized, coefficients of expansion of wheel materials and adjacent members must be closely matched, even though shrink fits or other so-called "secure" means of fastening are used. With the rotor mounted on the gyrowheel, it is particularly important that temperature gradients be kept to a minimum by providing adequate heat paths of conductive materials and minimizing the power input. This is true even if the coefficients of expansion of wheel and rotor are matched.

10-4. Gyro Motor

The design criteria for the motor will be discussed in some detail in Chap. 11, so that a few words will suffice in this chapter. The choice between a synchronous motor and an induction motor depends on the available power supply and the application. For those applications where precision torquing is necessary, a synchronous motor and a power supply with closely controlled frequency will be required. The principal disadvantage of the synchronous motor, usually of a hysteresis type, is its relatively poor efficiency. This can be improved considerably by overexcitation, which essentially transforms it into a permanent-magnet motor. However, this generally requires an additional switch position, and because of the demagnetizing effect due to hunting, the motor must be periodically overexcited to maintain efficiency. Changes in efficiency mean changes in the input power, with consequent changes in temperature and balance.

Induction motors may be used profitably in untorqued or nonprecision torqued systems. The efficiency is higher and the power-supply regulation is less critical. A change in speed, whether due to a change in frictional level with time or power-supply variations, will cause a precession torque to be exerted on the gyro if the gimbal suspension axes are not exactly orthogonal to the spin axis. The precessional torque is

$$T = J\alpha\theta \tag{10-7}$$

where J is the polar moment of inertia of the rotating masses, α is the angular acceleration of the rotating masses in radians per second squared, and θ the orthogonality error in radians. The torque and polar moment of inertia may be expressed in any consistent units.

10-5. Pickoffs and Torquers

The design of pickoffs and torquers is discussed in detail in Chap. 11. Pickoffs and torquers, like every element, must be securely mounted and fabricated of stable materials. The pickoffs should be so designed that the magnetic, electrostatic, or other coercive forces be kept to negligible values.

10-6. Gyro Case

The complete structure supporting the rotating members of the sensitive element is variously called *inner gimbal, gimbal float, gyro case, float,* etc., depending on the manufacturer and the type of gyro. The term *gyro case* is preferred by the author, since it is descriptive and less ambiguous than the others. The gyro case serves two principal purposes: (1) It supports the spin bearings, stator, and pickoffs; (2) it provides a sealed enclosure.

Typical gyro case designs are shown in Figs. 10-8 to 10-11. The single-degree-of-freedom gyros (Figs. 10-10 and 10-11) are cylindrical in shape, and the two-degree-of-freedom gyros (Figs. 10-8 and 10-9) are essentially spherical. The reasons for these shapes are fairly obvious,

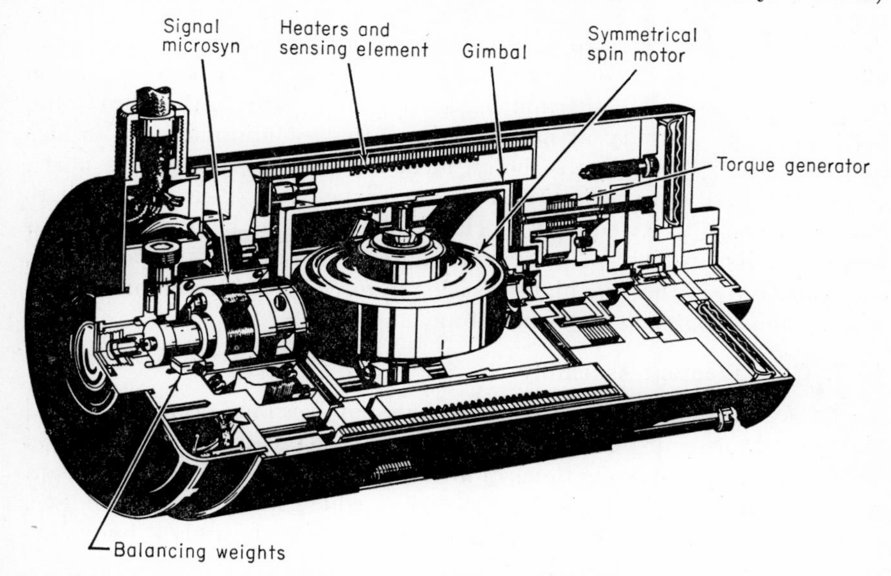

FIG. 10-11. Section of single-degree-of-freedom integrating gyro (HIG-6). (*Minneapolis-Honeywell Regulator Co.*)

since symmetry about the output axes is desirable in order to keep random fluid torques to a minimum.

The gyro case must rigidly support the spin bearings, stator, pickoff, torquers, and suspension; it must provide an isothermal environment; it must include access for electric leads and means for balancing about each of the principal axes; and it must provide a sealed enclosure. The need for a rigid and a symmetric structure, both thermally and electrically, has been emphasized many times and should not require restatement. The necessity for having an isothermal gyro case is recognized by most designers, and the trend toward the use of high-conductivity materials and thicker sections is continuing.

It is obvious that the total weight of the gyro element of a neutrally buoyant float is fixed and is equal to the weight of the displaced fluid. Usually less than half of this weight contributes to the angular momentum of the gyro. The older floated gyro designs sacrificed low temperature gradients and structural rigidity in order to obtain the maximum possible angular momentum. Inadvertently, these designs also sacrificed stability and accuracy.

At the present time most gyro cases are made of aluminum. This material has a good stiffness-to-weight ratio and is an excellent conductor, but it has about twice the coefficient of expansion of the steel parts of the gyroscope, such as the motor, bearings, and shaft. This mismatch in coefficient is certain to result in instability of the center of gravity. Several manufacturers are now developing gyroscopes using beryllium. This metal has a lower density than aluminum, a coefficient of expansion equal to that of steel, a thermal conductivity equal to that of aluminum, a modulus of elasticity about four times that of aluminum; it is also nonmagnetic. It appears to be an ideal material for many gyro parts, except for three drawbacks: (1) It is very expensive; (2) it is difficult to machine; and (3) it requires special machining and handling facilities because of its toxicity. However, because of its outstanding properties, it is quite certain that the high-precision gyroscopes of inertial navigation will use many parts made of beryllium.

10-7. Gyro Element Assembly

The sealed gyro case with its motor, spin bearings, gyrowheel, and pickoff and torquer elements attached to the case is called the *gyro element assembly*. The remaining items of interest in the design of a gyro element assembly are (1) sealing and leak checking, which will be covered in Sec. 10-13; (2) gas filling; (3) feed-throughs for electric leads; and (4) buoyancy and balance.

Gas Filling. The inert gas with which all modern gyro elements are filled performs two functions: (1) It prevents oxidation of the lubricant, thus prolonging the life of the bearings; (2) it acts as a coolant for motor and bearings, thereby preventing hot spots and high temperature gradients.

Unfortunately, a gas in the gyro case is the cause of windage losses and should be kept at a minimum pressure consistent with satisfying the function of item 2 above and should provide sufficient dielectric strength. The windage loss, of course, is very dependent on the speed and the particular configuration of the gyrowheel and gyro case, as well as being a function of the type of gas and the pressure.

Except for hydrogen (H_2), which has a viscosity of about 88 micropoises at 23°C, all the common gases (air, helium, carbon dioxide, nitrogen, and oxygen) have viscosities of 150 to 200 micropoises at 23°C. However, it has been found that, due to turbulence, the windage loss is nearly independent of viscosity and is roughly proportional to the density of the gas. Therefore, the following represent approximately the relative windage loss of the various gases at any given pressure: hydrogen = 1, helium = 2, nitrogen = 14, air = 14, carbon dioxide = 22.

Hydrogen and helium are the gases most widely used for filling the gyro element. Helium is favored by most manufacturers because of its greater safety, even though the windage loss is greater. This loss can be brought down to negligible values in most cases by reducing the pressure of the gas, since the windage loss is almost directly proportional to density

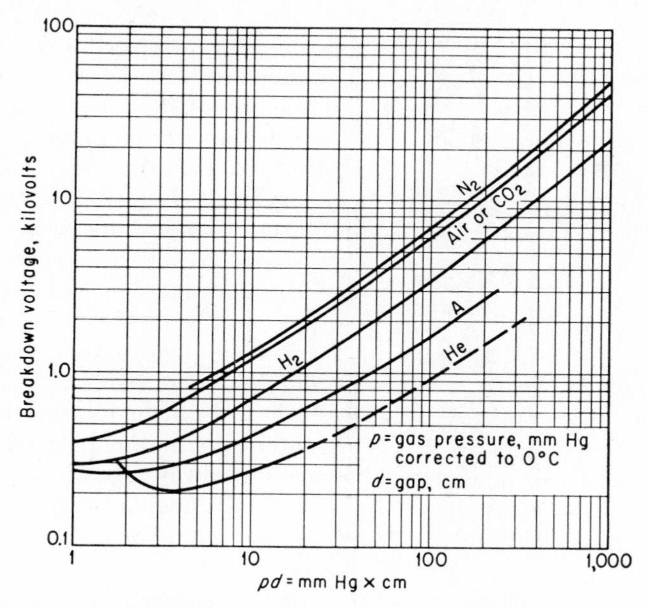

FIG. 10-12. Typical breakdown-voltage curves for various gases between parallel plate electrodes.

and thus to pressure. Helium is also easier to use in detecting leaks in the gyro case by applying any commercially available leak detector.

The dielectric strength (volts per centimeter) of helium, unfortunately, is quite low, and there is danger of breakdown and arcing between terminals or bare leads at low values of the product *pd*, where *p* is the gas pressure, in millimeters Hg corrected to 0°C, and *d* is the gap between electrodes, in centimeters. Typical breakdown-voltage curves[17,18] for various gases between parallel plate electrodes are given in Fig. 10-12. The breakdown-voltage curve for helium has been extrapolated, as indicated by the dashed line. The breakdown voltage for CO_2 is approximately 95 per cent of that for air, and its curve is shown in Fig. 10-12 as being coincident with that of air. For values of *pd* less than 1, the breakdown voltages for N_2, air, CO_2, H_2, and A increase sharply, as does helium, for values of pd less than 4. The dielectric strength of gases also depends on the material of the electrodes and on the ratio d/r of the gap to the radius of the electrodes in a rather complex manner. The curves of Fig. 10-12 are satisfactory within 20 per cent for anodes of Fe, Zn, Al, brass, stainless steel, Ni, Ag, or Pt at all values of pd; however, with Mg, Ba, Na, or K, the breakdown voltage is lowered by as much as 40 per cent for values of $pd < 20$. The effect of the electrode material becomes negligible for $pd > 200$. The curves of Fig. 10-12 generally hold for values of $(d/r) < 1$ and are too high for values of $(d/r) > 1$ by as much as 3 to 1 for sharp, pointed electrodes.

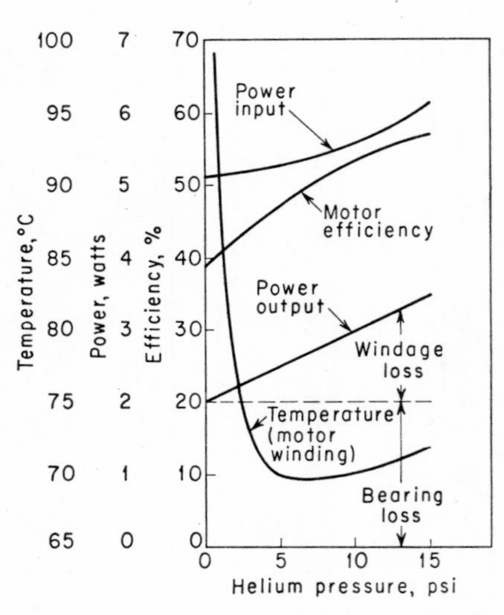

FIG. 10-13. Typical effect of gas pressure on temperature.

In one gyro design arcing occurred across a gap of 0.040 in. between slip rings at 180 volts in 1 atm of helium. The situation was alleviated by contaminating the helium with 5 per cent CO_2 or 10 per cent N_2, which raised the breakdown voltage to 450 volts without unduly increasing the windage loss. There is little information in the literature on the dielectric strength of mixed gases, but it is known that it is frequently less than that of either component.[17,23]

As stated previously, the windage loss in a gyro element is roughly proportional to the pressure (density) for any given gas with all other conditions held constant. A typical curve of power output and temperature versus helium pressure in a gyro is shown in Fig. 10-13. In the case of a gyro motor, the bearing and windage losses are considered the "output." Because of the motor-efficiency curve, the power input to the gyro does not decrease linearly with the helium pressure but first decreases and then levels off as the helium pressure is reduced. At 1 atm pressure most of the heat generated in the motor (power input) is dissipated by convection, but a larger proportion of the heat must be dissipated by conduction as the pressure is reduced. Therefore, the temperature of the stator windings will first drop, as the pressure is decreased, and then start to rise rapidly at a low pressure when most of the heat must be dissipated by conduction. The temperature curve for the stator windings is dependent on the ratio of windage loss to bearing loss and on the motor performance characteristics, as well as the ratio of conducted to convected power. The other common gases would give similar results. A reasonable figure of merit for a gas is the ratio of thermal conductivity to density; this ratio is given for a few gases in Table 10-2.

TABLE 10-2. THERMAL EFFICIENCIES OF SELECTED GASES*

Gas	Density ρ, g/l	Thermal conductivity K, cal/(sec)(cm)(cm²)(°C)	K/ρ
Air	1.293	5.68×10^{-5}	4.39×10^{-5}
Nitrogen	1.251	5.24×10^{-5}	4.19×10^{-5}
Helium	0.178	34.4×10^{-5}	192×10^{-5}
Hydrogen	0.0899	41.6×10^{-5}	462×10^{-5}

* Data given is at 0°C and 760 mm, except conductivity for nitrogen is at 7 to 8°C.

Most gyro manufacturers pressurize the gyro cases at well above the pressure of the minimum temperature (Fig. 10-13) in order to avoid a sharp temperature rise if the bearing or windage losses should increase for any reason. The temperature rise is essentially constant over a fairly large range of pressures. Gyro pressures are usually in the range of ½ to 1 atm absolute in order to avoid too low a dielectric strength.

It should be noted that the gyro case will be more closely isothermal when most of the heat is dissipated by convection rather than by conduction.

Electric Leads. The electric leads to the motor, and in some cases to the pickoffs and torquers, must often be carried through an hermetically sealed gyro case. Usually, glass insulated terminals are either soldered or cemented into through-holes in the case. Typical types of glass insulated terminals are illustrated in Fig. 10-14. Figure 10-14*a* shows a terminal whose center rod and eyelet are made of a metal such as Kovar which is wetted by glass and has the same coefficient of expansion as glass. The other two terminals (Fig. 10-14*b* and *c*) illustrate compression-type glass terminals which depend on the compression of the glass by the metal elements (tinned steel) to form a seal. The type shown in Fig. 10-14*a* usually has its glass element extending beyond the length of the eyelet, with a fillet at the central terminal rod. Since the glass is in compression in Fig. 10-14*b* and *c*, it cannot extend appreciably beyond the ends of the eyelet. Glass insulated terminals may be pro-

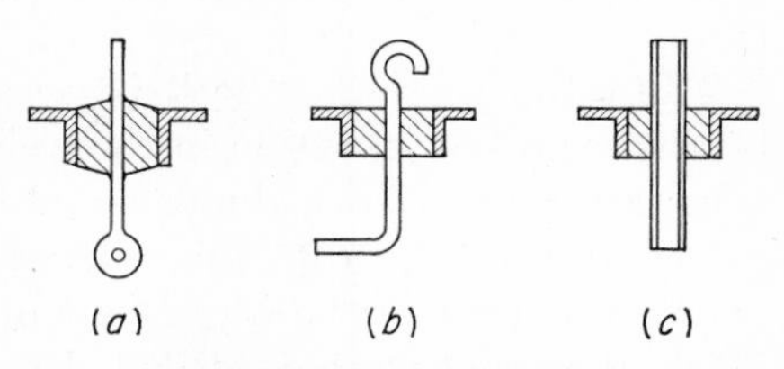

FIG. 10-14. Typical glass-insulated terminals. (*a*) Glass bonded with matched coefficient of expansion, swaged and pierced rod; (*b*) compression type with hooked rod; (*c*) compression type with hollow rod.

cured in many different sizes and in single or multiterminal types. The compression type is favored by most gyro manufacturers because it is sturdier and more reliable than others. Also illustrated in Fig. 10-14 are a few of the various types of terminal endings available: swaged and pierced, straight, hooked, bent, and hollow.

In some cases insulated wire is fed through holes in the gyro case which are then sealed with a plastic, usually epoxy. It is imperative that the insulation on the wire be bonded to the wire and compatible with the cement if the seal is to be hermetic. Teflon, nylon, and vinyl do not normally bond to the wire and are therefore unsatisfactory. Formvar and similar varnishes do bond well and are compatible with epoxy. The leak rates on all plastics are very much higher than those for metals and are proportional to the cross-sectional area of the leakage path and inversely proportional to its length. Therefore, the thickness of the insulation and sealant should be as small as possible, preferably 0.005 to 0.010 in., and the length as long as possible. In no case should the length of the leakage path in a plastic be less than $3/16$ in. (see section on Adhesive Joining and Sealing).

Buoyancy and Balance. As stated in Chap. 9, provision must be made (1) to adjust the total weight of a floated gyro element so that it will be at neutral buoyancy at the operating temperature (the added weights are called *buoyancy weights*), and (2) to adjust the center of gravity and/or the center of buoyancy into coincidence with the center of suspension (these adjustment weights are called *balance weights*). The buoyancy weights usually perform both functions; i.e., they are used for coarse balancing as well as for adjusting the total weight.

The total weight of the balance and buoyancy weights is determined by the expected variation in the weight of the gyro element. The variations are due to both dimensional and density tolerances. As may be expected, the total weights required vary widely with the design, but an average figure may be 5 per cent of the gyro element weight. The fine balance capacity required will depend on the accuracy with which the coarse balancing may be performed. The latter, in turn, is dependent on the balancing techniques as well as on the design.

For convenience, coarse balancing of floated gyro elements is frequently performed on a pair of parallel knife-edges in air, even though low-torque gimbal bearings are probably superior.* Though knife-edges are widely used, their limitations are not well known, and some deserve explanation. It is quite evident that pivot pins with flats will cause considerable uncertainties in balancing a body; however, it is not so evident that even a slight out-of-roundness is the cause of considerable uncertainty. Thus,

* See section on Gimbal Ball Bearings.

Fig. 10-15 shows a view of an elliptically shaped pivot on which a gyro is being balanced. The assembly is in balance when the knife-edge is tangent to the pivot at point P, since the load vector $\bar{W}$ passes through the point P. However, if the gyro is rotated 180°, the knife-edge will be tangent at the conjugate point P', and the unbalanced moment $M = WL$. It can be shown that the maximum moment arm $L \simeq a - b$, where a and b are the semimajor and semiminor axes, respectively. The uncertainty in balancing is

$$M \simeq W(a - b) \tag{10-8}$$

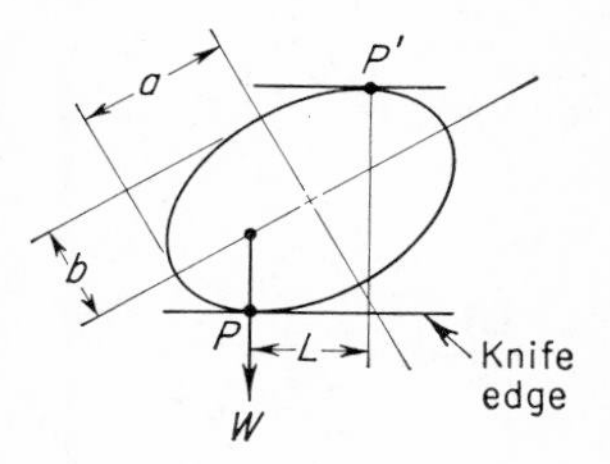

FIG. 10-15. Balancing a gyro element assembly on elliptical pivots.

Example. A gyro element weighing 22 oz is being balanced on pivots which have a nominal diameter of ⅛ in. The pivots are elliptical in cross section with a major-axis diameter of 0.1250 and a minor-axis diameter of 0.1248. For this case, the uncertainty in balance is

$$M = WL = \frac{22(0.1250 - 0.1248)}{2} = 2{,}200 \times 10^{-6} \text{ oz-in.}$$

If the knife-edges, or a portion of them due to waviness, are inclined at an angle θ (Fig. 10-16), the sensitive element will be apparently balanced when the weight vector passes through the point of contact P. The minimum uncertainty in balance will occur when the center of gravity is at point O'. If the sensitive element is rotated 180°, the apparent unbalance is

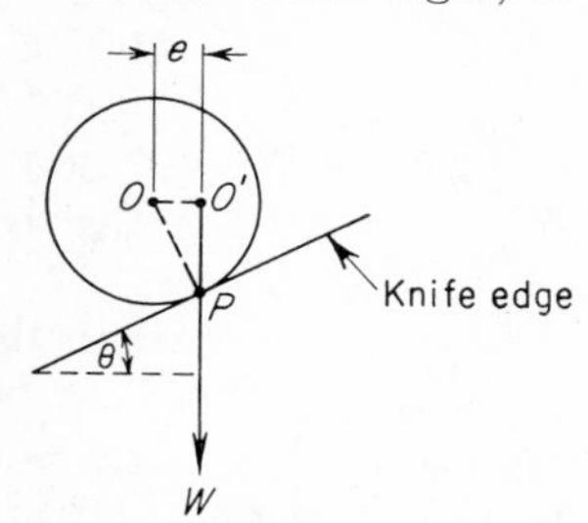

FIG. 10-16. Balancing a gyro element on inclined knife-edges.

$$M = 2We = 2WR \sin \theta \tag{10-9}$$

Example. The gyro element of the previous example is being balanced on knife-edges which are inclined at an angle of 5′. The minimum uncertainty in balance, by Eq. (10-9), is

$$M = 2 \times 22 \times 0.0625 \times 0.0015 = 4{,}125 \times 10^{-6} \text{ oz-in.}$$

The frictional resistance to rolling increases rapidly when the contact stresses exceed the elastic limit. According to R. C. Drutowski,[22] the frictional resistance at low loads of a ball on a steel plate varies as the 1.2 power of the load; but at higher loads, in which the contact stresses exceed the elastic limit, the frictional resistances vary as the 2.4 power of the load. The average contact stress is $S = P/A$, where P is the normal load and A is the contact area. The maximum stress occurs at the center of the contact area and is

$$S_m = \frac{3P}{2A} \tag{10-10}$$

The contact area is dependent on the radii of curvature of the contacting bodies and on the elastic properties of the materials. Using the notations indicated in Fig. 10-17, the area of the contact ellipse may be found as follows:[1,2]

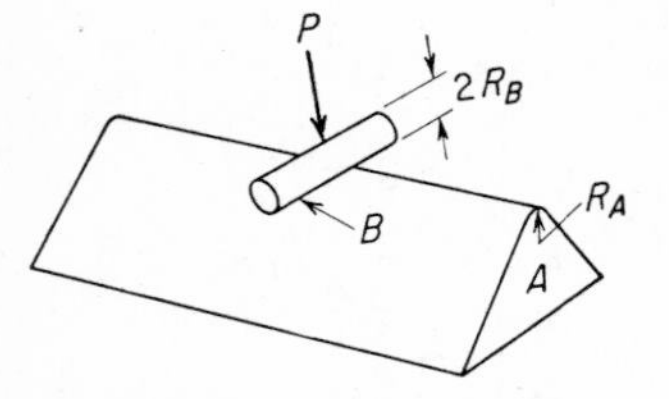

FIG. 10-17. Knife-edge and pivot.

$$A = \pi ab = \pi m R^2 \tag{10-11}$$

where

$$R = \left[\frac{\dfrac{3P(C_A + C_B)}{8}}{\dfrac{1}{R_A} + \dfrac{1}{R_B}}\right]^{1/3} \tag{10-12}$$

C_A and C_B are elastic constants of the two bodies which depend on the modulus of elasticity E and Poisson's ratio ν. Explicitly,

$$C_A = \frac{4(1 - \nu_A^2)}{E_A}$$

$$C_B = \frac{4(1 - \nu_B^2)}{E_B}$$

If both bodies are made of steel with a modulus of elasticity of 29×10^6 lb/in.^{2} and a Poisson's ratio of 0.25, the value of R is

$$R = 0.00459 \left(\frac{P}{\dfrac{1}{R_A} + \dfrac{1}{R_B}}\right)^{1/3} \tag{10-13}$$

The value of m depends on the conformity of the contacting bodies and is determined by the auxiliary angle τ.

$$\cos \tau = \left|\frac{1}{R_A} - \frac{1}{R_B}\right| \div \left(\frac{1}{R_A} + \frac{1}{R_B}\right) \tag{10-14}$$

Values of m for various values of $\cos \tau$ are plotted in Fig. 10-18. Substitute the value of m and the value of R from Eq. (10-12) or (10-13) in Eq. (10-11) to find the contact area. The maximum stress is determined from Eq. (10-10). If the maximum stress is below the elastic limit of the material, the frictional resistance may be neglected as compared to other errors which occur.

Example. A gyro element weighing 22 oz is supported on a pair of knife-edges by means of ⅛-in. steel pins. The knife-edges are rounded with a $1/16$ in. radius. Find the maximum contact stress.

Referring to Fig. 10-17, we see that the parameters are

$$R_A = R_B = \tfrac{1}{16} \text{ in.}$$
$$P = 11 \text{ oz} = 0.688 \text{ lb}$$
$$R = 0.00459 \left(\frac{0.688}{16 + 16}\right)^{1/3} = 0.001275$$

$\cos \tau = 0$, and, from Fig. 10-18, $m = 1$. Therefore, the contact area $A = \pi(1.275)^2 \times 10^{-6}$ in.^{2} and the maximum stress is

$$S_m = \frac{3}{2}\frac{0.688}{\pi(1.275)^2} \times 10^6 = 201{,}000 \text{ lb/in.}$$

The stress would be too high for most steels and might cause brinelling of pivot and/or knife-edges.

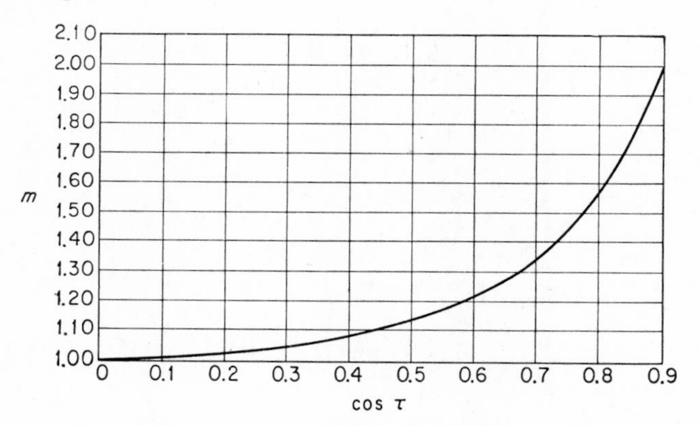

FIG. 10-18. Conformity factor m.

Surface finish of the contact surfaces, the parallelism of the two knife-edges, and the orthogonality of the pivot axes to the knife-edge axes also limit the degree to which the gyro element may be balanced. However, a surface finish compatible with the required tolerances and reasonable care in the setup would make these effects negligible.

The position of the center of buoyancy with respect to the pivot axes is seldom known accurately at this stage of assembly, so that extreme care in coarse balancing is not usually warranted. Final determination of the buoyancy weights and fine balancing are generally performed in open tanks of flotation fluid maintained at the proper density. It is imperative that the tank of flotation fluid be as nearly isothermal as possible. At the end of this stage of assembly, the fine balance weights should be approximately at the center of travel so that sufficient capacity remains for final adjustment at gyro test.

There are many types of buoyancy weights and balance weights used in practice; they range from the simple pin with an interference fit in a hole to a spring-loaded differential screw or nut. The pin is a very simple one, and it may be used wherever there is sufficient thickness of metal. Generally several are inserted into the end plates of the gyro case on single-degree-of-freedom gyros. They do have several limitations: (1) The pins and holes must have very accurate interference fits of the order of 0.001 in. per inch of diameter; (2) coefficients of expansion of the mating parts must be closely matched if the gyro is to be operated or stored over a great range of ambient temperature; (3) the holes must be vented to prevent entrapment of air which could later change the balance.

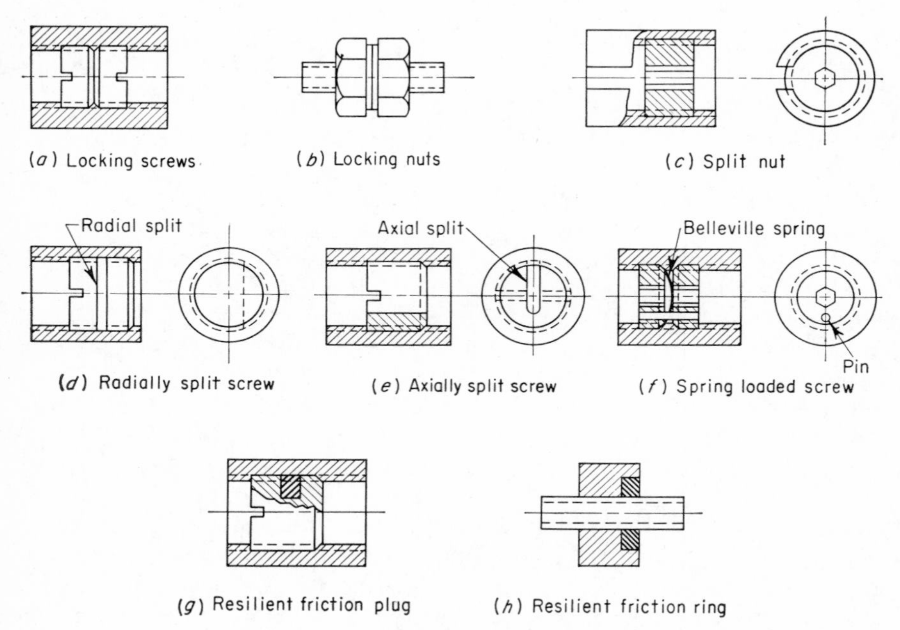

FIG. 10-19. Locking devices for balance weights.

Balance weights and buoyancy weights are generally of the screw-adjusted type. These may be mounted in brackets attached to the gyro case or in cavities in the gyro case. The principal problem with threaded weights is that of locking against vibration and shock. Figure 10-19 illustrates several types of locking devices. The opposed screws or nuts (Fig. 10-19*a* and *b*), though not always convenient, are satisfactory, provided care is taken to check that they are properly tightened. Fine adjustments can be made by further tightening one of the screws or nuts. Split screws or nuts (Fig. 10-19*c*, *d*, and *e*) have the disadvantage that it is difficult to control the spring pressure, and they have a tendency to act as taps or dies even though the leading edges are well rounded. The spring-loaded screws (Fig. 10-19*f*) are very effective, but they are expensive to manufacture and the smallest diameter that can be used is about ⅜ in.; a pin with a tight fit in one screw but loose in the other prevents relative rotation. Resilient plugs or rings (Fig. 10-19*g* and *h*) are quite popular. The resilient member is generally made of nylon, which is not too much affected by the usual environment and which retains its resilience without creep for long periods of time.

There are many other weight-adjustment devices which are used or have been proposed, such as the spring-loaded differential screw, the bimetallic strip bent by heating, or the transfer of metal from one electrode to another, but most of them are too complex and have not proved themselves. Eccentric weights, singly or in pairs, have been used, but the weight shift is not linear with respect to rotation, and they are difficult to lock in position.

As stated in Chap. 9, the effective weight of a balancing screw or nut is its weight in the surrounding fluid. If the effective weight is greater than zero, then the shift in the center of gravity will be greater than the shift in the center of buoyancy for a given displacement of the weight. If the effective weight is zero, then the shift in center of gravity is equal to the shift in the center of buoyancy. If the effective weight is negative, then the shift in the center of buoyancy is greater than the shift in the center of gravity. With low-density flotation fluids, it is more convenient to shift the center of gravity of the gyro element without appreciably shifting the center of buoyancy. Adjustment weights are generally made of a tungsten alloy with a density of about 0.61 lb/in.^{3} whereas the flotation fluids generally used have a density of about 0.07 lb/in.^{3}. If the gyro element is floated in a liquid metal, it may be advantageous to use weights of low-density material, such as aluminum, magnesium, or beryllium, and shift the center of buoyancy into coincidence with the center of gravity.

10-8. Gimbal—Two-degree-of-freedom Gyro

The gimbal of a two-degree-of-freedom gyro supports the outer end of the gyro element suspension and the inner end of the outer suspension. Each suspension is soft torsionally about its own axis and relatively very stiff torsionally about the other two axes and in translation along the three axes. Ideally, the suspension axes are orthogonal* to the spin axis and intersect at the centers of buoyancy and gravity of the gyro element. The floated gimbal is a light, neutrally buoyant structure made of magnesium or beryllium for the usual flotation fluids. Since it is always necessary to attach parts of high density, such as screws or springs, and

* See Sec. 10-4 for the effect of nonorthogonality.

since magnesium and beryllium are almost as dense as the flotation fluid, much care must be taken to avoid excess weight.

Reference to Fig. 10-20 shows that acceleration torques due to unbalance will be zero when (1) the gyro element is balanced along the y and z axes, (2) the gimbal is balanced along the z axis, and (3) the combination of gyro element and gimbal is balanced along the x axis. Torques due to an unbalance along the y axis of the gimbal will be resisted by the outer suspension and will not result in torques acting on the gyro. If the gimbal is symmetrical about each axis and the total weight is small, it may not be necessary to provide a means of balancing it along the z axis.

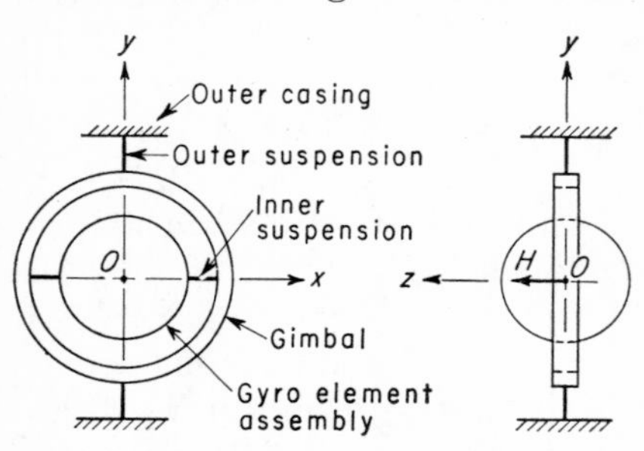

FIG. 10-20. Balance axes of a two-degree-of-freedom gyro.

10-9. Flotation Fluids

The important characteristics of a flotation fluid are as follows:

Density. The density should be sufficiently high to float a gyrowheel of high angular momentum without sacrificing rigidity of gyro case or other elements. An ideal density would probably be between 4 and 6 g/cm³.

Coefficient of Expansion. It should be low in order to minimize convection currents due to temperature gradients and to reduce the expansion bellows. However, a high coefficient of expansion permits vernier adjustment of the fluid density for neutral buoyancy of the gyro element.

Viscosity. A single-degree-of-freedom gyro requires close control of viscosity; therefore, the temperature coefficient of viscosity should be low. Viscosity is not critical over a range of at least 5 to 1 in a two-degree-of-freedom gyro.

Vapor Pressure. The vapor pressure must be low to prevent excessive loss during degassing and, in the case of mixtures, to avoid loss of the volatile components which would cause a change in density.

Freezing Point. Since many fluids become non-Newtonian near the freezing point, the operating temperature should be at least 10°C above the freezing point.

Stability. The fluid must be stable and must not separate, chemically or otherwise, into its components or continue to polymerize.

Thermal Conductivity. High thermal conductivity is desirable to minimize convection torques.

Electrical Conductivity. A fluid with the low conductivity of an insulator is desirable.

Toxicity and Reactivity. It is obviously simpler to work with fluids that do not require special hoods, an inert-gas environment, or other special facilities. The fluid must be compatible with the gyro materials and must not react with them chemically.

The commonly used flotation fluids are the fluorocarbons such as Fluorolube* or Kel F† (polymers of chlorotrifluoroethylene) and the silicone fluids (polydimethyl siloxane). Both the fluorocarbons and the silicones are available in a wide range of viscosities but in only a narrow range of densities. The density of the fluorocarbons varies from about 1.8 g/cm^3 at 100°C for the light fractions to about 2.0 g/cm^3 at 25°C for the heavy fractions, whereas the silicones vary from about 0.81 g/cm^3 at 100°C for the low polymers to about 0.97 g/cm^3 at 25°C for the high polymers. Both fluids are stable and nontoxic, have low vapor pressures, have good electrical insulation properties, but possess high coefficients of expansion [approximately 8.3×10^{-4} cm^3/(cm^3)(°C) for the fluorocarbons and 9.5×10^{-4} cm^3/(cm^3)(°C) for the silicones].

The slopes of the ASTM temperature-viscosity curves of the silicone fluids are very flat; the slopes for good petroleum oils and for the fluorocarbons are about 2.7 and 3.5 times greater, respectively, than those for the silicones. The low temperature-viscosity coefficient of the silicones is particularly desirable for single-degree-of-freedom gyros, but this advantage is usually more than offset by their low density. For this reason, most floated gyros are filled with the fluorocarbons. Close temperature control and/or temperature compensation is required for integrating gyros to control the viscous torques.

Though the fluorocarbons are the most widely used flotation fluids, other fluids such as Densilube‡ (poly-iodo-meta-bromo-benzo-trifluoride with a density of 2.3 g/cm^3) have been developed and show considerable promise because of their greater density without undue sacrifice of other desirable characteristics. Several gyro manufacturers are working on the development of gyros neutrally floated in liquid metals, such as mercury or low-melting-temperature alloys. The high specific gravity of liquid metals permits a high angular momentum in a very small float; in fact, it is a problem to design a gyro element of sufficient density, except with generous use of tungsten or similarly heavy metals. The liquid metals are excellent conductors, and the coefficients of expansion are of almost an order of magnitude less than the fluorocarbons or the silicones, thus reducing convection torques by about two orders of magnitude.

* Registered trademark, Hooker Electrochemical Corp.

† Registered trademark, Minnesota Mining & Manufacturing Co.

‡ Registered trademark, American Bosch Arma Corp.

The principal drawbacks of the liquid metals are their chemical reactivity and their high electrical conductivity. The latter problem is probably the most difficult one to solve, since even a tiny pinhole in the insulation of the electric circuit within the fluid may be catastrophic.

10-10. Suspension Elements

There are many different means of centering and controlling the gyro element within the outer case of the sensitive element. Torsion bars, suspension wires or tapes, jewel pivots, ball or air bearings, and electrostatic or electromagnetic bearings have all been tried with various degrees of success. Each method has certain advantages and certain limitations which will be briefly covered.

Torsion Bars; Suspension Wires or Tapes. Torsion bars are used in many rate gyros to provide an elastic restraint about the output axis of a single-degree-of-freedom gyro (see Chap. 4). Floated rate gyros usually have a torsion bar at one end of the gyro element which acts both as a torsional spring and as a centering device, while a jewel pivot provides the centering action at the other end of the element. Torsional microslip at the clamps results in spurious torques which act like pivot friction torques. These hysteresis-type torques may be minimized by enlarging the clamped ends of the torsion bars, since the total shear reactive force of the clamp varies inversely as the diameter, while the shear gradient along the axis of the clamp varies inversely as the third power of the diameter. The torsional stiffness and the maximum shear stress of a round bar or wire of diameter d and active length L may be expressed by formulas

$$\frac{T}{\theta} = \pi \frac{d^4 G}{32L} \tag{10-15}$$

and

$$\tau = \frac{16T}{\pi d^3} \tag{10-16}$$

where θ is the angle of twist, in radians; T is the torque; G is the shear modulus of elasticity; and τ is the shear stress, all in consistent units.

Suspension wires in tension are used in many floated two-degree-of-freedom gyros between the gyro element and the gimbal and also between the gimbal and the outer case, as shown in Fig. 10-20. Depending on the instrumentation of these displacement-type gyros, the suspension wires may act as centering members only or also may serve as torquers by applying proper bias voltages to the platform servos (see Chap. 11).

The suspension wires are kept under tension by soft preload springs designed for parallel motion. One type of a parallel-motion spring is illustrated in Fig. 10-21; each spring consists of two leaves rigidly separated by a block B, which is also the wire clamp. There are several other types of parallel-motion springs which are both simpler to manufacture and easier to assemble; the principal advantage of the type illustrated is that it can be made very soft in the preload direction and yet be very resistant to all other loads. The stops on the gyro (or gimbal) and the preload spring rate should be such that the maximum relative motion between gyro element and gimbal (or between gimbal and outer case) along the wire axis is less than the initial deflection e in order to avoid damaging the suspension wire by placing it in compression.

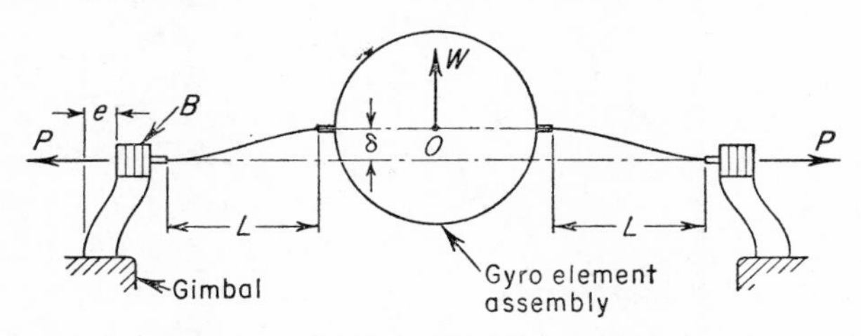

FIG. 10-21. Wire suspension system with transverse load.

The transverse deflection of the gyro element of Fig. 10-21, which is due to a buoyancy-error load W, is, as can be shown,

$$\delta = \frac{W}{2P}\left\{L - \frac{2[\cosh (nL) - 1]}{n \sinh (nL)}\right\} \tag{10-17}$$

where L = effective length of the wire suspension member
P = tension load
$n = (P/EI)^{1/2}$
E = modulus of elasticity
I = area moment of inertia of the suspension wires in bending

For the case where the bending stiffness is low, Eq. (10-17) may be closely approximated by

$$\delta = \frac{W}{2P}\left(L - \frac{2}{n}\right) \qquad \text{for } nL > 4 \tag{10-18}$$

The maximum bending moment occurs at either support and is

$$M_0 = \frac{W[\cosh (nL) - 1]}{2n \sinh (nL)} = \frac{P\delta}{\dfrac{nL \sinh (nL)}{\cosh (nL) - 1} - 2} \tag{10-19}$$

or

$$M_0 \simeq \frac{W}{2n} = \frac{P\delta}{nL - 2} \qquad \text{for } nL > 4 \tag{10-20}$$

The maximum tensile stress is the sum of the uniform stress due to the preload P plus the maximum bending stress due to the moment M_0. For a wire of diameter d, the maximum stress is

$$\sigma = \frac{4P}{\pi d^2} + \frac{32M_0}{\pi d^3} \tag{10-21}$$

Small-diameter wires act almost like strings, and the bending occurs close to the supports, with resultant sharp curvatures and high stresses. Equations (10-17) to (10-20) are true for all suspension wires of uniform cross section, provided the load W is applied parallel to a principal axis of the section. The torsional stiffness equation (10-15) and the stress equations (10-16) and (10-21) apply only to a circular cross section. For the corresponding equations relative to noncircular cross sections consult

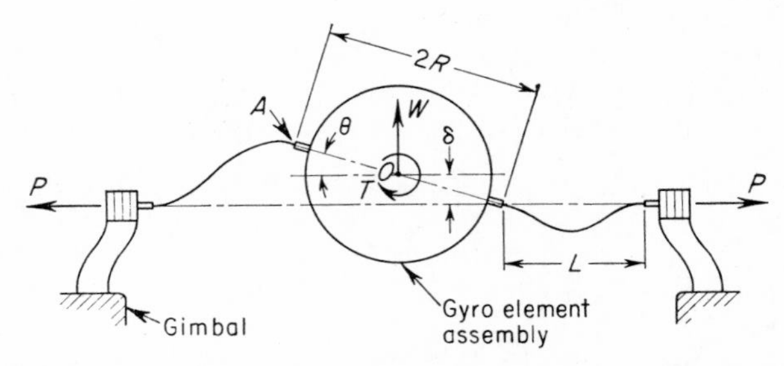

FIG. 10-22. Wire suspension system with transverse load and torque.

any good textbook on strength of materials.[10,24] The torsional stiffness of a gyro about the axis of the wires is twice that indicated by Eq. (10-15), since there are two wires in series resisting the applied torque.

The maximum stress will occur when the gyro element is displaced transversely and then twisted through an angle of θ radians, as indicated in Fig. 10-22. The maximum deflections will most likely occur when the gyro is not operating or during assembly. The maximum bending moment will occur at point A and is

$$\begin{aligned} M_A = P\delta &\left\{\frac{\cosh(nL) - 1}{nL\sinh(nL) - 2[\cosh(nL) - 1]}\right\} \\ &+ \frac{P\theta}{n}\left\{\frac{nR[\cosh(nL) - 1] + nL\cosh(nL) - \sinh(nL)}{nL\sinh(nL) - 2[\cosh(nL) - 1]}\right\} \end{aligned} \tag{10-22}$$

The first term in this equation is the bending moment due to the transverse deflection and is the same as provided by Eq. (10-19) in a slightly different form; the second term is the bending moment due to the twist θ. For $nL > 4$, the maximum bending moment is

$$M_A \simeq \frac{P\delta}{nL - 2} + \frac{P\theta}{n}\left[\frac{n(R + L) - 1}{nL - 2}\right] \tag{10-23}$$

The torsional stiffness about an axis perpendicular to the suspension wires, as shown in Fig. 10-22, amounts to

$$\frac{T}{\theta} = \frac{2P}{n}\left\{\frac{nL[\cosh(nL) - 1] + n^2R(R + L)\sinh(nL) - \sinh(nL) + nL}{nL\sinh(nL) - 2[\cosh(nL) - 1]}\right\} \tag{10-24}$$

For values of $nL > 4$, Eq. (10-24) becomes

$$\frac{T}{\theta} \simeq \frac{2P}{n}\left[\frac{nL + n^2R(R + L) - 1}{nL - 2}\right] \tag{10-25}$$

It is seen from Eq. (10-24) that the torsional deflection is independent of the transverse load; similarly, the transverse deflection is independent of an applied torque and is given by Eq. (10-17).

Jewel Pivots. The Massachusetts Institute of Technology Instrumentation Laboratory first introduced the use of jewel pivots for precision floated gyros in the late 1940s. An early version consisted of a

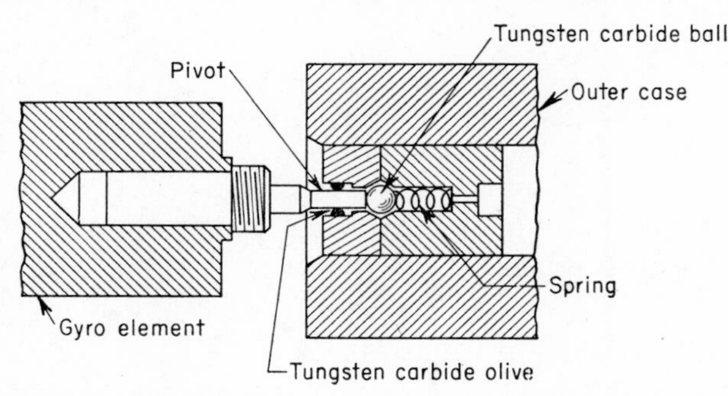

FIG. 10-23. Typical jewel pivot assembly. (*Courtesy of M.I.T. Instrumentation Laboratory.*)

0.030-in.-diameter tungsten carbide pin and a sapphire jewel (called an *olive* in the jewelry trade) with a diametral clearance of 0.0004 to 0.0006 in. Sapphire end stones with end plays of 0.0001 to 0.0005 in. were used to resist thrust loads. Because of their brittleness, however, these end stones chipped and shattered, and they had to be replaced by a ball of tungsten carbide. At the same time the pivot-pin diameter was increased to 0.050 in., and the olive was made of tungsten carbide in order to increase the load-carrying capacity.

A later version of the jewel pivot had a spring added behind the thrust ball to afford protection against shock and severe vibration. The need for this protection is questioned by several gyro manufacturers. A jewel pivot with spring-preloaded thrust ball is shown schematically in Fig. 10-23.

In general, the maximum loads on the pivots will occur during assembly, and extreme care must be taken to avoid shock-loading which will result in chipping or breaking of olives or end stones. After complete assembly of the gyro, the load on the pivots is the difference between the gravity or acceleration load and the buoyancy force. This pivot load per g of acceleration is

$$W_P = W_A(\alpha_F - \alpha_G)\,\Delta T \tag{10-26}$$

where W_A is the weight of the gyro element assembly in air; α_F and α_G are the volume coefficients of expansion of the flotation fluid and the gyro element, respectively; ΔT is the temperature change from condition of neutral buoyancy.

Example. A gyro element with an outer case fabricated of aluminum weighs 1,800 g in air and is neutrally buoyant in Fluorolube at 80°C. What is the load on the pivots when the fluid is cooled to the solidification temperature of 50°C?

Let $\alpha_G = 70 \times 10^{-6}$ cm³/(cm³)(°C) and $\alpha_F = 830 \times 10^{-6}$ cm³/(cm³)(°C)

$$W_P = 1{,}800 \text{ g } (830 \times 10^{-6} - 70 \times 10^{-6}) \times -30$$

$$W_P = -41.04 \text{ g} = -40{,}219 \text{ dynes} = -1.45 \text{ oz}$$

Therefore, the net load is approximately 40,000 dynes or 1.45 oz, acting upward.

The changes in diametral clearances between pivot and olive are generally negligible. The coefficients of expansion of tungsten carbide and sapphire are 5×10^{-6} and 5.4 to 6.2×10^{-6} in./(in.)(°C), respectively. Thus, even for a 0.050-in. stainless steel pivot in a tungsten carbide jewel, the diametral clearance will change by less than 0.0001 in. for a change in temperature of 150°C. However, the end clearance may be seriously affected by temperature changes, and these must be considered.

Example. A gyro element assembly has an aluminum case 3 in. long with a coefficient of expansion of 24×10^{-6} in./(in.)(°C). The outer case of the gyro, which supports the jewel, is also made of aluminum, with the same coefficient of expansion. When the gyro is cooled quickly, the average temperature of the gyro element is 10°C hotter than the outer casing. What is the change in the end clearance?

$$\Delta L = 3 \times 24 \times 10^{-6} \times 10 = 0.0007 \text{ in.}$$

A spring-loaded ball would prevent damage to the pivots or end stones.

Data are comparatively scarce on the fluid friction of jewel bearings, but the coefficient of friction is about 0.001 to 0.003, although the value probably depends on the viscosity of the flotation fluid and the unit pressure. The dry coefficient of friction of sapphire and tungsten carbide is about 0.2.

Example. A 700-g gyro element assembly is supported on a pair of jewel pivots of 0.040 in. diameter. The flotation fluid is a fluorocarbon with a coefficient of expansion of 8.3×10^{-4} in.³/(in.³)(°C). The temperature is 2°C above that of neutral buoyancy. What is the frictional torque T_f if the coefficient of friction $f = 0.0015$?

The load on the pivots (neglecting the expansion of the gyro element assembly) is

$$W_P = \frac{700 \text{ g}}{28.35 \text{ g/oz}} \times 8.3 \times 10^{-4} \frac{\text{in.}^3}{(\text{in.}^3)(°\text{C})} \times 2°\text{C} = 0.041 \text{ oz}$$

The frictional torque, sometimes called *stiction torque*, is $T_f = fW_PR = 0.0015 \times 0.041$ oz $\times$ 0.020 in. $= 1.23 \times 10^{-6}$ oz-in.

In the case of a single-degree-of-freedom gyro, the unbalance about the pivot axis may be measured and adjusted. However, it is difficult to balance about the spin axis, and it is sometimes said that it is necessary to balance the gyro element assembly accurately only about the pivot axis. This statement is unjustified. Any unbalance about the spin axis must be absorbed by the pivots and will result in friction torques which are small but not necessarily negligible. This factor is most important in a pendulous gyro accelerometer, particularly in a high-gravity-acceleration field. Because of small pivot clearances, there may be frictional torques as well as fluid torques acting on single-degree-of-freedom gyros owing to servo errors in a stabilized platform. For these reasons, M.I.T. has developed electromagnetic centering to prevent the pivots from touching the jewels.

In a two-degree-of-freedom gyro with jewel pivots the unbalances of the gyro element about both the inner and the outer axes and of the gimbal about the outer axis can be easily measured and adjusted. However, the unbalance of the gyro element or the gimbal about the spin axis of a two-degree-of-freedom gyro cannot be eliminated any more accurately than a similar operation in a single-degree-of-freedom gyro and is subject, therefore, to the same type of error torques in both designs.

Because of its construction, a two-degree-of-freedom gyro will be much less subject to frictional torques or fluid torques due to platform servo errors. Any servo error will cause components of rotation about the two pivot axes, with negligible friction torques.

Gimbal Ball Bearings. Low-torque ball bearings have been used as gimbal bearings for many years. Open curvature, close tolerances, and improved retainer designs have resulted in bearings with remarkably low friction torques, which are still too high, however, for the free gimbal bearings of precision gyroscopes. The principal sources of friction torque appear to be due to geometrical errors and to loss of energy due to deformation of balls and races. An instrument-bearing torque tester is described in reference 25.

One cause of geometric torques in ball bearings is illustrated in the exaggerated sketch of Fig. 10-24. As the bearing rotates, the weight on the bearing moves from one ball to another, and the inner race rides up and down. The weight of the gyro always tends to rotate the bearing forward or backward to a position midway between a pair of balls.

Waviness or eccentricities of the raceways and variations in ball size will also generate geometric torques. These torques, as well as any other friction torque acting on the gyro, will cause random drift of the gyro.

It had been observed for many years that a gyro-stabilized platform had improved performance if the gimbal bearings were kept in mild motion, as on a vehicle or on a Scorsby table. An improvement was obtained by introducing a *dither* into the platform servos, and still further improvement was achieved by counterrotating the bearings at either side

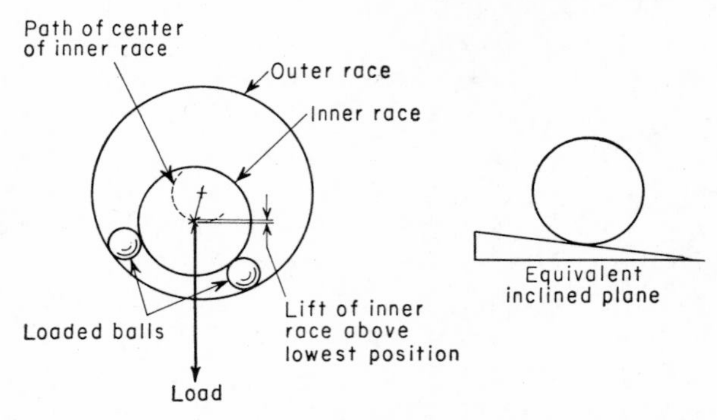

FIG. 10-24. Geometric torques due to weight on bearing moving from one ball to another.

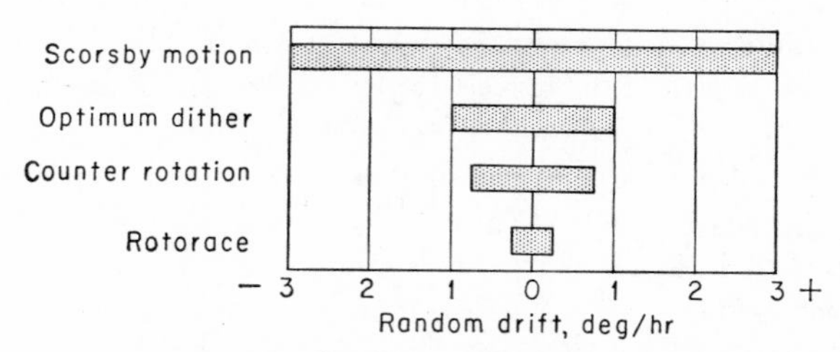

FIG. 10-25. Effects of four different methods of controlling gimbal ball-bearing action to reduce random drift of a typical gyro. (*Sperry Gyroscope Co.*)

of the gimbal axis. If the friction torques of each of the counterrotating bearings were exactly the same at all times, the net torque acting on the gyro would be zero. Unfortunately, these friction torques do not cancel, but a much reduced random drift rate is obtained; typical results are shown in Fig. 10-25. Rotation of the bearings has a secondary benefit in that it prevents pitting and wearing of balls and raceways which are essentially static in most applications.

If the counterrotating bearings are periodically reversed in direction of rotation, the differences in the torque levels of the opposed bearings are also effectively canceled, and the drift rate is reduced by an order of magnitude from that obtained with conventional bearings on a Scorsby table.

The Sperry Gyroscope Co. has developed a Rotorace* mechanism in which counterrotating bearings are periodically reversed. A typical Rotorace mechanism is shown in Fig. 10-26. Motor *A* drives gear *B* to rotate the bearing race counterclockwise. Motion is transmitted through gears *C* and *D* to turn the bearing race in gear *E* in a clockwise rotation. The counterrotation reduces the net friction torque. Mechanism *F* periodically reverses the direction of rotation, which effectively cancels

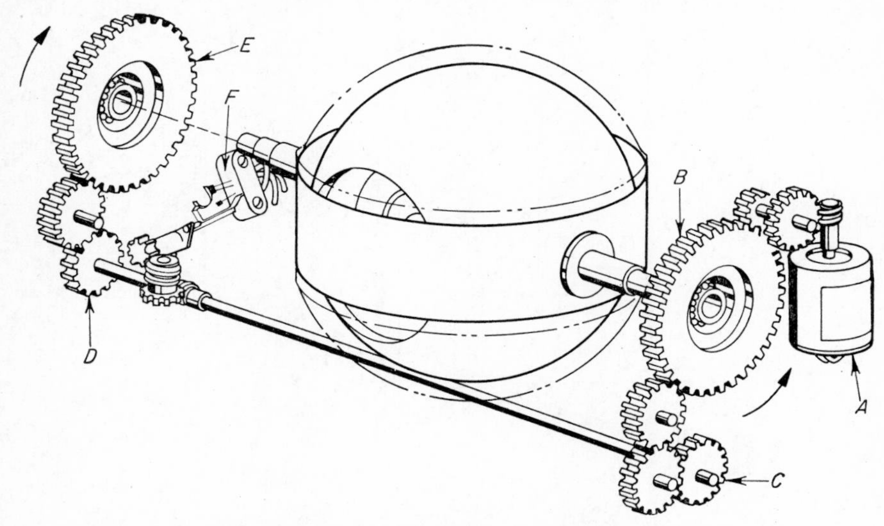

FIG. 10-26. Typical Rotorace mechanism. (*Sperry Gyroscope Co.*)

much of the remaining friction torque. Typical effect on random drift rates is shown in Fig. 10-25.

The Barden Corporation has developed the Dynamic Bearing.† The outer ring of the bearing is electromagnetically oscillated with an amplitude of about 22½°. This is enough to make one ball roll into the position of another, since retainerless, full-complement bearings are used in order to reduce the effect of the geometric friction torques. The outer-race oscillation integrates the friction torque to close to zero, or at least to an order of magnitude lower than the friction torque of an unoscillated bearing.

The means for oscillating the Dynamic Bearing are a six-pole permanent magnet and a three-pole electromagnet activated by a low-frequency (13 to 20 cps) oscillator using about 1 watt per bearing. A typical overall size of a Dynamic Bearing with a bore of 0.1875 in. is 0.500 in. OD and 0.500 in. wide.

* Registered trademark.

† Patent pending.

Without preload the running torque of the Dynamic Bearing is less than one-tenth the torque of the highest-quality instrument bearing. Under preload its running torque increases only slightly, whereas the torque of the conventional instrument bearing shows a pronounced increase. The starting torque of the Dynamic Bearing is the same low value as the running torque, whereas the conventional bearing may have a starting torque twice as high as that of the running torque. Typical restraining torque values are shown in the torque-load curves of Fig. 10-27.

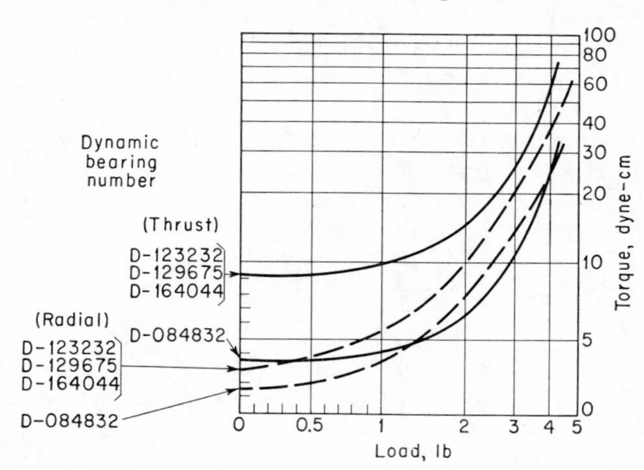

FIG. 10-27. Typical torque values for Dynamic Bearing. (*Pat. pending, Barden Corp.*)

Gas-lubricated Bearings. There is an increasing interest in gas-lubricated bearings by gyro manufacturers, particularly for gimbal bearings, though some development work is also being undertaken on gas-lubricated spin bearings. This interest is engendered primarily by the phenomenally low friction torque displayed by these bearings.

The nomenclature of oil-lubricated bearings also holds for the gas-lubrication field. Thus, a gas bearing is said to be "hydrodynamically" lubricated if the gas film between the bearing members is formed by the dynamic action of the rotating or sliding member acting on the gas. If the gas film is formed by a supply of pressurized gas to the bearing, it is said to be "hydrostatically" lubricated. Gas-lubricated spin bearings are generally hydrodynamically lubricated, whereas gimbal bearings, because of their almost negligible velocities, must be of the hydrostatic type.

It would be impossible to cover adequately the subject of gas-lubricated bearings in a book of this scope. It would require several chapters to introduce the subject, and without a previous understanding of the theory, a series of equations or charts might be confusing and misleading.

A good introduction to lubrication theory is given in "Theory and Practice of Lubrication for Engineers" by D. D. Fuller.[36] Additional recommended reading will also be found in the Bibliography at the end of this chapter.[37–46]

Although gas-lubricated bearings are being developed by many gyro manufacturers, they are fraught with many problems. As yet, the random torques acting on hydrostatically lubricated gimbal bearings are not as low as those obtained on the better fluid-suspended gyros. Accurate geometry, close clearances, and an excellent surface finish are required. Surface finishes of 5 μin. rms or better are needed, and the symmetry must be nearly perfect if the flow of air is not to cause rather large random torques to act on the gyro. Since rigidity is also a requirement, a compromise must be made between this and low random drift rates, one requiring a high pressure supply and the other a low pressure supply to keep the flow rate down. It must be remembered that the air bearing has to support the full weight of the gyro, whereas the pivot bearings or other suspensions of a fluid-suspended gyro may have to support substantially less than one-thousandth of the gyro weight, depending upon the temperature control (see section on Jewel Pivots).

10-11. Expansion Bellows

Most fluid-suspended gyros have outer casings which are hermetically sealed. There are two obvious advantages of a sealed gyro over a vented gyro.

1. There is no danger of spilling the fluid if the direction of the acceleration vector varies over a wide angle.

2. There will be no mass flow of the fluid and consequent torques, because of a change in the direction of the acceleration vector, as there would be with a free surface.

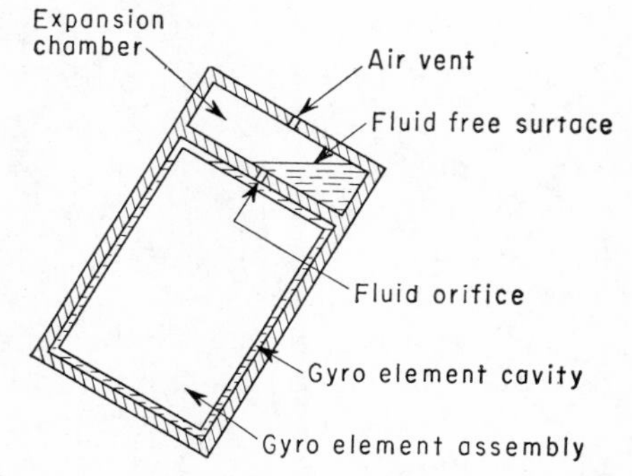

FIG. 10-28. Free surface of fluid extending into gyro element cavity.

If the free surface of a vented gyro is in a separate expansion chamber and connected by a small orifice to the gyro element cavity, the mass flow due to a change in the acceleration vector direction will not cause a torque on the gyro, unless the free surface is extended into the gyro element cavity, as illustrated schematically in Fig. 10-28.

There are several other serious disadvantages to a vented gyro.

1. Environmental pressure changes will change the pressure loading on the gyro element, possibly resulting in weight shifts.

2. Dirt may enter into the gyro element cavity and cause random torques.

3. A deep pipe may be formed in the fluid on solidification and may entrap air, which will cause torques during subsequent operation.

4. During long storage periods great quantities of air may go into solution in the fluid which will later be released at the operating temperature with resulting torques due to the entrapped air.

In order to keep the fluid pressure essentially constant in spite of temperature or environmental pressure changes, most fluid-suspended gyros are provided with sealed expansion bellows. There are two types of commercial bellows available: one is a one-piece, circularly corrugated brass tube and the other is fabricated of a series of conical disks which are alternately welded or brazed at the inner and outer edges. The latter type is made in a wide variety of materials and is considered superior, though much more expensive. (See manufacturers' catalogues for materials, spring constant, effective area, and permissible extension or compression.)

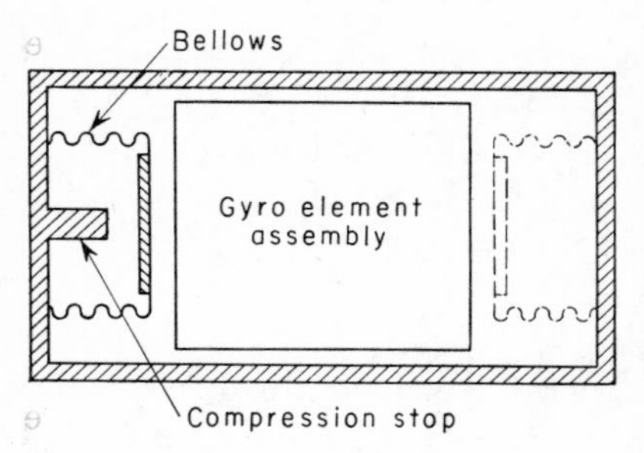

FIG. 10-29. Expansion bellows installation.

If the pressure in the fluid is to be independent of the environmental pressure, then it is most convenient to have the bellows compress as the temperature of the fluid is increased. A bellows installation is shown schematically in Fig. 10-29. The compression stop is provided to prevent overstressing of the bellows; similarly, an extension stop, not shown, must also be provided. Maximum loads on the expansion bellows usually occur during assembly or in processing (e.g., leak checking) rather than in a sealed and operating gyro (see Fig. 10-8 for typical bellows installation). The bellows should be designed so that:

1. The pressure in the fluid at the operating temperature is the same, as within the gyro element.

2. The bellows is compressed to its stop at the maximum operating temperature.

3. It does not touch its extension stop until the fluid has cooled at least 15°C below the operating temperature.

The pressure P_F in the fluid is

$$P_F = P_B + k\delta_c \tag{10-27}$$

where P_B is the pressure of the gas in the bellows and k and δ_c are, respectively, the spring constant [lb/(in.^{2})(in.)] and the compressive deflection of the bellows.

It is improper to provide two widely separated expansion bellows, since a change in the acceleration vector will in general cause a flow of fluid past the gyro element. Figure 10-29 shows a second bellows in phantom. It is quite evident that if the acceleration vector were directed to the right, the bellows on the left would be compressed more than the one on the right. If the acceleration vector were reversed, the bellows on the right would be compressed more than the other, and there would be a flow of fluid. This flow of fluid will give rise to random fluid torques.

10-12. Outer Casing and Covers

The outer casing of a precision floated gyro must serve several purposes.

1. It must confine the flotation fluid and prevent the entry of dirt.
2. It must prevent the entry of air.
3. It must provide a nearly isothermal environment for the gyro element.
4. It must isolate it from environmental pressure changes.

The materials used in the outer casing must be dimensionally stable and compatible with the other materials used in the gyro or be suitably protected therefrom.

Generally heaters and temperature sensors are mounted on the outer casing, which also acts as a support for the fixed part of the pickoffs and torquers. (The design of the heater and temperature sensors is covered in Chap. 11, as is the design of pickoffs and torquers.) Figure 10-11 illustrates a typical cross section of an outer casing, showing the heaters and temperature sensors as well as the support of the pickoff and torquer for a single-degree-of-freedom gyro. The casing is made of aluminum of heavy cross section which is an excellent conductor and aids in maintaining an essentially isothermal environment for the gyro element.

Covers are provided over the outer casing on many gyros. These covers may be added for one or more reasons.

1. They may be there for the sake of appearance, i.e., to cover unsightly wiring or to provide a smooth surface for a name plate.
2. They may provide mechanical protection to delicate parts such as terminals or temperature sensors.
3. They may act as a thermal shield and thus reduce temperature variations at the gyro element.
4. They may provide magnetic shielding for the gyro element and thus reduce random torques (see Chap. 11).

Some means must be provided for properly orienting and securely mounting the gyro on its platform. Either a synchro or a flange type of mount, with the mounting plane passing near the center of gravity of the gyro, is preferred.

10-13. Seals and Leak Detection

In every gyro there are many joints which must be hermetically sealed and checked. In addition to the main seals of the gyro case and the outer casing, there are seals for terminals, evacuation tubes, expansion bellows, and weight-adjustment accesses. All methods of joining and sealing have been used successfully; these include welding, brazing, silver soldering, soft-soldering, gasketing, O rings, adhesive bonding, and press fitting.

Welding, Brazing, and Silver Soldering. There is a great variety of information on these processes which is easily available, and no attempt will be made to describe them in detail. Inert-gas welding is commonly used for the fabrication of expansion bellows made of ferrous materials, such as stainless steel or Monel. However, regardless of the type of welding process, the weld is likely to be porous unless extreme care is taken.[34]

The ordinary brazing solders are copper-zinc alloys which melt and flow in the range of 1700 to 2000°F and may be used for the joining of most ferrous or cuprous alloys.[27] The silver solders, often called *silver braze alloys* or *hard solders,* may be used to join practically all metals except aluminum-, magnesium-, and beryllium-base alloys and those alloys which melt at a lower temperature than the flow temperature of the silver solders. A number of metals and alloys, however, are difficult to silver-solder and require special procedures.[27]

Brazing of aluminum and aluminum-base alloys is accomplished with the aluminum-silicon brazing alloys. Brazing of aluminum to other metals is also possible with special techniques.[28] Titanium and tantalum are difficult to join, and the joints are likely to be brittle, particularly with tantalum, unless special fluxes and procedures are used.[29–31]

Beryllium copper is commonly used for springs and suspension members in gyros because of its high strength, low modulus of elasticity, formability during hardening, and dimensional stability. In the solution-treated condition, it can be brazed at 1200 to 1300°F, quenched as soon as the brazing alloy has solidified, and then precipitation-hardened. Skill and care are required to obtain consistent results. Flux entrapped in the joints is the principal cause of low strength or failure.

The tensile strength of a brazed joint is a function of many factors, such as the brazing temperature, time, surface finish, and joint thickness. In general the brazing temperature should not exceed the flow temperature, nor should the time exceed that required to cause a complete wetting of the joint. Excess temperature or time may cause the formation of oxides, brittle intermetallic compounds, and gas inclusions; it may also result in the contamination of the brazing alloys by dissimilar-base metals with consequent de-wetting. It has also been found that the maximum strength of a brazed or silver-soldered joint occurs with a gap of about 0.002 in. A drop in strength of as much as 50 per cent can be expected if the gap is increased to 0.010 in.[32] In wide gaps the capillary forces are so weak that insufficient filling occurs, and the number and size of gas inclusions increase with the joint thickness.[33] Both these effects tend to weaken the joint and to increase the leakage rate. In general it is necessary to have an overlap of at least 3/16 in. in order to obtain a consistently good hermetic brazed lap joint.

Arma has successfully silver-soldered hundreds of nonmagnetic stainless steel gyro cases or complete gyro element assemblies with soft-soldered terminals not more than 1 in. away from the joint being brazed. They were induction-brazed at about 1150°F, with the induction coils energized for 11 sec. The terminal joints were kept cool with either small blocks of aluminum or moistened felt. All flux deposits were removed by washing with hot water and then isopropyl alcohol in order to prevent corrosion and chemical reactions with the flotation fluid.

Soft-soldering. Soft solder, an alloy of tin and lead, is universally used for wiring; it is also widely used for attaching glass insulated terminals and the principal sealed joints in gyros. Soft solder is specified by the percentage of each constituent, with that of tin appearing first. The most commonly used solder for gyro work is the 60-40 alloy (60 per cent tin, 40 per cent lead); this alloy is close to the eutectic and therefore flows at a comparatively low temperature.

A phase (equilibrium) diagram for tin-lead alloys is given in Fig. 10-30. An alloy of 63 per cent tin and 37 per cent lead is called the *eutectic alloy*, since it has a melting point of 361°F in which the liquid and solid states may be in equilibrium in all proportions. In other words, it acts like a simple element or chemical compound. All other alloys except pure tin or pure lead, which melt at 621 and 450°F, respectively, will pass through a pasty state on heating. For example, the 40-60 alloy (see Fig. 10-30) will remain solid until the temperature reaches the solidus line at 361°F (point a), when it will begin to melt. As the temperature is further increased, the alloy becomes pasty (i.e., a mixture of solid and liquid) until the temperature reaches that of the liquidus line at point b (460°F); at this point the alloy becomes completely liquid and flows readily. On cooling this alloy below 460°F, the reverse takes place, and the alloy becomes increasingly pasty until 361°F, where it is again solid.

If several successive soldering operations are to be performed on a single assembly, it is common practice to use soft solders with successively lower liquidus temperatures. It is evident from the phase diagram that the so-called "high-temperature" soft solders have a greater pasty range, but all commercial tin-lead solders have the same solidus temperature.

Solders in the pasty range have no strength, and the parts must be mechanically supported to prevent relative motion while the solder is in the pasty state. The advantage of the high-temperature soft solders is that the solder does not readily flow out of a finished joint until the liquidus temperature is reached.

For clean copper, brass, or tinned surfaces, a water-white rosin flux is most satisfactory. It possesses a natural acid which is not active at normal room temperature but which melts below the solidus temperature and frees the acid at about 300°F. The flux residue is nonconductive, noncorrosive, and nonhygroscopic. At 550°F the acid is almost completely volatilized and has no fluxing action; therefore, the soldering

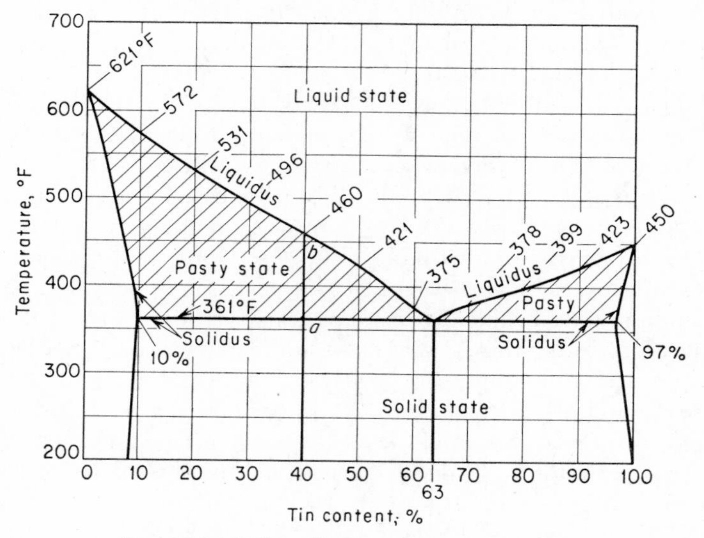

FIG. 10-30. Phase diagram for tin-lead alloys.

temperature should be kept below this temperature. Excessive temperatures are likely to cause surface oxidation in addition to destroying the fluxing action, and it will take longer for the joint to cool to a temperature of about 300°F, when it will be safely intact.

Soldering of beryllium copper or stainless steel generally requires a stronger flux, since the oxides formed are quite refractory. Generally chloride fluxes are used, which become active around 500°F and therefore require temperatures of about 600°F for good fluxing action. These fluxes are quite corrosive even at room temperature and must be thoroughly removed with a solution of baking soda in a pure hot-water rinse and then cleaned with alcohol. Particular care must be taken with precipitation-hardened beryllium copper, since it becomes quickly overaged at 650°F and higher.

As for brazing, the strength of a soft-soldered joint is a maximum when the gap is about 0.002 in. and drops rapidly as the gap increases. The strength of a soldered joint also drops rapidly as the temperature increases; thus, the operating temperature should never exceed about 200°F. There are limited available data on the creep strength of soft solder, but it probably does not exceed 50 to 75 lb/in.^{2} in shear at 200°F in a good joint. Some designers assume that the strength is essentially zero, and the solder is used only to provide a hermetic seal.

With present methods and solders it is very difficult to achieve hermetic sealing of aluminum. Special aluminum solders containing zinc will bond well to aluminum, as will ordinary soft solder, using ultrasonic or friction methods to remove the refractory oxides; but they are not consistently hermetic. The best available method for soldering aluminum is to plate it with a readily solderable metal.

In plating aluminum for soldering the basic metal is first given a zinc flash a few molecules thick, and then a copper or nickel plate about 0.0003 to 0.0005 in. thick. Nickel plate, particularly the hard-coat type obtained with electroless plating,* is considered superior, since it acts as a stop to prevent the formation of deleterious intermetallic compounds. However, nickel oxide is very difficult to remove when soldering, and the nickel plate must be protected by a gold plate (or plating with other noble metals) at least 20 μin. thick. The gold dissolves in soft solder, and bond is formed with the nickel. If plated aluminum joints are unsoldered, care must be taken not to wipe off all the tinning; otherwise, it will be practically impossible to resolder without stripping and replating.

Adhesive Joining and Sealing. The following are some of the advantages in using adhesives over other methods of joining and sealing:

1. Ability to join dissimilar materials, both metallic and nonmetallic
2. Reduction of the temperature required for joining
3. Electrical insulation it provides if necessary
4. Vibration damping properties
5. Higher strengths than the soft solders

Unfortunately, the joining and sealing of parts or assemblies with adhesives also have disadvantages:

1. They are dimensionally less stable than most metals.
2. They are much more permeable to gases and require a longer leakage path.
3. They have higher coefficients of expansion than any of the metals. With the proper filler, however, some resins may be made to have approximately the same coefficient of expansion as magnesium or aluminum.

* Metal deposition by catalytic reduction of nickel in a nickel-salt solution without the use of electrodes and electrolysis.

The thermosetting resins, such as the phenolics and epoxies, are high-molecular-weight polymers, which react in curing to form a three-dimensional, cross-linked molecular network possessing high strength, rigidity, and resistance to heat and chemical attack. These resins cannot be melted by heat and rehardened on cooling.

Thermoplastic resins such as the polyvinyls and the acrylics are also high-molecular-weight polymers but have few cross links and can be melted with heat or softened with solvents and then rehardened by cooling or drying. These resins have comparatively low cohesive strengths. Due to their excellent adhesive properties, they are often used in formulation with thermosetting resins as modifiers or plasticizers for increased flexibility.

The elastomeric adhesives are similar to the thermoplastic resins in structure and properties, possessing great flexibility due to their natural or synthetic rubber base. These materials are often used in nonstructural applications and as modifying agents for thermosetting resins, where reduction of brittleness and increase in impact, bending, or peeling strength are desired.

The formulation of an adhesive for joining and hermetic sealing of a gyro must provide the following characteristics:

1. Chemical inertness at the operating temperature with respect to the materials being joined and the environment, including the flotation fluid, if any
2. Good bonding strength, i.e., adhesion, to the joined parts
3. Good cohesive strength, i.e., internal strength
4. Excellent dimensional stability
5. Low permeability to gases
6. A coefficient of expansion reasonably matched to that of the joined parts
7. No gases formed during curing that might cause voids
8. Good workability

Only the thermosetting resins provide a strong cohesive force; this is due to molecular cross linkages. With proper surface treatment all the metals presently used in gyro fabrication (aluminum, magnesium, steel, beryllium, copper, stainless steel) may be joined by the thermosetting adhesives. One of the most suitable formulations was found to be the following epoxy resin:

	Per cent by weight
Araldite 6010 epoxy resin (Ciba)	35
Hardener HN-951 (Ciba)	5
Filler, Stupalith A2410 (200 mesh) (Stupakoff)	60

The addition of the filler provides a bonding formulation with a coefficient of expansion approximately equal to that of aluminum and a viscosity which is still workable. Numerous other nonreactive substances may be used as fillers to adjust the coefficient of expansion. The modified epoxies, i.e., those with plasticizers added to improve workability, were found to be incompatible with the fluorocarbon flotation fluids.

Substances known as reactive diluents are sometimes used to offset the increase in viscosity due to the filler; however, caution is required, since they tend to decrease the cohesive strength of the resin. In general, optimizing the sealant viscosity, expansion coefficient, and bond strength is a process involving careful adjustment of the formulation.

Surface preparation, of course, is extremely important. The surfaces to be bonded must be completely free of oil, loose dirt or scale, and moisture. Ultrasonic cleaning (using acetone, alcohol, or any other solvent which leaves no residue) is effective for removal of oil and loose dirt or scale. Etching to remove oxides and other films is generally effective and improves the bond strength. A certain amount of surface roughness also probably aids the adhesive strength because of the increased area and mechanical bonding. The parts should be joined soon after cleaning and should not be allowed to accumulate deposits of oil and dirt, which are present even in well-filtered air. It should also be self-evident that the prepared surfaces should not be touched except with clean tools or clean gloves.

The following surface preparation is recommended for aluminum.

1. Clean surfaces with acetone, preferably in an ultrasonic cleaner.
2. Etch for 15 min at 115°F in the following solution:
   Distilled water—30 parts by weight
   Concentrated sulfuric acid—10 parts by weight
   Sodium or potassium dichromate—1 part by weight
3. Rinse in clean water for 15 min.
4. Acetone-dip for 1 min and air-dry.

Where acid etching may be a problem, chromic acid anodizing per MIL-A-86725A Type I, followed by an acetone wash prior to applying the adhesive, is nearly as effective. When neither acid etching nor anodizing is practical, ultrasonic cleaning with acetone is recommended, but the strength of the bond is greatly reduced, possibly to one-third of its value with the acid etch.

It is difficult to obtain good adhesive bonds with copper or copper alloys. A gold flash (20 μin.), or nickel plate over the copper followed by a gold flash, will greatly improve the strength of the bond.

In general, for maximum strength and stability the adhesive should be cured at an elevated temperature immediately after joining, in accordance with the manufacturer's instructions. Though some adhesives are formulated so that they will cure at room temperature, improved properties will be obtained if they are cured at a higher temperature. In order to avoid porous joints, the adhesive should not produce volatile gases or undergo great changes in volume during the curing cycle.

The most commonly used joint configurations are the lap, scarf, and butt joints. The adhesive joints are generally strongest in pure shear and weakest in resisting a tearing action. Figure 10-31*a* indicates the tearing action obtained in a lap joint where the members being joined are flexible and bent so that the tensile forces are in line, as required by the equilibrium equations. With rigid members (Fig. 10-31*b*), there is little bending at the joint, and it is very nearly in pure shear. For maximum strength, the thickness of the adhesive should preferably be 0.002 or 0.003 in. With epoxy resins and an adhesive thickness of 0.002 in., shear strengths of at least 4,000 lb/in.² should be obtained with properly prepared aluminum surfaces. For an adhesive thickness of 0.020 in., the strength may drop to 1,200 lb/in.².

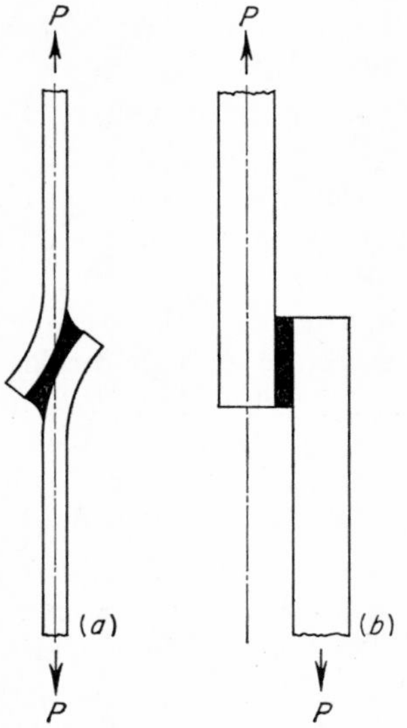

FIG. 10-31. Lap joints. (*a*) Tearing action due to local bending of weak members; (*b*) shearing action with rigid members to resist local bending.

A few typical joints used in sealing gyros are shown in Fig. 10-32. In each case the adhesive is placed on one or both members and then brought together in the directions indicated by the heavy arrows. The leakage path through the adhesive has been made at least 3/16 in. long and of small cross-

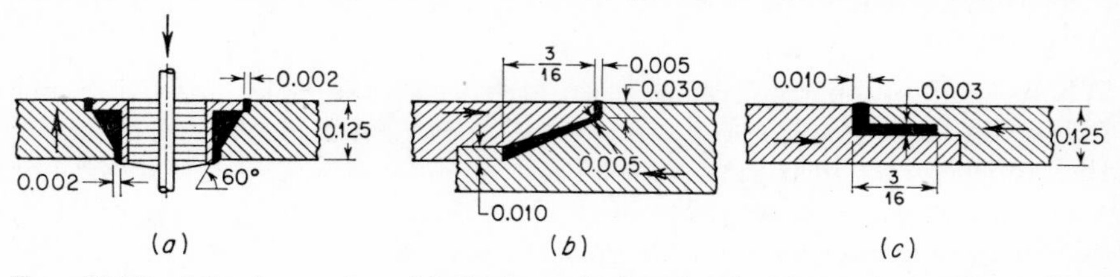

FIG. 10-32. Adhesive seals. (*a*) Sealing of glass-insulated terminal; (*b*) modified scarf joint with wedging action; (*c*) modified lap joint.

sectional area because of the high permeability of resins to all gases. All the joints are designed so that there is a wedging action to aid in the complete filling of the cavity and to minimize the possibility of entrapping air. Figures 10-32*b* and *c* are cross sections through cylindrical joints with piloting sections for centering. Since these are blind joints, the pilots also act as wipers to prevent excess adhesive from being squeezed into the gyro where it might break off and cause erratic weight shifts. Drawing a partial vacuum on the inside of assemblies such as those of Fig. 10-32*a* and *b* minimizes air entrapment, augments the wedging action, and forces the adhesive into close contact with both members. Heating of the members reduces the high viscosity of the filled resins and ensures complete wetting of the surfaces, although speed is necessary to prevent curing before the joint is completed.

Compared to metals, the resins are all very permeable to gases, and this phenomenon must be considered in the design of hermetic joints to be sealed with resins. The permeation constant at 100°C for the rigid epoxy resins most frequently used in hermetic sealing is in the range of 1.0×10^{-5} to 1×10^{-6} cubic centimeter (at 20°C and 760 mm) per hour per square inch of area per inch of thickness (length of leakage path) per atmosphere of partial pressure difference. The permeation constant is dependent on the gas, as well as on the sealant. In general, the permeation constant with helium is somewhat lower than with hydrogen, but both are greater than with air or nitrogen. The permeation constant of gases through metals is negligible except for hydrogen through palladium or iron. The permeation constant of hydrogen through palladium at 100°C is 8×10^{-3} (cm³)(in.)/(hr)(in.²)(atm) and through iron about 3×10^{-5} (cm³)(in.)/(hr)(in.²)(atm).

Gaskets and O Rings. In general, gaskets and O rings do not provide satisfactory hermetic seals for gyros, although they are successfully used in many other applications. Gaskets and O rings made of elastomers tend to creep and lose their compression with time; the silicone rubbers are particularly poor in this respect. Among metals, lead, tin, and soft copper have a similar tendency.

The elastomers are also quite permeable to all gases. The permeation constant K_p of nearly all elastomers at about 100°C is in the range of 3×10^{-2} to 1.5×10^{-3} (cm³)(in.)/(hr)(in.²)(atm).

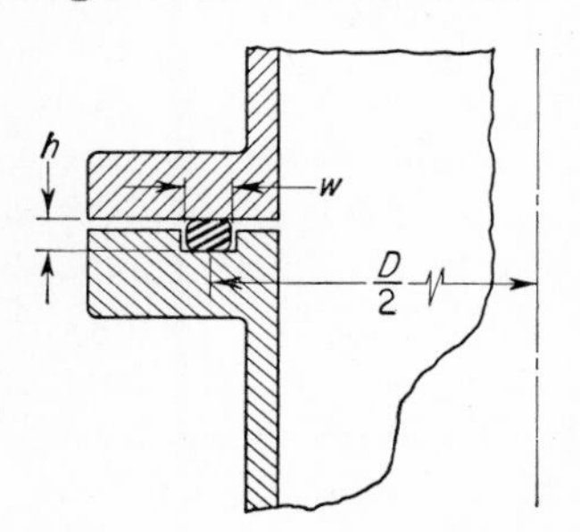

FIG. 10-33. Cross section through O-ring seal.

Example. Find the leakage rate for helium through a rubber O ring which is compressed to an essentially rectangular cross section (see Fig. 10-33) of $h = 0.060$ in. and $w = 0.105$ in. The mean diameter of the ring $D = 3.5$ in., the permeation constant $K_p = 1.0 \times 10^{-3}$ (cm³)(in.)/(hr)(in.²)(atm), and the difference in pressure $p = 1$ atm.

$$Q = K_p \times \frac{\pi D h}{w} \times p = 1.0 \times 10^{-3} \times \frac{\pi 3.5(0.060)}{0.105} \times 1 = 6.28 \times 10^{-3} \text{ cm}^3/\text{hr}$$

This is considered to be a very high leakage rate and would not be satisfactory for a gyro.

Where a seal is only temporary, e.g., used during tests for making adjustments and replaced or backed up with a superior seal, an O ring or gasket may be quite satisfactory. In floated gyros it is of utmost importance that no air be trapped by the seal design which may later be released into the fluid space and cause a torque.

Leak Detection. There are a number of methods available for detecting leaks which range from the comparatively simple soap-bubble test to the mass-spectrometer leak detector. Some of these methods are suitable for either detecting or locating leaks, but only a few may be used for quantitative measurements.

The soap-bubble test is a simple and fairly sensitive method for locating leaks in all kinds of seals, applicable even to those which are difficult to locate with a helium jet and a mass spectrometer. The usual procedure is to pressurize the inside of the component being tested with any convenient gas, such as air, at several atmospheres. Hydrogen gas will give superior results because of its lesser viscosity and consequent greater flow rate. The suspected area should be painted with a soap solution. Bubbles will form at the source of the leak. The sensitivity of this method is usually underestimated, since it is possible to locate leaks only 100 times larger than those just detectable on a mass spectrometer.

The thermocouple and the Pirani gauge are used to measure pressures below 0.1 mm Hg; but neither is very sensitive, and the results are not quantitative. However, they are not damaged by exposure to atmospheric pressure as are some other types.

The hot-cathode-ion gauge is suitable for pressures below 1 μ Hg. Very small leaks can be located by spraying the suspected area with acetone or ether and by watching for changes in pressure within the component. The pressure must not rise above 1 μ or the filament will burn out. The hot-cathode-ion gauge has the disadvantage, however, that it is not sensitive to only one gas, which makes it possible for gases other than the test gas flowing through the leak to affect the results.

The hydrogen-ion-gauge leak detector uses a highly evacuated ionization gauge tube which is sealed off with a palladium window. When the palladium is heated, it becomes permeable only to hydrogen, and any hydrogen passing through a leak into the vacuum system will enter the ion gauge through the palladium window. The hydrogen in the gauge is ionized by electron emission from a heated cathode and goes to an ion collector. The resulting current is proportional to the leakage rate and is read on a meter. The maximum sensitivity of the hydrogen-ion gauge is about 45 $\mu cm^3/hr$ of hydrogen reduced to standard conditions, which is equivalent to about 30 $\mu cm^3/hr$ of helium at standard conditions. The principal advantage of the hydrogen-ion gauge is that it will not be damaged by very high leakage rates nor by accidental exposure to atmospheric pressure.

The mass-spectrometer leak detector responding only to helium gas is used almost universally in gyro testing, since it is sensitive to leakage rates as low as from 1 to 5 $\mu cm^3/hr$ of helium at standard conditions. Helium, along with any other gas present, enters the vacuum system and is ionized by electron emission from a heated filament in the mass-spectrometer tube. The ions are accelerated by electric fields and separated by magnetic fields according to their mass-to-charge ratio. The instrument is adjusted so that only the helium ions are collected, and thus the current is proportional to the leakage rate. The vacuum system must reduce the pressure to less than 1 μ (0.001 mm Hg) to avoid the danger of destroying the filament. Therefore, it cannot measure large leakage rates, and it may be damaged if the leakage rate should accidentally increase.

Normally the unit being tested is placed in an atmosphere of helium and the inside connected to the vacuum system, or the inside is pressurized and the space outside the unit, say a bell jar, is connected to the vacuum system. These methods will detect and measure the leak quantitatively, but they will not determine the location of the leak. To locate a leak the inside of the unit may be connected to the vacuum system and a small jet of helium directed on the suspected area, or it may be pressurized with helium and a probe (fine capillary tube) connected to the vacuum system and held near the various suspected areas. These methods, unfortunately, are not very sensitive and may not be superior to the soap-bubble test.

A word of caution is necessary. The pressures or vacuums used should not put unnecessary strains on the parts tested that might cause leaks to be formed or the parts to be overstressed. With the aid of proper fixtures and choice of side to be pressurized, this faulty operation can usually be avoided.

Another common error is to use rubber gaskets or rubber tubing in the vacuum system without necessary precautions. Rubber is very permeable to all gases, including helium, and may cause unnecessary rejection of parts or assemblies due to faulty reading of leakage rates. In addition, rubber exposed to helium will absorb large quantities which will be evolved when connected to the vacuum system and result in faulty leakage-rate reading. These effects can be controlled by maximizing the length of the leakage path, minimizing the exposed area, completely degassing, and minimizing the time exposure to helium or other test gas. Resins used for bonding windings will also adsorb gases, and even metals will adsorb many gases. Therefore, if any parts on the vacuum side of the system have been exposed to the test gas, they should be thoroughly degassed (preferably at an elevated temperature) before testing for leaks.

When rubber or resins are used for sealing gyros, it may require 15 min or more before the full equilibrium leakage rate is obtained, because of adsorption of the test gas.

Gas may flow through channels such as a crack or a series of pores in either of two modes, known as viscous flow or molecular flow. Viscous flow occurs when the mean free path of the gas molecule is small as compared with the length of the channel and amounts to

$$Q_V = K \frac{p_2^2 - p_1^2}{\mu} \tag{10-28}$$

where Q_V = leakage rate for viscous flow
K = constant for a given leak
p_1, p_2 = pressures on opposite sides of leak
μ = coefficient of viscosity of gas at ambient temperature

Molecular flow occurs when the mean free path of the gas molecule is greater than the length of the channel. The magnitude of the flow is

$$Q_M = k \left(\frac{T}{M}\right)^{1/2} (p_2 - p_1) \tag{10-29}$$

where T = absolute temperature of gas
k = constant for a given leak
M = molecular weight of gas

Between these extremes the flow will be neither viscous nor molecular but will have some of the characteristics of both. The mean free path of most of the common gases is around 40×10^{-7} in. at standard conditions and varies inversely as the density. At 1 mm Hg, the mean free path would be about 0.003 in., and the flow would probably be viscous. At 1 μ Hg, the mean free path would be 3 in., and the flow would probably be molecular. For leak testing, one side of the unit is exposed to a vacuum at 1 μ or lower and the other side to an appreciable pressure; therefore, the flow will generally be partially viscous and partially molecular.

The leakage rates for several gases relat ve to helium are given in Table 10-3.

By making leak-rate measurements at two different pressures, the proportionality of the two types of flow may be determined for the test gas using Eqs. 10-28 and 10-29. With the aid of Table 10-3, the leakage rate for the other gases may be calculated approximately.

There is a great deal of controversy as to the allowable leakage rates for the gyro element assembly and the outer casing of a floated gyro.

This difference in opinion is probably due to the differences in design. The author has generally specified for use at Arma a maximum leakage rate of 20×10^{-6} cm^3/hr of helium at standard conditions for soldered, brazed, or welded main assemblies, such as the gyro element assembly or the complete assembly of a floated gyro, and a maximum rate of 12×10^{-6} cm^3/hr for soldered, brazed, or welded subassemblies. It is the author's experience that a good soldered, brazed, or welded joint has no measurable leak, or if it has, it is either very bad or becomes progressively

TABLE 10-3. RELATIVE LEAKAGE RATES OF GASES (REFERRED TO HELIUM)

Gas	Viscous flow	Molecular flow
Helium	1.00	1.00
Hydrogen	2.20	1.42
Oxygen	0.95	0.39
Air	1.10	0.37
Water vapor	2.00	0.40

worse with temperature or pressure cycling. Therefore, such low leakage-rate specifications appear to be justified for this type of joint or seal.

If gaskets, O rings, or adhesive-type seals are used, the allowable leakage rate must be increased because of the permeability of these materials. In fact, it may have to be many hundreds of times greater than that for a solder seal. At these high rates it becomes difficult to distinguish between the leakage due to permeability and that due to a crack or porosity, which may become progressively worse with time and result in a complete failure of the gyro. It is this latter aspect which is critical rather than the relatively high leakage rate.

10-14. Materials

The gyro designer's interest in material properties is generally confined to rigidity, density, coefficient of expansion, and dimensional stability. Table 10-4 lists these properties and a few others for a wide variety of materials. The data were taken from the Massachusetts Institute of Technology Instrumentation Laboratory Report R-137. M.I.T. has been a pioneer in determining the dimensional stability of most of the materials used in precision instruments. Since it is difficult to present the data in tabular form, the reader is urged to consult the reference[48] which describes the procedures, heat-treatments, and results.

It should be noted that the elastic limits listed in Table 10-4 are generally lower than those given in other sources. These limits are based on some very sensitive measurements of permanent strain by Dr. B.

TABLE 10-4. PROPERTIES OF MATERIALS

Material	Modulus of elasticity, lb/in.² × 10⁻⁶	Elastic limit, lb/in.² × 10⁻³	Yield point, 0.2% offset, lb/in.² × 10⁻³	Ultimate tensile strength, lb/in.² × 10⁻³	Elongation, % in 2 in.	Hardness R = Rockwell B = Brinell
Aluminum 356 (cast)	10.5	12	24	33	4	R34B
Aluminum 6061	10	12	40	45	15	R35B
Aluminum 7075	10.4	40	80	88	10	R88B
Aluminum 2017	10.5	30	40	62	22	R66B
Aluminum 2024	10.4	22	46	68	22	R68B
Beryllium copper 25	19	58.5	80 (0.01%)	175	5	R37C
Brass 60–40	15	24	50 (0.1%)	70	5	R80B
Brass 70–30	15	27	49 (0.1%)	60	19.5	R81B
Phosphor bronze 5%	16	72	82	92	5.5	R98B
Hastelloy B	32.1	114	120–150	160–200	30–15	R95B
Inconel	30.1	15	25–30	80–100	50–35	R65–85B
Z nickel	32.1	114	120–150	160–200	30–15	R40C
Ni Span C	26.5	57.5	100	115	18	R29C
Gyrolloy	28	20	....	....	....	....
Mumetal	30	....	18.5	64	27	....
K Monel	28.2	110	100–130	140–170	30–15	R27–33C
R Monel	26	42	30–100	79–115	50–20	R60–100B
Monel	26	54	55–120	85–125	35–10	R85B–23C
Stainless steel 310	29	30	45	100	50	R85B
Stainless steel 440C	29	190	275	285	1	R61C
Stainless steel 410	31.4	108	152	193	15	R41C
Stainless steel 303 (cold-drawn)	28	41	170	215	5	B97
Stainless steel 303 (annealed)	28	10.4	30	90	50	B83
1020 steel	30.1	50	63.7	75	20	R89B
1045 steel	30	17	28	72	16	R92B
1112 steel	28.4	63	74	87	17	R77B
1144 steel	30	40	70	100	16	R23C
4140 steel	29	100	140	165	18	R23C
10100 steel	29	90	250	300	10	R64C
52100 steel	29.2	89	250	300	10	R61C
Nitralloy 135 (modified)	29–30	120	181.5	206	13.2	R44C (core)
Silicon steel	29	45	54–62	63–75	7.2–6.3	R70B
Ductile titanium (pure)	16	52	80	90	20	R50–59A
Titanium 75A	15.5	....	70	80	15	R90B
Titanium 150A	16	75	120	160–135	15	R53C
Titanium 3 Al 5 Cr	16.7	115	145	155	13.5	R24C
Elgiloy	29.5	230	280	368	....	R58C
Tantalum	27	....	....	50	40	R60E
Tin	6.8	nil	nil	1.6	70	B3
Mallory 1000	40	25	75	94–112	2.5	R24–30C
Gyro Met (Mallory)	44	62	114	135	2	R30–36C
Hevimet (GE)	50	27	75	95	2	R20–30C
Fansteel 77	40	30	85	105	3.5	R28C
Beryllium (QVM Brush)	44.3	12.0	44	95	10	R59–83B
Coin silver	11	....	....	55	8	R65B
Magnesium-Nickel-Silver alloy	12	43–46	53–56	65–68	15–5	....
Magnesium M	6.5	9	28	38	10	R36E
Magnesium A292A	6.5	12	22	40	3	R48B
Tungsten carbide (94WC–6Co)	88	625 (compression)	....	680–750 (compression)	....	R90–92A

USED IN GYROSCOPE DESIGN

Density, g/cm³	Thermal conductivity, cal/(cm²)(cm)(°C)(sec)	Coefficient of expansion, in./(in.)(°C) × 10⁶	Resistivity, microhm-cm	Recommended use; dimensional stability
2.68	0.36	20.8	4.42	Best casting alloy for high-strength dimensionally stable parts
2.7	0.37	20.0	4.3	Very good corrosion resistance; good workability and strength; fair stability
2.8	0.29	23.6	5.75	Highest strength of the aluminum alloys; not particularly stable
2.79	0.29	21.5	5.75	High-strength alloy; good formability; relatively stable
2.77	0.29	21.6	5.75	Higher strength than 2017; fair stability
8.23	0.25	15.9	6.8–9.8	High strength, high elastic limit, nonmagnetic, easy to heat-treat; good dimensional stability
8.39	0.29	20.8	6.2	General-purpose for fixtures and noncritical parts; good machining
8.53	0.29	19.4	6.2	Good deep-drawing characteristics; not stable
8.86	0.19	17.8	9.6	For springs, bellows, lock washers; readily cold-formed
9.24	0.027	10.4	135	Very high strength; high corrosion resistance; excellent stability
8.51	0.036	12.8	98.1	High-temperature oxidation resistance, high creep strength; good stability
8.26	0.04	12.4	43.3	High strength, good corrosion resistance; good stability
8.15	0.02	7.2	79.7	Age-hardenable; can replace Be Cu, particularly where brazing is necessary; poor stability
8.26	.....	11.3–11.9	....	Coefficient of expansion to match 52100 steel; elastic limit a function of heat-treatment
8.58	.....	12.5	62	For magnetic shielding, high permeability, low creep strength; strain-sensitive
8.47	0.045	13.4	58.3	Good elastic properties and age-hardenable; good corrosion resistance; good stability
8.84	0.062	14.0	48.2	Same as Monel but with greater machinability
8.84	0.062	14	48.2	Strength coupled with excellent resistance to corrosion; cold-drawn for max. strength; fair stability
7.88	0.033	14.4	73	Nonmagnetic; high heat and corrosion resistance; good general-purpose stainless steel; fair stability
7.75	.057	10.2	59	Hardenable stainless; highest hardness of the stainless steels; good stability
7.73	0.059	10.2	56	General-purpose chrome stainless; hardenable by heat-treatment; corrosion resistant; good stability
7.9	0.038	16.1	69	Slightly magnetic; excellent corrosion resistance
7.9	0.038	16.1	69	Nonmagnetic unless cold-worked; low elastic limit; very good stability
7.85	0.122	12.2	15.9	General structural; not particularly stable
7.85	0.121	11.2	15.9	Hardenable plain carbon steel; good stability
7.85	0.124	11.8	12.6	Low-carbon free-machining steel of moderate strength and good stability
7.82	0.121	11.1	15.9	Free machining, hardenable plain carbon steel; excellent stability
7.85	0.102	11.1	22.3	A deep-hardening, hard, tough steel; may be hardened without excessive distortion; good stability
7.83	0.107	11.8	25.2	High hardness and high strength; fair stability
7.83	0.108	11.9	22	Bearing use; excellent stability
7.84	0.124	12.1	27–29	Extreme wear resistance; excellent stability
7.55	0.039	11.5	56	A magnetic steel, typically for transformers requiring low loss; poor stability
4.5	0.036	8.8	55	Good corrosion resistance; readily joined
4.51	0.022	8.6	54.8	Hardenable by cold-working only; ductile, weldable, good corrosion resistance; good stability
4.61	0.037	8.2	60	Good corrosion resistance, high strength-to-weight ratio; hardenable by heat-treatment; excellent stability
4.59	0.036	8.6	145	Hardenable by cold-working; good corrosion resistance; excellent stability
8.3	.....	12.7	100	High elastic limit and fatigue strength; springs and suspension
16.6	0.130	6.5	13.5	Ductile, high corrosion resistance; rectifier plate
7.3	0.155	23.5	12.8	
16.7	0.225	5.4	12.45	High-density material
16.7–17.0	0.235	5.88	12.45	High-density material, high strength
16.9–17.2	0.225	5.6	6.8	High-density material, Monel binder; fair stability
17	0.226	6.5	12.3	High-density material
1.85	0.40	11.3	4–6	High modulus-to-density ratio; good stability
10	1	19	1.8	Precipitation-hardening alloy for good strength and conductivity
10.5	0.75	19	2.32	Contacts; good conductivity, wear resistance, and strength; better creep strength than coin silver
1.76	0.30	24.2	5.0	Wrought, may be sand-cast; fair stability
1.8	0.17	26	14	Excellent stability
14.8	0.13	5	20	Very high hardness; tools, pivots, bearing surfaces

Averbach of M.I.T. He defined the elastic limit as the maximum stress to which the material may be loaded without having a positive permanent strain. It is thought, though not yet proved, that any material stressed above this elastic limit will creep under the applied load.

PROBLEMS

10-1. The load-deflection equation for each bearing of a spring-loaded pair is given by Eq. (10-2). If the preload is 12 lb and $k = 2 \times 10^{-4}$, what are the compliances of the bearing pair when subjected to an axial acceleration of $4g$ first in one direction and then in the other? The gyrowheel and other rotating parts weigh 1 lb.

10-2. If the bearings of Prob. 10-1 were preloaded to 12 lb by being rigidly mounted in opposition, as indicated in Fig. 10-6*a*, what would the compliances be when subjected to accelerations of $4g$, as in Prob. 10-1?

10-3. The angular momentum of a gyro rotating at 11,900 rpm is 3×10^6 g-cm²/sec. If the voltage of the motor power supply is dropped 15 per cent, the gyrowheel decelerates at the rate of 2 radians/sec². If the gimbal axis is at 89° to the spin axis, what is the precession rate of the gyro due to the deceleration? If the gyro speed at equilibrium drops to 11,800 rpm, what is the total precession?

10-4. A gyro element weighing 13 oz is being balanced on pivots which have a nominal diameter of 0.120 in. The pivots are elliptical in cross section with a maximum diameter of 0.122 in. and a minimum diameter of 0.119 in. What is the uncertainty in balance due to ellipticity, in ounce-inches? In dyne-centimeters?

10-5. Let the gyro element of Prob. 10-4 be balanced on perfectly round pivots. However, one knife-edge is inclined upward at an angle of 2′, whereas the other is slanting downward at an angle of 1′. If the knife-edges are 6 in. long, what is the uncertainty in the balance?

10-6. A gyro element weighs 18 oz and is supported on a pair of knife-edges by means of 0.093-in.-diameter steel pins. The knife-edges are rounded with a one-sixteenth radius. Find the maximum contact stress.

10-7. A gyro element supported by a pair of suspension wires, as in Fig. 10-21, is neutrally buoyant in the fluid at 65°C with a density of 1.89 g/cm³. Assume that the gyro element weighs 800 g in air. The beryllium copper suspension wires are 0.009 in. in diameter and are 0.750 in. long with an initial tension of 65 g. If the temperature is dropped to 55°C, what is the deflection of the gyro element? What is the maximum stress in the suspension wires? The volume coefficient of expansion of the fluid is 830×10^{-6} cm³/(cm³)(°C), and that of the gyro element is 70×10^{-6} cm³/(cm³)(°C).

10-8. If the gyro element of Prob. 10-7 is supported on pivots, what is the maximum load on each pivot? What is the frictional torque if the coefficient of friction is 0.002?

10-9. Find the leakage rate of helium through a butyl rubber O ring which is compressed to an essentially rectangular cross section (see Fig. 10-33) of $h = 0.070$ in. and $w = 0.125$ in. The mean diameter of the ring $D = 4.05$ in., the permeation constant $K_p = 0.5 \times 10^{-2}$ (cm³)(in.)/(hr)(in.²)(atm), and the difference in pressure $p = \frac{1}{2}$ atm.

BIBLIOGRAPHY

1. Hertz, H.: "Collected Papers," The Macmillan Company, New York, 1926.
2. Jones, A. B.: Analysis of Stresses and Deflections, New Departure Division, General Motors, 1946.

3. Mackenzie, K. D.: Spin Axis Bearings, The Barden Corporation Report R-13, M.I.T. Instrumentation Laboratory, February, 1951.

4. Ball Bearing Yield and System Isoelasticity, The Barden Corporation, 1957.

5. Ortman, F. W., and H. M. Green: Isoelasticity in Gyro Rotor Bearings, ASME Paper 57-F-34, August, 1957.

6. Lundberg, G., and A. Palmgren: Dynamic Capacity of Rolling Bearings, *J. Appl. Mechanics,* vol. 71, 1949.

7. Irwin, R. F.: Guide to Lubricants for Instrument Ball Bearings, *Prod. Eng.,* June, 1958.

8. Jones, A. B.: The Life of High-speed Ball Bearings, *Trans. ASME,* July, 1952.

9. Timoshenko, S.: "Theory of Plates and Shells," McGraw-Hill Book Company, Inc., New York, 1940.

10. Roark, R. J.: "Formulas for Stress and Strain," 3d ed., McGraw-Hill Book Company, Inc., New York, 1954.

11. Stodola, A.: "Steam and Gas Turbines," Vols. I and II, translated by L. C. Loewenstein, Peter Smith, Publisher, Inc., New York, 1945.

12. Conway, H. D.: Axially Symmetrical Plates with Linearly Varying Thickness, *J. Appl. Mechanics,* vol. 18, no. 2, 1951.

13. Conway, H. D.: The Bending of Symmetrically Loaded Circular Plates of Variable Thickness, *J. Appl. Mechanics,* vol. 15, no. 1, 1948.

14. Chenea, P. F., and P. M. Naghdi: Graphical Analysis of Axially Symmetrical Plates with Variable Thickness, *J. Appl. Mechanics,* vol. 19, no. 4, 1952.

15. Ham, C. W., E. J. Crane, and W. L. Rogers: "Mechanics of Machinery," 4th ed., McGraw-Hill Book Company, Inc., New York, 1958.

16. Den Hartog, J. P.: "Mechanical Vibrations," 4th ed., McGraw-Hill Book Company, Inc., New York, 1956.

17. Meek, J. M., and J. D. Craggs: "Electrical Breakdown of Gases," Oxford University Press, New York, 1953.

18. National Research Council of the U.S.A.: "International Critical Tables," McGraw-Hill Book Company, Inc., New York, 1929, Vol. VI.

19. Mims, B. L.: Yield of a Ball and Grooved Plate and Its Relation to Yield in a Ball Bearing, The Barden Corporation Report PR-18, 1948.

20. Mims, B. L.: Axial Yield and Rate of Yield, The Barden Corporation Report PR-9, 1948.

21. Mims, B. L.: Yield of Preloaded Ball Bearings under Combined Loads, The Barden Corporation Report PR-22, 1949.

22. Drutowski, R. C.: Energy Losses of Balls Rolling on Plates, Record of Proceedings, Instrument Ball Bearing Conference, New Departure Division, General Motors, March, 1958.

23. Milamed, R. L.: Hermetic Sealing of Electrical Instruments, *Elec. Mfg.,* March, 1954.

24. Timoshenko, S.: "Strength of Materials," D. Van Nostrand Company, Inc., Princeton, N.J., 1940–1941, Vols. I and II.

25. Asch, A. B.: Antifriction Instrument-bearing Torque Testing and the Resistance to Motion of Such Bearings, ASME Paper No. 58-SA-34, 1958.

26. Bedwell, D. C., and E. A. Meyer: Leakage Testing of Sealed Electronic Enclosures, *Elec. Mfg.,* December, 1955.

27. American Welding Society: "The Brazing Manual," Reinhold Publishing Corporation, New York, 1955.

28. Miller, M. A.: Joining Aluminum to Other Metals, *Welding J. (N.Y.),* vol. 32, 1953.

29. Dececco, N. A., and J. M. Parks: The Brazing of Titanium, *Welding J. (N.Y.)*, vol. 32, 1953.

30. Smith, L. W., and L. A. Yerkovich: Strength of Joints in Titanium Brazed with Several Alloys, *Prod. Eng.*, July, 1953.

31. Chatfield, C. H.: Silver Brazing of Refractory Metals, *Welding J. (N.Y.)*, vol. 33, 1954.

32. Setapen, A. M., and W. D. Warren: Silver Alloy Brazing Beryllium Copper Alloys, *Welding J. (N.Y.)*, vol. 28, 1949.

33. Bredzs, Nikolajs: Tensile Strength of Brazed Joints, Product Design Handbook Issue for 1956, *Prod. Eng.*, October, 1955.

34. "Procedure Handbook of Arc Welding Design and Practice," 11th ed., Lincoln Electric Company, 1957.

35. Phillips, A. L.: "Welding Handbook," 4th ed., American Welding Society, 1957.

36. Fuller, D. D.: "Theory and Practice of Lubrication for Engineers," John Wiley & Sons, Inc., New York, 1956.

37. Grinnell, S. K., and H. H. Richardson: Design Study of a Hydrostatic Gas Bearing with Inherent Orifice Compensation, *Trans. ASME*, vol. 79, January, 1957.

38. Gottwald, F.: Computations and Measurements on the Air Bearing, Archive 16/15, Foreign Document Evaluation Branch, Ordnance Research and Development Center, Aberdeen Proving Ground, Maryland, March, 1943.

39. Gottwald, F.: Proposal for an Air Supported Course Gyroscope, Archive 16/16, Foreign Document Evaluation Branch, Ordnance Research and Development Center, Aberdeen Proving Ground, Maryland, April, 1943.

40. Gottwald, F.: Tests on Air Supported Course Gyros, Archive 16/17, Foreign Document Evaluation Branch, Ordnance Research and Development Center, Aberdeen Proving Ground, Maryland, November, 1943.

41. Sternlicht, B., and R. C. Elwell: Theoretical and Experimental Analysis of Hydrodynamic Gas Lubricated Journal Bearing, *Trans. ASME*, vol. 80, May, 1958.

42. The Development of a Gas Supported Rotating Sphere for Use as a Stable Element, Curtiss-Wright Corporation, Report R49-22.

43. Ausman, J. S.: The Fluid Dynamic Theory of Gas-lubricated Bearings, *Trans. ASME*, August, 1957.

44. Corey, T. L., C. M. Tyler, Jr., H. H. Rowand, Jr., and E. M. Kipp: Behavior of Air in the Hydrostatic Lubrication of Loaded Spherical Bearings, *Trans. ASME*, July, 1956.

45. Kochi, Kikuo C.: Characteristics of a Self-lubricated Stepped Thrust Pad of Infinite Width with Compressible Lubricant, ASME Paper 58-A-194, 1958.

46. Fischer, G. K., J. L. Cherubim, and D. D. Fuller: Some Instabilities and Operating Characteristics of High-speed Gas-lubricated Journal Bearings, ASME Paper 58-A-231, 1958.

47. Schetky, L. M.: The Properties of Metals and Alloys of Particular Interest in Precision Instrument Construction, M.I.T. Instrumentation Laboratory Report R-137, January, 1957.

48. Lement, B. S., and B. L. Averbach: Summary Report #1; Measurement and Control of the Dimensional Behavior of Metals, M.I.T. Department of Metallurgy Report R-95.

CHAPTER 11

ELECTRICAL DESIGN OF GYROS

By Francis W. Wessbecher

Nomenclature

H = angular momentum
I = moment of inertia
ω = angular velocity of spin
ω_p = angular velocity of precession
T, T_d = torque applied
ω_s = synchronous speed
f = frequency
p = number of poles
S_s = number of stator slots
S_r = number of rotor slots
P = permeance
K = dielectric constant
F = magnetomotive force
N_1, N_2 = number of turns
subscripts p, c = pattern winding; control winding
subscripts B, C = bias; control

11-1. Introduction

The electrical designer is concerned with three or four distinct areas in the design of a precision gyroscope. The first area, common to most present-day gyroscopes, is the spin motor used to drive the gyrowheel. The second and third areas which are, as a rule, intimately connected with each other, are the pickoff and torquer, necessary to sense the orientation of the gimbal and to position it as required, respectively. The fourth area is the electrical control system, the role of which is to center the gimbal structure inside the gyroscope. It is evident even from this superficial list that the electrical engineer has a variety of electromagnetic devices to cope with, internal to the gyroscope, without considering the complex equipment required to utilize profitably the information derived from the gyro.

As all electromagnetic designers, the design engineer, concerned with electrical components for gyroscopes, is confronted with the many-sided task of reducing the size, weight, and cost of a variety of devices while trying to improve their performance and reliability. Electrical devices for gyroscopes have two additional requirements imposed on them. First, the input power must be reduced to a minimum in order to avoid thermal weight shifts in the gimbal structure and thermal convection currents in the flotation fluid. Second, mechanical stability is required to eliminate excessive drift rates. This combination of small size and weight, high performance, and mechanical stability makes what would be a routine electrical design problem a major engineering effort.

11-2. Spin Motors

A survey of gyroscopes presently being produced shows that the vast majority of them are driven by either an induction motor or a synchronous hysteresis motor. There are, of course, gyroscopes that rely on d-c or eddy-current motors or even on chemical propellants for the wheel drive, but they constitute only a small fraction of those being manufactured. Therefore, this chapter will be principally concerned with the induction and hysteresis motors as used in gyrowheel drives.

Both last-mentioned types of motors have been produced for many years in numerous sizes and shapes for commercial or military applications. While the principles of operation are the same for any given type of motor, regardless of its application, the design objectives and construction techniques used in motors for gyro drives are so different from those applied in commercial practice that the gyro spin motor should be considered as a special type. Indeed, there are many commercially available motors that a gyro designer may select which could provide the necessary torque at the desired speed; yet almost every new gyro incorporates a new motor design. To understand this apparently wasteful practice we must understand the spin motor's function and performance requirements.

Operation of Spin Motors. The spin motor is used to drive the gyrowheel inside the inner gimbal. Let us recall that the gyrowheel, more commonly called the *wheel,* has inertia due to its physical dimensions and mass. When this wheel is rotated, it acquires an angular momentum, expressed by

$$H = I\omega \tag{11-1}$$

where I denotes the moment of inertia and ω is the angular velocity of the wheel expressed in radians per second. It has also been pointed out that a spurious precessional rate

$$\omega_p = \frac{T_d}{H} \tag{11-2}$$

is created when a disturbing torque T_d is applied to the gimbal. It is apparent that this precessional rate will be lower for a given disturbing torque if the angular momentum of the wheel is increased. This can be accomplished by raising either the moment of inertia or the angular velocity of the wheel. Increasing the inertia will result in a direct increase in weight, while the angular velocity may be raised by changing the motor characteristics, which may or may not contribute to an increase in weight.

The initial design problem to be solved by the gyro designer is to determine how high an angular momentum is desired, and what price must be paid for it. While theoretically the designer may strive for as large an angular momentum as possible, practically he must weight the resulting over-all gyro performance against the increase in weight required to attain the desired moment of inertia. Also, one has to consider the increased power consumption of the motor and the expected reduction in bearing life as the speed is raised. The solution of this problem will dictate restrictions in the spin motor design, affecting the following:

1. Speed-torque characteristic
2. Size and weight
3. Ambient temperature
4. Mechanical stability

The electrical designer will then have to produce a motor to meet these often contradictory requirements. Usually a compromise is reached between the design goal and the actual performance level that can be realistically achieved with the restrictions imposed upon the motor.

Speed-Torque Characteristic. Once the available power supply has been specified, the maximum synchronous speed of the motor is essentially fixed. The relationship between this speed, the supply frequency, and the electric poles in the motor winding is expressed by the relationship

$$\omega_s = \frac{120f}{p} \tag{11-3}$$

where ω_s = synchronous speed, rpm
f = supply frequency, cps
p = number of poles

Present-day gyroscopic equipment, operating on the standard 400 cps power supplies, is practically restricted to either 12,000 or 24,000 rpm. Induction motors which cannot operate at a synchronous speed may have their speed reduced by as much as 10 per cent due to the slippage between the rotor and the rotating magnetic field created by the stator.

The use of higher-frequency supplies of, say, 500 or 600 cps would help in increasing the angular momentum; but a really significant improvement will not occur until the power-supply frequency is raised to the order of 2,000 or 3,000 cps. The adoption of these frequencies may happen in the future, but present designs use standard 400 cps power supplies and rely on motors wound for either two-pole or four-pole operation.

The relationship which exists between the speed of the motor and the torque developed is of great importance to the gyroscope designer. Since the only load on the spin motor is the friction and windage torque, it is essentially operated at no external load. Both the induction motor and the hysteresis motor can be used in this application. The difference between these is that the speed of the induction motor varies with friction or windage torque, while the hysteresis motor tends to operate at synchronous speed for all values of torque less than the pull-in torque. The hysteresis motor is indeed a truly synchronous motor, the speed of which depends only on the frequency of the applied voltage. Therefore, in a gyroscope which requires a constant angular momentum, at least for purposes of precision torquing, the hysteresis motor is used exclusively. There are other types of synchronous motors, but the only one that is self-starting and requires no slip rings is the hysteresis type. When there is no need for exact knowledge of the angular momentum, an induction motor might be used, mostly because of its higher efficiency. Typical speed-torque curves for a hysteresis motor and an induction motor are given in Fig. 11-1. In Fig. 11-1a, the curve pertains to a hysteresis motor and shows that the motor operates at synchronous speed for all values of torques less than the pull-in value. In Fig. 11-1b, the curve represents a low-slip induction motor, the speed of which varies with load.

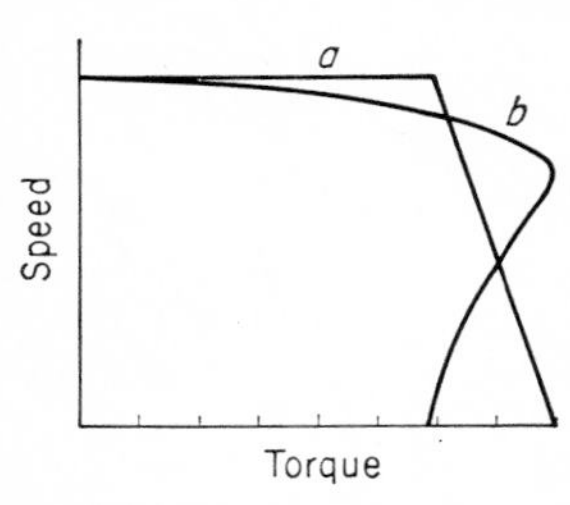

FIG. 11-1. Motor speed-torque curves. (a) Hysteresis motor; (b) induction motor.

Size and Shape of Motors. The constant attempts to reduce the over-all size of gyroscopic components requires that the spin motor designer utilize all the existing space as advantageously as possible. This in turn means that the materials in the motor should be utilized to their maximum capability within limits imposed by the over-all gyro design. From the sole point of view of motor design it would be possible to determine the best ratio of physical dimensions in order to achieve optimum performance at a particular load. However, the motor designer is usually restricted by other design considerations which prohibit the use of these ideal dimensions. Typical examples of these restrictions are motors required to have a large air-gap diameter and short length in order to fit over a structural member, as shown in Fig. 11-2. The other extreme is a long, thin motor, the axial length of which is made several times the air-gap diameter in order to use an existing bearing. Both of these instances represent poor solutions from an electrical design viewpoint, but quite necessary in light of over-all gyro design considerations.

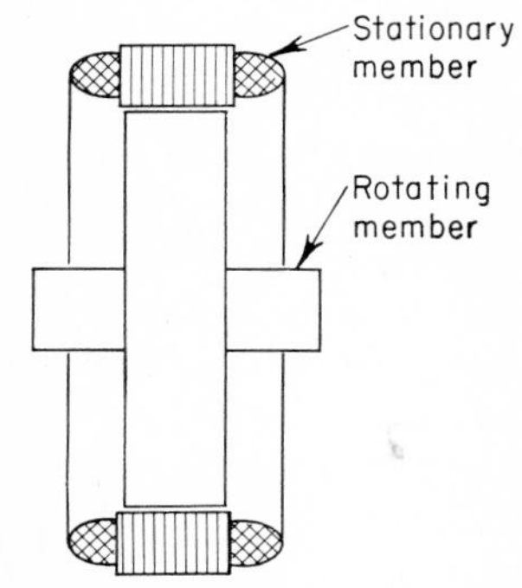

FIG. 11-2. Conventional motor configuration, showing a narrow stack with large diameter.

A gyro motor can take one of several shapes. In the first and most conventional design the stationary part encloses the rotating part, similar to the conventional commercial motor as shown in Fig. 11-3.

A second design approach consists of a rotating element external to the stationary member, as shown in Fig. 11-4. This inside-out construction is widely used in gyros because the weight of the rotor is placed in an advantageous position inertia-wise. The other advantages and disadvantages pertaining to each of these types of construction must be weighed for the particular application. Of course, each type of motor can be designed to deliver the required torque at the desired speed. The selection of any particular type of motor design over another will be determined first by its ability to fit into the space available in the over-all gyro design. The choice is influenced secondly by relative advantages of

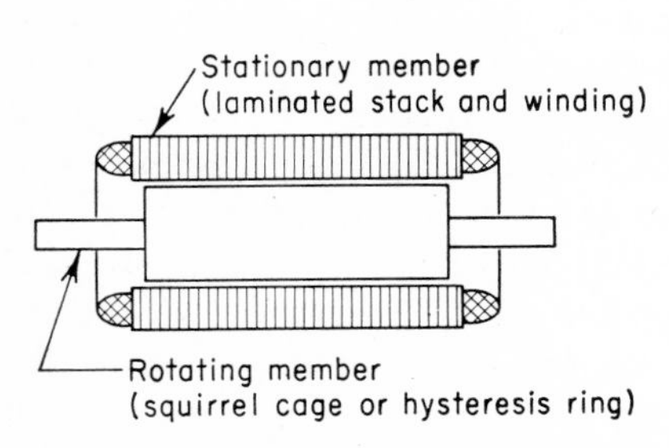

FIG. 11-3. Conventional motor configuration, showing a long motor with small diameter.

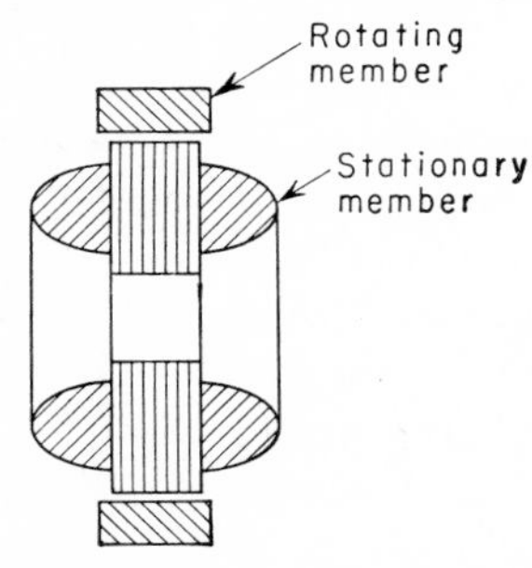

FIG. 11-4. Inside-out motor configuration, showing extremely narrow stack with large diameter.

one type of construction over another with regard to weight, power consumption, and dimensional stability.

Temperature Rise. The usual precision gyroscope is operated at an elevated temperature in order to adjust and control buoyancy and dimensional stability. The internal temperature rise of the motor must then be added to the elevated ambient value in order to determine the operating temperature of the motor.

The over-all size and weight of a motor (required to drive a given load) is often reduced, within limits, of course, by simply allowing the internal temperature rise of the windings to increase. This additional internal temperature rise will require the use of special insulating materials capable of withstanding these higher temperatures. Unfortunately, this type of operation usually results in local hot spots, which cause various areas on the inner gimbal to be at different temperatures. This temperature difference may create convection currents in the flotation fluid and thus produce disturbing torques on the gimbal. Also, high-temperature operation of the spin motor is frequently associated with severe bearing problems. The motor and the bearings are physically close enough together for the heat from the motor to reach the bearings. If the bearing lubricant is oil, it might be driven off as a vapor, allowing the bearings to run dry and thus shorten their life. If, on the other hand, the lubricant is a grease, the latter may melt and flow away from the bearings, also leaving them to run dry. The grease will recongeal at some other point on the gimbal structure, causing an undesirable weight shift. Neither of these conditions can be tolerated in a precision gyroscope; therefore, most spin motors are operated with a conservative internal temperature rise so that the bearing lubrication is not jeopardized.

Dimensional Stability. To be of any practical use a gyroscope must be very sensitive to low-level torque inputs. In order to obtain this sensitivity the gimbals must be precisely balanced during manufacture and must maintain this balance through the whole useful life of the equipment. Any mechanical shift of the various components mounted on the gimbal structure will, of course, disturb this fine balance.

The largest single problem in dimensional stability centers around the spin motor with its wires and insulators. The wires should be completely insulated from the iron-core structure in order to prevent grounding failures. This is usually accomplished by the insertion of an insulation material in each slot and on both ends of the stack. In a simple 12-slot stack, for instance, this would require 24 or more pieces of insulating material, each held in place by wedging or cementing. Admittedly the weight of the individual pieces of the insulating material is small, but it should be remembered that the objectionable torques are in the order of micro-ounce-inches. To overcome this possible weight shift, processes have been developed which allow for the use of film-type insulations applied directly to the stack prior to winding which serve as both slot and end-lamination insulation. It is firmly attached to the iron surfaces and affords adequate insulation, even at elevated operating temperatures, without the possibility of weight shifts.

A second problem pertains to the bonding together of the individual laminations to form the stator of the electric motor. Experiments have shown that normal lamination bonding does not adequately secure the laminations in gyro applications. Silicon steel laminations have an oxide coating on both sides. This coating serves to insulate each lamination from the next one and thus reduces the eddy currents in the stack. Tests have shown, however, that bonding such laminations together actually only bonds the oxide coatings of those adjacent. This oxide coating may peel off under stress and break the stack bond. In other usual application of motors in a housing (like a servomotor or a fan motor) this would be completely satisfactory, since the laminations would be mechanically held in place by the housing and any shift in the stator weight would go undetected. In gyro application, however, this condition is intolerable, since even small weight shifts cause unbalance torques. Therefore, the motor design must achieve the optimum bonding strength between individual laminations. This is approached only if the laminations are chemically cleaned to remove all the scale and grease that interfere with the bonding of the base metal. A clean lamination will rust at once if exposed in air; therefore, additional processing is required to inhibit the formation of rust during the handling necessary to make the stack. Finally, the laminations are coated with an adhesive and stacked under controlled temperature and pressure for mechanical stabilization.

In summary, the design of a gyro spin motor usually is beset with gyro-imposed limitations from start to finish. The basic requirements of a precision gyro spin motor are small size, light weight, low power input, and ability to provide the required torque-speed characteristic. The special requirements, such as physical shape, dimensional stability, allowable noise or vibration, and run-up time, are sometimes more troublesome to the motor designer than the basic electrical requirements.

Induction Motors. Induction motors used in gyroscopes are almost all polyphase machines with squirrel-cage rotors, since this type of design does not require slip rings for rotor excitation.

The three-phase stator most commonly used produces a rotating magnetic field. The winding has three groups or phases of coils spaced 120 electrical degrees apart from each other. The application of three time-varying currents, which are time-displaced by 120 electrical degrees, produces a magnetomotive force which has a constant amplitude but shifts its orientation along the winding as a function of time. The resultant field can be thought of as a single radial field of a uniform magnitude that rotates around the motor axis at a fixed speed. This fact may be demonstrated either by sketching the currents and magnetomotive force distributions at various instants of time or by writing the equations. The result of the analysis shows that the magnetomotive force wave travels at

$2/p$ revolutions for each cycle of input frequency. This is referred to as the synchronous speed of the field and can be expressed as

$$\omega_s = \frac{120f}{p} = \text{rpm}$$

The squirrel cage is made of a number of conductors cast directly into slots on the periphery of the rotor, each conductor being connected to end rings of conducting material at each end of the rotor. The squirrel cage has no outside electrical connections. Therefore, any current that flows in its conductors is produced by the voltage induced by the stator mmf. This voltage is directly proportional to the time rate of change of the flux linking the rotor coils, made up of two conductors and the connecting end rings.

If the rotor were moved at the same speed and in the same direction as the rotating field, there would be no rate of change of flux linking the rotor circuit. The rotor would appear as stationary with respect to the rotating field, and there would be no induced voltages or currents in the rotor bars. Since this occurs at synchronous speed, one may also say that at synchronous speed there are no rotor currents and that the induction motor cannot produce any torque. For any speed less than the synchronous speed, the time rate of change of the flux linking the rotor conductors will be proportional to the difference between the actual rotor speed and the synchronous speed of the field. This difference is usually expressed as a percentage of the synchronous speed, viz.,

$$\text{Per cent slip} = \frac{N_{\text{syn}} - N_{\text{act}}}{N_{\text{syn}}} \times 100\% \tag{11-4}$$

The rotor equivalent circuit consists of a resistance and an inductive reactance. The inductive reactance is dependent upon the apparent or relative frequency of excitation of the rotor conductors. Therefore, at speeds close to synchronous speed the reactance will approach zero, while at a speed much lower than synchronous speed the reactance becomes large.

The rotor current I_R may be expressed as

$$I_R = \frac{E}{\sqrt{R^2 + X^2}} \tag{11-5}$$

where the rotor reactance X is dependent on the relative speed.

The induction motor provides the classical condition of a current-carrying conductor in a magnetic field having a force developed on it. The force can be expressed as

$$F = \frac{BIL}{10} \tag{11-6}$$

where B = flux density, gauss
I = current, amp
L = length of conductor, cm
F = force, dynes

The torque developed is the product of this force and a number of constants which depend upon the dimensions of the motor and the system of units used. We have, generally, without going into specific details,

$$T = F \times k \tag{11-7}$$

The relationship between slip and torque is of particular interest in any induction motor application because of several conflicting requirements to be faced. Looking at typical slip-torque curves for induction motors, curve a in Fig. 11-5 is typical for low-slip motors. When the speed approaches within 2 to 3 per cent of the synchronous speed, the torque reaches its rated value. The stalled torque, as shown, is less than the rated load torque, which points out one of the shortcomings of this type of motor, namely, low stall torque. The starting input power requirements may be 10 times greater than the running power owing to the very low rotor resistance required to obtain the low-slip characteristic. This necessitates additional power-supply capacity and adds weight to the gyroscopic equipment. The advantages of such a motor in a gyro are (1) the relative flatness of the slip-torque characteristic over a wide range of torque loads and (2) the high angular velocity. These two factors provide a relatively constant velocity and angular momentum with a fairly high efficiency.

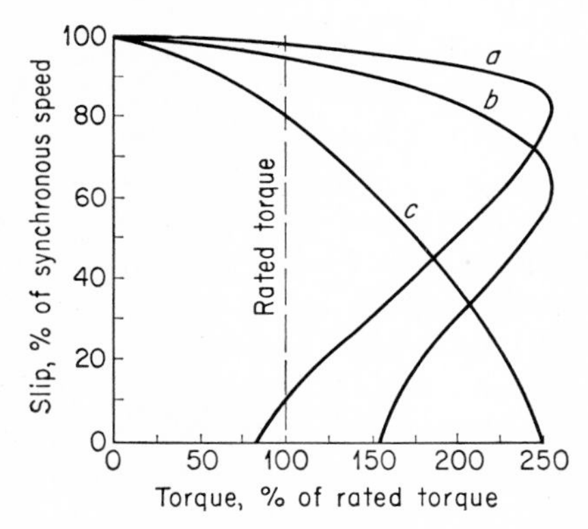

FIG. 11-5. Induction motor slip-torque characteristics for different values of rotor resistance.

In Fig. 11-5, curve c shows the typical characteristic of a servo-type induction motor. The slip-torque characteristic is almost linear over the entire range of torque loads from no load to stall. This motor has the opposite characteristic of the low-slip motor. The angular velocity varies linearly with any change in torque load and is relatively low, approximately one-half the synchronous speed at maximum power output.

In Fig. 11-5, b represents a safe middle ground between the two extremes in induction motor designs. The slope of slip-torque characteristic is between that for curves a and c. Therefore, any change in the load torque required will not result in a drastic change in speed. The starting torque is greater than the rated load torque. Finally, the speed can be relatively high, approximately 95 per cent of the synchronous speed of the field, to provide the additional angular momentum.

Experience has shown that motor b is probably the best engineering compromise for the conflicting requirements between low slip and high starting torque and low slip and low starting power.

Efficiency and Losses. As stated earlier, one of the requirements of a gyro spin motor is that it consume the least possible power which will enable it to perform satisfactorily under load. In order to accomplish this, the losses in the motor must be held to an absolute minimum. These losses can be divided into the following classifications: copper losses, I^2R iron losses, and hysteresis and eddy-current losses. The friction and windage losses, which are usually included in the losses of a commercial motor, are not present in the losses of a spin motor, since, as seen earlier in this chapter, they constitute the only useful output.

Motor losses can be further classified as stator or rotor losses. The largest single loss in most gyro spin motors is that of copper, owing to the current in the stator winding. The only way this can be reduced while still maintaining the ampere-turns needed to produce the stator field is to increase the cross-sectional area of the stator conductors. The latter can only be accomplished by allowing a greater volume for the stator iron and winding, thus adding weight to the motor. We now have two conflicting requirements, namely, to reduce the copper loss and still maintain a small, light motor. There is no single solution to this conflict, and it must be resolved in light of the over-all gyro design, weighing the effects of the increased size against those resulting from an additional internal temperature rise. Some gyros use motors requiring 20 or 25 watts of input power because the configuration of the gyro provides for the external dissipation of the stator copper loss, whereas other gyro designs suffer badly with as little as 5 watts dissipated in the stator.

The rotor copper loss is usually only a small fraction of the stator copper loss for all speeds except stall. At stall the copper loss of the stator and the rotor are nearly equal. The reduction in the rotor copper loss at higher speeds is due to the fact that the voltages induced in the rotor conductors are reduced, since the rotor and the field of the stator are rotating at nearly equal speeds.

The iron losses in both stator and rotor are small, because the iron in these circuits is operated at comparatively low flux densities. In some applications the low flux density has even allowed the use of nonlaminated rotors because of the improved mechanical stability that can be obtained with a very slight increase in iron losses.

Harmonics. In addition to the fundamental voltage, harmonic voltages are induced in the conductors of the induction motor. These may be divided into two basic categories: (1) those due to harmonics already present in the applied voltage and (2) those due to the space harmonics produced in the motor itself by the nonideal distribution of the stator winding.

The time harmonics can be considered as voltages of higher frequencies applied to the windings. The stator-winding impedances are much higher at the higher frequencies and effectively limit the higher-frequency currents in the windings. The torques produced by the time harmonics are very low compared with the one created by the fundamental voltage. The effect of these harmonic torques on the speed-torque characteristic of the induction motor is slight enough to be neglected in all but the most critical designs.

The really significant harmonics in an induction motor are the space harmonics caused by the imperfect distribution of the stator winding. The ideal winding distribution on the stator would require an infinite number of slots. In practice this number is limited to 12, 24, or 36, depending upon the diameter of the stator. Therefore, in addition to the fundamental field, the stator winding will produce an infinite number of harmonic fields. These fields are not to be confused with the time harmonics, since they all vary at the same time rate as the fundamental. The winding or space harmonic fields exist as multiple poles of the fundamental field. Thus a two-pole machine with a third space harmonic will act as if a six-pole machine were superimposed upon the two poles. The fifth space harmonic will appear, in effect, as a ten-pole machine. These superimposed poles produce torques which may or may not cause the motor to rotate in the same direction as the fundamental. Since most gyro applications involve three-phase motors, the harmonic fields which rotate in the same direction as the fundamental are the seventh and the thirteenth, while the fifth harmonic works against the fundamental. All these harmonics (since they appear as multipolar machines) will have synchronous speeds lower than the synchronous speed of the fundamental.

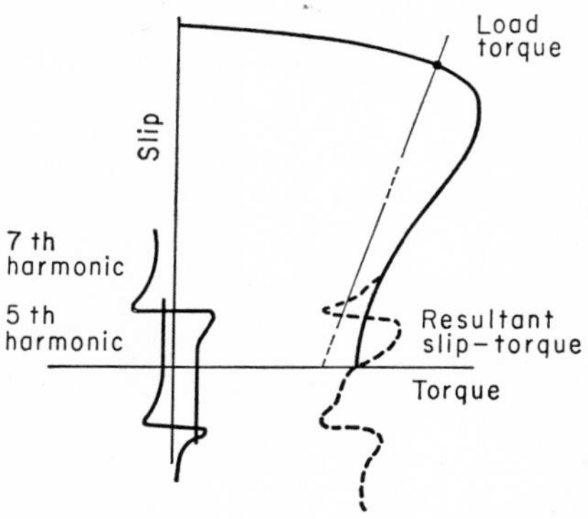

FIG. 11-6. Induction motor slip-torque characteristic, showing the effect of harmonic torques.

The effect of the space harmonic on the speed-torque characteristic is shown in Fig. 11-6. The fundamental torque shows that the motor is capable of delivering more torque than is required for the load. Therefore, the motor should drive the load until it reaches the operating speed s

and is delivering a torque T. When the loss in torque, which results from the fifth and seventh space harmonics, is considered, it appears that the spin motor is not capable of delivering the required load torque. At any point where the total developed torque is less than the required load torque, the motor will hang up or crawl. This will occur in the region of 2,000 to 4,000 rpm for a four-pole 400-cps motor. If the motor is driven beyond this point on the speed-torque curve, it would then be able to drive the load up to operating speed.

A second problem which arises from the space harmonics is the noise and vibration generated in the motor. These disturbances result from a combination of radial forces produced by the stator harmonics and the rotor harmonics. Neither one of these radial forces would be disturbing,

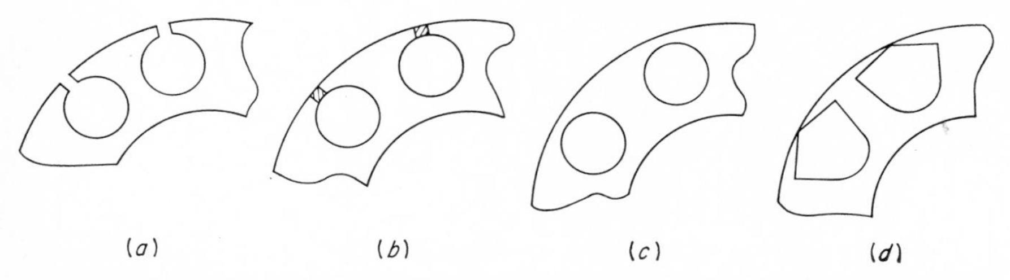

FIG. 11-7. Lamination slot openings. (*a*) Normal open slot; (*b*) slot closed with iron wedge; (*c* and *d*) two types of closed slots.

since their frequencies are either very low or very high as compared with the natural frequency of the motor. However, the resultant forces are close to the natural frequency of the motor and may be very disturbing, since they can physically distort the stator.

In order to avoid the undesirable effects of space harmonics, two-design methods are employed. The first is the selection of the proper stator and rotor slot combination to minimize the space harmonics, and the second is the skewing of the rotor bars to reduce the effects of the remaining space harmonics.

The selection of the proper combination of slots for the stator and rotor is usually done by empirical means. Starting with the stator, the usual motor design has a number of stator slots equal to some multiple of the number of poles times the number of phases. Thus a four-pole three-phase machine would have 12, 24, or 36 slots. In general it is desirable to have as many slots as possible in order to reduce the effects of any air-gap variation. However, because of the restrictions placed on spin motor size, the use of even 36-slot stators is rare. The limiting factor in selecting the number of slots for a given stator is mainly the ability to make laminations with very small tooth cross sections. Laminations of this design are too often damaged by handling during manufacturing. One solution to this problem has been to punch closed slots, similar to those shown in Fig. 11-7*c*, and then to machine the slots open after the lamination-stacking operation has been completed; but this procedure is costly and time-consuming. Therefore, it is quite common to have 12-slot stators for a three-phase four-pole motor.

Once the number of stator slots has been selected, the number of rotor slots can be determined by several simple rules. First, this number must never be equal to the number of stator slots. It must be 14 to 25 per cent larger or smaller than the number of stator slots for most designs.

The following restrictions are placed on the number of rotor slots in a three-phase motor:

$$S_s - S_r \neq \pm 1,\ \pm 2,\ \pm(p \pm 1),\ \text{or}\ \pm(p \pm 2) \qquad (11\text{-}8)$$

$$S_s - S_r \neq \pm 3p \text{ or any multiple of } \pm 3p \qquad (11\text{-}9)$$

$$S_s - S_r \neq \pm p,\ \pm 2p,\ \pm 5p \qquad (11\text{-}10)$$

where S_s = number of stator slots
S_r = number of rotor slots
p = number of poles

The second means of reducing the effects of space harmonics is to skew the stator or the rotor. This means that either the stator or the rotor slots will curve in a manner similar in appearance to Fig. 11-8. The individual slots are twisted or skewed with respect to the axis of rotation. This is done so that one half of each rotor conductor will be under a north pole of the harmonic to be discriminated against, while the other half of the same bar lies under a south pole of this harmonic. Two equal and opposing harmonic voltages will be induced in the same bar, and the net voltage due to the harmonic will be close to zero. The current due to the harmonic will also be zero, and no torque will be produced.

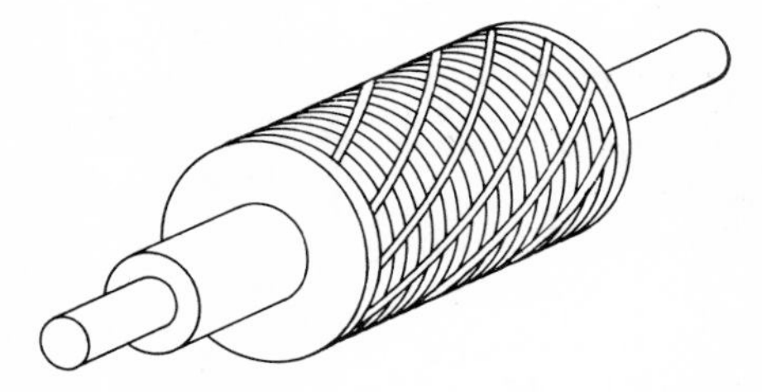

FIG. 11-8. Skewed rotor for induction motor.

Figure 11-6 shows that the principal space harmonic to be avoided in a three-phase four-pole motor is the seventh, since it can severely reduce the available torque. Therefore, it is desirable actually to skew against this harmonic.

In a four-pole machine the individual pole will cover 90° at the air-gap diameter. The seventh harmonic will have 28 poles; therefore, the north and south poles of the seventh will cover $\frac{1}{14}$ of 360°. The rotor bars should then be skewed so that an individual bar lies under both the north and the south pole of the seventh harmonic. It may be necessary for mechanical reasons to skew the stator rather than the rotor, in which case the stator slots should be skewed one rotor bar.

The actual equations used to perform the design of an induction motor are given in many places in the literature and will not be repeated here.

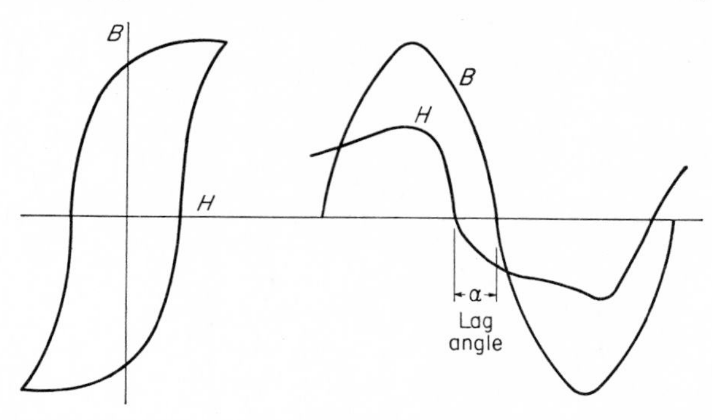

Fig. 11-9. The hysteresis lag angle between magnetizing force and magnetization.

Hysteresis Motors. The synchronous hysteresis motor consists of a polyphase-wound stator and a magnetically hard rotor. The motor requires no rotor excitation, is self-starting, and is capable of pulling large inertia loads into synchronism. It is superior to an induction motor as a gyro spin motor because it operates at synchronous speed and thus provides a constant angular momentum. The use of the hysteresis motor is restricted, however, by its low efficiency, usually less than 80 per cent at best, and by the fact that the motor will respond very rapidly to small changes in frequency.

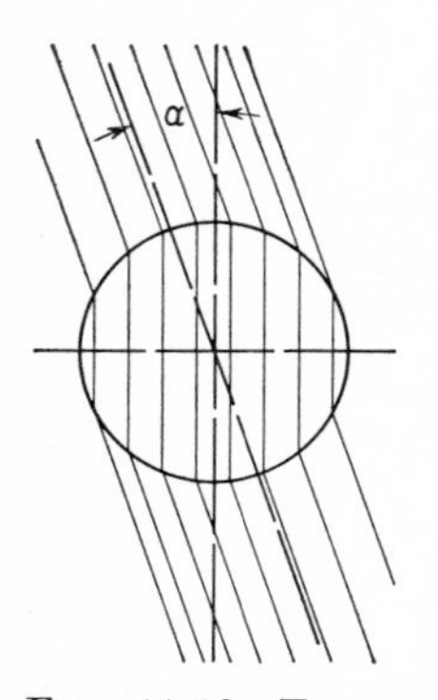

Fig. 11-10. Torque angle between stator and rotor magnetic fields in hysteresis motor.

The ability of a hysteresis motor to produce torque can be explained by referring to Fig. 11-9. The nonlinear relationship which exists between the magnetizing force H and the magnetization B produced by it, and the difference between the magnetization produced by increasing and decreasing the magnetizing forces, is usually depicted as a hysteresis loop. Assuming that the magnetization is sinusoidal, as would be true for a sinusoidal excitation and back electromotive force, Fig. 11-9 shows that the magnetization appears to lag the magnetizing force that produced it. Although this magnetizing force, as shown, is only the rotor magnetizing force, since it will be much larger than either the air-gap or stator-iron magnetizing forces, we may consider it as the entire magnetizing force. The magnetic field is redrawn in Fig. 11-10 to show the hysteresis lag angle α between the rotor magnetization and stator magnetomotive force.

The torque produced by the hysteresis motor is proportional to the product of the rotor magnetizing force, the rotor magnetization, and the sine of the lag angle α. The torque developed tends to lower the lag angle and is independent of the speed of rotation. A constant torque is developed for all speeds up to synchronous speed. The hysteresis torque can be expressed as

$$T = W_h \times V \times p \times K \tag{11-11}$$

and

$$W_h = B_m H_m \sin \alpha \times \text{const} \tag{11-12}$$

where W_h = hysteresis loss per cycle, proportional to area of hysteresis loop
V = volume of hysteresis material in rotor
p = number of poles in stator winding
K = constant, depending upon system of units used
B_m = flux density in rotor (peak value)
H_m = rotor magnetizing force (peak value)
α = lag angle between H_m and B_m

The performance of the hysteresis motor is deteriorated by such secondary effects as parasitic losses caused by local variations in the field distribution and induction motor torques caused by the eddy currents induced in the magnetic material of the rotor.

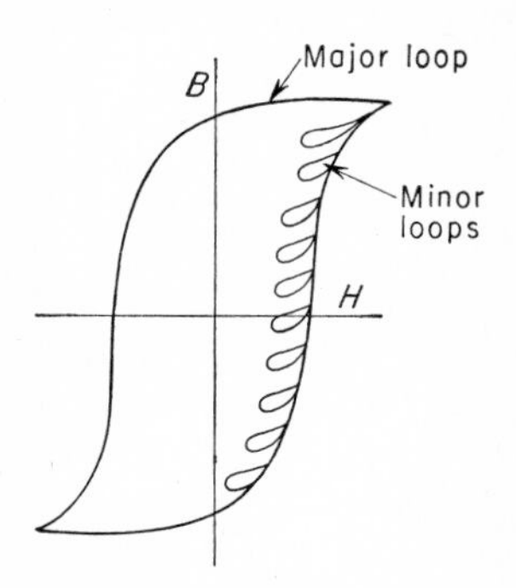

FIG. 11-11. Parasitic losses due to slot openings in hysteretic material.

The major parasitic loss is due, however, to the slot openings in the stator. Under a stator slot opening the rotor flux density falls to a low value, while under the next tooth it is increased to a higher value due to the changes in the reluctance of the magnetic circuit. This causes the rotor material to follow a series of minor loops, such as shown in Fig. 11-11, in addition to the major loop. The energy lost, which is proportional to the areas of these minor loops, is dissipated as heat in the rotor and results in a lower available torque. In order to alleviate this, stators have been made with very small slot openings or even closed slots (Fig. 11-7).

The eddy currents that are induced in the rotor also produce a field that interacts with the field produced by the stator to produce induction motor torques. The latter are superimposed on the hysteresis torque and, depending upon the resistance of the rotor, might be either large or small as compared with the hysteresis torque.

The fact that the hysteresis motor has the full torque available to pull the load up to synchronous speed means that it also has full torque available to follow any small frequency change. It will actually follow rapid frequency changes that the induction motors would filter out. This property of following fast frequency variations has reduced the effectiveness of hysteresis motors in gyroscopes with poor supply-frequency regulation.

Torque Characteristics. As was stated before, the main advantage of the hysteresis over the induction-type motor as a spin motor lies in its speed-torque characteristic. The hysteresis motor, once it has reached synchronous speed, will continue to operate at exactly this speed as long as the load is less than the pull-out torque. Therefore, the supply frequency must be held very close to the nominal value by the use of external regulating equipment to have the motor maintain a constant speed for all values of loading less than the pull-out value. The constant speed allows gyro performance calculations to be based on constant angular momentum and well-defined gyro response. However, this requirement increases the complexity of the over-all system.

Rotor Material. In designing a hysteresis motor the significant difference between this and the induction motor lies in the hysteretic material used in the rotor. Obtaining the desired characteristics for this material is the major design task and often requires the fabrication of several working models prior to finalization.

Since the magnitude of the torque developed depends upon the hysteresis lag angle between the flux density and the magnetizing force of the rotor, and since this angle in turn depends upon the remanence and the coercive force or the area of the hysteresis loop of the hysteretic material, the latter should be selected to have a high remanence and coercive force and a large hysteresis loop area. Most magnetic materials which have these properties also have low permeability and require a large magnetizing force as compared to the soft magnetic materials used in the stator. In order to provide this magnetizing force the stator requires a large exciting current. This is the reason for the large stator copper loss, which is the principal loss in the well-designed hysteresis motor.

Attempts have been made to reduce the copper losses of hysteresis motors by the "overexcitation" technique. This technique requires that a voltage in excess of the normal value be applied to the windings until the motor reaches synchronous speed and then be reduced to the rated level. This kind of operation greatly increases the motor efficiency, but at the expense of operational reliability. The reduction in the voltage reduces the current in the winding; therefore, it lowers the stator copper losses and raises the efficiency. Such an overexcited hysteresis motor is subject to being pulled out of synchronism, however, by any slight increase in load, reduction in line voltage below a critical value, or momentary change in frequency that causes the motor to slip even a single pole. If the reduced voltage is lower than the value necessary to pull the load back into synchronism, the motor will not be able to return to synchronous speed. In order to use "overexcitation" properly additional circuitry should be provided that will periodically apply the high excitation voltage to ensure that the motor is in synchronism.

A more profitable area for improvement is in the hysteretic material itself. The most useful of such materials for hysteresis motors are cobalt and chrome steels and alloys of cobalt-nickel, vanadium, and iron. Most hysteresis motors are designed around the cobalt or chrome steels, which offer a compromise between the desirable hysteretic properties and

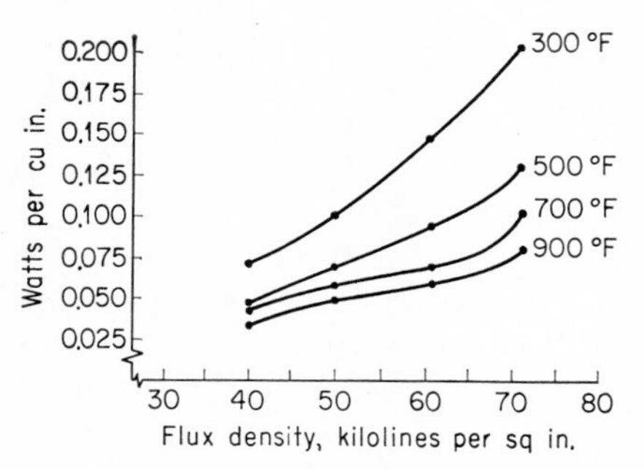

FIG. 11-12. Effect of heat-treatment on the hysteresis loss of 3½ per cent chrome steel.

Efficiency, %
80
60
40
20
0
0.010
0.015
0.030
Solid
0
0.2
0.4
0.6
0.8
1.0
Torque, in.-oz

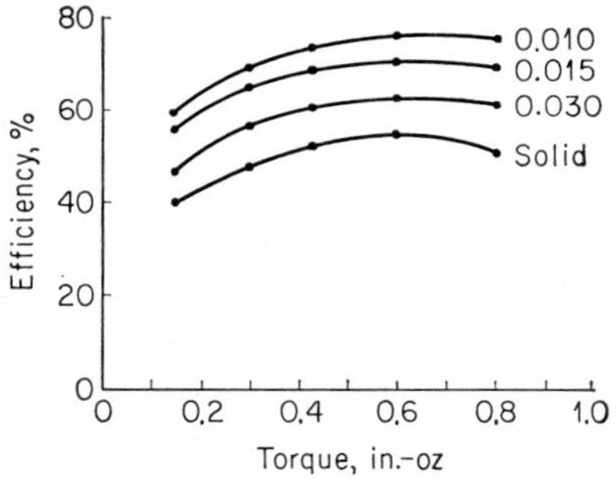

FIG. 11-13. Hysteresis motor efficiency for various ring-lamination thicknesses, in inches, all other motor parameters remaining constant.

the undesirable low permeability. Nearly as important as the selection of the material itself is the heat-treatment that the material receives during fabrication. The proper application of heat will improve motor performance, while improper heat-treating will actually reduce the maximum torque and efficiency that can be obtained. The effect of various heat-treating temperatures on the area of the hysteresis loop is shown for 3½ per cent chrome steel in Fig. 11-12. Alloys of cobalt-nickel-vanadium now in development promise more efficient motors in the future.

One of the previously mentioned advantages of the hysteresis motor over the induction motor in gyro applications is the fact that the rotor is a single homogeneous mass rather than a combination of laminations and a casting. This advantage is often discarded in order to obtain improved motor performance. Instead of using a single piece of hysteretic material for the rotor, the material is divided into laminations similar to those of the stator. This construction reduces the effect of eddy currents in the rotor and improves the efficiency of the machine. Figure 11-13 shows the improvements in efficiency at pull-in obtained by building the rotor with laminated hysteretic material rather than with a solid ring. The advantage of increased efficiency gained by laminating the hysteretic material of the rotor was secured at the expense of mechanical rigidity and ease of manufacturing.

At the opposite end of the laminated versus nonlaminated hysteresis rotors argument is the fact that some hysteresis motors are designed with copper end rings attached to the hysteretic material. The end rings provide a complete electric path for the eddy currents induced in the rotor. The reason given for the use of these rings is that the induction motor characteristics will be stronger and thus provide a greater stalled torque. The use of nonlaminated rings, without end rings, is generally accepted as a compromise for many noncritical designs.

Efficiency. A major objection to the use of the hysteresis motor is its low efficiency. The efficiency is low mostly because of the large stator ampere-turns required to produce the flux in the low-permeability hysteretic material. In order to overcome this the overexcitation technique has been devised for applying a higher than normal voltage to the stator during starting, the voltage then being reduced after the load has reached synchronous speed. The efficiency of a hysteresis motor can be raised above 90 per cent by this technique if the running voltage is reduced to a low enough value. The overexcited motor must be designed to operate at the higher voltages, however, without saturating the magnetic circuit; therefore, at the lower running voltages much lower pull-in torques will be produced than the size of the motor would suggest.

A more promising approach to increasing the efficiency of the hysteresis motor is to incorporate permanent magnets in the rotor to provide part of the air-gap magnetization. The motor would have the self-starting feature of the hysteresis motor and the efficiency of a permanent-magnet motor. Unfortunately, the mechanical stability of such a motor leaves much to be desired for a gyroscopic application, which is probably reason enough to discourage its development. Similar improvement in performance could be achieved, however, by the use of a heat-treatment to produce both hard and soft magnetic material in one solid ring.

Summary. There are applications for both the induction motor and the hysteresis motor in precision gyroscopes. The former is essentially fixed in performance as a 5 to 10 per cent slip motor with whatever stalled torque is required by the load. Any future refinements in induction motors can only be expected in the construction used to achieve greater mechanical stability. The hysteresis motor, on the other hand, is awaiting technical improvements in materials and designs that will increase the available output torque and over-all efficiency.

11-3. Pickoffs or Signal Generators

The pickoff or signal generator in a gyroscope is used to monitor the angular displacement of the gimbal with respect to the support structure and to produce an electric signal proportional to this displacement. This function could be performed by a wide variety of electromechanical devices which range from resistance potentiometers to photoelectric devices requiring optical and electronic components. The more common gyroscopic pickoffs are of the induction or variable magnetic coupling type, the variable capacitance type, or the electrolytic type, in their order of relative importance. Some of the other designs, such as potentiometers and synchros, are discussed at great length in the literature, while the remaining pickoffs, such as the photoelectric and Hall-effect types, are not used widely enough yet to warrant an elaborate discussion.

A gyroscopic pickoff must conform to the general requirements of any other pickoff. First, it must be able to convert mechanical motions into electric signals with adequate sensitivity or gradient to operate the associated circuitry. Second, it must have high resolution in order to detect the very small increments of motion usually encountered in gyroscopes. Third, it must have an electrical null position that is clearly defined and repeatable. These requirements must be achieved with an input power as low as possible in order to avoid any internal heating that would create disturbing torques on the gyroscope. The pickoff must also be free of self-generated electrical noise that could mask an output signal. There can only be negligible torques produced by the pickoff as the gyro gimbal is displaced. This low-torque requirement eliminates many otherwise good pickoffs, such as resolvers or synchros, for precision gyro applications. The torque level of even a good resolver or synchro is 0.1 oz-in. while the allowable reaction torque of a gyro pickoff must be in the order of micro-ounce-inches or less. The final (or what could well be the first) consideration is the allowable size and shape of the pickoff. The pickoff configuration must be compatible with the over-all gyro design, since part of it will be mounted on the gimbal and part on the support structure. The part on the gimbal should, of course, have the least possible weight and require as few electric leads as possible.

There are many different pickoff configurations used in gyroscopes. In order to review even a few of these, it is necessary to divide the pickoffs into groups according to their applications. Since gyroscopes are built with either a single degree of freedom or two degrees of freedom available for precession, the inductive, capacitive, and electrolytic pickoffs must be capable of either single-axis or two-axis sensitivity and operation.

Inductive Pickoffs. The inductive pickoff probably has the widest application in present gyroscopes. These pickoffs produce a signal voltage that is proportional to the change in the magnetic coupling between two windings. This change may be due either to an actual change in the relative positions of two windings or to changes in the permeance of the magnetic path linking these windings.

Single-axis Inductive Pickoffs. The most widely used single-axis inductive pickoff is the microsyn. Microsyn devices are built in a variety of sizes and configurations to meet special applications. The

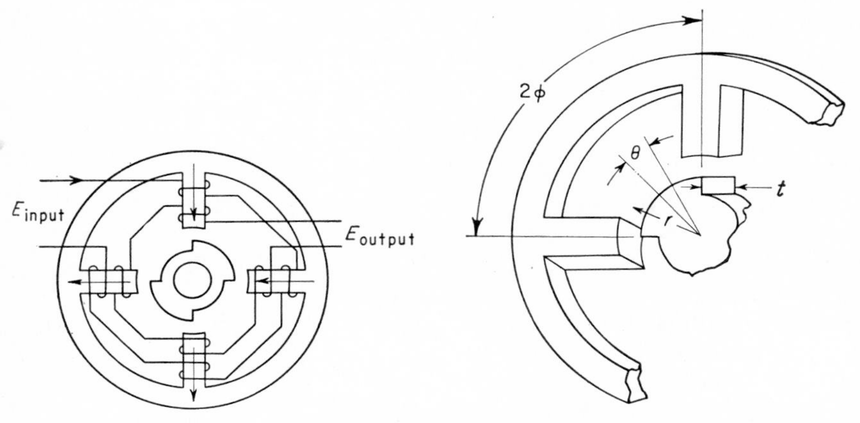

FIG. 11-14. Four-pole microsyn pickoff. Arrows indicate instantaneous direction of magnetic flux.

FIG. 11-15. Microsyn geometric relationships.

basic device is a laminated four-pole structure with a laminated dumbbell-shaped rotor. The rotor is attached to the gimbal, while the pole structure is mounted on the stationary tank or housing. The primary and secondary windings are both mounted on the pole structure. The primary windings are connected in series or series-parallel and excited with an alternating current. The secondary windings are connected in series, in opposition, so that with the rotor at the null or reference position the output voltage is zero. As a displacement is imparted to the rotor from the null position, the phase of the output voltage indicates its direction, and the magnitude represents its position. This pickoff operates on the variable-reluctance principle in that the changes in output voltage are due to changes in the reluctance path of the magnetic circuit consisting of stator poles and rotor.

Figure 11-14 shows a four-pole microsyn stator and the two-pole rotor used with it. The rotor pole covers approximately one-half of the area of the stator pole face at the air gap. The complete magnetic path consists of the high-permeability magnetic material in the stator and rotor and an air gap with low permeability. Therefore, any change in the total reluctance of these series paths is almost all due to the change in reluctance of the air gap. A change in the reluctance of the magnetic circuit with a fixed primary excitation causes a proportional change in the amount of flux linking the secondary coils to produce the change in signal voltage.

The output voltage gradient is calculated from the change in reluctance or its reciprocal, the change in permeance, as the rotor moves from the null position. Since the reluctance of the magnetic circuit is mainly the reluctance of the air gap, it can be expressed in terms of the air-gap dimensions given in Fig. 11-15 and the basic equation for reluctance

$$\mathcal{R} = \frac{L}{\mu A}$$

The area A of the rotor under one pole can be expressed as

$$A = rt\left[\frac{\phi}{2} + (-1)^p\Theta\right] \tag{11-13}$$

where r = radius of rotor
t = thickness of rotor
ϕ = pole angle
Θ = displacement angle from null position
p = number of poles on stator (either an even or an odd number)

The reciprocal of the reluctance is the permeance and can be expressed as

$$P = \frac{1}{\mathcal{R}} = \frac{\mu A}{L} = \frac{\mu rt}{h}\left[\frac{\phi}{2} + (-1)^p\Theta\right] \tag{11-14}$$

where h is the radial length of the air gap. The change in permeance with displacement of the rotor is expressed as

$$\frac{dP}{d\Theta} = (-1)^p\,\frac{\mu rt}{h} \tag{11-15}$$

This shows that the change in permeance with angular rotation is linear and independent of position. This conclusion is reached because of the limitations imposed on the dimensional relationships between the rotor and the poles. First, the area of the pole is less than the area of the rotor. Second, the rotor moves less than one-half the angle between poles. This allows for the assumption that the leakage flux between the poles and the rotor will not change significantly with rotor position.

The output voltage gradient of an ideal pickoff can then be expressed by using this change in permeance as a function of Θ. We have

$$\frac{dE_0}{d\Theta} = 10^{-9}\omega p I_p N_p N_s \frac{dP}{d\Theta} \tag{11-16}$$

where p = number of poles in stator
ω = supply frequency, radians/sec
I_p = primary current, amp
P = permeance in cgs units, i.e., cm
N_p, N_s = turns on primary and secondary windings

From the above equation it is apparent that the output voltage can theoretically be increased by increasing any of the above parameters. Actually, there are restrictions imposed upon doing this. One is that output voltage is usually required to have the same frequency as the rest of the system pertaining to pickoff operation. This limits the frequency to 400 cps in most cases. The reliability of the pickoff will be decreased and manufacturing costs increased if the gradient is raised by increasing the number of poles. The output voltage could also be increased by increasing the secondary turns, but this gives the pickoff a high output impedance and may cause difficulties with the associated circuitry. Any increase in the primary ampere-turns I_p will cause an increase in the reaction torque developed between the poles and the rotor. This torque, in dyne-centimeters per radian, is expressed as

$$T = \frac{1}{8\pi} F^2 \frac{dP}{d\Theta} \tag{11-17}$$

where F is the magnetomotive force of the air gap in gilberts and P the permeance in centimeters.

The air-gap magnetizing force in Eq. (11-17) is the result of the primary and secondary ampere-turns. Since the secondary winding is normally operated into a high-impedance circuit, the secondary current is quite small. Therefore, the magnetomotive force in the air gap is essentially proportional to the primary ampere-turns squared. It is generally more advantageous to design for a given output voltage gradient by making the rate of change of permeance with angle as high as possible and by using as few primary ampere-turns as possible.

The same design considerations are true for most induction-type pickoff devices, namely, that the gradient can best be obtained by proper shaping of the magnetic circuit rather than by increasing the primary ampere-turns or the secondary turns.

Two-axis Inductive Pickoffs. A simple two-axis inductive pickoff can be made with an a-c-excited primary magnet and a group of four secondary coils. Two secondary coils are connected so that the sum of their output voltages will be proportional to the displacement of the primary magnet about an axis at right angles to the first axis.

The primary coil produces a flux which links the secondary coils. When the primary coil is centered above the four secondary coils at the reference position, there are equal and opposite voltages induced in each pair of the secondary coils, and the net output voltage across each pair is zero. As the primary coil is moved away from this reference position, the phase of the output voltage indicates the direction of the motion, while its magnitude corresponds to the position of the primary coil with respect to the secondary coils. In the usual application of this configuration the primary coil is mounted on the gimbal, while the secondary coils

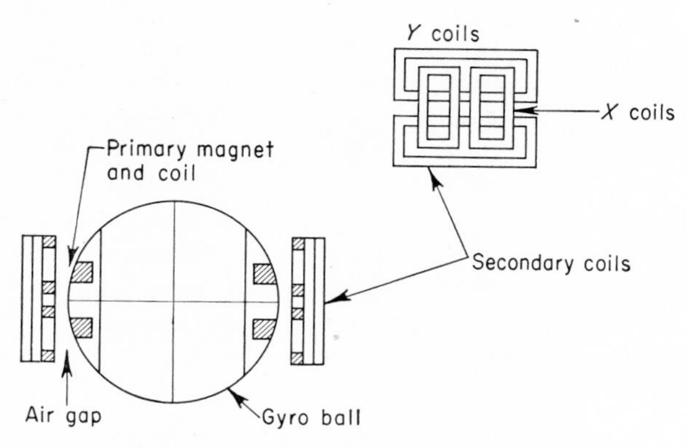

FIG. 11-16. Two-axis inductive pickoff.

are attached to the stationary tank structure. Figure 11-16 shows the arrangement of coils for detecting motions along the x and y axes. The pickoff functions as a two-degree-of-freedom device when the additional pair of secondary coils is placed at 90° to the x axis coils. These windings will detect motions along the y axis.

The design considerations of this device are noteworthy. First, the secondary coils are supported on a nonmetallic board. This eliminates any reaction torques due to changes in reluctance of the magnetic path with position. Second, the primary coil is surrounded by a magnetic material to shape and constrain the magnetic field produced by the coil. Third, the primary or excited winding is mounted on the gyro gimbal to reduce any stray torques due to the interaction between the magnetic field of the pickoff and the gyro motor mounted on the gyro ball or spin assembly. Fourth, the secondary windings are operated into a high-impedance circuit to achieve low secondary currents in order to keep the reaction torques between secondary and primary windings to a minimum.

The pickoff produces an electric signal which can be expressed by

$$E_0 = K_1 \frac{d}{dt}(N_2\Phi_m) = K_2 I_1 X_m \tag{11-18}$$

and

$$\frac{dE_0}{d\Theta} = K_3 \frac{dX_m}{d\Theta}$$

where $dE_0/d\Theta$ = rate of change of no-load output voltage with angle Θ
X_m = mutual reactance between primary and secondary windings
$dX_m/d\Theta$ = rate of change of mutual reactance between primary and secondary with angle Θ
I_1 = constant rms alternating current
Φ_m = mutual flux

When $dX_m/d\Theta$ is a constant, the output voltage gradient is a linear function of the angular displacement; this is true for all angles close to the zero output or reference position. The output voltage gradient can be increased by adding magnetic materials to the secondary-coil support structure to increase the flux linking the secondary coils. The pickoff will then become subject to varying reluctance torques as the primary magnet moves with respect to the secondary-coil support. To achieve the desirable higher output gradients without the undesirable reluctance torques, a modified pickoff has been designed. The primary magnet is similar to Fig. 11-16 except that its structure is extended to provide a high-permeance return path for the flux. Figure 11-17 shows a cutaway view of this pickoff. The primary winding which surrounds the center leg of the magnetic structure produces the flux in the air gap. The secondary coils are mounted internally to the magnetic path but are attached to the stationary member of the gyro. As the magnet moves from its null position, an output voltage appears across the two secondary windings. This pickoff functions in two axes when an additional pair of secondary coils is mounted at right angles to the first set.

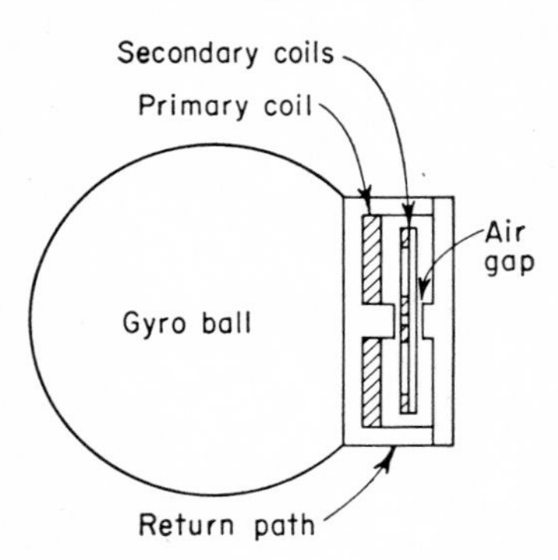

FIG. 11-17. Two-axis inductive pickoff with return magnetic path.

A comparison of the performance of these two inductive pickoffs shows that, for a given application and primary input power, the magnetic return-path pickoff has approximately twice the voltage gradient, without extraneous torques being produced due to the additional magnetic material. Such a pickoff is, of course, more difficult to build, and since it is made of many small parts, it does not offer the same mechanical stability as the simpler pickoff does.

A third type of two-degree-of-freedom induction pickoff can be made by mounting four E-shaped magnets around the tank structure and completing their magnetic paths with I-shaped keepers mounted on the gimbal. However, as the gimbal moves, this pickoff develops reluctance torques between the primary magnets and the magnetic return paths mounted on the gimbal.

Capacitive Pickoffs. Capacitive pickoffs operate on the principle that the mechanical displacement to be detected produces a change in capacitance which can be measured or detected by the output circuit.

The capacitance between two flat plates can be expressed as

$$C = \frac{1}{9 \times 10^5} \frac{KA}{4\pi h} \qquad \mu f \tag{11-19}$$

where A = effective area of plates, cm^2
K = dielectric constant of material between plates (unity for air)
h = distance between plates, cm

From Eq. (11-19) it is apparent that the change in capacitance can be brought about by changing either the effective area A or the spacing h between the plates, such as shown in Fig. 11-18. The relationship between capacitance and area is linear, but the relationship between capacitance and spacing between plates is a hyperbolic function. In order to use the change in capacitance due to the change in spacing, it is necessary to restrict the mechanical displacements to very small values over which this hyperbolic function may be considered as linear.

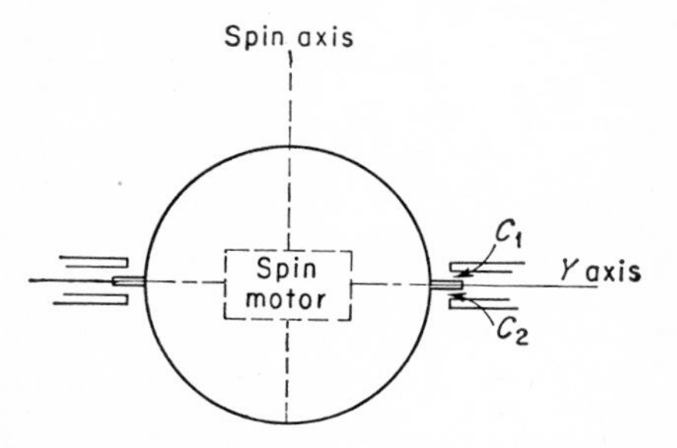

FIG. 11-18. Capacitance pickoff, showing capacitors for a single axis.

When the distance between plates is very small, it is necessary to provide mechanical stops which prevent the plates from shorting should the motion of the gimbal be excessive. The limit stop must be able to protect the pickoff if the plates are driven together with an appreciable force.

The dielectric constant K in Eq. (11-19) varies, of course, with the type of material used between the capacitor plates. In gyroscope applications this material is usually the flotation medium and is commonly selected on the basis of the buoyant force it provides rather than its dielectric constant. The flotation medium may be air, a nonconductor, or a conductor, depending on the over-all design. If the flotation material selected is a conductor, it is necessary to insulate electrically the pickoff gap from the flotation medium. This creates so many additional problems that it is rarely done. Also, the use of a capacitance pickoff is limited because of the viscous drag torques developed between the moving and the stationary plates of the condensers. These act on the gyroscope by causing disturbing torques. Electrical reaction torques, which are theoretically equal to

$$T = \frac{1}{9 \times 10^4} \frac{KA}{8\pi} \left(\frac{V}{h}\right)^2 \times r \tag{11-20}$$

are also developed. In this formula

V = potential difference between plates, volts
h = gap in capacitance, cm
r = effective radius that reaction forces act on, cm
T = torque, dyne-cm/radian

A single-degree-of-freedom capacitance pickoff for a gyroscope application is shown in Fig. 11-18. As the gyro spin axis tilts about the x axis, capacitance C_1 increases, while capacitance C_2 decreases. A second set of capacitors, placed at right angles to the first ones, will detect tilting about the y axis.

The most satisfactory application for a capacitance-type pickoff is a gyroscope that uses a gas suspension between the gimbal and the stationary tank. But even in this design the inductive-type pickoff is more widely used. In order to perform satisfactorily the capacitance pickoff is operated at relatively high frequencies compared to the gyroscopic control system. Frequencies in the order of 5,000 or 10,000 cps are commonly used. The variable capacitance produced by the pickoff may be inserted in a resonant circuit to cause a change in frequency proportional to displacement or in a bridge circuit, the unbalance of which is proportional to the displacement. In general, any technique used to take advantage of the variation of capacitance with the displacement of a gimbal will be just as sensitive to extraneous changes in other capacitances in the circuit. Therefore, the performance of the capacitance pickoff depends on the cable capacitances in the circuit. These must be kept as low and constant as possible. It should be mentioned that the capacitance pickoff inherently has a high output impedance due to the very low values of capacitance that can be achieved with an air dielectric. The high output impedance causes the output circuits to be sensitive to pickup and noise. These two characteristics greatly reduce the usefulness of capacitance pickoffs.

Electrolytic Pickoffs. The electric potentiometer functions as a pickoff by changing the resistance between its wiper arm and the ends of the resistance wire. An analogous operation can be performed by the electrolytic pickoff, in which the resistance wire is replaced by an ionized solution, while electrodes take the place of the wiper arm and the ends of the wire. As the distance between the electrodes is varied, the effective electric resistance between the electrodes is changed. The ionized solution, called the *electrolyte*, conducts electric currents according to Ohm's law in the same way as a metallic conductor behaves.

The resistance of an electric conductor, in ohms, is expressed as

$$R = \rho \frac{L}{A} \tag{11-21}$$

where ρ = resistivity, ohm-cm
L = length of conductor, cm
A = cross section, cm^2

The equivalent of this in an electrolytic circuit is expressed as

$$R = \frac{L}{\sigma A} \tag{11-22}$$

where σ is the conductivity of the electrolyte.

In both instances R represents the electric resistance of a conducting path of length L and cross section A in above-mentioned units.

The variable resistance which exists between the electrodes is used as the arm of a bridge circuit. The circuit is excited with an alternating voltage to avoid the electroplating of electrodes that takes place with direct current. The electrolyte would also be changed by the electroplating process and would cause the pickoff to give erroneous results. It has been suggested that the frequency of the alternating voltage be as high as 1,000 cps, but satisfactory electrolytic pickoffs are made to operate at 400 cps. The effective resistance provided by the electrolyte must be high in order to minimize the effects of polarization at the electrodes over the total resistance, but it is also desirable to operate the bridge with a low output impedance to reduce circuitry problems. A compromise between these conflicting demands is shown in Fig. 11-19.

This particular pickoff has an electrolytic resistance with a nominal value of 20,000 ohms. By operating the bridge into an isolation transformer with a stepdown of 10 to 1, the output impedance is reduced to 200 ohms. The desired conditions of high internal resistance and low output impedance are both satisfied in that the electrolytic resistance is high enough to avoid the effects of polarization and the output is low enough to work with a reasonable external circuit. Of course, the output transformer reduces the output voltage gradient by a factor of 10. Even with this 10 to 1 reduction, the gradient is still higher than that of many other pickoffs. A trimming capacitor is usually added to balance out the capacitance of the electrodes in the bridge circuit.

The circuit in Fig. 11-19 can be modified to include two such bridges. The electrolytic resistance values in one circuit correspond to displacements about the x axis of Fig. 11-20, while the values of the second set of electrolytic resistances correspond to displacements about the y axis. As a central conductor is moved about either or both the x or y axes, the output voltages from the two bridges correspond to the displacement of the central conductor.

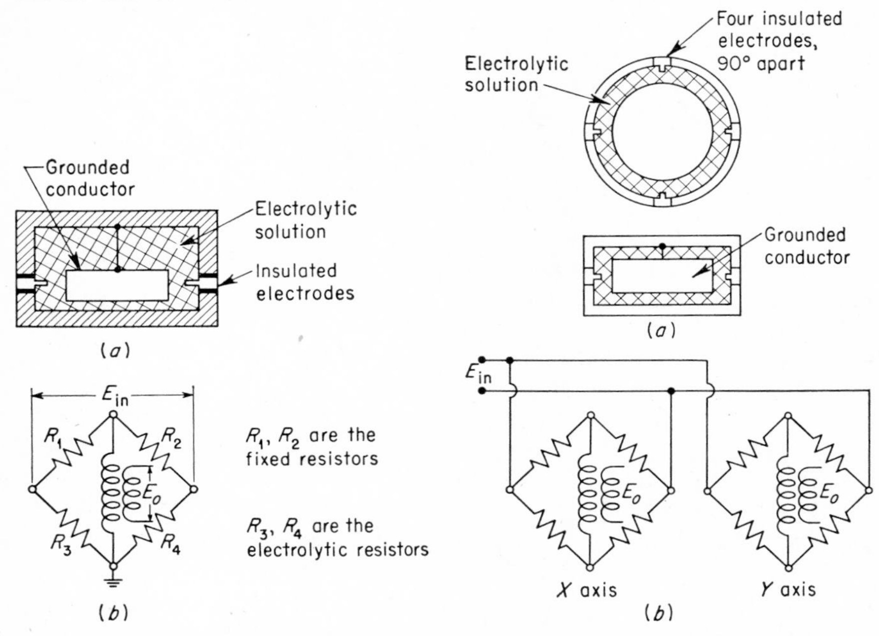

FIG. 11-19. Single-axis electrolytic pickoff. (a) Mechanical configuration; (b) electric circuit.

FIG. 11-20. Two-axis electrolytic pickoff. (a) Mechanical configuration; (b) electric circuit.

The principal problem with electrolytic pickoffs is in the development of the ionized solution. The latter must have the proper level of resistivity and must be stable for long periods of time under varying temperature conditions. The solutions with the best electrical properties are usually corrosive and require that the pickoff be encased in glass or that the metal container be coated to resist corrosion.

11-4. Torquers

The function of the torquer in a gyroscope is to produce a mechanical torque proportional to an electric signal. This torque is used to position the gimbal to some desired location or to compensate for a known unbalance.

The principal single-axis torquers are microsyn-type components, excited by either alternating or direct voltages, depending upon the instrumentation and application. Mechanically, the torquer microsyn is similar to the pickoff device. The stator and rotor are made of laminated stacks shaped as in Fig. 11-11. The difference between the torquer microsyn and the pickoff microsyn is in the windings on each pole and their connections to the external circuit. There are two types of windings used on torquer microsyns: the Z type for d-c excitation and the differential type winding for a-c excitation. Torquer microsyns are also made with various numbers of poles—4, 8, 12, 16—depending upon the application.

A four-pole a-c-excited torquer microsyn has a winding connected as shown in Fig. 11-21. This microsyn might be designed with additional poles if required. Each pole has two windings, viz., a control winding and a surrounding pattern winding, which are electrically insulated from each other. The pattern winding has a fixed excitation, while a variable excitation is applied to the control winding. The direction of the pattern- and control-winding currents at a given instant is also shown in Fig. 11-21, with the direction of the flux produced by these currents. By following the direction of the flux produced in each pole, we see that the flux produced by the two coils adds in poles 1 and 3 and subtracts in poles 2 and 4. The flux density in poles 1 and 3 is greater than that in poles 2 and 4, and the rotor tends to turn clockwise. The torque developed by an individual pole can be expressed as

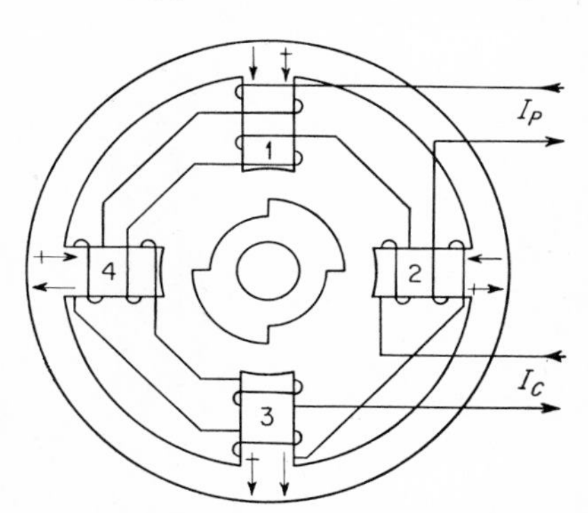

FIG. 11-21. Microsyn a-c torquer.

$$T_p = 2\pi 10^{-2}(NI)^2 \frac{dP}{d\Theta} \tag{11-23}$$

where NI = total ampere-turns applied to pole

$dP/d\Theta$ = rate of change of permeance with angular displacement, cm/radian

T_p = torque per pole, dyne-cm/radian

NI can be considered to be the sum of the pattern- and control-winding ampere-turns. Assuming, for simplicity, that the pattern and control windings have an equal number of turns N, the torque produced by the microsyn can be expressed as

$$T_p = 2\pi 10^{-2} N^2 (I_c + I_p)^2 \frac{dP}{d\Theta} \tag{11-24}$$

where the notations and units are those defined in Eq. (11-23). I_c and I_p are the control and pattern currents, expressed in amperes.

The microsyn has its air gap so shaped that $dP/d\Theta$ is essentially constant over an angular range of approximately 30°. Therefore, the torque equation per pole reduces to

$$T_p = a(I_c + I_p)^2 \tag{11-25}$$

where a denotes an appropriate constant.

The total torque developed by a microsyn is the sum of the torques developed by the individual poles. With poles 1 and 3 in Fig. 11-21 producing counterclockwise torques and poles 2 and 4 creating clockwise torques, the resultant or net torque generated is the difference between the clockwise and the counterclockwise torques.

$$T_{\text{net}} = T_{\text{ccw}} - T_{\text{cw}} = a(I_p + I_c)^2 - a(I_p - I_c)^2 \tag{11-26}$$

Equation (11-26) is true only when the pattern-winding current and the control-winding current are in phase. If these two currents are out of phase, the net torque is reduced by a value equal to the cosine of the angle between the currents and is expressed as

$$T_{\text{net}} = 4aI_pI_c \cos (\Theta_p - \Theta_c) \tag{11-27}$$

If the currents are 180° out of phase, the cosine of the angle between them is equal to -1, and the net torque will be negative. This indicates that the net flux in poles 2 and 4 is greater than the net flux in poles 1 and 3, and thus the rotor will rotate in a clockwise direction.

The net torque produced by the microsyn can be raised by increasing the number of poles, while maintaining the same number of ampere-turns on each pole, or by increasing the current in each winding, while maintaining the same number of poles. Both of these procedures increase the output torque but require additional input power.

Some gyro applications require larger torques than are possible to obtain from the a-c-excited torquer microsyn. With the same laminated core structure it is possible to obtain a greater torque from the microsyn by changing the winding and exciting it with a direct voltage. The winding change requires that each pole be wound with a single winding and that the four windings be connected as shown in Fig. 11-22. The arrows in Fig. 11-22 indicate the direction of the magnetic flux in each pole. When the rotor is centered with respect to the stator poles, the magnetic flux in the opposite poles is equal for any position of the rotor. This is true because the opposite poles are electrically connected in series, so that the same current flows in each winding and each winding has the same number of turns. Since the reluctance of the air gap under a pole is equal to the reluctance of the air gap under the opposite pole, the magnetic flux in a given pole must be equal to the magnetic flux in the opposite pole. The currents in the two separate windings of the microsyn do not have to be equal. Therefore, higher flux can be present in the even poles, for example, than in the odd poles of the microsyn in Fig. 11-22. This unbalance in magnetic flux results in a net force or torque on the rotor that causes it to turn in a direction of alignment with the stronger poles. This torque is the difference between the counterclockwise and the clockwise torques that tend to align the rotor with the respective poles.

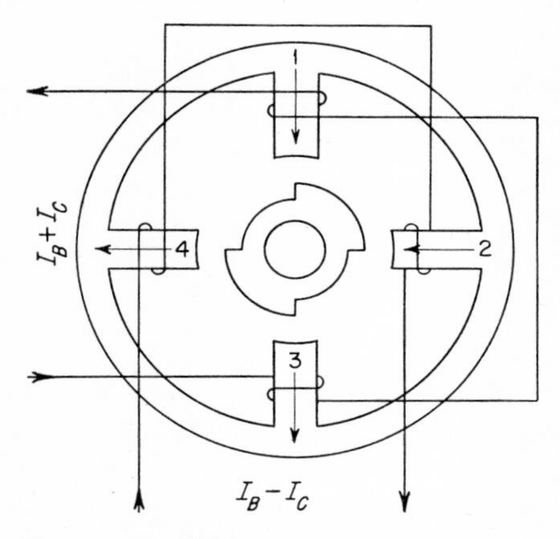

FIG. 11-22. Microsyn d-c torquer. Arrows indicate instantaneous direction of magnetic flux.

Since the torque per pole is proportional to the square of the current in the winding, the net torque is proportional to the difference of the squares of currents in each winding. This relationship is undesirable from an instrumentation point of view. A technique used to overcome this is to bias both windings with a fixed or bias current I_B. The addition of a control current I_C into the windings on one pair of poles and the subtraction of the same current from the current windings on the other poles results in a linear relationship between control current and net torque. Explicitly, with a scale factor a, as used in Eqs. (11-25), etc., the net torque becomes

$$T = a(I_B + I_C)^2 - a(I_B - I_C)^2$$

or, after simplification,

$$T = 4aI_BI_C \tag{11-28}$$

Present discussion of torquer microsyns has been limited to the ideal microsyn, namely, a unit which produces no torque when the control current is zero. In actual practice this ideal condition is seldom, if ever, achieved. Due to unequal turns on the individual poles, or lack of magnetic or geometric symmetry, there is always a small torque produced when the control current is zero. This torque is referred to as a reaction torque and requires compensation during manufacturing. The effect of this torque is to make either the odd or the even pair of poles appear to be stronger than the other pair. The rotor rotates toward alignment with the apparently stronger pole pair. A method of compensating for this effect is to shunt the stronger pair of windings with a resistance until the net torque on the rotor is within the specified value for a zero control current. The shunting resistor provides an alternate path for the current that would normally pass through the winding and produce a torque. By reducing the current in the stronger winding, the unbalance is effectively eliminated.

Elastic Restraint Microsyn. A third type of torquer microsyn is called the *elastic restraint generator*. This electromagnetic device serves the same basic function as a torsional spring or bar in that it produces a torque proportional to the deflection of the rotor. It is superior to the purely mechanical devices because its effective spring constant can be modified (within limits) by simply raising or lowering the excitation to its windings. The elastic restraint generator does not deviate from Hooke's law as a spring does. Therefore, the torque produced is a linear function of the angular displacement of the rotor from a reference or null position.

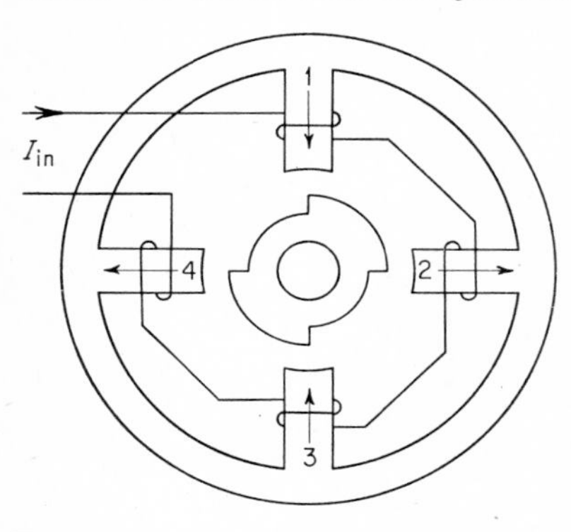

FIG. 11-23. Elastic restraint generator. Arrows indicate instantaneous direction of magnetic flux.

Mechanically, the elastic restraint generator is the same as the pickoff and torquer microsyn. It consists of the same type of laminated stator and dumbbell-shaped rotor. The winding consists of a single coil on each pole, with all coils connected in series. The direction of the coil windings is such that the adjacent poles produce fluxes in opposite directions. Therefore, the flux pattern in the elastic restraint generator is different from that in the other types of microsyn, where the adjacent poles produce fluxes in the same direction. Figure 11-23 shows the direction of the magnetic flux in an elastic restraint generator.

The operation of this device may be explained by analyzing what happens when the rotor moves away from the null or reference position between two poles. As the rotor moves, the reluctances of the air gaps under one pair of poles are reduced, while the reluctances of the air gaps under the other pair of poles are increased. The assumption that the magnetic circuit consists of only the reluctances of the air gaps is again valid. The total reluctance of two series-connected poles is a fixed value when there is a negligible change in the leakage paths with angular position. Since the rotor and stator are designed to have a minimum change in leakage with position, this assumption is certainly justified. With the application of a constant magnetomotive force and an essentially fixed total reluctance, the total flux produced is constant, independent of the rotor position. However, the flux density in the air gap under pole 2 of Fig. 11-23 is reduced by a clockwise rotation because the area of the rotor under the pole is increased. The flux density in the air gap under pole 1 is increased by clockwise rotation as the area under this pole is reduced. Therefore, the flux density under each pole is a function of the angular displacement of the rotor from its null position, and the torque produced by each pole is proportional to the square of the flux density in the air gap under that pole. The total torque developed by the elastic restraint generator is the sum of the torques produced by the individual poles. The sum of these torques can be simplified and expressed by the equation

$$T = bI^2\Theta \tag{11-29}$$

where T = torque

I = excitation current

Θ = angular displacement from null position

b = appropriately selected constant, depending on calibration and system of units used

Equation (11-29) shows the major advantages of the elastic restraint over a mechanical spring as a means of restoring a gyroscope gimbal to a null or reference position. The torque gradient of the elastic restraint can be increased simply by raising the excitation level rather than by disassembling and changing springs. Also, the torque produced by the elastic restraint is directly proportional to the angular deflection from the null position without the usual inherent nonlinearities of the spring.

Two-axis Torquer. Because of its application in a two-degree-of-freedom gyroscope, the two-axis torquer must be able to provide torques about two axes, either simultaneously or separately, as the need arises.

A two-axis torquer can be made in the same configuration as the two-axis pickoff (Fig. 11-14), except that both the primary magnet winding and the secondary-coil windings are excited by d-c voltages. The magnet winding produces a magnetic field of fixed magnitude, while the secondary currents are usually adjusted to provide a particular level of desired torque. The torque produced by this device is due to the magnetic field produced by the secondary winding as it acts on the magnetic field set up by the primary magnet. The force on the conductor or the reaction on the magnet, which is attached to the gimbal, is expressed by the fundamental equation

$$F = \frac{BIL}{10} \tag{11-30}$$

The torque produced by the torquer also depends upon the effective radius of the magnets (usually the radius of the gimbal) and the number of secondary turns. The torque equation is, therefore,

$$T = \frac{N_2 \times I_2 \times B \times L \times r}{10} \quad \text{dyne-cm} \tag{11-31}$$

where r = gimbal or air-gap radius between magnet and secondary winding, cm
B = flux density in air gap, gauss
I_2 = current in secondary winding, amp
L = effective length of secondary conductor, cm
N_2 = number of secondary conductors

The performance of such a torquer is required to be optimized in terms of power input and volume available for the primary magnet. The d-c power input P_{in} into the magnet depends upon the magnitude of the primary current I_p and the d-c resistance $R_{\text{d-c}}$ of the winding. We have

$$P_{\text{in}} = I_p^2 R_{\text{d-c}} = I_p^2 N_p^2 b$$

$$\Phi = \frac{0.4\pi}{\mathcal{R}} \sqrt{\frac{P_{\text{in}}}{b}} \tag{11-32}$$

where P_{in} = input power to magnet winding, watts
I_p = direct current into magnet winding, amp
$R_{\text{d-c}}$ = resistance of magnet winding, ohms
N_p = number of turns on primary winding
b = winding factor, ohm^2
Φ = total flux produced by magnet, maxwells
$\mathcal{R}$ = reluctance of primary magnet circuit, cm^{-1}

From Eqs. (11-31) and (11-32), the torque, in dyne-centimeters, produced per unit of secondary current can be expressed by the formula

$$\frac{T}{I_2} = \frac{4\pi}{10^2} \frac{N_2 r L}{\mathcal{R} A} \sqrt{\frac{P_{\text{in}}}{b}} \tag{11-33}$$

where I_2 = current in secondary winding, amp
A = cross-sectional area of primary magnet, cm^2

All the terms in Eq. (11-33), except the input power, are functions of the geometry of the magnet housing. $\mathcal{R}$ is the reluctance of the magnetic circuit and depends on the dimensions; b is the winding factor and depends on the area inside the housing allowed for the winding; and A is the area of the magnet circuit. In general, the larger the area for the winding, the smaller the value of $\mathcal{R}$. Therefore, for a given physical size and configuration, it is possible to optimize the value of T/I_2 for a given level of input power.

One of the advantages of this type of torquer is that it can be easily combined with the pickoff (Fig. 11-16) to provide both torquing and signal functions in a single device. The primary magnet in such applications has both d-c and a-c excitation applied at the same time to the same winding. The number of secondary coils is doubled to provide for two sets of concentric windings, one for the pickoff output voltage and one for the secondary current of the torquer. Since the average torque produced by the interaction of the primary a-c field with the secondary d-c field is zero, no additional torque is produced by the pickoff. Also, since the relative speed of the magnet to the secondary coil is negligible, no signal is produced by the d-c primary excitation. Any harmonic ripple on the d-c supply is undesirable, since the a-c components would be coupled to the secondary pickup windings.

Summary. Wide use is made of the various electromagnetic types of pickoffs and torquers because they usually combine the highest performance with simplest construction and external circuitry. The most exhaustive analysis and development work has been performed on the single-degree type of devices, while relatively little work has been done on two-axis configurations. One reason for this is that the work on the two-axis devices is limited to specific gyroscope application, while the single-axis pickoff and torquer are useful servo components as well as being widely used for a group of gyroscopic applications.

11-5. Electromagnetic and Electrostatic Centering

Appreciable engineering effort has been spent in attempts to develop an electromagnetic or electrostatic system for centering the inner gimbal of a gyroscope. The goal of such a system would be a servo-type suspension that could automatically adjust itself for spurious inputs affecting the centering of the gyro. This suspension would reduce the performance requirements now demanded of the traditional mechanical suspension, i.e., pivots or wires, and would provide a means of modifying the suspension of a completed gyro without disassembly.

Electromagnetic Centering. Most of the development work has been devoted to the single-degree-of-freedom microsyn components to provide electromagnetic centering of the gimbal. One approach has been to develop a microsyn that provides only centering forces to return the gimbal to its null position if it is radially displaced. The second approach has been to develop microsyns capable of performing both the centering function and the normal torquing or pickoff operation.

A microsyn similar to Fig. 11-24 can be used to provide the centering forces. When the rotor is displaced axially, a force is developed along the line of displacement that tends to return the rotor to its original position. This force, in dynes, is expressed as

$$F_x = \frac{1}{2} 10^{-5} \times I^2 \times \frac{dL}{dx} \tag{11-34}$$

where F_x = force along x axis due to a displacement toward pole 1
I = current in coil on pole 1, amp
dL/dx = change of inductance of coil due to a displacement, henrys/cm

Since any axial displacement means that the rotor moves toward one pole and away from another, there is a second force developed at the

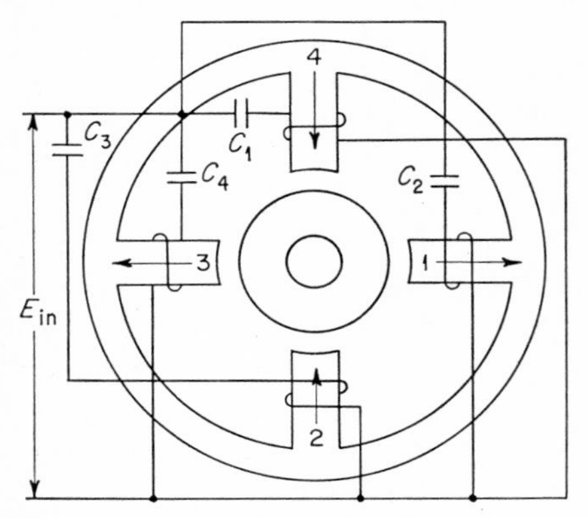

FIG. 11-24. Four-pole microsyn used for electromagnetic centering.

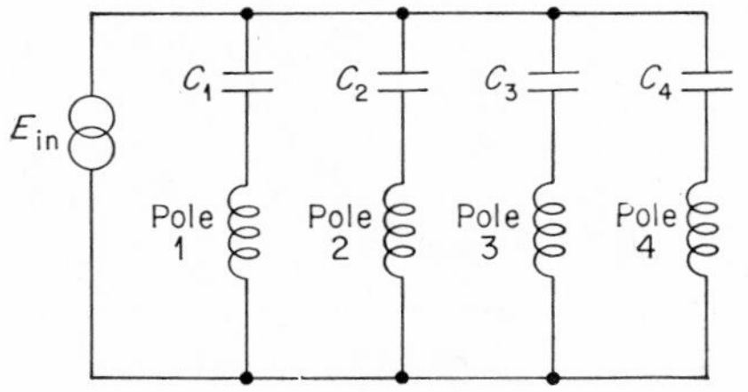

FIG. 11-25. Circuit of four-pole microsyn used for electromagnetic centering.

second pole which is opposite to that developed at the first pole. The net force acting on the rotor is

$$F_x = (F_x)_1 - (F_x)_3$$

or

$$F_x = \frac{1}{2} 10^{-5} \left(I_1{}^2 \frac{dL_1}{dx} - I_3{}^2 \frac{dL_3}{dx} \right) \tag{11-35}$$

expressed in the same units as Eq. (11-34).

A similar force is developed for displacements along the y axis or for combinations of x and y displacements.

In order to develop the negative torque required to return the rotor to its original position, the primaries are connected according to Fig. 11-25. The value of the condensers is selected such that at the null or centered position the currents in each coil are equal. When the rotor is displaced toward pole 1 and away from pole 3, the inductance of pole 1 increases and its current decreases according to Fig. 11-26. The opposite is true for pole 3, where the inductance decreases and the current increases.

Using Eq. (11-35), it is apparent that the net force will be negative or opposing the force that moved the rotor.

This suspension can be stiffened by using the voltage developed across each primary to drive a feedback amplifier. The voltage across each winding is determined by the relative position of the rotor and indicates its displacement. This signal is used to drive an amplifier that furnishes a current to the windings in a direction to increase the restoring force. By adjusting the parameters of this feedback amplifier, the "stiffness" of the suspension to axial forces can be varied.

The microsyn in Fig. 11-24 cannot be used to provide the torquing or pickoff functions because there is no change in inductance with angular

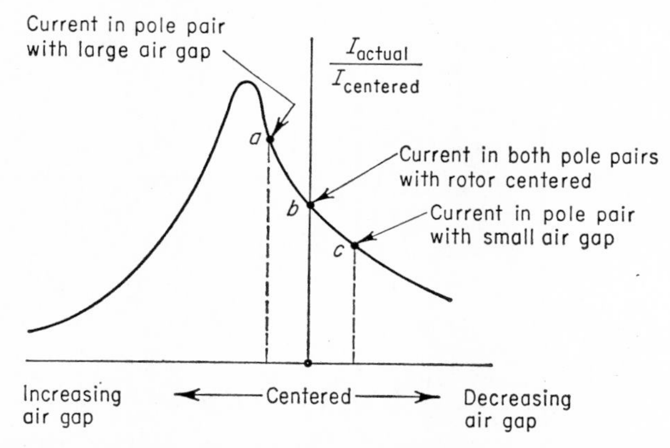

FIG. 11-26. Change in microsyn primary current with displacement of rotor from center or null position.

rotation of the cylindrical rotor. If the same flux pattern is maintained and a dumbbell-shaped rotor employed as in the conventional microsyn, the flux per pole remains constant for small angular displacements. This is true because the same flux prevails in pole 1 as in pole 4, since the two poles are in a series magnetic circuit. Any reduction in the reluctance of the air gap at pole 1 (caused by rotation) is counterbalanced by an increase in the reluctance of the air gap at pole 4. Therefore, this microsyn cannot function either as a torquer or as a pickoff. The microsyn will produce a torque that is proportional to the angular displacement. Referring to Fig. 11-23, we can see that the flux pattern is the same as that used in the elastic restraint generator, the torque output of which is proportional to a displacement. Since the flux relationship between adjacent poles must be the one shown in Fig. 11-23 in order to provide the centering forces, and since only the elastic restraint generator of the four-pole microsyn can fulfill this requirement, it is the only four-pole microsyn used for electromagnetic centering.

If the microsyn is made with an eight-pole stator and a four-pole rotor, similar to Fig. 11-27, it can be used to accomplish both the centering function and the normal pickoff or torquer function. In this case the primary windings would be connected as shown in Fig. 11-28. The stator poles would be divided into pairs. Each pair acts as a single pole in the four-pole microsyn. As the rotor is displaced toward one pair of poles, the inductance relative to that pair is increased while that of the opposite pair is reduced. The same type of curve as in Fig. 11-26 can be used to show the change in current which takes place as the rotor is displaced.

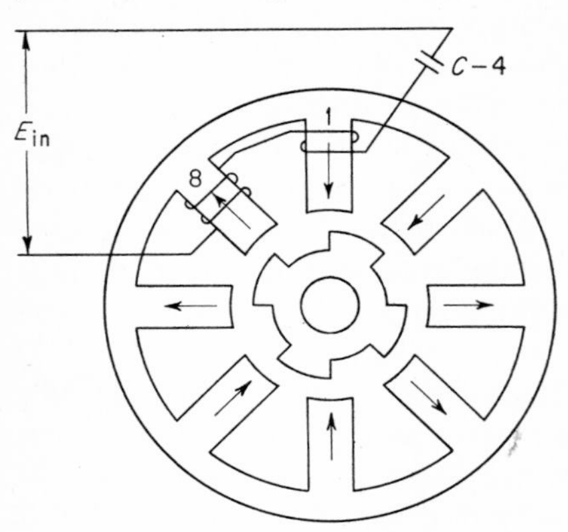

Fig. 11-27. Eight-pole microsyn, primary windings shown only for poles 8 and 1. Arrows show the instantaneous direction of magnetic flux.

The same type of electromagnetic centering can be used to center axially the output axis of a single-degree-of-freedom gyro similar to Fig. 11-29. The microsyns are usually mounted on each end of the gyro output axis, one to provide torquing and one to generate a signal. The stators and rotors of both microsyns are tapered as shown in Fig. 11-29. When a force is applied to the shaft to cause it to move toward the signal generator end, the inductance of the signal generator increases

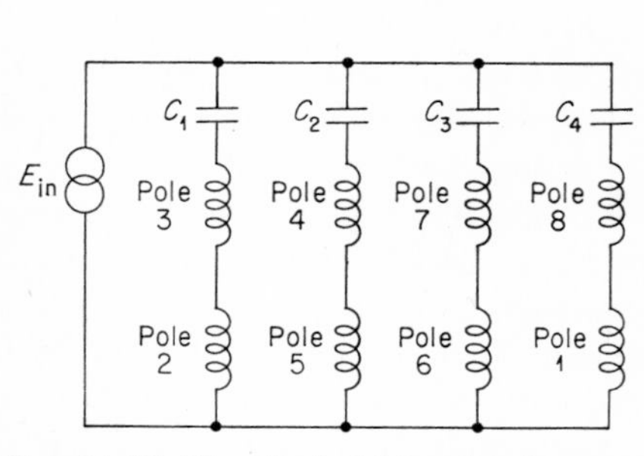

Fig. 11-28. Circuit of eight-pole microsyn used for electromagnetic centering.

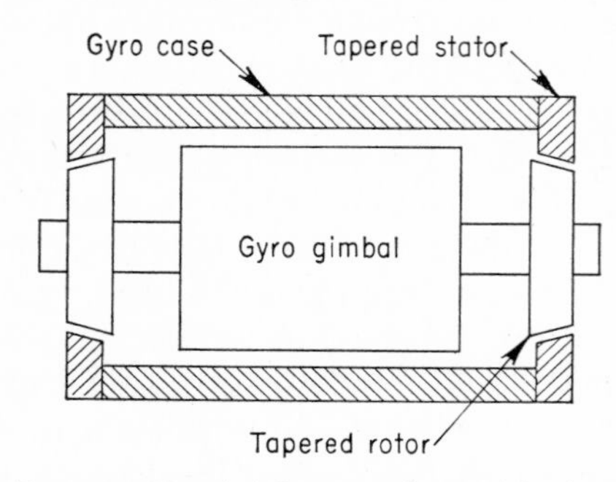

Fig. 11-29. Axial centering with two tapered microsyns.

and the inductance of the torquer is reduced. By using a circuit similar to Fig. 11-28, the primary currents can be made to follow the curve shown in Fig. 11-26. By using an eight-pole microsyn with a tapered stator and rotor, it is possible to center the gimbal about all three axes.

Electrostatic Centering. The electrostatic suspension of a gyro is more sophisticated than the electromagnetic approach, mostly because of the problems raised by the relatively high voltages encountered. In order to minimize the weight to be supported by the electrostatic field without unduly sacrificing the angular momentum, a rather unconventional design has been suggested which consists essentially of a spinning spherical shell or ball supported in an evacuated chamber or tank by a set of electrodes. These are energized by a servo system, assuring the proper centering and torque-free support of the spinning ball. This design eliminates the need for spin bearings and their loading arrangement. Electrostatic suspension of this kind therefore provides frictionless spin and gimbal "bearings," the stiffness of which can be adjusted by varying the voltage applied to the electrodes or by designing the gyro with appropriate gaps adjacent to the electrodes or, again, by properly selecting the area of the electrodes.

The gyroscopic element of this gyro is generally made in the shape of a sphere, with the electrostatic supporting forces acting in radial alignment through the center of the sphere. In operation the rotating sphere is brought up to speed prior to being used by electromagnetic means and is allowed to coast down in the evacuated tank. The coast-down time may be several days or more, since the sphere is in a vacuum and free of external forces, except perhaps those produced by displacement currents, which create an all but negligible dissipation of energy and thus loss of angular momentum. Such a design theoretically embodies the properties of an ideal gyro—high angular momentum and freedom from external forces and internal heat.

The use of the electrostatic suspension is severely limited by the fact that it is extremely difficult to obtain the mechanical configuration needed to realize the ideal performance. Among others, the rotating ball must be machined to approach a perfect sphere, even allowing for dynamic distortion. The enclosing tank must also approach a perfect internal sphere and be able to maintain vacuum of 10^{-6} mm or better. The sphere must be made of a material that has a uniform density. The nearer the parts of the gyro approach the ideal configuration, the better the performance.

Both the electromagnetic and the electrostatic suspension are developments which may lead to better gyros, but both are limited by the fact that ideal parts are not easily manufactured. As the manufactured parts approach the desired ideal parts, the performance of these suspensions will be improved. The same is true for other types of gyro suspension. Any major improvement in the electromagnetic or electrostatic suspension should open up new and interesting possibilities in gyro design.

PROBLEMS

11-1. Determine the possible stator and rotor slot combinations that can be used for a four-pole three-phase induction motor.

11-2. When a spin motor is proportioned similar to Fig. 11-2, it is not always possible to skew the rotor one slot due to the large skew angle required. What are the alternatives?

11-3. Explain why skewing the stator of a hysteresis motor would not reduce the parasitic losses shown in Fig. 11-11.

11-4. The simplified equivalent circuit of a 400-cps microsyn is shown in Fig. 11-30.

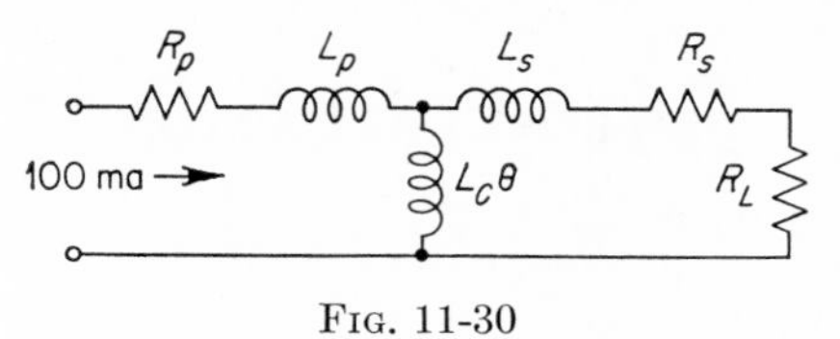

FIG. 11-30

Assuming $R_p = 10$ ohms, $L_p = 5$ mh, $L_s = 1.5$ henrys, $R_s = 800$ ohms, $L_c = 150$ mh, find the voltage gradient and phase shift with a 10,000-ohm load over the angular range of $\Theta = \pm 0.2$ radian.

11-5. Using the circuit in Prob. 11-4, find the reaction torque developed when the torque is proportional to

$$T = K \times I_p \times I_s \times \cos (\Theta_p - \Theta_s)$$

where K is the torque gradient equal to 1.5 dyne-cm/ma^2.

11-6. Using the circuit in Prob. 11-4, determine what effect the addition of a 0.04-μf condenser across the load will have on the gradient and phase shift.

11-7. If the two secondary coils on each side of the gyro in Fig. 11-16 are not at right angles to each other, what error will this cause in pickoff accuracy?

BIBLIOGRAPHY

1. Liwschitz-Garik, M., and C. C. Whipple: "Electric Machinery," D. Van Nostrand Company, Inc., Princeton, N.J., 1946, Vol. II.

2. Fitzgerald, A. E., and C. Kingsley, Jr.: "Electric Machinery" McGraw-Hill Book Company, Inc., New York, 1952.

3. Puchstein, A. F., and T. C. Lloyd: "Alternating Current Machines," John Wiley & Sons, Inc., New York, 1954.

4. Teare, B. R., Jr.: Theory of Hysteresis Motor Torque, *Trans. AIEE*, vol. 59, p. 907, 1940.

5. Roters, H. C.: The Hysteresis Motor—Advances Which Permit Economical Fractional Horsepower Ratings, *Trans. AIEE*, vol. 66, p. 1419, 1947.

6. Gilinson, P. J.: Microsyn Magnetic Suspension Elementary Principles, M.I.T. Instrumentation Laboratory TP 1582, 1956.

7. Gilinson, P. J.: The 8 Pole Microsyn Magnetic Suspension Signal and Torque Generator, M.I.T. Instrumentation Laboratory TP 1580, 1956.

8. Hume, E. L.: Theory of Microsyn Electromagnetic Components, M.I.T. Instrumentation Laboratory Report R-11, 1951.

9. Gilinson, P. J., and R. G. Haltmaier: Engineering Data for 2.0-inch Series of Microsyn Electromagnetic Components, M.I.T. Instrumentation Laboratory Report R-16, 1951.

10. Haltmaier, R. G.: Coupled Circuit Analysis of Microsyn Signal Generators, M.I.T. Instrumentation Laboratory Engineering Notes E-266, 1953.

CHAPTER 12

GYRO EVALUATION

By Sidney Osband

Nomenclature

IA = input axis
OA = output axis
SA = spin axis
Θ_{IA} = gyro input angle
$\dot{\Theta}_{IA}$ = gyro drift rate
$\Delta\Theta_{IA}$ = gyro drift angle
T, T_u, T_e = torque
H = angular momentum
K_t = sensitivity of torquing device
ω_E = earth angular rate
ω_V = vertical component of earth rate
ω_H = horizontal component of earth rate
λ = geographical latitude
U_{IA} = input axis unbalance
U_{SA} = spin-axis unbalance
C_{SA} = compliance along spin axis
C_{IA} = compliance along input axis
α = direction of applied acceleration relative to spin axis

12-1. Introduction

In previous chapters the basic theory of gyroscopics was developed, the functional characteristics of a number of gyroscope types were evolved, and the relationships between design principles and performance were explored.

The gyro designer strives to attain a gyro performance goal through the selection of an optimized functional configuration and the application of appropriate design principles and compromises. He thus creates a design-data package in which every detail of construction is specified. The success of the design is revealed by an engineering test program on gyros built in accordance with the design package. This testing is called *gyro evaluation.*

Gyro evaluation is the determination of the performance abilities of gyroscopes and the assessment of whether or not a design is suitable for a particular application. A gyro performance specification may be evolved from the evaluation-test results. This specification may differ from the initial gyro design goal, the degree depending upon the success of the design effort.

In the process of evaluation, performance limitations and deficiencies are uncovered. This results in efforts to improve design and fabrication techniques. Research may become necessary in certain areas. The cycle is then repeated by the construction of new gyros of an "improved" design and the evaluation of these units. Thus evaluation is both a spur toward the improvement of gyros and a link in the development chain of design, build, test.

Evaluation data can be obtained from tests on gyro subassemblies, from tests on gyros as components, from tests on equipment containing gyros, and finally from tests on vehicles or weapons systems containing gyroscopic equipment. The prime source of data, however, is from tests on component gyros in engineering laboratories.

This chapter is devoted primarily to the laboratory testing of gyroscopes and is particularly concerned with the testing of precision stabilization instruments. These gyros require the utmost in refinement of testing techniques, particularly since they are intended to be used in closed loops. However, many of the test principles described in this chapter are applicable to other types of gyros.

12-2. The Gyro in a Stabilization Loop

The stabilization gyroscope is a transducer which provides an output error signal generated by the rotation of the gyro housing from an inertial reference direction. As such, the output signal may be used to control the structure to which the gyro is mounted, called the *stable platform,* to hold the latter fixed angularly in inertial space, thereby nulling the gyro output. This stabilization loop is illustrated in Fig. 12-1 for a single axis. Most applications involve simultaneous stabilization on three orthogonal axes.

When the vehicle containing the platform turns, it tends to turn the platform with it. This generates a gyro output signal which controls the platform drive to turn the platform relative to the vehicle in an amount equal and opposite to the turn of the vehicle relative to a space-fixed reference.

In some applications it is desired to rotate the reference system for purposes of initial alignment or to maintain a relationship with a rotating coordinate system, such as one fixed to the earth. As explained in preceding chapters, this is accomplished by the application of control torques which precess the gyro at an angular rate that is proportional to the torque.

These functions of the gyroscope are diagramed in Fig. 12-2 for one channel of a two-axis gyroscope and for the particular channel of a single-axis stabilization gyroscope. Figure 12-2*a* shows an angle difference.

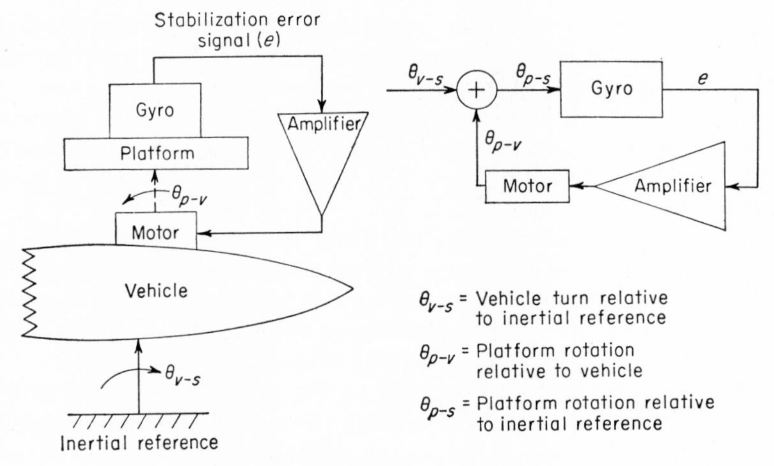

FIG. 12-1. The single-channel stabilization loop.

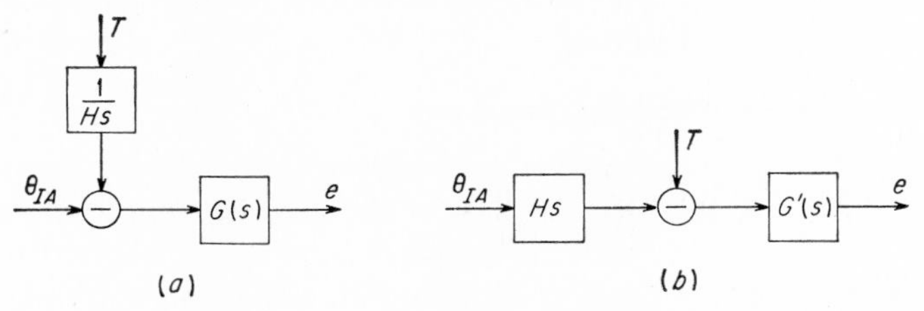

FIG. 12-2. Gyroscope transfer diagrams. (*a*) Two-axis gyro; (*b*) single-axis gyro.

This difference exists between the housing and the inner gimbal, the orientation of which is theoretically undisturbed by input angular motions of the housing.

Figure 12-2*b* shows a torque summation on the gimbal as a result of forced precession due to input angular motions. Note that torques cause output changes in single-axis gyros without involving the angular momentum in the absence of the stabilization loop. In both gyros the control torques act on an axis orthogonal to both the input and the spin axes. Both input angular rotation and torque can change the output signal.

The transfer functions $G(s)$ and $HsG'(s)$, which relate the output signal to the angular rotation of the gyroscope housing about the input axis, include the sensitivity of the pickoff or error signal generator.

The functional block diagram of a stabilization loop, including the gyro functional diagram, is shown in Fig. 12-3. Even though a two-axis gyro diagram is used, the following discussion applies equally to a single-axis gyro. $A(s)$ is a transfer function which includes characteristics of the amplifiers, damping devices, motors, inertias, gyro reaction torques, etc., in the platform equipment. The input angle Θ_{IA} of the gyroscope is identical to the stable platform position because the gyro housing is bolted to the platform.

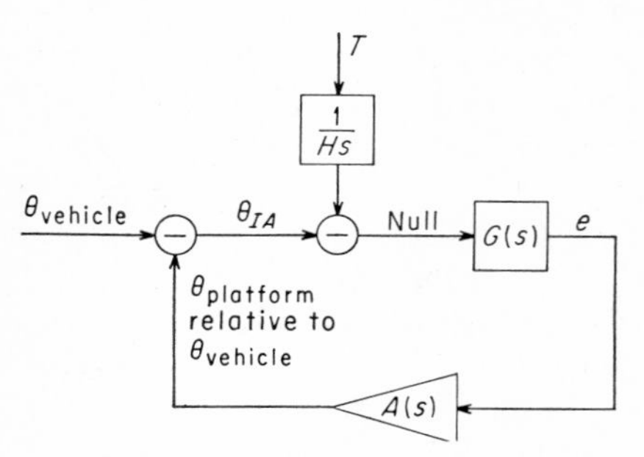

FIG. 12-3. The gyro in a stabilization loop.

As a result of the loop-nulling characteristic, the average error signal is zero. This assumes, however, a highly precise stabilization loop at low frequencies and sufficient gyro and servo linearity and symmetry so that negligible average output offset results due to higher-frequency vehicle dynamics.

The functional characteristics of stabilization gyros are such that a null of the output signal is accompanied by a null at the gyro summation point at the input of $G(s)$ or $G'(s)$.

Consequently, in a steady-state condition we have

$$\Theta_{IA} = \frac{T}{Hs} \tag{12-1}$$

where T is the summation of the control torque (usually applied via electromagnetic torque motors built into the gyros) and the error and uncertainty torques due to imperfections in the construction of the gyro. H is the angular momentum of the gyro.

Thus the platform will rotate (precess) relative to an inertial reference at a rate proportional to the total torque applied. The total angle of rotation is proportional to the time integral of the torque and inversely proportional to the angular momentum. This torque-integration feature of the gyro is also equivalent to a filtering action. Higher-frequency torque variations, such as those due to vibration, cause negligible angular displacements of the platform at the torque frequency. However, should torque rectification take place (as a result of anisoelastic compliance, for example), the steady average torque value causes an angle of drift which may increase continuously with time. This low-pass filtering

action is generally characteristic of all integration mechanisms. The precision gyro is perhaps the most nearly perfect integration mechanism available.

12-3. Gyro Performance

As indicated above, a gyroscopic platform will rotate or precess relative to an inertial space reference at a rate proportional to the total amount of torque applied. When the control torques are zero, the platform may still rotate owing to the space integration of the gyro error and uncertainty torques; this is defined as the *drift* or *drift rate* of the gyroscope. In the main, gyro testing is the measurement and study of these torques. The gyro itself is an essential instrument in the torque measurement. The integrating nature of the gyro also means that very small torques may be measured, since with sufficient time a finite drift angle is accumulated by integration.

Drift is the prime factor which determines gyro accuracy. Other accuracy factors are pickoff (output signal generator) resolution and hysteresis and torque-generator linearity and hysteresis. In general the pickoffs of contemporary gyroscopes are sufficiently accurate to provide negligible errors. Depending upon the application, that is, whether the platform is fixed in inertial space coordinates or torqued to operate in coordinates fixed in orientation to the earth, the torquer inaccuracies will either be of no consequence or be comparable to the drift inaccuracy in importance.

In addition to accuracy, the total gyro performance picture includes reliability, functional characteristics, and operational suitability to a specific application. These may be defined as follows:

Accuracy. The precision with which the gyro provides an angular reference and output error signals. The manner in which precision is affected by actuating, modifying, and interfering inputs.

Reliability. Either the mean time to failure or the probability that the gyro will operate according to specifications in a given mission.

Functional Characteristics. The nominal or idealized output response to the actuating inputs and the variation of the response with the modifying inputs.

Operational Suitability Characteristics. Convenience factors of which warm-up time, wheel run-up time, heating characteristics, and power requirements are the most noteworthy.

The above description of gyro performance areas makes reference to actuating, modifying, and interfering inputs with respect to accuracy and functional characteristics.

The actuating inputs are the input angular rotation of the gyro housing and the torquing current fed into the torque generator. These inputs are

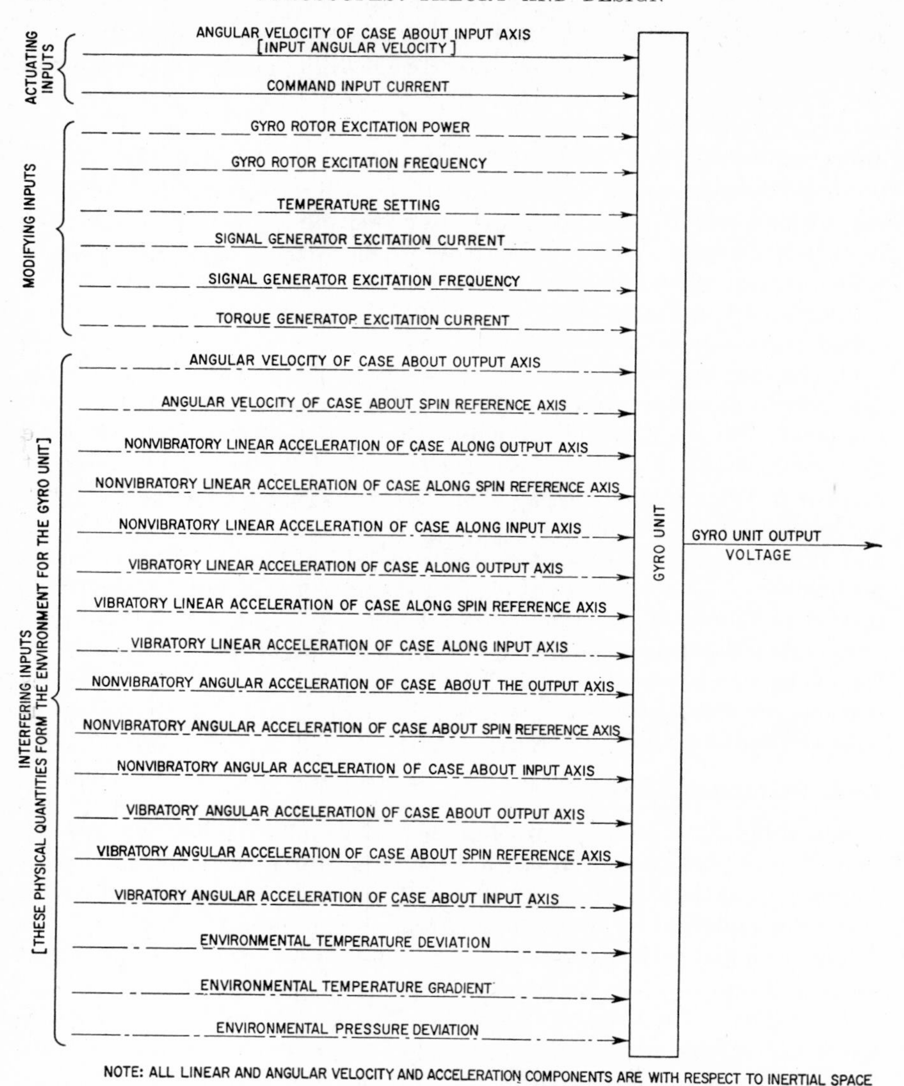

FIG. 12-4. Classification of gyro inputs. (*Courtesy of M.I.T. Instrumentation Laboratory.*)

intended to provide a desired output response, which in turn may be changed by the modifying inputs. The prime modifying inputs are spin motor excitation frequency, which determines the angular momentum; torque-generator and pickoff primary excitations, which determine the electrical sensitivities; and temperature, which determines the damping factor in floated gyros. The accuracy of the gyro, particularly the drift rate, is affected by the disturbing inputs such as linear vibration, temperature variations, and magnetic fields. In addition, the actuating and modifying inputs are disturbing inputs. Sinusoidal variation of the input angular rotation, or angular oscillation, is an actuating input which produces output signals. Angular oscillation may also produce disturbing torques which affect drift. Power changes may accompany spin frequency changes. These power changes can cause temperature effects which in turn affect gyro drift.

Figure 12-4 indicates many of the inputs to which gyros respond and classifies them into the three categories mentioned above.

Of the four performance areas—accuracy, reliability, functional characteristics, and operational suitability—accuracy and reliability are the most vital features and consume the major portion of the effort in gyro evaluation. Functional and operational suitability characteristics involve rather straightforward, simple measurements. Reliability testing explores other performance areas (programed environmental inputs) and makes use of a specialized mathematical theory of statistics and probability. This is a whole field in itself and will not be discussed further in this book.

Accuracy determination, particularly drift measurement, will be, then, the evaluation phase of greatest interest to this chapter. The following sections on test instrumentation and methods are concerned primarily with the drift testing of precision stabilization gyroscopes.

12-4. Performance Criteria

It is difficult to establish a complete or universally applicable tabulation of gyro performance criteria. The following definitions are merely suggestions of the author, who hopes that they will soon be supplanted by standards endorsed by both industry and the armed services.

The principal performance criteria of significance to stabilization gyros are as follows:

Drift Rate. The time rate of change of input angle relative to inertial space which maintains the output at null when control torques are not applied. Typical units are degrees per hour.

Sensitivity. The ratio of specified output to input variations determined by the slope of the best straight line that can be fitted to input-output data. Typical units are volts per radian for pickoffs or ratio of output signal to input angle for the steady state.

Torquing Sensitivity. The ratio of gyro precession rate to torquer input current. Typical units are degrees per hour per milliampere or degrees per hour per milliampere squared, depending on the type of torquer used.

Linearity. The greatest deviation of the input-output data from the best straight line, expressed as a percentage of the maximum output. This can be applied to input angle response, pickoffs, or torquers.

Resolution. The maximum amount by which the input can change without producing a change in output. Typical units are seconds of arc.

Gimbal Freedom. The maximum angular displacement relative to the housing about the output axis of the gimbal supporting the gyro rotor. Typical units are degrees.

Output Null. The minimum rms output, expressed in millivolts.

Nutation Frequency (Two-axis Gyros). The natural frequency of oscillation of the gimbal supporting the rotor, determined by the angular momentum and the gimbal inertia. Typical units are cycles per second.

Characteristic Time (Time Constant). The logarithmic response time (63 per cent of final value for a step input) of the output for a step input angle change for single-axis gyros; the logarithmic decay time of nutation for two-axis gyros; expressed in seconds.

Cross Coupling (Two-axis Gyros). The maximum ratio of the nonintended output to the intended output due to a single input, expressed as a percentage.

Warm-up Time. The maximum time required for the gyro to attain specified performance after power is applied at a specified condition, expressed in minutes.

Reliability. The mean time to failure or the probability that the gyro will conform to specification.

Of the above, aside from reliability, drift rate (or drift) is the most vital. Drift rate, linearity, and resolution are accuracy-performance criteria. Sensitivity, torquing sensitivity, nutation frequency, characteristic time, and cross coupling are functional performance criteria. Gimbal freedom, output null, and warm-up time are suitability criteria.

12-5. The Nature of Gyro Drift

The torques which cause gyro drift may be separated into two main categories:

1. Error torques: The systematic components for which adjustment or compensation may be applied
2. Uncertainty torques: The random components which bear no correlation with any inputs

The drift due to error torques is of three types:

1. Nonacceleration-sensitive drift: Generally caused by elastic or magnetic torques. The units are degrees per hour.
2. Acceleration-sensitive drift: Generally caused by mass unbalance. The units are degrees per hour per g.

3. Acceleration-squared-sensitive drift: Generally caused by structure compliance. The units are degrees per hour per g^2.

Other sources of systematic drift-rate errors may be temperature-sensitive torques due to differential expansion or change in buoyancy force in floated gyros, torques due to nonorthogonality of the principal axes and wheel speed change, and torques due to elastic and viscous coupling between housing and gimbals, combined with some particular housing motions.

The random drift is due to small uncertainty torques such as caused by bearing noise, friction, temperature gradients, etc., all of which are time-variable. Random drift is generally determined by statistical analysis of a large number of drift tests.

The uncertainty of drift is the limiting accuracy factor in gyro performance. The uncertainty may consist of changes in the systematic torques as well as in purely random drift. For example, a gyro may have a mass unbalance which causes a drift rate of 2°/hr/g. Repeated observations in the gravity field indicate that the drift rate caused by this mass unbalance varies over a range of 0.5°/hr. The 2°/hr error drift may then be reduced by rebalancing or be compensated for. However, the best that can be accomplished is ±0.25°/hr, owing to the 0.5°/hr variation. Variations in the systematic drift rates may be designated instabilities. The purely random drift is usually of unknown origin.

In specifying random drift or nonrepeatability a statistical approach is desirable. The standard deviation from the mean (rms or 1σ) is the preferred quantity. Since disturbing inputs and time are significant factors influencing drift rate, it is necessary to specify them along with the drift rate. This leads to such performance statements as "The standard deviation from the mean of the nonacceleration-sensitive drift rate, as measured once daily with shutdowns between successive readings, is 0.1°/hr over a one-month period" or "The 1σ deviation of vertical-axis drift rate, as determined from five successive 20-min drift runs in the gravity field, was 0.05°/hr." Obviously, an unlimited variety of drift-rate statements may be made for each gyro. The types of drift-rate measurements to be made should be determined from the knowledge of the operational and environmental conditions in the intended application and from the manner in which gyro drift affects system accuracy.

12-6. Gyro Test Instrumentation

Gyro testing may be conducted in any one of three instrumentations:

1. Servo table
2. Torque feedback
3. Open loop

Servo table and torque feedback are closed-loop operations and are much more common than open-loop approaches in the testing of precision stabilization gyros. Combinations of these methods, particularly of the first two, are used simultaneously in two-axis gyro testing. The choice of instrumentation is determined by such considerations as the type of system and vehicle in which the gyro is to be used, the measurement objectives of a particular test, the environmental conditions of the test, and test hardware availability and cost. As a result, different instrumentations will be employed in the various phases of a gyro evaluation program.

Servo-table Instrumentation. The servo-table instrumentation is akin to the stable-platform instrument in which the gyro is utilized. A rigid, precise turntable is attached to the laboratory floor. The gyro in turn is mounted to the turntable with an input axis aligned to the table axis. The table is slaved to the gyro reference by electronics and motor drives such as to null the gyro stabilization error output signal. A perfect gyro without control current input would result in a table position angularly fixed in inertial space. With an imperfect gyro the table rotates relative to inertial space at a drift rate proportional to the magnitude of the imperfection torque. It is desired to measure this drift of the table.

The base of the servo table, as a result of being attached to the earth (the floor of the test laboratory), is rotating in space about the earth's polar axis at the earth's sidereal rate of 15°/hr.* Were the turntable axis aligned parallel to the earth's axis, as shown in Fig. 12-5, it would appear to the observer in the test laboratory that the turntable stabilized by a perfect gyro rotates at 15°/hr.

Deviations of the turntable rotation rate from the earth's sidereal rate are due to gyro drift. If the turntable rotation rate is measured to be 16.3°/hr, for example, then the gyro drift rate is

$$16.3 - 15 = 1.3°/\text{hr}$$

As will be discussed in the section on Earth's Rotation, the earth's rate effect about the servo-table axis varies with different table orientations to the earth. The orientation of the turntable axis must be known with sufficient accuracy to permit determination of the gyro drift rate by subtraction of the earth's rotation from the observed table rotation rate.

Figure 12-6 is a block diagram of the servo-table instrumentation within which is the functional diagram of one axis of a two-degree-of-freedom gyro. The servo-table instrumentation as applied to single-axis gyros is

* More precisely, at one revolution in 23 hr, 56 min, and 4.09 sec; or about 15.04°/hr.

similar in principle. The servo loop is designed for a maximum static gain and stability. Higher-frequency response is not critical.

An essential part of this instrumentation is the table rotation readout for precisely determining the table angle as a function of time. Both electrooptical and electromechanical devices are used. A graduated scale with photocell pickoffs or trip pins with mechanical or magnetic pulse generators may be used to actuate time-interval recorders at discrete table rotation angles. Continuous angle-indicating devices, such

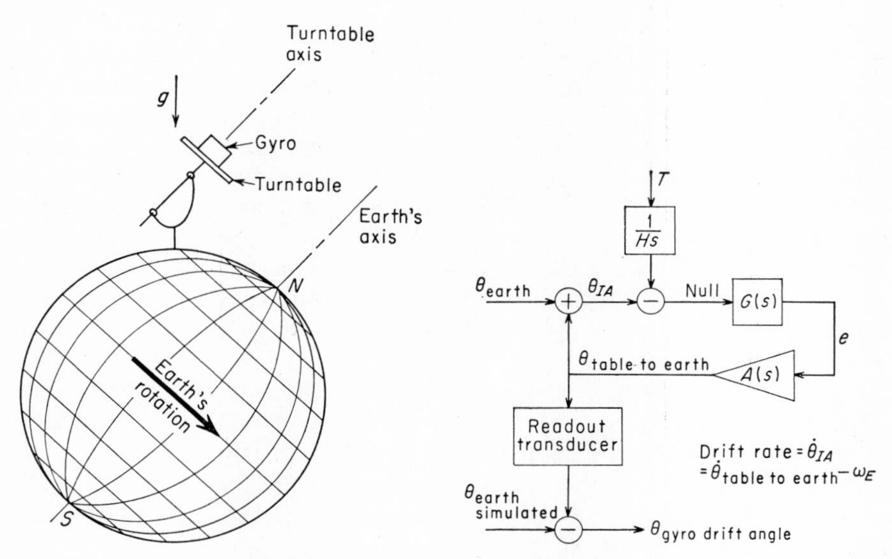

FIG. 12-5. Turntable with axis parallel to earth's axis.

FIG. 12-6. Servo-table instrumentation.

as synchros, inductosyns, or microsyns, may be used. To obtain a direct and precise recording of gyro drift angle as a function of time, the housing of these indicating devices may be driven by a sidereal clock drive at the earth's rate component about the table axis. The rotor attached to the servo-table shaft then produces outputs relative to a stator fixed in inertial space.

This earth's rate cancellation is shown in Fig. 12-6 at the readout. The earth's rate may be eliminated as well at data reduction, particularly with readouts of the time-interval type.

In general,

$$\text{Gyro drift angle} = \Delta\Theta_{IA} = \Delta\Theta_{\text{table to earth}} - \omega_{\text{earth(component)}} \cdot \Delta t$$
$$\text{Gyro drift rate} = \dot{\Theta}_{IA} = \dot{\Theta}_{\text{table to earth}} - \omega_{\text{earth(component)}}$$

Figure 12-7 illustrates a servo-table test installation at the Massachusetts Institute of Technology Instrumentation Laboratory. Figure 12-8 is a line diagram of the servo-table construction. The azimuth rotation freedom, provided in the base, and the tilt rotation freedom, provided in the trunnion, permit the particular orientation of the gyro stabilized

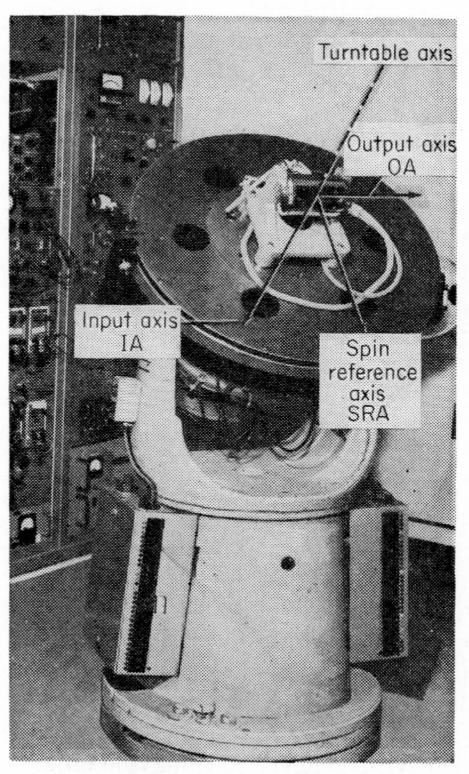

FIG. 12-7. Gyro on a servo turntable. (*Courtesy of M.I.T. Instrumentation Laboratory.*)

turntable axis, as desired. For any test, these adjustments are locked, and rotation occurs about the turntable axis only.

Torque-feedback Instrumentation. In this instrumentation the torque required to cancel gyro drift is supplied electrically. The torquing current is measured and related to drift rate by prior calibration data.

If the gyro housing is fixed angularly in inertial space coordinates, the output signal of the gyro will change because of disturbing torques. This output is amplified and converted to a current which is fed to the gyro torque generator. This control torque then serves to null the output signal. When the nulling transient has expired, the settled value of torquing current is a measure of the gyro drift rate. If an input angular rate is impressed upon the gyro by either the earth or an angular rate table, the torquing current becomes a measurement of the sum of the gyro drift rate and the impressed input rate.

Figure 12-9*a* is the block diagram of torque-feedback instrumentation as applied to one channel of a two-axis or two-degree-of-freedom gyroscope.

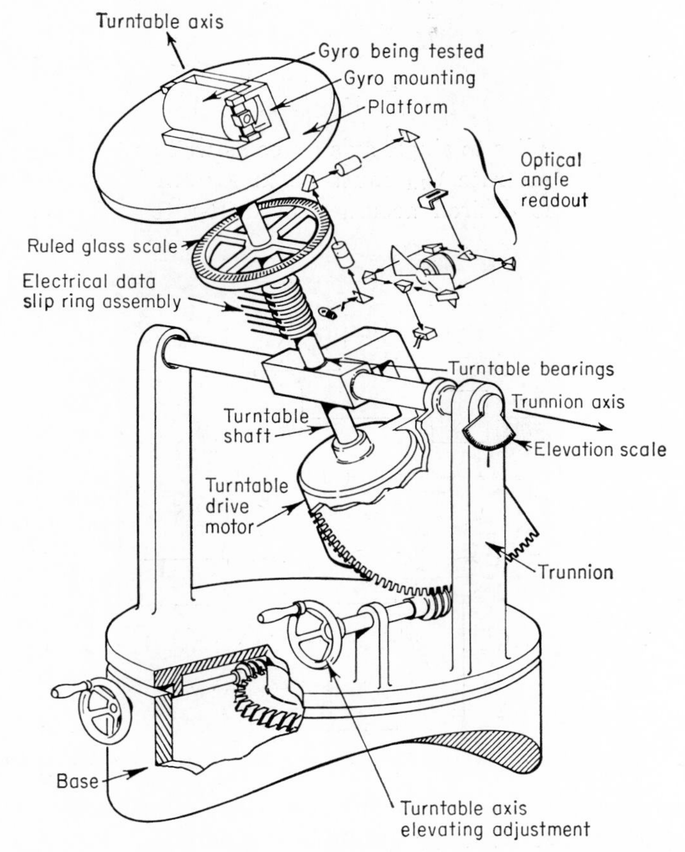

FIG. 12-8. Pictorial schematic of the model D turntable. (*Courtesy of M.I.T. Instrumentation Laboratory.*)

$B(s)$ is the transfer function of the electronic equipment which supplies the torquing current as a result of the gyro error output; T_e is the torque due to the current; T_u is the sum of all the gyro internal torques (systematic plus random); and K_t is the sensitivity of the torquing device.

When no input rotation is supplied, $\Theta_{IA} = 0$. The loop-nulling action provides an average torque balance between the internal gyroscope torques and the applied electrical torque. With applied angular inputs the average null condition is

$$\frac{T_u - T_e}{Hs} - \Theta_{IA} = 0 \tag{12-2}$$

and the equivalent drift rate is

$$\frac{T_u}{H} = \dot{\Theta}_{IA} + \frac{T_e}{H}$$
$$= \dot{\Theta}_{IA} + \frac{K_t i}{H} \tag{12-3}$$

Equation (12-3) applies to single-axis gyros as well as to two-axis gyros. Obviously, the input rate $\dot{\Theta}_{IA}$ must be known with a precision commensurate with the desired accuracy of drift-rate determination. If

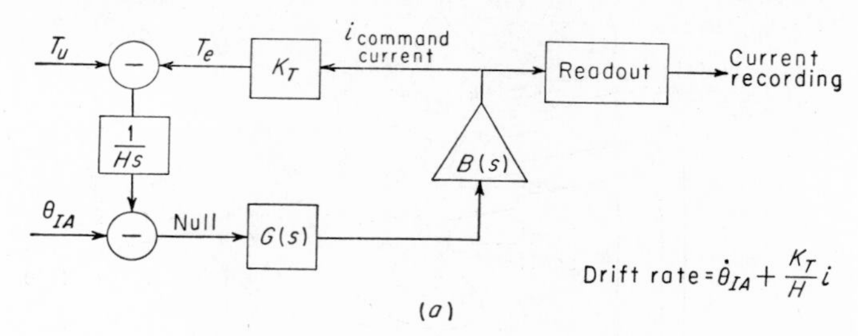

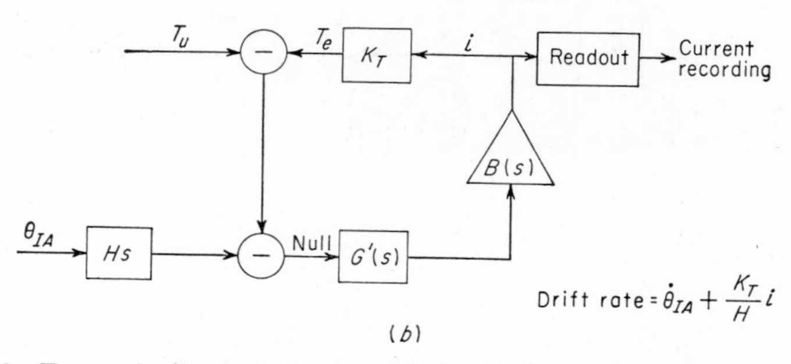

FIG. 12-9. Torque-feedback instrumentation. (*a*) Two-axis gyro; (*b*) single-axis gyro.

$\dot{\Theta}_{IA}$ is due to earth's rotation, the orientation of the input axis (or axes) to the earth must be known precisely.

K_t/H is usually determined as a unified constant by comparing drift-rate changes to changes in control current. In Sec. 12-4 this constant was defined as torquing sensitivity. With torque-feedback instrumentation this calibration is accomplished by varying the input rate $\dot{\Theta}_{IA}$ and noting the change in settled torquing current.

Figure 12-9*b* provides a representation of torque feedback as applied to single-axis gyros. The block diagram shows the torque summation on the output axis between the internal torques, the electrical command torque, and the torque due to forced precession about the input axis. In the absence of an angular input ($\dot{\theta}_{IA} = 0$), the torque balance is independent of the gyroscopic action due to the angular momentum H. Relatively little difference in response would be noted between the

Fig. 12-10. Equatorially mounted rate table. (*American Bosch Arma Corp.*)

wheel's spinning and stationary conditions. The only difference would be the presence of reactions in the output axis bearings when the wheel is spinning. These reactions form a couple about the input axis proportional to the gimbal rotation rate about the output axis, or

$$T_{IA} = Hs\theta_{OA} \tag{12-4}$$

In contrast, torque-feedback response for a two-axis gyro is decidedly affected by shutting off the spin motor. With the spin motor running, the loop is closed through precession. The torque-sensitive and gimbal rotation axes are orthogonal. When the spin motor of a two-axis gyro is shut off, however, they are coincident, and the loop is closed without precession, as in a single-axis gyro.

Figure 12-10 illustrates the electronics and equatorially mounted rate table in use at the Arma Division for gyro testing by torque feedback. In this case the rate-table axis is aligned with the earth's axis. The earth's rate may be canceled by the table rate drive operating at minus earth's rate (−ER). Otherwise the gyro input axis (or axes) may be established orthogonal to the polar-aligned table axis. In both cases no input rates are applied to the gyro, and the settled value of torquing current provides a direct determination of the gyro drift rate.

A variation of torque-feedback instrumentation includes placing the gyro in a servo-table or platform stabilization loop. A rotation pickoff

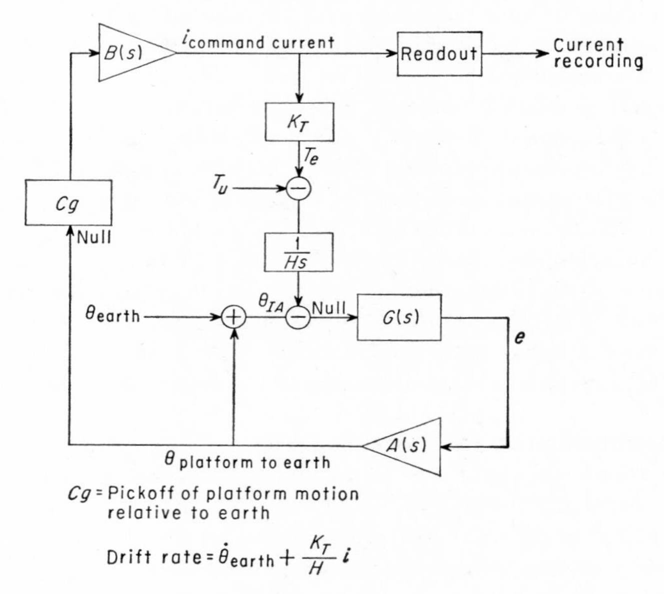

FIG. 12-11. Torque feedback with gyro in stabilization loop.

on the stabilized table is then used to control the torquing current to the gyro to prevent rotation of the table relative to the earth. The current is a measure of the gyro drift rate plus earth's rotation inputs. Figure 12-11 is a block diagram of this system.

Open-loop Instrumentation. The third instrumentation is "open loop," for which Fig. 12-2*a* and *b* applies. Changes in the error output voltage are due to torque or applied input angular rates. The determination of gyro drift from a recording of the output signal involves the transfer function of gyro response to input angular rotation. In two-axis gyros and highly damped single-axis gyros the response is such that a simple constant, the output voltage to input angle sensitivity, is used to relate output signal to gyro drift.

The error output signal is not held to a null. Thus the gyro gimbal (or gimbals) is permitted to rotate relative to the housing. This may generate torques which would not be present in the intended use of the gyro in a nulled closed loop. For example, rotation of the gimbal may wind up flexible power leads or elastic centering members. The relative rotation rate between gimbal and housing may produce damping torques in floated gyros. In a single-axis gyro these torques directly affect the drift measurement, since the output axis is the torque-sensitive axis. In a two-axis gyro these torques create drift about the input axis other than the axis about which the gimbal rotation occurs.

It is desirable to limit the rotation of the gimbal by the application of electrical control torques because of limited gimbal freedom; the torques described above should be limited as well. The gyro is normally held fixed to earth so that a constant earth's rotation rate may be applied about an input axis, and gravity-produced disturbing torques are constant. Thus a constant electric current may be applied to the torquers to hold the gyro output near null. Changes in output will be due either to random drift or instabilities as a function of time or to drift rate caused by the application of a disturbing input such as vibration.

The prime virtue of open-loop instrumentation is that drift-angle data can be obtained with a minimum of test hardware, mainly through the elimination of a servo table and readout. The prime detriment is the potential for creation of extra drifts due to the departure from error signal null.

Test Instrumentation for Two-axis Gyros. The functioning of a two-axis gyro about one input axis is relatively independent of its behavior about the other input axis. Thus, a two-axis gyro may be tested with either identical or different instrumentations on the two axes.

The most common test setups are with servo-table or torque-feedback instrumentations on both axes. Servo table on one axis and torque feedback on the other is also used, particularly when only single-axis servo tables are available.

Open-loop instrumentation can be applied on one axis in conjunction with torque-feedback or servo-table instrumentation on the other axis. This nulls the output about the second axis and limits the torques due to gimbal rotation which would otherwise affect the drift measurement about the open-loop input axis.

When a two-axis gyro is tested on a two-axis servo table, table rotation about the second input axis disturbs the alignment of the first gyro input axis with the first servo-table axis, as is shown in Fig. 12-12. The servos will continue to function to null the gyro output signals at large angles of misalignment. However, torque control may be utilized about the second input axis to limit the drift in order to maintain the desired accuracy of drift measurement about the first axis.

Applicability of Test Instrumentations. There are two basic classes of inertial navigation systems which employ precision stabilization gyros. In one class are the navigation systems on land and sea vehicles, manned aircraft, and long-range cruise missiles (pilotless aircraft). In the other class are the navigation systems utilized to control the initial launch phase of ballistic missiles, satellite vehicles, and space probes.

The first class may be called *long-term systems,* characterized by a mission time in the range of a few hours to a few days. The second class may be called *short-term systems,* which involve a gyro use time of the order of a few minutes. In both classes of systems gyros contribute to

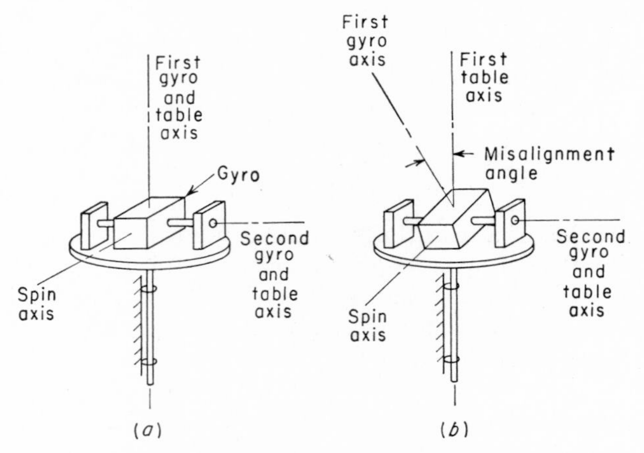

FIG. 12-12. Two-axis gyro on a two-axis servo table. (*a*) Initial position; (*b*) after drift about second axis.

system error by allowing the platform to drift from the reference coordinate system.

In long-term systems the acceleration environment is essentially that due to the earth's gravitational attraction. Vibration and maneuvering accelerations are a small part of the over-all acceleration picture. Therefore, servo-table and open-loop tests over long periods of time (hours to days) in the gyro test laboratory provide an essentially direct indication of the over-all drift-angle deviation of gyros in long-term systems operating in the gravity field. Servo-table instrumentation has found greater applicability than open-loop tests because it provides test conditions most nearly equivalent to actual operating environment and avoids the error drift caused by departure from output null in open-loop testing.

In short-term system applications the high-acceleration environment is not readily duplicated in the gyro test laboratory. It becomes necessary to obtain drift-rate measurements in the gravity field, to determine the dependence of drift rate on acceleration, and then to predict the drift accuracy at accelerations actually encountered in the rocket vehicle. It is necessary to separate out the drift-rate (torque) factors which are either nonacceleration-sensitive or proportional to acceleration or again proportional to the square of acceleration. Torque-feedback instrumentation has found application in this testing, since it provides a convenient measurement proportional to the drift rate. With accurate torquers drift-rate measurements may be taken over short periods of time (minutes) with high precision.

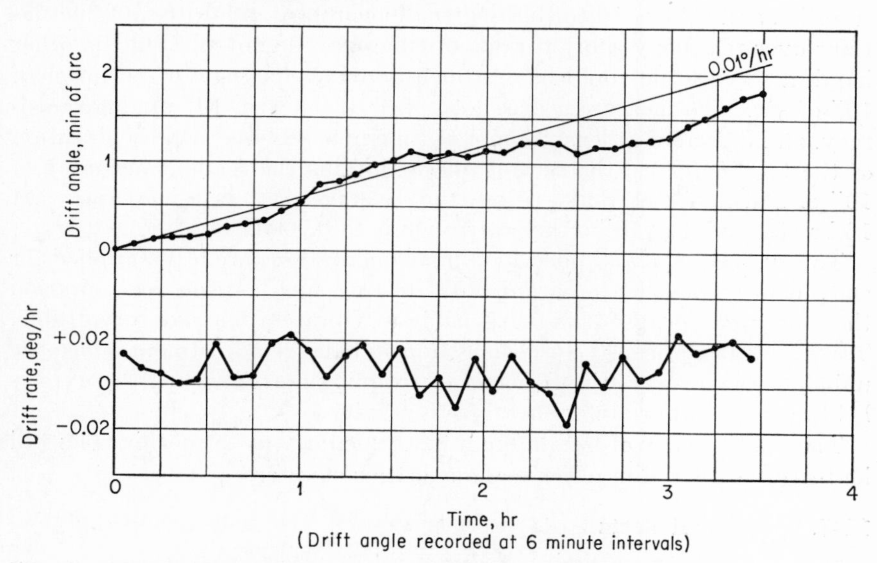

FIG. 12-13. Comparison of drift-angle and drift-rate plots.

The drift angle of a gyro as measured by servo-table or open-loop instrumentation is the time integral of the drift-rate (torque) measurement of torque-feedback instrumentation. This integration is a filtering process which attenuates the effect of high-frequency torque variations on the drift angle. Figure 12-13 is a comparison of drift-angle and drift-rate plots of data taken from a gyro drift test. Note the smoothing in the drift-angle plot.

The long-term drift pattern recorded by a servo table therefore indicates the effect of the average and low-frequency disturbing torques. Torque-feedback instrumentation tends to give equal emphasis in the readout to all frequencies of torque variation. Generally the frequency response is modified in the electronics to deemphasize the higher frequencies to an extent compatible with the desire to note relatively short-term drift variations.

As the duration of a drift test increases, a servo table maintains its angular readout accuracy, therefore increasing the possibility of measuring smaller average drift rates. Torque-feedback instrumentation maintains its drift-rate-measuring accuracy independent of test duration. If it is applied to long-term drift testing, it becomes increasingly difficult, as the run progresses, to integrate torque-feedback current recordings to determine accurately total drift angles or average drift rates.

It is practical to utilize torque feedback for measurements down to 0.01°/hr. The electric current entering the torquer may be readily recorded and calibrated to this degree of accuracy, and drift-rate fluctuations over relatively short periods of time may be noted. On the other hand, a servo table could have a measurement accuracy of better than 10″ of arc. To measure a drift rate of 0.01°/hr with 10″ angular accuracy, an interval of at least 15 min of time must elapse. As the duration of the test increases, the servo table maintains the readout accuracy of 10″ of arc, and the ability to measure average drift rate increases. At 10 hr of operation, 10″ of arc corresponds to 0.0003°/hr.

Torque-feedback and open-loop instrumentations are often applied for convenience. During environmental testing such as that for vibration they are used because it is not feasible to vibrate a massive servo table. Torque feedback is also convenient during balance adjustment, since the unbalance is measured by a value of torquing current when the gyro is held in the appropriate orientation to gravity.

The applicability of the different instrumentations to specific tests will be further explored in other sections of this chapter.

12-7. Functional Tests

In functional testing the inaccuracies and errors of the gyroscope are ignored. Only the nominal output response to the actuating inputs and the variation of the response with the modifying inputs are measured. As a result, the nominal gyro transfer functions may be established.

The prime relationships to be determined are the transfer function between input rotation and output signal and the transfer function between torquing current and input or precession rate when the gyro is operated in a closed loop which nulls the output. The electrical and mechanical cross couplings of two-axis gyros are also important functional parameters.

In order to define clearly the response to the actuating and modifying inputs, and for convenience, individual coefficients which are part of the transfer functions are often measured separately. Among these are pick-off sensitivity, gimbal inertia, elastic restraint, wheel inertia, and damping factor, some of which are determined on subassemblies in the process of fabrication.

The response to input angular rotations is determined by open-loop measurements. The input angle is actuated by either a step input or an angular-oscillation table, and the output is recorded. The angular-oscillation table is usually set for a constant-amplitude sinusoidal motion which is varied in frequency. A direct frequency-response measurement is obtained. In short-time-constant gyros it may be desirable to determine the sensitivity alone. In this case the input angle is changed (not necessarily as a step input), and the steady-state change of output is noted. The input angle is varied over a specified range, and an input angle versus output voltage plot is made. The slope of the best straight line is the sensitivity.

The sensitivity to torquing current is determined in either servo-table or torque-feedback instrumentation. With servo-table instrumentation the prime turntable axis is set vertical so as to avoid any change in the acceleration-sensitive drift rates caused by changing orientation to gravity as the test progresses. The torquing current is set at various constant levels, and the corresponding table rates are measured. A current-versus-precession-rate plot is used to establish the torquing sensitivity. With torque-feedback instrumentation the gyro may be positioned to accept various components of earth's rotation rate, and the corresponding steady-state torquing currents are recorded. Repositioning to obtain the various earth's rotation inputs should be about a vertical axis to keep gravity-produced drift rates constant. For rates greater than that of the earth, a vertical-axis rate table is used.

Nutation characteristics of two-axis gyros are determined with the application of large step changes in torquing current. A high-gain–high-speed oscillograph recording of the pickoffs will reveal the nutation frequency and damping time constant. This test may be run with any of the three instrumentations, since the nutation frequency is above the response region of the closed-loop instrumentations. Since the closed loops are thereby inactive, the gyro is effectively in open loop at the nutation frequency.

12-8. Gravity Testing

In the drift testing of stabilization gyros it is desirable to test initially under ideal conditions, i.e., with a minimum of disturbing inputs, and then to evaluate the nature of the drift as disturbing factors are introduced, one at a time or in desired combination.

Since the testing is conducted predominately in an engineering test laboratory on the surface of the earth, one must always contend with at least two disturbing inputs: earth's rotation and the gravitational attraction of the earth. During this testing with a minimum of disturbing inputs, the gyro orientation with respect to gravity may be changed in order to separate the drift-rate factors which are independent of acceleration from those which are acceleration-sensitive. Hence, the name "gravity testing."

The gravitational acceleration vector and the earth's rate vector form an angle in the meridian plane which is the complement of the latitude angle. Hence, a change in orientation with respect to gravity may involve a change in earth's rate input. For each position of the gyro the components of gravity and earth's rotation rate on the principal gyro axes must be taken into consideration.

Earth's Rotation. The earth's rotation rate is represented by a vector directed from south to north, parallel to the earth's polar axis. This

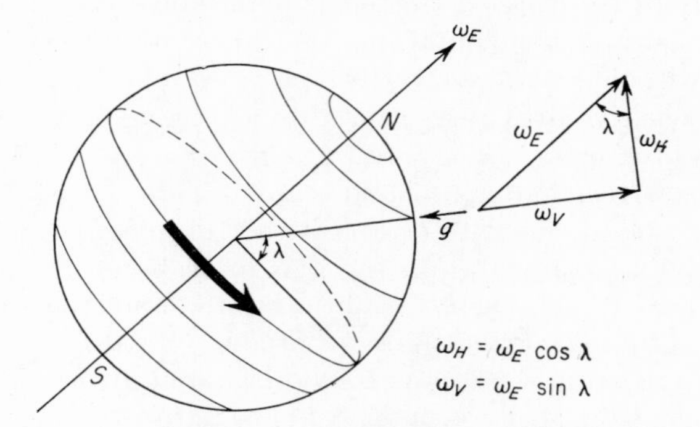

FIG. 12-14. The components of earth's rotation rate.

vector may be resolved directly into components about the gyro input axes. However, in many cases it is convenient to resolve the earth's rate into vertical and horizontal components and then to determine the portions of these components along the input axis or axes.

As illustrated in Fig. 12-14, the vertical component of earth's rotation is

$$\omega_V = \omega_E \sin \lambda$$

and the horizontal component is

$$\omega_H = \omega_E \cos \lambda$$

where ω_E = earth's sidereal rotation rate
λ = local latitude

The horizontal component of earth's rate ω_H is a vector directed from south to north.

Gyros are sensitive to angular rates applied about input axes only. They do not respond to rotation rates about either the spin or the output axis. In single-axis gyros only one input axis is involved, and this is designated IA. The other axes are the spin axis and output axis, and these are designated SA and OA, respectively. In two-axis gyros the three principal axes are the spin axis and two input axes. The spin axis is designated SA and the input axes are designated X and Y, where X is the inner axis and Y is the outer axis, as shown in Fig. 12-15.

Gyros are often operated and tested with a principal axis aligned with the vertical. Consider the single-axis gyro. If the IA is vertical, ω_V is an input. If the IA is horizontal and directed north-south, ω_H is an input. If the IA is horizontal and east-west, there is no input due to earth's rotation. The latter orientation is one in which the IA is orthogonal to the earth's axis. Any orientation with the IA orthogonal to the earth's axis eliminates an input due to earth's rotation. However, IA being horizontal and east-west is the only orientation in which gravity may be directed along a principal axis, namely, the spin or output axis, without the effect of earth's rotation.

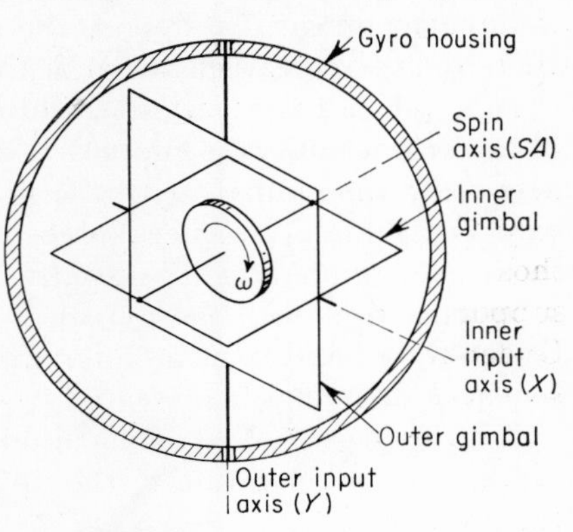

FIG. 12-15. Two-degree-of-freedom gyro gimbal diagram.

Likewise, if an input axis of a two-axis gyro, for example, the X axis, is positioned horizontally and east-west, there will not be any earth's rotation effect on this axis. However, if in addition a principal axis is to be vertical, either the spin or Y axis should be vertical. The horizontal earth's rate component ω_H is an input about the Y axis when the spin axis is vertical, and the vertical earth's rate component ω_V is an input about the Y axis when the Y axis is vertical. The only orientations in which earth's rate is not an input to a two-axis gyro are those in which both input axes are orthogonal to the earth's axis. This is equivalent to the spin axis parallel to the earth's axis and is not a case of a vertical principal axis.

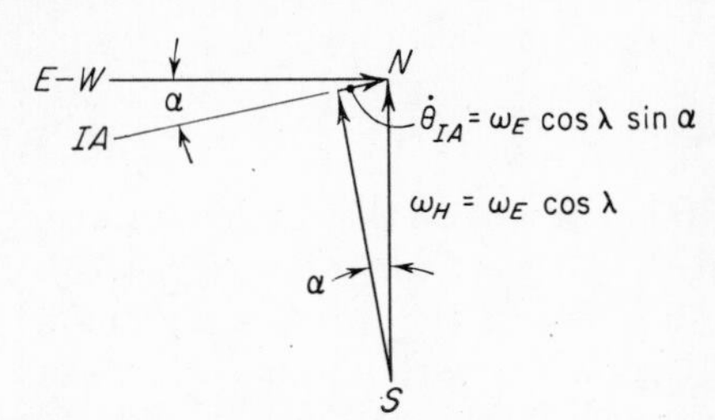

FIG. 12-16. Deviation of input axis from east-west about the vertical.

Consider again the position with an input axis horizontal and east-west. Be this a single-axis or a two-axis gyro, there is no effect due to earth's rotation about this axis. As the gyro is rotated about a vertical axis, the horizontal component of earth's rate ω_H is introduced about the horizontal input axis as follows:

$$\dot{\theta}_{IA} = \omega_H \sin\alpha = \omega_E \cos\lambda \sin\alpha \tag{12-5}$$

where α is the angle of rotation from the position in which the input axis is directed east-west. This situation is shown in Fig. 12-16 and has been discussed because of its frequent occurrence in both application and testing of gyros.

The Gyro in the Gravity Field. When a gyro is located on the earth's surface, the gimbal or gimbals are pulled downward by the gravitational attraction of the earth. The gimbal support system exerts a thrust which is directed upward to oppose the gravitational pull on the gimbals and thereby prevents acceleration of the gyro toward the center of the earth.

In a vehicle, say a missile, which is accelerated upward by the thrust of the engine, the gyro support system also provides an upward thrust to accelerate the gimbals with the vehicle. Therefore, a gyro on a laboratory test table experiences forces (and torques) in the same direction as those encountered due to upward vehicle accelerations. If the test table support is removed, the gyro will fall freely with an acceleration of $1g$. Under these conditions no internal forces exist, and only nonacceleration-sensitive drifts may be created.

If a thrust is applied which accelerates the gyro upward relative to the earth at an acceleration a, the upward thrust of the support system on the gimbals is

$$F = M(a + g)$$

where M = mass of gimbal including wheel
a = net upward acceleration relative to earth
g = acceleration due to gravity

In free fall

$$a = -g$$
$$F = 0$$

On the earth's surface

$$a = 0$$
$$F = Mg$$

If the two forces acting on the gyro gimbal at rest on the earth's surface, namely, the gravitational pull Mg and the support force F, are not collinear, a gravity-sensitive torque is produced. If the forces act along a principal axis of elasticity, which usually coincides with a principal axis of the gyro because of symmetry of construction, the torques are due to unbalance alone and do not include compliance effects. For this reason and for convenience, the gyro unbalances are usually identified along three mutually perpendicular axes which coincide with the principal axes. Drift rates due to unbalances are most directly identified as a result of the application of acceleration along the principal axes. Note that the torque due to an acceleration along a principal gyro axis acting on an unbalance is about an axis orthogonal to both the acceleration and the unbalance direction.* If the acceleration is in a direction other than along a principal axis, the components of acceleration along the principal axes are computed, and the effects of these acceleration components on the drift rates due to the unbalances are computed separately and then superimposed. Table 12-1 is a summary of the drift-rate factors produced by accelerations along principal axes acting on unbalances along these principal axes.

TABLE 12-1. DRIFT RATES DUE TO UNBALANCE

Gyro type	Acceleration along	Drift rate about	Due to unbalance along
Single-axis	Spin axis (SA)	Input axis (IA)	Input axis (IA)
	Input axis (IA)	Input axis (IA)	Spin axis (SA)
	Output axis (OA)	None	None
Two-axis	Spin axis (SA)	Inner axis (X)	Inner axis* (X)
		Outer axis (Y)	Outer axis* (Y)
	Outer axis (Y)	Outer axis (Y)	Spin axis† (SA)
	Inner axis (X)	Inner axis (X)	Spin axis‡ (SA)

* See Fig. 12-15. Unbalance along Y is that of the inner gimbal alone. Unbalance along X is that of both gimbals together.
† Unbalance of the inner gimbal alone.
‡ Unbalance of both gimbals together.

When the total acceleration is in a direction other than along a principal axis, drift rates due to compliance may result in addition to those due to the unbalances along the principal axes. To produce a drift rate due to compliance, the acceleration must have components along the spin axis and an input axis. The torque due to the acceleration along these two principal axes is about the third principal axis. Table 12-2 is a summary of the drift-rate factors produced by accelerations acting on compliances.

Gravity-constant Tests. Gravity-constant testing is a form of gyro testing in the gravity field on the earth's surface. Constant-gravity testing implies that during any test the orientation of the gyro with respect to the vertical is unchanged. Gravity-constant tests permit the direct measurement on nonacceleration-sensitive drift rates, measurements of unbalance, and stability and random drift studies involving specific gyro parameters, such as spin-axis balance. In addition, a gyro to be used in a level platform is best tested in the constant-gravity position which nearly duplicates its condition of use.

The combination of the results of three tests, each one with a different principal axis oriented vertically, yields a convenient determination of

* The unbalance along a principal axis means a separation of center of mass and center of support along that axis.

the drift-producing parameters other than compliance. If a torque-sensitive axis (the OA of a single-axis gyro, either input axis of a two-axis gyro) is vertical, the resulting tilt drift rate about a horizontal input axis is the nonacceleration-sensitive drift rate, since unbalances cannot create torques about a vertical axis. When another principal axis is vertical, the torque-sensitive axis is horizontal, and the total drift rate is due to

TABLE 12-2. DRIFT RATES DUE TO COMPLIANCE*

Gyro type	Acceleration along	Drift rate about	Due to difference in compliances along
Single-axis..........	Any principal axis	None	None
	Spin axis (SA) and input axis (IA)	Input axis (IA)	Spin axis (SA) and input axis (IA)
	Output axis (OA) and spin axis (SA)	None	None
	Output axis (OA) and input axis (IA)	None	None
Two-axis...........	Any principal axis	None	None
	Spin axis (SA) and inner axis (X)	Inner axis (X)	Spin axis (SA) and inner axis (X)
	Spin axis (SA) and outer axis (Y)	Outer axis (Y)	Spin axis (SA) and outer axis (Y)
	Inner axis (X) and outer axis (Y)	None	None

* It is assumed that the principal axes of elasticity coincide with the principal gyro axes. This implies that an acceleration along any principal axis results in deflection of the center of mass relative to the center of support along that principal axis.

the sum of the nonacceleration-sensitive drift rate and the drift rate due to an unbalance. Obviously, the difference in the drift rates measured in the two orientations is a drift rate due to unbalance.

Consider first a single-axis gyro. To measure the nonacceleration-sensitive drift rate, the OA is vertical and the IA is horizontal. It is desirable to orient the IA east-west. In this orientation there is no component of earth's rotation about the IA. If a servo table is being utilized, motions about the turntable axis aligned to the input axis result in a change in orientation with respect to gravity. However, these changes are small over long periods of time for a gyro of high quality because of the low drift rate and the absence of earth's rotation effects. In a case where rotation of the turntable results in an undesirable change of orientation to gravity, torque-feedback instrumentation has merit, since the gyro housing is held fixed to the earth. For example, the variations in nonacceleration-sensitive drift rate of a single-axis gyro may be studied over extended periods of time by continuous chart and pen recording of the torque-feedback current. Orienting the IA east-west reduces the current level to that of the drift-rate equivalent only [see Eq. (12-3)] and increases the measuring accuracy.

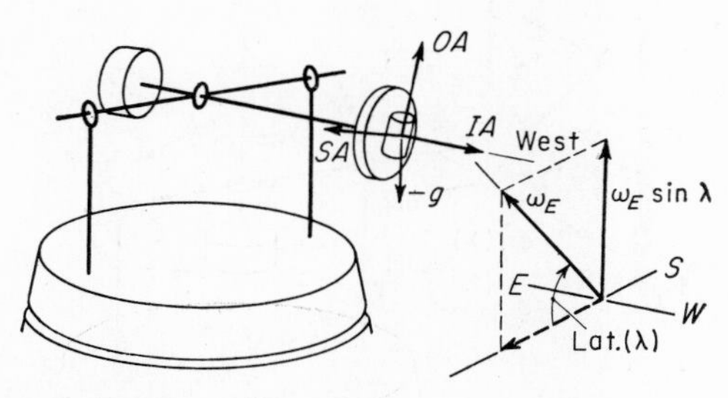

FIG. 12-17. East-west axis servo-table test:

A. Test arrangement:
 Turntable axis: Horizontal and east-west.
 Gyro axes: IA parallel to turntable axis. SA and OA in vertical plane.
 Closed loop: Stabilization loop from gyro signal generator to turntable drive.

B. Test conditions:
 Earth's rate: No component parallel to IA.
 Gravity: Components along SA and OA, depending upon turntable rotation angle.

C Ideal performance: Turntable stationary for any turntable rotation angle.

D. Value of test: Convenient test since turntable rate equals drift rate. With turntable rotation angle such that OA is vertical, there is no torque-producing component of acceleration perpendicular to OA. With OA horizontal, gyro is subjected to full gravity component along SA; useful to evaluate unbalance weight shifts along IA. These two positions allow the separation of SA acceleration-sensitive components of drift from nonacceleration-sensitive components. (*Courtesy of M.I.T. Instrumentation Laboratory.*)

When the spin axis is vertical, the drift rate is due to the sum of the nonacceleration-sensitive drift rate and that due to the unbalance along the input axis. Above considerations concerning the use of servo-table and torque-feedback instrumentations and the orientation of the IA east-west apply equally to this test. Figure 12-17 illustrates the servo-table testing of a single-axis gyro with the input axis east-west.

When the IA is vertical, the drift rate is due to the sum of the nonacceleration-sensitive drift rate and the one due to spin-axis unbalance. However, the vertical component of earth's rate is being applied as an input rate. Thus the torque-feedback current would correspond primarily to the earth's vertical rate, with the addition of the relatively small gyro drift rate. Small percentage errors in measurement caused by torquer primary excitation variation and recorder scaling error create large errors in drift-rate measurement.

However, this constant-gravity test may be performed with a vertical-axis servo table, as shown in Fig. 12-18. Rotation of the turntable about the vertical axis does not disturb the orientation to gravity. A perfect gyro (zero drift rate) would result in a table rotation rate equal to

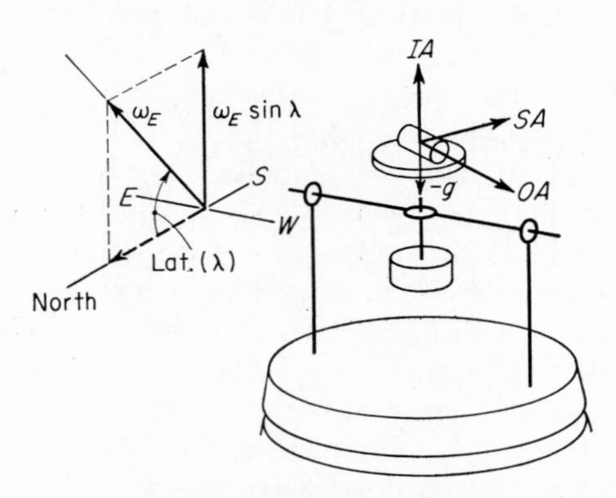

FIG. 12-18. Vertical input axis servo-table test:

A. Test arrangement:
Turntable axis: Vertical.
Gyro axes: IA parallel to turntable axis. SA and OA in horizontal plane.
Closed loop: Stabilization loop from gyro signal generator to turntable drive.

B. Test conditions:
Earth's rate: Sine latitude component along IA.
Gravity: Direction along IA.

C. Ideal performance: Turntable rotates at constant angular velocity of one earth's rate times the sine of the test-station latitude.

D. Value of test: Subjects gyro to constant-gravity component along IA. Useful to evaluate unbalance weight shifts along SA. (*Courtesy of M.I.T. Instrumentation Laboratory.*)

the vertical component of earth's rate ω_V. The difference in table rate from the earth's rate vertical component is equal to the gyro drift rate. This drift rate is the sum of the nonacceleration-sensitive drift rate and that due to spin-axis unbalance. Since in a precision gyro the drift rate due to spin-axis unbalance is far more variable than the nonacceleration-sensitive drift rate, vertical-axis servo-table tests are useful for extended studies of variations in spin-axis unbalance. In addition, this orientation corresponds to the application of the azimuth gyro in a level (Schuler tuned) platform, and this test is used to determine over-all azimuth drift accuracy for application to long-term navigation systems.

Similar techniques may be applied to a two-axis gyro, except that the drift rates about each of the two axes are measured at each of the three orientations with a principal axis vertical. A difficulty is incurred in that a component of earth's rotation rate is applied to at least one input axis for each position in which gravity is along a principal gyro axis.

For example, to measure nonacceleration-sensitive drift rates about one axis of a two-axis gyro, this axis, say X, should be horizontal and east-west, with the other input axis, Y, vertical. If torque feedback is applied, the current recorded as an indication of X axis drift ideally represents the X axis nonacceleration-sensitive drift rate. Simultaneously, however, the Y axis torque control current reflects the sum of the Y axis nonacceleration-sensitive drift, the drift rate due to spin-axis unbalance of the inner gimbal, and the vertical component of earth's rotation rate. The earth's rate component is typically orders of magnitude greater than the nonacceleration-sensitive drift of a precision gyro. Consequently, a small percentage of cross coupling from the torquer, which reflects the vertical component of earth's rate to the torquer on the other axis, can cause significant errors in the measurement of the nonacceleration-sensitive tilt drift. For example, with an earth's rate component of 10°/hr and a 1 per cent torquer cross coupling, a drift-measuring error of 0.1°/hr results. The measurement of the gyro drift rates can be accomplished without the earth's rotation effect through the use of the equatorially mounted rate table shown in Fig. 12-10. This table holds the gyro fixed in inertial space coordinates when it is driven at a rate equal and opposite to the earth's sidereal rate. The gyro is therefore rotated with respect to gravity at about 15°/hr. If the gyro is mounted to the table such that at one point the Y input axis is vertical, the torque-feedback currents recorded at that instant are the required measurements without earth's rate. However, continuous study of variations of either nonacceleration-sensitive drift or spin-axis balance is not possible with this setup because the gyro rotates relative to gravity. In effect, this is no longer a gravity-constant test.

When a vertical-axis servo table is applied to a two-axis gyro, one input axis, say Y, is vertical and the other, X, is horizontal. As the turntable rotates about the vertical due to the vertical component of earth's rate plus the gyro drift rate, the X axis orientation changes. If it is initially east-west, where no earth's rate is impressed, it will move so as to pick up a portion of the horizontal component of earth's rate, as per Eq. (12-5). If a two-axis servo table is being applied such that the X axis is also in servo-table instrumentation, the horizontal earth's rate effect will cause tilting about the X axis. Since in a gravity-constant test it is desired to prevent tilting, leveling-torque control must be applied either in conjunction with the servo table or in the form of torque feedback where the gyro housing is locked to the vertical-axis turntable about both axes. In either case this leveling torque varies as a sinusoidal function of the rotation about the vertical turntable axis. Cross coupling of this torque to the other torquer axis affects the measured drift rate about the vertical axis except when the X input axis is east-west.

Similar considerations apply when gravity-constant tests are run on a two-axis gyro with the spin or the X axis vertical.

A very useful orientation for gravity-constant studies of stability and random drift of two-axis gyros is realized with the spin axis aligned with the polar axis. In this orientation, the earth does not apply an input rate to either axis. If one input axis is horizontal, only nonacceleration-sensitive drift and drift due to the unbalance along this input axis are present. The drift on the other axis is nonacceleration-sensitive, due to the unbalances along this and the spin axis, and a compliance torque in turn, due to the acceleration in the plane of the spin axis and this axis.

Gravity-varied Tests. Gravity-varied testing is a form of gyro testing on the earth's surface in which the orientation of the gyro with respect to gravity changes continuously. A complete test consists of at least one rotation of the gyro in the gravity field. Gravity-varied tests permit the measurement of the various gyro drift factors (nonacceleration-sensitive drift, drift due to unbalances, drift due to compliance) as does a series of gravity-constant tests. The advantage of gravity-varied tests over a combination of constant-gravity tests is in the continuous nature of the data obtained. If a gyro error parameter should shift during a series of constant-gravity tests, it need not be immediately apparent. Analysis of the data may either be confused or give fallacious results. During gravity-varied tests the drift rate should be related to table angle in specific patterns, as will be shown in the following paragraphs. Oddities in this pattern will give an immediate indication of gyro abnormalities. In addition, the gyro drift is observed over a continuous and wide range of acceleration orientations, which makes this a more thorough test.

Studies of gyro drifts in a fixed gyro orientation, such as with spin axis horizontal, may not reveal random drifts due to loose parts free to shift along the spin axis. Gravity-varied tests are therefore a more stringent and thorough means of random-drift evaluation. Such tests are also used to evaluate the random-drift characteristics of gyros to be used in untorqued long-term navigators in which they tumble in the earth's gravitational field owing to the rotation of the earth relative to the space-fixed gyros.

The most common forms of gravity-varied tests involve a test table with a turntable axis parallel to the earth's axis. This may be applied to single-axis and two-axis gyros equally. The test methods are usually as follows:

1. Single-axis gyros
   a. Servo table with input axis parallel to earth's polar axis.
   b. Torque feedback with output axis parallel to earth's polar axis. Table is driven at a multiple of earth's rate.
2. Two-axis gyros
   a. Servo table with one input axis parallel to earth's polar axis. Other input axis orthogonal to earth's polar axis with either servo-table or torque-feedback instrumentation on this axis.
   b. Torque feedback on both axes with spin axis parallel to earth's axis. Table is driven at a multiple of earth's rate.

As shown in Fig. 12-19, the acceleration due to gravity along the table axis, which is parallel to the earth's axis, is constant for all table angular positions at $a = g \sin \lambda$, where λ is the latitude angle. Since a principal axis of the gyro is aligned to the table axis, the other principal axes are orthogonal to the table axis, and the accelerations along these axes are, respectively,

$$a_1 = g \cos \lambda \sin \Theta \qquad \text{first axis}$$

and

$$a_2 = g \cos \lambda \cos \Theta \qquad \text{second axis}$$

where Θ is the table rotation angle from a starting position, with the first of these two principal axes oriented horizontally.

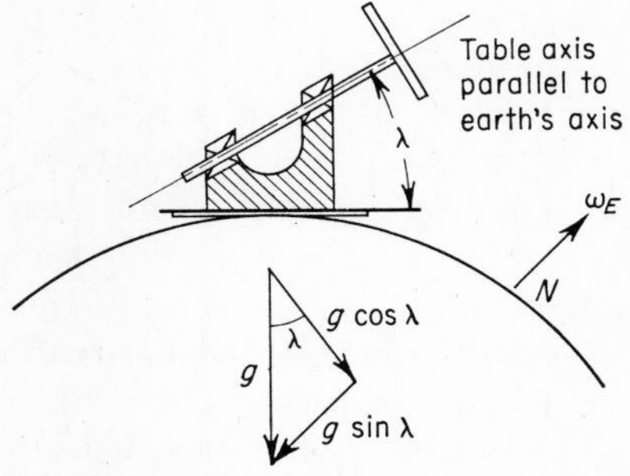

Fig. 12-19. The components of gravity relative to the earth's axis.

Single-axis Servo Tests. When a single-axis gyro is tested on a servo table with an input axis parallel to the earth's axis, as shown in Fig. 12-20, the table rotates about this input axis relative to the earth at the sidereal earth's rate plus the gyro drift rate. For an ideal gyro the table completes one revolution in 23.94 hr. This is equivalent to 15.04°/hr. The actual rate will differ from this by the gyro drift rate. This drift rate is a function of the table angle due to the varying direction of gravity with respect to the gyro.

Consider the drift-rate factors during a servo-table test in which an input axis is parallel to the earth's axis (IA ∥ EA). The constant component of acceleration along the table axis acting on the spin-axis unbalance results in a constant drift-rate component which adds to the non-acceleration-sensitive drift rate $\dot{\Theta}_0$. This component is

$$\dot{\Theta}_{SA} = \frac{1}{H} \cdot U_{SA} g \sin \lambda \qquad (12\text{-}6)$$

where $\dot{\Theta}_{SA}$ is the drift rate due to spin-axis unbalance and U_{SA} denotes the unbalance along the spin axis. If zero table angle is chosen when the spin axis is horizontal, the drift rate due to input axis unbalance is

$$\dot{\Theta}_{IA} = \frac{1}{H} \cdot U_{IA} g \cos \lambda \sin \Theta \tag{12-7}$$

where $\dot{\Theta}_{IA}$ is drift rate due to input axis unbalance, U_{IA} is unbalance along the input axis, and Θ represents the table rotation angle from a position in which the spin axis is horizontal.

This drift-rate component is a first harmonic of the table rotation

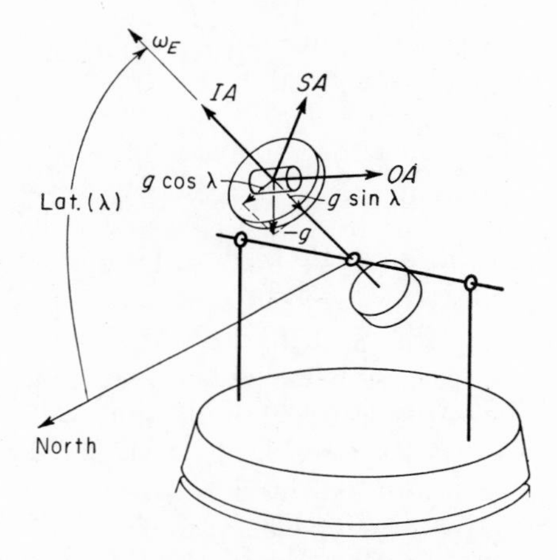

FIG. 12-20. Input axis parallel to earth's axis servo-table test:

A. Test arrangement:
- Turntable axis: Parallel to earth's axis.
- Gyro axes: IA parallel to turntable axis. SA and OA in slant plane, perpendicular to turntable axis.
- Closed loop: Stabilization loop from gyro signal generator to turntable drive.

B. Test conditions:
- Earth's rate: Earth's rate all along IA.
- Gravity: Sine latitude component along IA. Cosine latitude component resolved along SA and OA, depending upon turntable rotation angle.

C. Ideal performance: Turntable rotates at constant angular velocity of one earth's rate for any turntable rotation angle.

D. Value of test:
1. This arrangement subjects the gyro to acceleration components along all three axes. The components along SA and OA are variable, depending upon turntable rotation.
2. Since, in this position, the ideal turntable rate is the full earth's rate, it is the quickest arrangement for tumbling the gyro in the gravity field under platform-stabilization conditions. (*Courtesy of M.I.T. Instrumentation Laboratory.*)

angle. The drift rate due to compliance is

$$\dot{\Theta}_C = \frac{M^2(C_{SA} - C_{IA})}{H} g^2 \sin \lambda \cos \lambda \sin \Theta = \frac{M^2}{2H}(C_{SA} - C_{IA})g^2 \sin 2\lambda \sin \Theta \quad (12\text{-}8)$$

where C_{SA} = effective compliance along spin axis
C_{IA} = effective compliance along input axis
M = mass supported by compliances

This drift-rate component is also a first harmonic of the table rotation angle.

How is the constant nonacceleration-sensitive drift to be separated from the constant drift due to spin-axis unbalance, and how is the first harmonic drift due to input axis unbalance to be separated from that due to compliance? This is accomplished by a pair of "24-hr" tests during which the IA is directed along the table axis in both tests. During the second test the positive input axis direction is opposite to that during the first test. The change in orientation between the two tests is accomplished by a 180° rotation of the gyro about its output axis with respect to the table. The polarity of the fixed table rotation component due to nonacceleration-sensitive drift and the first harmonic component due to compliance torques will reverse between the two tests. The table rotation rate components due to spin axis and input axis unbalance do not change between the two tests. Separation of the fixed and first harmonic components and addition and subtraction of the similar components of the two tests result in separation of each of the four drift-rate components.

IA ∥ EA (input axis parallel to earth axis) servo-table tests are also utilized for random-drift studies, particularly on gyros employed in certain types of inertial navigation systems in which one of the gyros has its input axis parallel to the earth's axis and the stabilization gyros tumble about this axis. These random-drift studies can be run simply by operating over successive 24-hr periods and by comparing the drift-rate patterns for each of the complete rotations of the table.

Another random-drift measurement technique employs drift-compensating electrical command torques which are programed as a function of the table angle. The programing is based on the data of a previous 24-hr run. During the test with programed compensation any deviation of the table from earth's rate is considered an error due to random-drift variations. This technique of drift compensation may actually be utilized in the navigation system.

Single-axis "Tumbling Tests." Tumbling tests use torque-feedback instrumentation and a rate table. The table axis is aligned with the earth's axis. The input axis is positioned orthogonal to the table axis, as shown in Fig. 12-21. This eliminates both the earth's rate and the test table rotation as inputs to the gyro.

The test table is driven at a rate which is a multiple of the earth's rate. Rates of 8, 10, 16, and 24 times earth's rate are common. One revolution

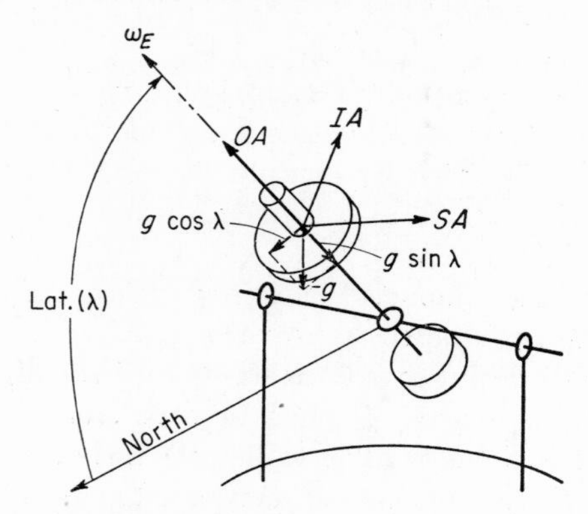

FIG. 12-21. Tumbling test, torque feedback:

A. Test arrangement:
- Turntable axis: Parallel to earth's axis.
- Gyro axes: IA and SA perpendicular to turntable axis.
- Closed loop: Feedback loop from gyro signal generator to gyro torque generator.
- Turntable drive: Turntable rotated about turntable axis by constant-speed drive at some convenient rate.

B. Test conditions:
- Earth's rate: No component parallel to IA.
- Gravity: Cosine latitude component resolved along IA and SA, depending upon turntable rotation angle.

C. Ideal performance:
- Recorded current fed back to torque generator is zero.

D. Value of test:
1. Provides continuous torque-generator current readout of drift rate.
2. Provides fast information on drift characteristics with gyro tumbling in the gravity field. (Ten times earth's rate is a common turntable constant speed used.)
3. Provides variable acceleration components along both IA and SA. Is very useful, therefore, for providing data in studying all components of drift. (*Courtesy of M.I.T. Instrumentation Laboratory.*)

is therefore completed within a period in the range of 1 to 3 hr, as opposed to 24 hr for servo-table tests. The torque feedback maintains the error pickoff output at null. A continuous recording of the torquing current is a direct measure of drift rate as a function of table angle.

For this test the gyro could be positioned to any number of orientations in which the input axis is orthogonal to the table (and earth's) axis. The most frequently used orientation with single-axis gyros is the output axis parallel to the table axis. In this orientation alone the various drift-rate factors may be resolved by harmonic analysis without the need for a second test with a 180° reversal of orientation.

If zero table angle is chosen with the spin axis horizontal, the acceleration along the spin axis is

$$a_{SA} = g \cos \lambda \sin \Theta \tag{12-9}$$

The acceleration along the input axis is given by

$$a_{IA} = g \cos \lambda \cos \Theta \tag{12-10}$$

and the drift-rate component due to spin-axis unbalance is

$$\dot{\Theta}_{SA} = \frac{1}{H} U_{SA} g \cos \lambda \cos \Theta \tag{12-11}$$

The drift-rate component due to input axis unbalance may be written

$$\dot{\Theta}_{IA} = \frac{1}{H} U_{IA} g \cos \lambda \sin \Theta \tag{12-12}$$

The drift-rate component due to compliance becomes

$$\dot{\Theta}_{C} = \frac{M^2}{2H} (C_{SA} - C_{IA}) g^2 \cos^2 \lambda \sin 2\Theta \tag{12-13}$$

Thus, a separation of the fixed component, the two orthogonal first harmonics, and the second harmonic components of torquing current leads directly to values of nonacceleration-sensitive drift and drifts due to spin-axis unbalance, input axis unbalance, and compliance.

Tumbling tests provide a relatively rapid means of determining the gyro error parameters with continuous observation of the drift-rate characteristics. The precision of the table-rate drive is not too important, since the gyro input axis is perpendicular to the table axis and hence the gyro will not sense fluctuations in table rate. The slower rates (8 or 10 times earth's rate) are used in order to relax the alignment requirements. For example, if the table rotates opposite to the earth's rotation at 8 times earth's rate, a net rate in space of $7 \times 15 = 105°/\text{hr}$ results. If the gyro is misaligned relative to the table by 1′ of arc, a constant input to the gyro of 0.03°/hr is encountered. The error rate for a constant misalignment is proportional to the net table rate in space and increases with more rapid tumbling. This error does not affect the measurement of unbalance or compliance, however. Only the nonacceleration-sensitive drift-rate measurement is affected.

Two-axis Servo Tests. In two-axis gyro servo-table tests one input axis is aligned to a turntable axis parallel to the earth's axis. The drift-rate patterns on this axis are identical to those for the single-axis gyro servo-table test, described previously, and a 180° reversal is required for resolution of the drift-rate factors.

The second input axis is orthogonal to the earth's axis, and for a perfect gyro zero table motion results. If torque feedback is used on the second axis, no earth's rate or table rate is measured. The drift patterns on this input axis are similar to those for the single-axis gyro with output axis parallel to the earth's axis. The axis about which the drift-producing torque is developed is parallel to the table axis and corresponds to the output axis of the single-axis gyro.

Note that the drift rate on the second input axis must be low in order to maintain the alignment between the first gyro input axis and the first servo-table axis. The servos will continue to function at large angles (even as high as 30°) of misalignment. However, the first axis drift reading will no longer correspond to the drift of the gyro about the input axis. Also, a few degrees of rotation could result in significant aberrations in the drift patterns owing to the unusual changes in orientation to gravity taking place during the test.

For these reasons, it may be desirable to employ torque-feedback instrumentation on the second drift axis. Then the gyro housing is clamped about the axis so that alignment is maintained.

Two-axis Tumbling Tests. Tumbling tests on two-axis gyros must be conducted with the spin axis aligned with the table axis which is in turn parallel to the earth's axis. This is the only orientation in which the gyro will not respond to the table and earth motions.

Due to the orientation to gravity, the drift components due to the nonacceleration-sensitive torques and input axis unbalances will be fixed during the test. The drift components due to the spin-axis unbalances (one due to unbalance of the inner gimbal and the other to unbalance of the combination of inner and outer gimbals) and the drifts due to compliance will be first harmonics of the table rotation. Separation and identification of the drift-rate components are accomplished via a pair of tests between which the spin-axis orientation is reversed by a 180° rotation about an input axis. The drifts due to the unbalances reverse in polarity between the two tests. The polarity of the nonacceleration-sensitive drifts and the drifts due to compliance is unchanged between the two tests.

Eight drift components are determined (four for each axis): nonacceleration-sensitive drift, drift due to input axis unbalance, drift due to spin-axis unbalance, and drift due to compliance.

12-9. Environmental Testing

The discussion of gravity testing was limited to tests with disturbing inputs held to a minimum. During gravity tests three environmental factors are always present. These are the gravitational attraction of the earth, the earth's rotation, and the passage of time.

Environmental testing is the extension of gravity testing to evaluate performance as affected by a wide range of additional disturbing inputs. These are chosen in accordance with the prediction of the typical and extreme environments to be encountered in the application of the gyro.

For convenience in gyro testing, the environmental conditions may be separated into four groups:

1. Disturbing inputs convenient to gravity testing
2. Nonoperative environmental inputs
3. Operative environmental inputs
4. Limiting environmental inputs

Disturbing Inputs Convenient to Gravity Testing. Certain environmental inputs are conveniently applied to gyros while they are instrumented into the systems used for gravity testing. The effects of these inputs are determined by comparing the results of gravity tests with and without these inputs applied.

One such input is temperature. Precision gyros require temperature control to sustain a stable mass balance, to maintain buoyancy in floated gyros, and to minimize the effects of temperature transients and gradients. Temperature conditions may be readily changed while the gyro is mounted on either a servo or tumbling table. The average temperature of the gyro may be altered, that of the surrounding air may be changed in a suitable enclosure, and temperature gradients and transients may be induced on the gyro housing. The effect on drift rate is noted while these temperature inputs are applied.

Other disturbances which can be similarly handled are input power variations, particularly in the spin motor voltage and frequency; ambient pressure; magnetic fields; and high rates of forced precession. Magnetic fields may be uniform, as induced by large field coils, or concentrated, as induced, for example, by permanent magnets. High rates of forced precession are intended to simulate the condition of loss of synchronization of platform servos, which is known as *platform tumbling*. These rates are induced by rotating the test table over large angles so as to apply rapid turning rates about a gyro input axis. As with temperature inputs, the effect on drift rate of the above inputs is noted either while the inputs are applied or shortly thereafter.

Nonoperative Environmental Tests. Nonoperative environmental tests are performed to determine the ability of a gyro to withstand the conditions encountered in shipping, handling, and storage. Shutdowns for relatively short periods are included under storage.

Nonoperative environmental tests consist of a comparison of performance in the gravity field before and after the application of environmental conditions.

These nonoperative environmental conditions include vibration, as encountered in shipping; shock, as encountered in shipping and handling; temperature, as encountered in shipping and storage; and humidity, sand, dust, and fungus, as encountered in storage. Nuclear radiation is included as required.

Shutdowns to room temperature are convenient for gravity testing in that the gyro need not be removed from the test table. Shutdowns to lower temperatures and the application of the other nonoperative environments usually require the removal of the gyro from the test table.

Operative Environmental Tests. Operative environmental tests require that the performance of the gyro, particularly the drift, be measured while the environmental inputs are applied. The environments chosen simulate the conditions expected in the gyro application being considered.

The dynamic environmental tests (linear vibration, centrifuge, and angular oscillation) are of prime interest. Each of these tests requires special electromechanical equipment for the application of the disturbing inputs. Torque-feedback instrumentation is most often used for the drift measurement. Occasionally open-loop instrumentation may be used. Servo-table instrumentation is rarely utilized because the servo table is too great a burden to be carried by the environmental test equipment. This is particularly true of vibration tests, where the transmissibility of the servo table makes it difficult to control the vibration applied to the gyro.

Linear Vibration Tests. Vibration tests serve many purposes, among which are the determination of the anisoelastic nature of the gimbal structure supporting the wheel, the resonant frequencies of this structure, the response of the gimbal suspension to vibration, the effect of vibration on spin-bearing performance, and the drift performance under the acceleration conditions, particularly random vibration encountered in the proposed application of the gyro.

Electrodynamic shakers are used in most cases because they can operate over a broad frequency range with accurately controlled waveform. However, it is necessary, for extreme precision of measurement, to supplement the shaker with an auxiliary linear-motion table which is driven horizontally by the shaker. This table positions the gyro angularly to maintain a constant earth's rate input and provides a purely linear vibration. It also supports the gyro at what would otherwise be excessive overhang of the shaker. A sufficient distance is obtained between the gyro and the shaker electromagnet to minimize magnetic effects on the gyro. For moderate-accuracy measurements the gyro may be mounted on a pedestal on top of the shaker and vibrated vertically. This is advantageous over wide frequency ranges because resonances of supplemental mechanical equipment are minimized.

Whenever possible the shaker and gyro should be oriented to minimize earth's rate inputs to the gyro and thereby increase the accuracy of the torque-feedback drift measurement.

In order to generate torques due to anisoelasticity, a component of vibration must be present along the spin and an input axis. Most vibration tests are conducted with linear vibration applied in the plane of these axes. To determine the anisoelastic nature of the gimbal structure supporting the wheel, two tests are performed at a frequency well below that at which the first (lowest frequency) gyro resonance occurs. In one test a moderate level of sinusoidal vibration is applied at various directions in a spin axis–input axis plane, and the change in drift rate as a result of the applied vibration is recorded for each orientation. In the second test the sinusoidal vibration is applied at a direction approaching 45° from the spin axis at varying levels of acceleration, and the drift rate change is noted at each level. It may then be determined how well the theoretical equation is satisfied both as to variation with the square of acceleration (a^2) and as to the sine of the double angle ($\sin 2\alpha$).

$$\dot{\theta}_C = \frac{M^2}{2H}(C_{SA} - C_{IA})a^2 \sin 2\alpha \tag{12-14}$$

where $\dot{\theta}_C$ = drift rate due to compliance
M = effective mass supported
H = angular momentum
C_{SA} = compliance along spin axis
C_{IA} = compliance along input axis
a = effective value of acceleration, rms
α = direction of acceleration applied at this angle to spin axis

The major axes of elasticity are determined as the directions along which vibration produces no drift. The departure of these directions from the principal axes, if any, may be noted. If the above equation is reasonably well satisfied, the anisoelastic constant

$$\frac{M^2}{2H}(C_{SA} - C_{IA})$$

may be quoted for $\alpha = 45°$ in degrees per hour per g^2.

The resonant frequencies of the gimbal structure and the response of the gimbal suspension to vibration are measured by applying sinusoidal vibrations at low levels. The vibration is varied in frequency over a range on the order of 5 to 2,000 cps, usually at a constant octave rate; the frequency doubles in equal time intervals. The vibration may be applied along the spin and the input axis and at 45° to the spin axis. Resonances are noted by extreme peaks in drift rate as measured by the torque-feedback current. The variation in response between the tests at different directions of vibration application can be revealing of structural characteristics in the gimbal and gimbal suspension.

Vibration can affect spin-bearing performance in two ways. The running torque about the spin axis may be increased owing to additional bearing loading, and the preload may be overcome. The latter effect is investigated by applying vibration along the spin axis when the spin axis and a torque-sensitive axis are horizontal. As the vibration level is increased, the drift rate will rise when the preload is overcome.

Random vibration is created by driving the shaker from amplified random-noise recordings. This type of vibration is more representative than the sinusoidal vibration of the environments encountered in many applications. The drift change resulting from the application of realistic levels of random vibration is recorded.

Centrifuge Tests. Centrifuge tests have limited value in gyro evaluation because of the high angular rotation rates of the machine. For example, a large centrifuge with an arm radius of 20 ft requires an angular rate of greater than 500,000°/hr to create an acceleration five times that due to gravity. Thus, an extreme accuracy of alignment of the spin axis to the centrifuge rotation axis is required to reduce input rates to the gyro. The accuracy needed is far beyond feasible limits.

Centrifuge tests on gyros are usually conducted with the wheel stationary. This is unsatisfactory, however, from the viewpoint that it represents a significant departure from actual gyro operating conditions. In addition, large torques may be created proportional to centrifuge speed owing to the product of inertia effects. Also, should the wheel rotate during testing, uncertainties will result.

Centrifuge tests serve the limited purpose of verifying that unbalance and compliance torque factors with a stationary wheel, as measured at $1g$, vary with the acceleration and square of acceleration within suitable limits at higher acceleration values. These tests also serve to determine the capability of the gyro to withstand high levels of acceleration without subsequent deterioration in performance as measured by gravity tests.

Angular-oscillation Tests. Angular-oscillation tests are performed with the gyro mounted on a turntable which is driven in sinusoidal motion via a crank mechanism. The drift of the gyro due to the application of various levels and frequencies of angular oscillation at different orientations is determined.

Sometimes tests are conducted with angular oscillation applied about two or three axes simultaneously.

Environmental Limit Tests. Environmental limit tests are destructive. They consist of applying a series of increasingly severe environmental conditions until a gyro failure occurs. These tests are both operative and nonoperative and involve many of the disturbing inputs.

12-10. Gyro Test Programs

The test program applied in the evaluation of a gyro depends upon the type and the intended use of the gyro. Among the factors which influence the selection of gyro tests are the type of navigation system (whether long or short term), the orientation of the gyro relative to vehicle acceleration and gravity, the type of gimbal suspension (whether air bearing or floated), the frequency and conditions in which the gyro may be compensated, the environmental conditions to be encountered, and finally the nature of the equipment (platform and electronics) with which the gyro will be associated.

Nonetheless, all gyro test programs consist of five phases: inspection, functional tests, adjustment, gravity tests, and environmental tests. The detailed tests, particularly in the gravity-test and environmental-test phases, vary.

A typical test program is outlined below for a floated stabilization gyro used in a system in which both short-term and long-term drift stability is important.

Typical Test Program

1. Inspection
   a. Visual inspection. Identify obvious defects in external construction.
   b. Wiring. Check continuity, insulation, and resistance checks of all circuits in the gyro.
   c. Suspension. Check for friction and/or bubbles in suspension by observing gimbal motion as result of torquing (wheel not running).
   d. Wheel tests. Check spin motor and bearings for power, torque, winding temperature, speed, wheel run-up time.
   e. Buoyancy. Determine and set buoyant temperature and check temperature control.
2. Functional tests (see Secs. 12-4 and 12-7)
   a. Output sensitivity. Test pickoff output as a function of input angle displacement.
   b. Torquing sensitivity. Test precession rate as a function of torquing current.
   c. Characteristic time, viscous damping, cross coupling. Check to define transfer functions utilizing step inputs or oscillating tables.

d. Elastic restraint. With output axis vertical, determine the electrical torques required to hold various gimbal rotation angles.

3. Adjustment

a. Balance. With series of constant-gravity tests or via tumbling, measure unbalances. Adjust balance and recheck. Operations usually carried out with torque feedback. Check on balance-adjustment sensitivity.

b. Nonacceleration-sensitive drift. With torque-sensitive axis vertical, adjust twist of elastic members or apply electrical compensation to bring torque-feedback current within acceptable limits.

4. Gravity tests

a. Temperature-sensitive drift. With gyro in various gravity-constant orientations, determine drift rate as gyro temperature is varied.

b. Spin voltage tests. With spin axis horizontal, determine drift rate as spin motor excitation voltage is varied. Measure wheel power.

c. Short-term drift stability (gravity constant). With gyro in constant orientation to gravity, measure variation of drift rate during 1 day with torque-feedback instrumentation.

d. Short-term drift (gravity varied). With torque feedback or servo table, measure drift over a period of 1 day. Turntable axis parallel to earth's axis. Compare drift-rate readings at same table angle for indication of stability.

e. Long-term drift stability. Measure all gyro drift parameters with series of gravity-constant tests or with gravity-varied tests. Keep gyro running for many months. Periodically (perhaps weekly) measure all gyro drift factors for comparison with initial values.

5. Environmental tests

a. Short-term drift stability with shutdown. Measure all gyro drift factors; shut down to required low ambient; start up gyro and measure again gyro drift factors.

b. Long-term drift stability. Measure all gyro drift factors once each month. In between measurements subject gyro to various environmental conditions, such as cold storage, vibration, shock, shelf storage, and periods of running.

c. Magnetic field tests. Mount field coils near gyro under test. Apply various levels of magnetic field strength at different orientations with respect to the gyro, and measure the drift change.

d. Operative environmental tests. Measure change in drift rate as a result of applying linear vibration of various levels and frequencies. Also measure change in drift rate as a result of applying angular oscillation.

PROBLEMS

For each of the problems assume an angular momentum of $H = 10^6$ g-cm²/sec and a rotor spin velocity of $\omega_z = 2{,}000$ radians/sec. Also assume that $I_x = I_y = 2I_{\text{rotor}}$.

12-1. A single-axis stabilization gyro is tested in the gravity field. With the +IA up (as shown in sketch), the drift rate is +2°/hr. With the +SA up, the drift rate is −1°/hr. With the +OA up, the drift rate is +0.3°/hr.

(*a*) What is the nonacceleration-sensitive drift rate?

(*b*) What is the drift rate due to spin-axis unbalance?

(*c*) What is the drift rate due to input axis unbalance?

(*d*) If the mass of the rotor is 100 g and the difference between spin-axis and input axis compliance ($C_{SA} - C_{IA}$) is +0.0001 in./lb, what is the total drift rate when the +IA is directed north along the polar axis at 30°N latitude and the +OA is horizontal to the west?

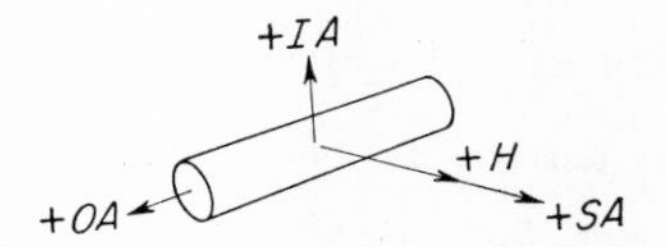

12-2. A two-degree-of-freedom gyro is tested in torque-feedback instrumentation with the spin axis vertical. When the X (inner) axis is positioned east-west, the torquing currents are

X axis drift control = +1.4 ma
Y axis drift control = +15.3 ma

When the X axis is positioned north-south, the torquing currents are

X axis drift control = −13.5 ma
Y axis drift control = −0.2 ma

The local latitude is 40°N.

(*a*) What are the torquing sensitivities of the two axes in degrees per hour per milliampere?

(*b*) If the nonacceleration-sensitive drifts are negligible, what are the magnitudes of the two input axis unbalances in equivalent degrees per hour per g?

12-3. A stabilization gyro is tested on a servo table with the table axis vertical at 40°N latitude. Time is recorded every degree of table rotation. For five successive 1° intervals, the elapsed time intervals are 6.25, 6.20, 6.23, 6.23, and 6.19 min.

(*a*) What is the average gyro drift rate?

(*b*) What is the standard deviation from the mean?

(*c*) Which gyro parameter probably contributes most to the variation in drift rate?

12-4. An angular oscillation of 2 milliradians double amplitude at 5 cps is applied to the housing of

(*a*) A rate gyro about its input axis; natural frequency is 20 cps and damping factor is 0.7.

(*b*) A floated rate-integrating gyro about its input axis; time constant is 0.002 sec.

(*c*) An air-bearing rate double integrating gyro about its input axis; time constant is 200 sec.

(*d*) A floated two-axis gyro about one input axis; nutation damping constant is 0.03 sec.

All the above gyros have electric pickoffs with a sensitivity of 10 volts/radian.

What is the amplitude and phase of the outputs? (Note that the two-axis gyro has two outputs.) What driving-torque amplitude must the angular oscillating table apply to the housing of the two integrating gyros if the inertia of the housing is neglected?

12-5. A two-axis stabilization gyro is subjected to a torque-feedback tumbling test at -10 times earth's rate at 40.7°N latitude. The spin axis is directed along the earth rotation vector $+Z$. At 0° table angle the $+X$ axis is horizontal and to the west. Unbalances are

$$U_x = +5 \text{ dyne-cm}/g \text{ (CM on } +X \text{ side of CS)}$$
$$U_y = -2 \text{ dyne-cm}/g$$
$$U_z = +10 \text{ dyne-cm}/g$$

Compliances are

$$C_x = C_y$$
$$C_z > C_x$$

Maximum compliance torque (when the acceleration is at 45° to the spin axis) on the X and Y axes is 3 dyne-cm$/g^2$.

(*a*) What are the torque patterns for one revolution on each of the stabilization axes X and Y?

(*b*) What are the maximum equivalent drift rates on the two input axes? At what table angles do the maximum rates occur?

BIBLIOGRAPHY

1. LaHue, P. M.: A Technical Discussion of Gyro Drift Rate, Minneapolis-Honeywell Regulator Company, Document U-ED 9714, Minneapolis, May, 1954.

2. Denhard, W. G.: Some Physical Configurations and Typical Data Forms Encountered in Laboratory Testing of Inertial Gyros, M.I.T. Instrumentation Laboratory Report R-112, April, 1956.

3. Draper, C. S., W. McKay, and S. Lees: "Instrument Engineering," McGraw-Hill Book Company, Inc., New York, 1952–1955, vols. 1–3.

4. Draper, C. S., W. Wrigley, and L. R. Grohe: The Floating Integrating Gyro and Its Application to Geometrical Stabilization Problems on Moving Bases, Institute of the Aeronautical Sciences, S.M.F. Fund Paper FF-13, January, 1955.

5. Sandeman, E. K.: Specification of Gyroscope Drift Rates for Users, The English Electric Company, Ltd., Report LI.t.026, Guided Weapons Division, Luton, England, April, 1958.

INDEX